THE ENCYCLOPAEDIA OF
MAMMALS:1

THE ENCYCLOPAEDIA OF
MAMMALS:1

Edited by Dr David Macdonald

George Allen & Unwin
London, Sydney

Project Editor: Graham Bateman
Editors: Peter Forbes, Bill MacKeith, Robert Peberdy
Art Editor: Jerry Burman
Picture Research: Linda Proud, Alison Renney
Production: Clive Sparling
Design: Chris Munday

AN EQUINOX BOOK

Published by:
George Allen & Unwin
40 Museum Street
London WC1A 1LU
England

Planned and produced by:
Equinox (Oxford) Ltd,
Mayfield House, 256 Banbury Road,
Oxford, OX2 7DH, England

Copyright © Equinox (Oxford) Ltd, 1984

Color and line artwork panels © Priscilla Barrett, 1984

British Library Cataloguing in Publication Data

Encyclopaedia of mammals. — (An Equinox
book)
1. Mammals—Dictionaries
I. Macdonald, David
599'.003   QL703
ISBN 0-04-500028-X

Origination by Alpha Reprographics Ltd. Harefield,
Middx; Excel Litho Ltd, Slough. Bucks; Fotographics,
Hong Kong.

Filmset by Keyspools Ltd, Golborne, Lancs, England

Printed in Spain by Heraclio Fournier S.A., Vitoria

Advisory Editors

Dr W. Nigel Bonner
British Antarctic Survey
Cambridge
England

Dr P. Charles-Dominique
Muséum National d'Histoire Naturelle
Brunoy
France

Dr Tim H. Clutton-Brock
University of Cambridge
England

Dr Peter Evans
University of Oxford
England

Professor Bob D. Martin
University College London
England

Dr Russell A. Mittermeier
World Wildlife Fund
USA

Dr Bernd Würsig
Moss Landing Marine Laboratories
California
USA

Artwork panels

Priscilla Barrett

with additional panels by
Malcolm McGregor

Left: Humpback whale (Anthrophoto); half-title: Snow leopard (Ardea);
ppii–iii: lion hunt (Bruce Coleman).

CONTRIBUTORS

PKA   Paul K. Anderson PhD
University of Calgary
Alberta
Canada

SSA   Sheila S. Anderson BSc
British Antarctic Survey
Cambridge
England

TNB   Theodore N. Bailey PhD
US Fish and Wildlife Service
Kenai, Alaska
USA

KB   Ken Balcomb PhD
Friday Harbor
Washington
USA

JDB   John D. Baldwin PhD
University of California
Santa Barbara, California
USA

SKB   Simon K. Bearder PhD
Oxford Polytechnic
England

BCRB   Brian C. R. Bertram PhD
Zoological Society of London
England

RB   Robin Best MSc
Instituto Nacional de
Pesquisas da Amazônia
Manaus
Brazil

JDSB   John D. S. Birks BSc
Universities of Exeter and Durham
England

AB   Anders Bjärvall PhD
National Swedish Environment
Protection Board
Solna
Sweden

SB-H   Sarah Blaffer-Hrdy
Harvard University
Cambridge, Massachusetts
USA

WNB   W. Nigel Bonner BSc FIBiol
British Antarctic Survey
Cambridge
England

WDB   W. D. Bowen PhD
Northwest Atlantic Fisheries Center
St John's, Newfoundland
Canada

DB-J   Douglas Brandon-Jones BSc
British Museum (Natural History)
London

PB   Paul Brodie PhD
Bedford Institute of Oceanography
Dartmouth, Nova Scotia
Canada

FB   Fred Bunnell PhD
University of British Columbia
Vancouver, British Columbia
Canada

PC-D   Pierre Charles-Dominique
Muséum National
d'Histoire Naturelle
Brunoy
France

DJC   David J. Chivers MA PhD
University of Cambridge
England

IC   Ivar Christensen
Institute of Marine Research
Bergen-Nordnes
Norway

THC-B   Tim H. Clutton-Brock MA PhD
University of Cambridge
England

JMD   James M. Dietz MS PhD
Michigan State University
East Lansing, Michigan
USA

DPD   Daryl Domning PhD
Howard University
Washington
USA

ND   Nicole Duplaix PhD
TRAFFIC
Washington DC
USA

AWE   Albert W. Erickson PhD
University of Seattle
Washington
USA

PGHE   Peter G. H. Evans PhD
University of Oxford
England

JEF   John E. Fa
University of Oxford
England

FHF   Francis H. Fay BS MS PhD
University of Alaska
Fairbanks, Alaska
USA

GWF   George W. Frame PhD
Utah State University
Salt Lake City, Utah
USA

RG   Ray Gambell PhD
International Whaling Commission
Cambridge
England

DEG   David E. Gaskin BSc PhD
University of Guelph
Guelph, Ontario
Canada

AHH   A. H. Harcourt PhD
University of Cambridge
England

FHH   Fred H. Harrington PhD
Mount Saint Vincent University
Halifax, Nova Scotia
Canada

SH   Stephen Harris PhD
University of Bristol
England

HJH   Berty J. van Hensbergen BA
Centro Pirenaico de Biologia
Experimental, Jaca, Spain/
University of Cambridge,
England

CHJ   Charles H. Janson
University of Washington
Seattle, Washington
USA

AJTJ   A. J. T. Johnsingh MSc PhD
Ayya Nadar Janaki Animal College
Sivakasi, Tamil Nadu
India

TK   Toshio Kasuya PhD
University of Tokyo
Japan

GK   Gillian Kerby BSc
University of Oxford
England

CMK   Carolyn M. King DPhil
Eastbourne
New Zealand

WGK   Warren G. Kinzey
City University of New York
N.Y.
USA

HK   Hans Kummer
Zurich University
Switzerland

RML   Richard M. Laws PhD FRS
British Antarctic Survey
Cambridge
England

BleB   Burney le Boeuf BA MA PhD
University of California
USA

JWL   Jack W. Lentfer
Department of Fish and Game
Juneau, Alaska
USA

CL   Christina Lockyer BSc MPhil
British Antarctic Survey
Cambridge
England

TRL   T. R. Loughlin
National Marine Mammal
Laboratory, Seattle, Washington
USA

DWM   David W. Macdonald MA DPhil
University of Oxford
England

JMacK   John MacKinnon DPhil
Bogor, Indonesia

KMacK   Kathy MacKinnon MA DPhil
Bogor, Indonesia

IAM   Ian A. McLaren PhD
Dalhousie University
Halifax, Nova Scotia
Canada

AJM   Audrey J. Magoun
University of Alaska
Fairbanks, Alaska
USA

JM   James Malcolm PhD
University of Redlands
Redlands, California
USA

RDM   Robert D. Martin DPhil FIBiol
University College
London

KM   Katharine Milton
University of California
Berkeley, California
USA

RAM   Russell A. Mittermeier
State University of New York
Stony Brook, New York
USA

Tarsiers (P. Barrett—see p 339).

PDM   Patricia D. Moehlman PhD
University of Yale
Newhaven, Connecticut
USA

CN   Carsten Niemitz
Freie Universität Berlin
West Germany

DKO   Daniel K. Odell PhD
University of Miami
Miami, Florida
USA

TJO   Thomas J. O'Shea BS MS PhD
US Fish and Wildlife Service
Gainesville, Florida
USA

KGVO   Karl G. Van Orsdol PhD
University of Cambridge
England

JMP   Jane M. Packard PhD
University of Florida
Gainesville, Florida
USA

FEP   Frank E. Poirier PHD
Ohio State University
Colombus, Ohio
USA

JIP   J. I. Pollock BSc PhD
Duke University Primate Center
Durham, North Carolina
USA

RAP   Roger A. Powell PhD
North Carolina State University
Raleigh, North Carolina
USA

GBR   Galen B. Rathbun BA PhD
US Fish and Wildlife Service
Gainesville, Florida
USA

AFR   Alison F. Richard PhD
Yale University
New Haven, Connecticut
USA

PRKR   Philip K. R. Richardson
McGregor Museum
Kimberley
South Africa

KR   Keith Ronald
University of Guelph
Guelph, Ontario
Canada

JR   Jon Rood PhD
Conservation and Research Center
National Zoological Park
Front Royal, Virginia
USA

TER   Thelma E. Rowell
University of California
Berkeley, California
USA

JKR   James K. Russell PhD
Formerly of National Zoological Park
Smithsonian Institution
Washington DC
USA

ABR   Anthony B. Rylands PhD
Instituto Nacional de
Pesquisas da Amazônia
Manaus
Brazil

DES   David E. Sergeant PhD
Arctic Biological Station
St. Anne de Bellevue, Quebec
Canada

BS   Barbara Smuts PhD
Harvard University
Cambridge, Massachusetts
USA

TTS   Tom T. Struhsaker PhD
New York Zoological Society
Bronx Park, New York
USA

MS   Mel Sunquist PhD
Conservation and Research Center
National Zoological Park
Front Royal, Virginia
USA

ABT   Andrew B. Taber BA
University of Oxford
England

JWT   John W. Terborgh
Princeton University
Princeton, New Jersey
USA

POT   Peter O. Thomas
University of California
USA

DRV   Dennis R. Voigt MS
Ministry of Natural Resources
Maple, Ontario
Canada

PMW   Peter M. Waser PhD
Purdue University
West Lafayette, Indiana
USA

RSW   Randall S. Wells
Moss Landing Marine Laboratories
California
USA

CW   Chris Wemmer PhD
Conservation and Research Center
National Zoological Park
Front Royal, Virginia
USA

AJW   Anthony J. Whitten
Centre for Environmental Studies
Medan, Indonesia

WCW   W. Chris Wozencraft BSc
University of Kansas
Lawrence, Kansas
USA

RWW   Richard W. Wrangham PhD
University of Ann Arbor
Ann Arbor, Michigan
USA

PCW   Patricia C. Wright
Duke University Primate Center
Durham, North Carolina
USA

BW   Bernd Würsig PhD
Moss Landing Marine Laboratories
California
USA

EZ   E. Zimen PhD
University of Saarbrücken
West Germany

CONTENTS

Left: male and female European weasels (P. Barrett—see p 111).
Overleaf: West Indian manatee and calf (Ardea).

PREFACE

To say that *The Encyclopaedia of Mammals* (volumes 1 and 2) covers all known members of the class Mammalia is an accurate but arid summary of these books. The newest discoveries of modern biology weave a thread amongst this array of 4,000 or so species, giving insight into the lives of animals so intricate in their adaptations that the reality renders our wildest fables dull.

In this first volume we shall include three main groups of mammal—the carnivores, sea mammals and primates. The second volume will contain the large herbivores (such as horses, deer, rhinos, hippos, elephants), small herbivores (such as squirrels, voles, mice and rabbits) and insect-eaters (such as shrews, moles, anteaters), as well as marsupials and bats.

The Carnivores section (order Carnivora) embraces creatures amongst whom are the epitomes of power, endurance, gentility, and quickness of wit and fang alike. The symbol of majesty is the lion, of tirelessness the wolf, of guile the fox and of our own ruination of wild places the Giant panda. Other images of savagery, menace and treachery may be undeserved, but they are no less vivid. There are some who think that to probe the real lives of the King of Beasts and others of his realm is to sully their poetic images. This encyclopedia proves them wrong. Some authorities split the order Carnivora into two major suborders; these are the marine carnivores (seals, sea lions and walruses) called Pinnipedia, and the terrestrial suborder whose members are known collectively as Fissipedia. There is no question that there are affinities between the marine and terrestrial carnivores (the blood proteins of seals, for example, are similar to those of bears) but the links are ancient and unclear. Consequently we have followed the alternative school in elevating both divisions to ordinal status, dealing in this section with the terrestrial order Carnivora and in the next with the order Pinnipedia and other sea mammals.

The section on sea mammals introduces three quite unrelated orders whose members are adapted to life at sea—the whales and dolphins (order Cetacea), seals and sea lions (order Pinnipedia) and sirenians (order Sirenia). Much more important, these pages bridge the waters between the faunas of our comfortably familiar terrestrial surroundings and the disquietingly alien world of ocean and ice-floe; a world where distances, empty landscapes and even some of the creatures are so immense that they might seem unreal in their remoteness. From a distance, the torpedo-shaped uniformity of marine mammals masks the character of each species and personality of each individual; the illusion may be of animals with less individuality than some of the more familiar terrestrial mammalian species. But with closer study, that illusion is banished, and the ways of whale and porpoise, of seal and walrus, spring intimately to life, and in so doing emphasize the subtlety and the frailty of the natural web, and the dependence of the monumental upon the minute.

As members of the order Primates, humans have much in common with all mammals, but our link with other primates, especially the apes, is so immediate that they are uniquely intriguing. There are those, perhaps fearful of the closeness of our relationship, who laugh, mockingly, at the behavior of monkeys and apes, deriding them as a shoddy zoological charade on humanity. In this section, however, the reader encounters creatures with whom we share our roots and, in the apes, in which the similarities between us are at least as compelling as are the differences. The primates are outstanding for their colorful athleticism, their intelligence and most of all for their intricate social relationships. Their societies encompass every variant between friendship and feud, and are engrossingly interesting, not only in themselves, but in what they tell us about ourselves.

To the non-scientist the intricacies of classification (the ordering of animals into groups of increasing size and comprehensiveness on the basis of common ancestry) are difficult to comprehend, although there is a tendency to believe that there can be only one correct answer. That this is far from the truth is indicated by changing ideas about the orders Scandentia (tree shrews) and Dermoptera (flying lemurs). Both these groups are small (18 and two species respectively) and have a long evolutionary history. Today they are treated as separate orders, but at various times in the past 100 years scientists thought them to be related to the order Primates. The animals have remained the same, but our knowledge and understanding has altered, and will probably continue to do so.

In planning this encyclopedia our aim was precise and rather ambitious. Recently, zoologists have had increasing success in discovering facts about the behavior and ecology of wild mammals, and in developing new and intriguing ideas to

LEFT Lion pride at rest (P. Barrett—see p 34). ABOVE Young Bare-ear marmoset (Bruce Coleman).

explain their discoveries. Yet so scattered is the information that much of it fails to reach even professional zoologists, far less percolate through to a general readership. Worse still, there is the idea that the public will, or can, only accept watered-down science, diluted to triviality and carefully sieved free of challenge. Our aim, then, has been to gather the newest information and ideas and to present them lucidly, entertainingly, but uncompromisingly. If we have succeeded, these pages will refresh the professional as much as they enthral the schoolchild. The best way to convey the excitement of discovery is through the discoverers, and for this reason the book is written by the researchers themselves. Aside from any other qualities, this encyclopedia must be unique among its class in amassing so much first-hand experience and international expertise. As already mentioned, there is no single "correct" classification of the animal kingdom, and so we have had to select from the views of different taxonomists. In general we follow Corbet and Hill (see Bibliography) for the arrangement of families and orders. However, within family or species entries authors have been encouraged to follow the latest views on "their" groups.

This encyclopedia is structured at a number of levels. Firstly for each order there will be a general essay which highlights common features and main variations of the biology (particularly body plan), ecology, and behavior of the group concerned and its evolution. For the small orders—the tree shrews and flying lemurs—these order essays will be a complete review of the group, but for the other groups it acts as a pivot for the next level of entries which it introduces. Thus the carnivores are divided into seven families, the cetaceans into two suborders—the toothed and baleen whales—and the primates into the prosimians, monkeys and apes. These essays cover various themes and highlight the particular interest of given groups, but each invariably includes a distribution map, summary of species or species groupings, description of skull, dentition and unusual skeletal features of representative species and, in many cases, color artwork that enhances the text by illustrating representative species engaged in characteristic activities.

The bulk of this encyclopedia is devoted to individual species, groups of closely related species or families of species. The text on these pages covers details of physical features, distribution, evolutionary history, diet and feeding behavior, social dynamics and spatial organization, classification, conservation and relationships with man.

An information panel precedes the textual discussion of each species or group. This provides easy reference to the main features of distribution, habitat, dimensions, coat and duration of gestation and life span, and includes a map of natural distribution (not introduction to other areas by man), and a scale drawing comparing the size of the species with that of a six-foot (1.8m) human. Where there are silhouettes of two animals, they are the largest and smallest representatives of the group. Where the panel covers a large group of species, the species listed as examples are those referred to in the accompanying text. For such large groups, the detailed descriptions of species are provided in a separate Table of Species. Unless otherwise stated, dimensions given are for both males and females. Where there is a difference in size between sexes, the scale drawings show males.

Every so often a really remarkable study of a species emerges. Some of these studies are so distinctive that they have been allocated two whole pages so that the authors may develop their stories. The topics of these "special features" give insight into evolutionary processes at work throughout all mammals, and span social organization, foraging behavior, breeding biology and conservation. Similar themes are also developed in smaller "box features" alongside most of the major texts.

Most people will never have seen many of the animals mentioned in these pages, but that does not necessarily mean they have to remain remote or unreal in our thoughts. Such detachment vanishes as these animals are brought vividly to life not only by many photographs, but especially by the color and line artwork. These illustrations are the fruits of great labor: they are accurate in minute detail and more importantly they are dynamic—each animal is engaged in an activity or shown in a posture that enhances points made in the text. Furthermore, the species have been chosen as representatives of their group. Unless otherwise stated, all animals depicted on a single panel are to scale; actual dimensions will be found in the text. Simpler line drawings illustrate particular aspects of behavior, or anatomical distinctions between otherwise similar species. Similarly, we have sought photographs that are more than mere zoo portraits, and which illustrate the animal in its habitat, emphasizing typical behavior; the photographs are accompanied by captions which complement the main text.

The reader may marvel at the stories of adaptation, the process of natural selection and the beauty of the creatures found herein, but he should also be fearful for them. Again and again authors return to the need to conserve species threatened with extinction and by mismanagement. About 350 of the 497 species described in these pages (including all cetaceans, cats, otters and all primates save man) are listed in the Appendices I to III of the Convention on International Trade in Endangered Species of Wild Flora and Fauna (CITES). The *Red Data Book* of the International Union for the Conservation of Nature and Natural Resources (IUCN) lists about 100 of these species as at risk, *excluding* the 22 lemurs, which are currently under review. In this book the following symbols are used to show the status accorded to species by the IUCN at the time of

going to press: E = Endangered—in danger of extinction unless causal factors are modified (these may include habitat destruction and direct exploitation by man). V = Vulnerable—likely to become endangered in the near future. R = Rare, but neither endangered nor vulnerable at present. I = Indeterminate—insufficient information available, but known to be in one of the above categories. ? = Suspected but not definitely known to fall into one of the above categories. We are indebted to Jane Thornback of the IUCN Monitoring Centre, Cambridge, England, for giving us the very latest information on status. The symbol * indicates entire species, genera or families, in addition to those listed in the *Red Data Book*, that are listed by CITES. Some species and subspecies that have EX or probably have EX? become extinct in the past 100 years are also indicated.

The success of books like this rests upon the integrated efforts of many people with diverse skills. I want to thank all of the authors for their enthusiastic cooperation, Priscilla Barrett for her painstaking attention to detail in the artwork, and all the other people, too numerous to list, who have helped to shape these volumes. I also thank my wife, Jenny, for her tolerance of the avalanches of manuscripts which, for two years, have cascaded from every surface of our home. In particular I am grateful to Dr Graham Bateman, Senior Natural History Editor at Equinox, for his good-humored navigation as we have paddled our editorial boat hither and thither, fearful of being smashed on the rocks of gauche sensationalism or becalmed in the stagnant pools of obsessive detail. Hopefully, the reader will judge that we have charted a course where the current is invigorating and the waters clear.

David W. Macdonald
DEPARTMENT OF ZOOLOGY
OXFORD

LEFT Male American Red foxes fighting (R. Peterson).
OVERLEAF South American sea lions and Killer whale (Bruce Coleman).

WHAT IS A MAMMAL?

IT would be correct to say that mammals are a group of animals with backbones, whose bodies are insulated by hair, which nurse their infants with milk and which share a unique jaw articulation. This, however, fails to convey how these few shared characteristics underpin the evolution of a group with astonishingly intricate adaptations, thrilling behavior and highly complex societies. Mammals are also the group to which humans belong, and through them we can understand much about ourselves. Another answer to the question "What is a mammal?" would therefore be that the essence of mammals lies in their complex diversity of form and function, and above all their individual flexibility of behavior: the smallest mammal, Kitti's hog-nosed bat, weighs 1.5g (0.05oz), the Blue whale weighs 100 million times as much; the wolf may journey through 1,000sq km (400sq mi), the Naked mole rat never leaves one burrow; the Virginia opposum gives birth to litters of up to 27, the orang utan to only one; the elephant, like man, may live three score years and ten, while the male Brown antechinus never sees a second season and dies before the birth of the first and only litter he has fathered. No facet of these varied lives is random; they are diverse but not in disarray. On the contrary, each individual mammal maximizes its "fitness," its ability, relative to others of its kind, to leave viable offspring.

Mammals are also a class comprising approximately 4,070 species, amongst which ancient relationships permit subdivisions into 1,000 or so genera, 135 families, 18 orders and 2 subclasses. These subclasses acknowledge a 200 million-year

separation between egg-laying Prototheria (the only survivors are the platypus and echidnas) and the live-bearing Theria. Not quite as longstanding is the 90 million-year-old split within the Theria, dividing the marsupials (infraclass Metatheria) from the placental mammals (infraclass Eutheria).

Even within taxonomy's convenient compartments there is a bewildering variation in the size, shape and life-histories of mammals. Indeed, it is especially characteristic of mammals that even individuals of the same species behave differently depending on their circumstances. Hence, individuals in one population of Spotted hyenas may live their entire lives in 50-strong, stable clans, whereas elsewhere a fleeting association of a few days constitutes the most enduring adult relationship. Within one pack of African wild dogs, two females may encounter another's pups and, depending on her social rank, one may offer unstinting care, the other a savage death. The student of mammal behavior may cease to be surprised at the unexpected, the intricate and the odd, but can hardly fail to remain enthralled.

From Reptiles to Mammals

In the Carboniferous period some 300 million years ago, the ancestors of today's mammals were no more than a twinkle in an ancient reptilian eye. The world was spanned by warm, shallow seas and the climate was hot, humid and constant. Amongst the reptiles of the late Carboniferous, one line heralded the mammal-like reptiles—the subclass Synapsida. The synapsids flourished, dominating the reptilian faunas of the Permian and early Triassic periods about 280–210 million years ago. Over millions of years their skeletons altered from the cumbersome reptilian mold to a more racy design that presaged the

▼ The precise origins of modern mammalian orders are lost in the past. This evolutionary tree summarizes one view of mammal ancestry. Dark green indicates the presence of a fossil record, paler green, possible lines of descent.

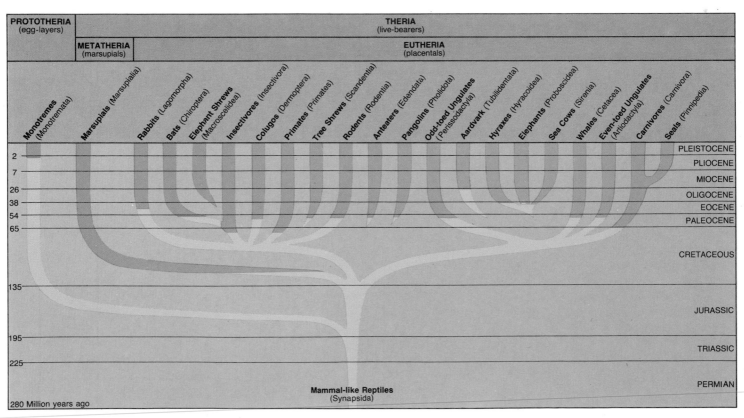

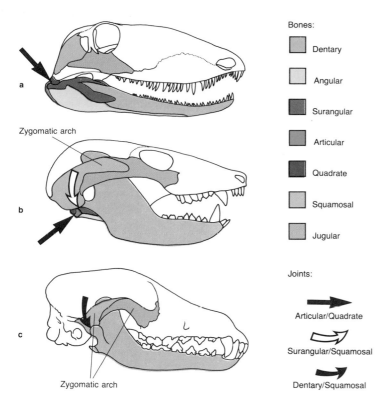

Bones:

- Dentary
- Angular
- Surangular
- Articular
- Quadrate
- Squamosal
- Jugular

Joints:

→ Articular/Quadrate

⇨ Surangular/Squamosal

➔ Dentary/Squamosal

▲ From reptile to mammal.
In the fossil record, the divergence of mammals from reptiles is indicated by changes in the hinge mechanism whereby the lower jaw articulates with the skull. (a) Originally the lower jaw of the reptilian skull, and that of early mammal-like reptiles (synapsids) such as the Permian pelycosaur *Ophiacodon*, shown here, was composed of several bones, including the articular, angular, surangular and dentary, the articular forming the hinge joint with the quadrate bone of the skull. (b) In a transitional form of the mid-Triassic, *Probainognathus*, the reptilian articular/quadrate articulation remains, but at the same joint there is a new articulation between the surangular and the squamosal bone of the skull, the surangular having reached this position due to considerable expansion of the dentary. Another noticeable change is the development of the zygomatic arch, to which the more powerful jaw muscles attached. (c) In the modern mammal (for example, a wolf, shown here) only the dentary/squamosal hinge remains, while the dentary is the principal bone of the lower jaw. The teeth of reptiles are unspecialized (homodont condition), while those of present-day mammals are specialized to fulfill different functions (heterodont condition).

early mammals. Yet, despite these auspicious Permian beginnings, this was a false start for the mammals. The late Triassic period saw the dazzling ascendency of the dinosaurs which in the Mesozoic era (225 to 65 million years ago) not only eclipsed the synapsids, but nearly annihilated them due to competitive superiority. Inconspicuous mammal-like reptiles survived and evolved during the Triassic period (225–195 million years ago) into true mammals, of which the first were 5cm (2in) long, nocturnal and probably partly arboreal. Their unobtrusive scuttlings gave little evidence of what was to become the most exciting radiation in vertebrate history when, 75–80 million years later, in the late Cretaceous period, the dinosaurs lumbered mysteriously into oblivion.

By the Triassic period, among synapsids the order Therapsida prevailed and in the fossils of these mammal-like reptiles lie the roots of modern mammals. Over millennia, as reptile metamorphosed into mammal, they developed an expanded tem-

poral skull opening and a corresponding rearrangement of the jaw musculature; a secondary palate appeared, forming a horizontal partition in the roof of the mouth (formed by a backwards extension of the maxillary and palatine bones); their teeth became diverse (heterodont); six of the seven bones of the reptilian lower jaw were reduced in size while the fifth, the dentary, was greatly enlarged; ribs were no longer attached to the cervical and lumber vertebrae, but only to the thoracic ones; the pectoral and pelvic girdles were streamlined, and angles on the heads of femura and humeri altered so that the limbs were aligned beneath, rather than to the side of, the body. These and other changes promoted more effective, agile and swift working of the body. For example, the false palate forms a bypass for air from the nostrils to the back of the mouth, facilitating simultaneous eating and breathing, made more efficient by the evolution of the diaphragm—a muscular plate separating the chest from the abdomen.

All modern mammals arose from a group called cynodonts. These advanced mammal-like reptiles of the middle and late Triassic were somewhat dog-like predators. For lack of any better point at which to split the reptile-to-mammal continuum, mammals are defined as those in which the early articular-quadrate jaw joint has been superseded by a new articulation between the dentary bone of the lower jaw and the squamosal bone of the skull (see diagram). Previously, a genus called *Diarthrognathus* from the late Triassic sandstone of South Africa was thought to represent this transition, having both types of jaw articulation in the same joint. However, in 1969 a stronger candidate was discovered in the mid-Triassic beds of Argentina. This cynodont, *Probainognathus*, retains only the flimsiest articular-quadrate joint and illustrates the development toward the articulation between the dentary and squamosal bones. Furthermore, the bones of the old reptilian jaw joint are juxtaposed so as to foreshadow their remarkable transformation into the ossicles of the mammalian middle ear apparatus (the articular, quadrate and stapes become, respectively, the malleus, incus and stapes). The remarkable schizophrenic anatomy of *Probainognathus*, simultaneously reptile and mammal, emphasizes the transience of nature glimpsed through the evolutionary keyhole—not only may a sturdy jawbone (itself part of a fish's gill-arches in a yet earlier incarnation) become a delicate part of the ear, but the separation of the origins of *Diarthrognathus* and *Probainognathus* is partly illusory since South Africa and Argentina were, in the Triassic, in the same region (Gondwanaland).

Since soft parts do not fossilize, the history of modern mammals must be traced from fragments of bones and teeth. In addition to their jaw articulation, modern mammalian skulls are distinguished by the entotympanic bone, an element of the auditory bulla. Furthermore, mammalian teeth develop only from the premaxillary, maxillary and dentary bones and they are generally diversified in function (heterodont, consisting of incisors, canines, premolars and molars). Typically, mammals have two sets of teeth, the milk, or deciduous, set often differing in form and function from the adult set. All mammalian teeth consist of a core of bone-like dentine wrapped in a hard case of enamel (largely calcium phosphate). In most mammals the pulp cavity seals, and the tooth ceases to grow, once adult.

The Central Heating System of Mammals

The two most fundamental traits of mammals lie not in their skeletons, but at the boundaries to their bodies—the skin. These two features are hair and the skin glands, including the mammary glands which secrete milk, and the sweat and sebaceous glands. None may seem spectacular and some or all may have evolved before the mammal-like reptiles crossed the official divide. But these traits are associated with endothermy, a condition whose repercussions affect every aspect of mammalian life.

Endothermic animals are those whose internal body temperature is maintained "from within" (endo-) by the oxidation (essentially, the burning) of food within the body. Some endotherms maintain a constant internal temperature (homoeothermic), whereas that of others varies (heterothermic). The temperature is regulated by a "thermostat" in the brain, situated within the hypothalamus. In regulating their body temperature independent of the environment, mammals (and birds) are unshackled from the alternative, ectothermic, condition typical of all other animals and involving body temperatures rising and falling with the outside (ecto-) temperature. Endothermic and ectothermic animals are sometimes, misleadingly, called warm- and cold-blooded respectively. However, since the major heat source for, say, a lizard is outside its body, coming from the sun, it can have a body temperature higher than that of a so-called warm-blooded animal, but when the air temperature plummets the reptile's body temperature falls too, reducing the ectotherm to compulsory lethargy. In contrast, the internal processes of the endothermic mammal operate independently of the outside environment. This difference is overwhelmingly important because the myriad of linked processes that constitute life are fundamentally chemical reactions and they proceed at rates which are dependent upon temperature. Endothermy confers on mammals an internal constancy that not only allows them to function in a variety of environments from which reptiles are debarred, but also assures a biochemical stability for their bodies. The critical effect of temperature on mammalian functioning is illustrated by the violence of the ensuing delirium if the "thermostat" goes awry and allows the temperature to rise by even a few degrees.

Endothermy is costly. Mammals must work, expending energy either to warm or cool themselves depending on the vagaries of their surroundings. There are many adaptations involved in minimizing these running costs and the most ubiquitous is mammalian hair. The coat may be adapted in many ways, but there is often an outer layer of longer, more bristle-like, water-repellent guard hairs which provide a tough covering for densely-packed, soft underfur. The volume of air trapped amongst the hairs depends on whether or not they are erected by muscles in the skin. Hair may protect the skin from the sun's rays or from freezing wind, slowing the escape of watery sweat in the desert or keeping aquatic mammals dry as they dive. Hairs are waterproofed by sebum, the oily secretions of sebaceous glands associated with their roots.

Mammals differ in their body temperatures—eg monotremes 30°C (86°F), armadillos 32°C (89.6°F), marsupials and hedgehogs 35°C (95°F), man 37°C (98.6°F) and rabbits and cats 39°C (102.2°F). Some mammals minimize the costs of endothermy by sacrificing homoeothermy: they do not maintain a constant internal temperature. The body temperature and hence metabolic costs of hibernating mammals drop while they are torpid, as do those of tenrecs and many bats during daily periods of inactivity. The body temperature of echidnas fluctuates between 25–37°C (77–99°F). Their temperature control is so rudimentary that they die of heat apoplexy in environments of 37°C (99°F). Because of the huge area for heat loss in their wings, bats cannot maintain homoeothermy when at rest, but allow their temperature to fall. They get so cold that when they awaken they have to go through physical jerks to raise their temperature before take-off.

Lactation and the Rise of Mammals

The decline of the huge, naked, ectothermic dinosaurs may have been triggered by the cooling climate of the Mesozoic era, with its daily and seasonal fluctuations in temperature. But these would have affected smaller (or infant) dinosaurs more than the giants that predominated among dinosaurs, due to the smaller reptile's relatively greater surface-area-to-volume ratio and hence more rapid heat loss (see p 12). So why did the mammals finally prosper, and the dinosaurs decline?

Early mammals may have avoided competition with dinosaurs by becoming nocturnal, and the key that unlocked this chilly niche to them may have been the evolution of endothermy (internal self-regulation of body temperature). In addition to allowing them to forage out of the sun's warming rays, endothermy may have improved mammals' competitive ability by allowing them to grow faster and therefore breed more prolifically than reptiles, whose bodies more or less "switch off" when they cool down.

Another possibility is that the mammals usurped the dinosaurs' supremacy on account of one critical difference which stemmed from the development of lactation and parental care in mammals. Young dinosaurs, like modern crocodiles, hatched as minuscule replicas of their parents; their small size required that they ate quite different food from the adults of their species. They grew slowly at a rate dependent upon their foraging success, gradually approaching adulthood, but inevitably as feeble inferiors until they finally attained full size. In contrast, the evolution of lactation enabled an infant mammal to grow rapidly towards adult competence under the protection of parental care (see p 7). At independence the young mammal is almost fully grown and, unlike the still infantile reptile of the same age, then enters directly roughly the same niche as adult members of its species. For example, a Grizzly bear is born at roughly the same percentage of its mother's weight (1–2 percent) as was a hatchling dinosaur, but remains dependent on her for protection for up to 4½ years. The dinosaur, on the other hand, had to fend for itself in a series of niches that changed as it grew. In the inconstant, unpredictable environment of the cooling Mesozoic, dinosaurs may have been at a disadvantage to mammals because they required a succession of different food supplies to become available exactly on cue as their young grew, and faced a protracted period when young were at a competitive disadvantage to adults. If this reconstruction is correct, then it was parental care (also evolved by birds), and particularly lactation, that assured the supremacy of mammals. The protracted parent-offspring bond established during nursing in turn set the scene for the subsequent evolution of intricate mammalian societies.

▲ Musk oxen, northernmost of hoofed mammals. Their long, coarse guard hairs and fine underfur exclude the arctic cold.

The coiled sweat glands in the skin of mammals secrete a watery fluid. When expressed onto the skin's surface this evaporates, and in so doing draws heat from the skin and cools it. Mammals vary in the distribution and abundance of their sweat glands: primates have sweat glands all over the body, in members of the cat and dog family they are confined to the pads of the feet, and whales, sea cows and golden moles have none. Species with few sweat glands resort to panting—losing heat by evaporation of saliva.

Mammals' Perfumes

Mammals are unique among animals with backbones in the potency and social importance of their smells. This quality also stems from their skin, wherein both sebaceous and sweat glands become adapted to produce complicated odors with which mammals communicate. The sites of scent glands vary between species: capybaras have them aloft their snout, Mule deer have them on the lower leg, elephants have them behind the eyes and hyraxes have them in the middle of their back. It is very common for scent glands to be concentrated in the ano-genital region (urine and feces also serve as socially important odors); the perfume glands of civets lie in a pocket between the anus and genitals and for centuries their greasy secretions have been scooped out to make the base of expensive perfumes. Glands around the genitals of Musk deer are a similarly unwholesome starting point of other odors greatly prized by some people. Most carnivores have scent-secreting anal sacs, whose function is largely unknown, although in the case of the skunk it is clear enough. The evolution of scent glands has led to a multitude of scent-marking behaviors whereby mammals deploy odors in their environment. Scent marks, unlike other signals, have the advantage of transmitting long after the sender has moved on. They are often assumed to function as territorial markers, exerting an aversive effect on trespassers, but evidence of this is scant. Probably the messages are much more complex, perhaps communicating the sex, status, age, reproductive condition and diet of the sender. Many mammals have several scent glands, each of which may send different messages, eg the cheek glands of the Dwarf mongoose communicate status, whereas their anal gland secretions communicate individual identity.

Milk and Reproduction

The mammary glands are unique to mammals and characterize all members of the class. The glands, which are similar to sweat glands, should not be confused with the mammillae or teats which are merely a means of delivering the milk and are absent in the platypus and echidnas. Only the glands of females produce milk. Numbers of teats vary from two in, for example, primates and the Marsupial mole, to 19 in the Pale-bellied mouse opossum.

Courtship among mammals varies from rape (elephant seals) to extravagant enticement (Uganda kob). Pairings may be ephemeral (Grizzly bears) or lifelong (Silver-backed jackals), and matings monogamous (elephant shrews) or polygynous (Red deer). In all cases fertilization involves intromission which can last for a few seconds (hyraxes) to several hours (rhinoceroses). Each of these variations correlates with the species' niche; for example, amongst cavy-like rodents duration of intromission is briefest in species which mate in the open, exposed to predators—the males of these species have elaborate penile adornments, presumably to accelerate stimulation of the female.

The three species of monotremes (order Monotremata), sole survivors of the egg-laying mammal subclass Prototheria, and some insectivores have a cloaca (common opening of urinary and reproductive tracts) and the testes are situated in the abdomen. As in birds, it is only the left ovary of the female platypus that sheds eggs into the oviduct, where they are coated with albumen and a shell, and laid after 12–20 days. Echidnas incubate their eggs in a pouch, platypuses keep theirs in a nest where they are incubated for about three weeks. Meanwhile the embryo is nourished from the yolk. On hatching the young sucks milk that drains from mammary glands onto tufts of hair on the female abdomen. Monotremes lack nipples.

Among marsupials (subclass Theria, infraclass Metatheria), eggs are shed by both ovaries into a double-horned (bicornuate) uterus. There the developing embryo spends 12–28 days, securing nourishment from its yolk sac and "uterine milk" secreted by glands in the uterine walls. The early embryo (blastocyst) rests in a shallow depression in the uterine wall, its vascular yolk sac (chorion) in contact with the slightly eroded wall of the mother's uterus. This point of contact allows limited diffusion between maternal and fetal blood and is called a chorio-vitelline placenta. At birth the marsupial infant is highly altricial (poorly developed), weighing only 0.8g (0.03oz) for the 20–32kg (44–70lb) female Eastern gray kangaroo. Nevertheless, its sense of smell and its forelimbs are disproportionately developed and enable it to battle through the jungle of fur on its mother's belly to reach the teats, often in a pouch. The infant attaches to a single teat, which swells so as to plug into the baby's mouth. Marsupials detach from the nipple at about the same weight as that at which a placental mammal of comparable size is born.

Amongst the placental mammals (infraclass Eutheria), which have been separate from the marsupials since the mid Cretaceous (about 90 million years ago), the major innovation is the chorio-allantoic placenta. This organ facilitates nutritional, respiratory and excretory exchange between the circulatory system of mother and infants. The mother's enhanced ability to sustain infants in the uterus permits prolonged gestation periods and the birth of more developed (precocial) young. The placenta permits a remarkable liaison between mother and unborn infant. The blastocyst first adheres to the uterus and then, with the aid of protein-dissolving enzymes secreted by its outer membrane, sinks into the maternal tissue, reaching an inner layer called the endometrium. The outer membrane of the embryo, the chorion, is equivalent to the one which lines the shell of reptile and bird eggs. Protuberances (villi) grow out from the chorion into the soup of degenerating maternal tissue known as the embryotroph. The villi absorb this nutritious broth. Blood vessels proliferate in the uterus at the site of implantation and the chorionic villi vastly increase the absorbtive surface—a human placenta grows 48km (30mi) of villi. Bandicoots (family Paramelidae) are the only marsupials with chorio-allantoic placentae, but they are grossly inefficient compared to the placental mammal's version, since they lack

villi. Mammalian orders differ in the extent to which the maternal and embryonic membranes of the placenta degenerate to allow mixing of parent and offspring fluids. Amongst lemurs, pigs, horses and whales the chorionic villi simply plug into the maternal endometrium. This is a huge advance on the marsupial system, but nevertheless is 250 times less efficient at salt transfer from mother to fetus than are the placentae of most rodents, rabbits, elephant shrews, New World monkeys and common bats. In their cases the maternal and embryonic tissues are so eroded that the fetal blood vessels are bathed in the mother's blood. The great significance of the placenta is that without it the mother's body would reject the baby like any other foreign body. It is this tolerance of the embryo that divides

▼ Olive baboon nursing young. When a mammalian infant sucks at its mother's nipple it may withdraw a little milk, but more importantly it stimulates "let-down," whereby muscles squeeze much more milk out of a honeycomb of tubes and cavities in the mammae; this milk collects in ducts from which it can be sucked. Some 30–60 seconds of preliminary sucking are required to stimulate let-down, which indicates that the process is not controlled simply by nerves (as they transmit messages almost instantaneously), but by a chemical envoy (a hormone) that travels within the mother's bloodstream. In fact sucking triggers a nerve impulse which races to the pituitary—a part of the mammal's brain—and in response this organ releases two chemicals into the blood. When these chemical couriers reach the mammae, one (lactogenic hormone) stimulates the secretion of milk by the glands, the other (oxytocin) prompts the ejection of stored milk from the nipple.

the placental mammals from the marsupials, and allows the former to have longer pregnancies and hence to bear precocial young.

The placenta facilitates feeding the embryo during gestation, and milk nourishes it after birth. Both, however, have an additional function, namely to transfer the mother's antibodies to her offspring, thus enhancing its immunity to disease. The "afterbirth" of placental mammals is the fetal part of the placenta.

Species differ in the duration of both gestation and lactation, and in their combined duration. Although marsupials tend to have shorter gestations and more prolonged nursing than do placental mammals, there is considerable variation between species in both groups. Gestation length is ultimately constrained by the size of skull which will fit through the mother's pelvis, but where agility, speed or long travels put a premium on the mother's athleticism, then pregnancy will be short compared with the period of lactation, and birth weight of the litter relatively small.

Parental Care and Milk

Mammals are not the only vertebrates to give birth to live young (viviparity), but they are unique in that the availability of milk buffers their infants from the demands of foraging for themselves while they are still small and inferior copies of their parents. To a large extent a young mammal prospers initially on the strength of its parents' competitive ability, as reflected in the supply of its mother's milk, until reaching an age and size when it can compete more or less on adult terms. Thus mammals, in comparison to other viviparous vertebrates, are born small (the average litter is about 10 percent of mother's weight), minimizing the encumbrance upon their agile mothers, but grow very fast and become independent of their mothers at a much larger size, a development sustained by lactation and hastened by endothermy. In the tree shrew, *Tupaia*, parental care is entirely nutritional, the mother visiting her infants once every two days solely to nurse them for a few minutes. However, especially where food is elusive, additional parental care eases the transition to adulthood; indeed, since the female can store fat

Evolution, Society and Sexual Dimorphism

In 1798 Malthus' *Essay on the Principle of Population* sowed a seed that was to germinate in Charles Darwin's mind as the theory of natural selection, published in the *Origin of Species* in 1859. Malthus had noted that although a breeding pair generally produce a total of more than two offspring, many populations do not grow as fast as this would imply, if at all. Darwin was impressed by the subtlety of species' adaptations and saw that individuals differed in the detail of their adaptation and thus their "fitness," ie the perfection of their adaptations to prevailing conditions. The variation between individuals arose from the mixing of genetic material involved in sexual reproduction, and from mutation, although the connection between these mechanisms and Darwin's theory was not realized until 1900 when Mendel's work of 1865 was rediscovered.

Since populations do not necessarily grow, many of the young born must die, and the variation between individuals facilitates selective death, allowing better adapted individuals to prosper. Traits which confer an adaptive advantage will thus spread, if they are heritable, since those who bear them will become an increasingly large proportion of the breeding population. Natural selection fashions individuals of succeeding generations to be ever better adapted to their circumstances. The characteristics of a species represent the sum of the actions of natural selection on similar individuals.

It is wrong to say that animals behave "for the good of the species"—rather, individuals are adapted to maximize their own fitness, which is equivalent to maximizing the number of their offspring which survive to breed. In fact, selection acts on the genetic material that underlies each individual's traits, and so individuals actually behave in ways that promote the survival of the genes for which they are temporary vehicles—hence Oxford biologist Richard Dawkins' now famous term, the "selfish gene." Sometimes an individual helps its relatives, behaving in a way that appears detrimental to its own interests but is on balance beneficial to its genes, and hence improves its overall (or "inclusive") fitness.

Individual mammals behave so as to maximize their reproductive success and since the pattern of reproduction is the core of society, adaptations to this end are reflected in the great variety of mammalian social systems. There is an asymmetry between males

and females in this respect: sperm are cheaper to produce than ova, and of course only female mammals bear the costs of pregnancy and lactation. Therefore males may more readily maximize their reproductive success by mating with many females. Females, in contrast, can mother only a comparatively small number of young and so maximize their reproductive success by investing heavily in the quality of each offspring and, in particular, securing the very best (evolutionarily "fittest") father. Infanticide, as practiced by males of some primates and some carnivores, is a striking example of the lengths to which males will go to spread their genes at the expense of their rivals'—the death of the rival males' offspring brings lactating females back into heat (estrus), in addition to disposing of potential competitors of the infanticidal male's own progeny.

Females are a resource over which male mammals compete. The stringent natural selection that therefore operates between competing males is called sexual selection. It explains why many mammals are polygynous (one male mates with several females), few are polyandrous (one female mates with several males) and why males are often bigger than females (ie the sexes are dimorphic). A big male defeats more rivals, secures more females in his harem and thus sires more offspring; if his size and prowess are passed to his sons they will in turn become successful, dominant males. Therefore, females adapted to behave in a way which enables their sons to prosper will select only the biggest, most successful, males as mates. The situation is different if the species' niche is such that a male's reproductive success is affected by the quality of his parental care rather than simply by the quality of his sperm; for example, amongst members of the dog family (Canidae) the survival of young depends on their father provisioning them with prey, and the male would find it impossible to provide for more than one or perhaps two litters. In that event natural selection favors monogamy and the size and appearance of male and female are less disparate. This explains why greater sexual dimorphism is associated with polygyny, but it is less obvious why sexual dimorphism is disproportionately marked among bigger species. One possible answer is that energy demands are relatively less on larger species (see p 12) and therefore they can afford to invest more heavily in bulging muscles and masculine armaments.

(and scarce minerals) in anticipation of nursing and thereafter convert it to milk, she is free to spend more time with her offspring if necessary. Carnivora carry prey back to their offspring and may (eg wolves and African wild dogs) regurgitate for them. Koalas feed on toxic eucalyptus leaves and produce special feces of partially digested and detoxified material on which the weanling feeds, whereas the Two-toed sloth overcomes a comparable problem by continuing to nurse for up to two years. Lactation not only prolongs infant dependence and accelerates growth, it detaches the infant mammal from the environment: short-term food shortages are ironed out as the mother continues to lactate, if necessary mobilizing her own tissue, minerals and trace elements to provide abundant, digestible and nutritious food for her young. For the young, suckling is hardly an arduous pursuit, so it can devote more of its energy to growth than it could if hunting, doubtless inefficiently, for itself. Last but not least, parental care prolongs the young mammal's apprenticeship in complex adult skills.

The evolution of lactation has facilitated a marked increase in the sophistication of mammalian teeth. Once formed, mam-malian teeth are encased in a dead shell of enamel and thus cannot grow in girth (some continue to grow outwards). Lactation postpones the time at which the teeth must erupt and this may have been a precondition for the evolution of the complex occlusion (fitting together) of cusps of teeth in upper and lower jaws (diphyodonty) that is characteristic of mam-malian teeth and necessary for chewing. In a growing jaw such teeth would be thrown out of alignment. The importance of lactation is that it postpones the need for teeth until much of the jaw's growth is complete. As part of this process, mammalian jaws grow quickly; after birth, the growth of a mammal's head suddenly spurts relative to the rest of the body, giving infants their typically big-headed appearance. Furthermore, the growth of jaws and teeth is very resistant to variation, proceeding almost unabated whether the infant is starving or overfed. Of course, some mammals are so huge that they take years to grow and this may result in special modifications to

▼ Cheetah mother and young. Prolonged parental care prepares carnivore young for generally complex adult society and hunting behavior.

their tooth eruption. It takes over 30 years for an elephant jaw to reach full size, but nevertheless the upper and lower teeth are perfectly aligned throughout because their premolars and molars (in both milk and permanent teeth) erupt sequentially, one at a time from the rear, a bigger tooth emerging as the animal grows and as the previous one wears out.

Milk contains water, proteins, fats, and carbohydrates, but in proportions which vary widely between species. Mammals whose milk has a higher protein content grow fastest, but the diets of many species preclude their producing protein-rich milk. Pinnipeds have very fat-rich milk: that of California sea lions is 53 percent fat, perhaps because of the need for rapid weight gain prior to immersion in cold wintry seas. Elephant seals born at 46kg (100lb) quadruple their weight in three weeks. Small mammals also grow very fast; Least shrews double their birth weight by the time they are four days old. The composition of milk may change during lactation: amongst kangaroos the early milk is almost fat-free, but later it contains 20 percent fat. When the mother kangaroo nurses two babies of different sizes each teat delivers milk with a fat content appropriate to the stage of development of the infant attached to it.

The timing of breeding is critical, and often triggered by the effect of daylength on the pineal body of the brain. The costs of pregnancy and, even more, lactation are high and the weaned youngsters will place an additional burden on the food resources within their parent's range. Consequently, in seasonal environments, many species give birth at periods when food is most abundant. This can lead to extreme synchrony in the time of mating—in the marsupial Brown antechinus all births occur within the same 7–10 days each year! The onset of heat (estrus) in some rodents is triggered by the appearance in their diet of material contained in sprouting spring vegetation.

A difficulty may arise when other factors intervene to make it disadvantageous to mate one gestation period in advance of the optimal birth season. For example, Eurasian badgers give birth in February, but their gestation period of eight weeks would seem to necessitate them mating at a time when they are normally inactive, conserving energy while living on their winter fat reserves. Mammals have evolved some intricate adaptations to combat this dilemma. In the case of the badger

(and some other members of the weasel family, some pinnipeds, some bats, the Roe deer and the Nine-banded armadillo) the adaptation is delayed implantation. This interrupts the normal progression of the fertilized egg down the oviduct to the uterus where it implants and develops: instead, the egg, at a stage of division called the blastocyst (where it consists of a hollow ball of cells), reaches the uterus where it floats in suspended animation, encased in a protective coat (zona pellucida) until the optimal time for its development. In the case of the Eurasian badger this means mating any time from February to September. The most protracted delay to implantation is in the fisher— a marten—whose total pregnancy lasts 11 months, the same as that of the Blue whale. The fisher's "true" gestation is two months. Cetaceans (whales and dolphins) have very short pregnancies relative to their body weight. The longest mammalian pregnancy is 22 months in the African elephant. The shortest on record is $12\frac{1}{3}$–$12\frac{1}{2}$ days in the Short-nosed bandicoot.

Some kangaroos and wallabies exhibit embryonic diapause. A female conceives after giving birth (post partum estrus) but so

▲ Red deer stag roaring. The male's greater size and strength and its antlers have evolved due to sexual selection—in the rutting season the most powerful combatants can monopolize a greater number of hinds. Stags can assess the prowess of their rivals by their capacities to bellow, and thereby are able to avoid challenges that would be hopeless or dangerous.

long as her current infant continues to suckle the new embryo does not implant in the uterine wall. The consequence is the ready availability of a replacement should one infant succumb, with the added advantage of a rapid succession of offspring to be squeezed into good breeding seasons.

A different method of ensuring that birth is at a convenient season is sperm storage. This is employed by the Noctule bat and other nontropical members of the families Rhinolophidae (horseshoe bats) and Vespertilionidae (common bats). All the males produce sperm in August (thereafter their testes regress). They continue to inseminate females, often while the latter hibernate throughout the winter. The sperm are stored for 10 weeks or more in the uterus, until ovulation in the spring.

Sons, Daughters and Favoritism

At first glance the uncoordinated wrigglings of a newborn mammal may give little indication of its sex. Yet, there are some mammals which treat their offspring differently depending on whether they are sons or daughters. In the two highly polygynous species of elephant seals, male pups are born heavier, grow faster, and are weaned later than their sisters. These differences arise partly because mother elephant seals allow their sons to suckle more than daughters. Similarly, male Red deer calves are born heavier than females, after longer gestation. Thereafter, males suckle more frequently and grow faster and evidently cost their mothers more, since hinds which bear sons are inclined either to breed later in the succeeding season than hinds which rear daughters, or not at all. In these species mothers seem to invest more heavily in sons than in daughters.

The opposite pattern prevails amongst dominant female Rhesus macaques, amongst which a mother that rears a son is more likely to breed the following year than one that has reared a daughter. The implication is that a daughter costs her more, depleting her resources further than does a son. Amongst macaques it seems that part of the extra burden of bearing daughters is, remarkably, that females pregnant with female fetuses are more frequently threatened or attacked by other females than are those bearing male fetuses.

What underlies this favoritism? The answer lies in the limited time, effort and resources which parents have at their disposal for investment in offspring. Natural selection will favor parents which invest more heavily in sons than daughters if that investment is repaid subsequently by the production of a larger crop of grandchildren. It is easy to see how just such a process has operated among elephant seals, Red deer and probably many polygynous mammals. In these species almost all females breed (indeed females are the "resource" over which males compete). However, a minority of very dominant males sire the great majority of the young.

Depending on their status, males vary hugely in evolutionary fitness from indefatigable studs to reproductive flops. Attaining dominant status depends largely on a male's size and strength, and these attributes are greatly influenced by early nourishment. A mother Northern elephant seal which lavishes nourishment on her son is weighting the odds in his favor for the day, long hence, when he joins battle to win a harem. If he emerges victorious his brief but orgiastic reproductive career may secure for his mother up to 50 grandchildren each year for as many as 5 years—an ample evolutionary return for that extra milk. Since in harem-living species all females breed, largely irrespective of their strength, comparable extra investment in daughters' muscle-power would be wasted in such societies. Put the other way around, producing a feeble son which fails to breed is worse than useless, for the parental investment of time and energy is wasted on an evolutionary dead-end. In short, if parents' investment influences their offsprings' subsequent reproductive success, then natural selection will favor those parents which invest more in offspring of the sex in which that contribution has the greatest benefit.

The same principle underlies the opposite result among dominant female macaques. Macaques live in matrilinear groups whose members are linked by a female line of descent. Young males disperse, while mothers form coalitions with their adult daughters who thereby inherit their mother's social rank. The breeding success of a female macaque improves with the strength of the other females in her coalition. An attempt to promote this strength may explain why dominant females allocate extra investment to daughters. The attacks on females bearing female embryos (and subsequently also upon female infants) may arise because mothers in rival coalitions react to these infants as potential competitors of their own daughters.

Not only do some species invest more in offspring of one sex than the other, some actually bear more of one sex. Amongst African wild dogs the sex ratio at birth is biased towards males (59 to 41 percent). This may have evolved because several males are required to rear the offspring of one female, so that parents producing a male-biased litter will thereby secure more grandchildren. In effect, a litter of African wild dogs requires the paternal investment of several "fathers" to survive; thus to gain equal returns (ie future descendants) from their investments in sons and daughters, parents of this species may require more sons.

In mammals for which investment in either sex of offspring is equally rewarding one would expect equal investment in and, on average, equal numbers at birth of male and female offspring. In fact, although an average sex ratio at birth of 1:1 is typical for many mammals, the ratio can vary between populations of the same species, which suggests that the ratio can be controlled by parents to maximize their reproductive success. Female coypu with abundant fat reserves, and hence the opportunity of investing heavily in a litter, selectively abort small, predominantly female litters. Later they produce larger litters, with the result that females in the best condition produce more sons. This is advantageous because sons of females in good condition grow to be stronger and thus, in a polygynous society, are at a competitive advantage over the less robust sons of less healthy mothers.

Among mammals a birth sex ratio favoring female offspring (eg the Collared peccary) is rare, but one favoring males is typical of Mule deer following mild winters, of wolves in higher density populations, of Grey and Weddell seals born early in the pupping season, of mink born in smaller litters, and of chimpanzees whose previous offspring was female. It is easy to speculate how bearing sons in these various conditions may promote the parents' fitness (ie increase the number of their future descendants), but it is very hard to count descendants in the wild. Nonetheless, the exciting point is that so intricate are the adaptations of mammals that even features as fundamental as the sex ratio at birth are not immutable.

Size and the Energy Crisis

To survive, each animal must balance its income of energy with its expenditure. The particular problem for mammals is that their endothermy remorselessly imposes high expenditure. A mammal's body temperature is unlikely to be exactly that of its surroundings, so even when totally inactive the mammalian system must work to maintain its constant temperature and to avoid heat flooding out of or into its body: when at rest, 80–90 percent of the energy "burned" by endotherms is used solely to maintain constant temperature (homoeothermy). As summer turns to winter, the fires in a human household must be fueled with more energy, incurring higher bills, in order to maintain the home at a constant temperatur . So too a mammalian body requires more energy the faster it loses heat to the environment. The heat from the mammal's core is lost through its skin, and as a small mammal grows larger its volume increases faster than does its surface area (the surface area of a body increases with the square of its length, whereas its volume increases with its cube). A bigger mammal has less skin surface per unit volume and consequently, all else being equal, loses heat more slowly. Big mammals are therefore relatively (not absolutely) cheaper on fuel than smaller ones; when inactive, the energy costs (and hence requirements) per unit weight of a horse are one-tenth of those of a mouse. This phenomenon, of bodily dimensions varying together but at different rates, is called allometry. A crucial consequence of this increase in surface area (and thus heat loss) relative to weight (and volume) in smaller bodies is that energy consumption rises so precipitously with diminishing body size that the smallest terrestrial mammal, the Pygmy white-toothed shrew (2–3.5g/0.07–0.12oz) has to eat almost incessantly. The 1.5g (0.05oz) Kitti's hog-nosed bat manages to be slightly smaller by going into torpor and thus "switching off" its metabolism when at rest. The rate at which all the body's chemical processes occur and at which it requires energy is called the metabolic rate, so the fuel-hungry small mammals are said to have a high, or fast, metabolic rate. By analogy with an internal combustion engine, small mammals are expensive on fuel, like racing cars with high-revving engines.

Larger mammals are at an advantage over smaller ones in conserving energy. On the other hand they are at a disadvantage when dissipating heat. Mechanisms for aiding heat loss include the elephants' ears and seals' flippers. The strictures of temperature are reflected in the wide geographical variation in the size of ears of North American hares: the Arctic hare's ears are slightly shorter than its skull, while those of the Antelope jack rabbit of Arizona are expansive radiators, twice the length of its skull.

Marine mammals face a special problem, since the thermal conductivity of water is greater than that of air. They all need abundant insulation and the problem is especially acute for smaller species. The great Blue whale has a tenfold more advantageous surface:volume ratio than a small porpoise. This, added to its far greater depth of blubber, puts the Blue whale at a 100-fold thermal advantage in cold water. The struggle against the drain of body heat to the surrounding oceanic heat-sink may explain why smaller whales have even higher metabolic rates than would be predicted from their size: they lead an energy-expensive life in order to generate adequate heat. By contrast, fossorial (subterranean) rodents have a lower metabolic rate than to be expected for their size, because of the difficulty of dissipating heat in their humid burrows.

If all else were equal, the energy-expensive metabolisms of smaller mammals would force them to eat relatively more than their larger cousins. However, all else is not equal, since foods differ in quantity and availability of energy. Animal tissues, fruits, nuts and tubers are all rich in readily converted energy, in contrast to most vegetation, where each cell's nutrients are

encased within tough cell walls of cullulose. The energy contained in a meal of meat is not only greater than that in a comparable weight of foliage, it is easier to digest. Thus a carnivorous weasel is 26 times more efficient in extracting energy from its food than is its herbivorous prey, the vole. Smaller members of a mammal order tend to sustain their high energy demands by eating richer foods than do their large relatives. The 7kg (15lb) duiker selects buds and shoots whereas the 900kg (2,000lb) Giant eland can survive on coarse grasses; a bush baby eats fruit but the gorilla eats leaves, and the Bank vole eats seeds and roots whereas the capybara eats grasses. Amongst carnivores large size facilitates the capture of larger prey, which thus exempts them from the general rule that quality of diet declines with larger body size.

Diets differ in their availability. "High quality" foods, such as live prey or fruits, are less abundant than "lower quality" ones like leaves. Overall, the abundance of food available to a species depends on which tier of the food chain it tries to exploit: since living things, like other machines, are imperfect, energy is wasted at each link in the chain and so less is available for creatures at the top. This is why the total weight (biomass) of predators is less than that of their prey and why that of herbivores is less than that of their food plants, which in turn are the primary converters of the sun's energy into edible form.

Body Size, the Cost of Living, and Diet

The general rule is that (due to the volume:area ratio) smaller species require more energy per unit weight than do larger ones and consequently smaller species are pushed towards more nutritious diets and bigger species can tolerate less nutritious, but often more abundant food. So, for example, although they are close relatives (both are microtine rodents) the 100g (3.5oz) Bank vole has a higher metabolic rate than the 1.4kg (3lb) Musk rat. Many of the species that defy this general rule do so in order to exploit a specialized diet: some groups of mammals are typified by slower metabolisms than expected for their weight. For example, despite their similar body sizes, tropical leaf-nosed and fruit bats which eat fruit or nectar have more expensive metabolisms than blood-eaters or omnivores, which are in turn greater energy consumers than the unexpectedly "economical" insect-eaters. Examples of mammal life-styles which are associated, across all orders, with slow metabolisms are ant- and termite-eaters, arboreal leaf-eaters, and flying insectivores. Mammals with these diets are united in their thrifty use of energy by the fact that their diets all preclude the possibility of a consistent and abundant supply of fuel necessary to run a fast metabolism; flying insects are highly seasonal in their availability, many tree leaves are loaded with toxins and deficient in nutrients, and quantities of indigestible detritus inevitably adhere together with termites to the anteater's sticky tongue and so diminish the rewards of its foraging efforts. The difficulty of securing and or processing fuel destines mammals in these niches to an economical "tick-over" metabolism sparing in its use of fuel, like a slow-running engine.

Other mammals have highly tuned, "souped-up" engines their metabolisms burning energy even faster than expected for their body sizes. Amongst these are the seals and sea lions, whales and dolphins, and river and sea otters, which must generate heat to survive in freezing waters.

Quantity versus Quality

Those, generally larger, mammals with a lower metabolic rate cannot grow so fast, and consequently their embryos have relatively longer gestations and their infants have slower postnatal growth. Litter-weight at birth is a smaller fraction of maternal body weight in larger species. Infants of larger mammals thus require even longer postnatal care because they are so small relative to adult size. The need for protracted parental care would be increased even further if the overall litter weight was divided into numerous smaller infants, rather than a few bigger ones, since the smaller infants would require even longer growing times. To minimize this problem larger mammals have smaller average litter sizes. These trends combine, so that mammals with lower metabolic rates have longer intervals between generations and a lower potential for population increase from one generation to the next.

Thus the rate of chemical reactions in the cells of a mammal species has repercussions throughout the species' life-history and even determines the pattern of their population dynamics. Mammal species with fast, expensive metabolisms have a greater capacity for rapid production of young; they are preadapted to population explosions. Viewed against the variety of mammalian sizes from 1.5g (0.05oz) to 150 tonnes, this

▲ ▼ The giraffe's neck and the Harvest mouse's small size are both adaptations enabling them to reach food that would otherwise be unavailable.

interaction between size, metabolic rate and reproductive potential raises the intriguing possibility that while some species have evolved a particular size largely in order to overcome the mechanical problems of exploiting a particular niche, others may be a particular size largely due to selection for high reproductive potential of which their size is a secondary consequence. A giraffe must be tall to exploit its treetop food and a Harvest mouse must be small to clamber nimbly aloft grass stalks, and their sizes shackle them respectively to the reproductive consequences of slow and fast metabolisms—by the time a giraffe bears its first single offspring, a Harvest mouse born at the same time has been dead four years, and potentially could have left more than ten thousand descendants.

On the other hand, mammals like voles and lemmings, with high reproductive potential, are at a great advantage in unstable environments. They need to be able to breed prolifically and at short notice to take advantage of an unexpected period of bountiful food, and the capacity to breed fast requires the rapid growth permitted by the high metabolic rates typical of small body size. Mammals dependent upon unpredictable resources are therefore generally small.

The key feature of unstable environments is that the supply of resources may exceed the demand, for example when the few survivors of a harsh period find their food supply is replenished. In these circumstances, survival is no longer so dependent on population density or direct competitive prowess, and an individual will increase its reproductive success by investing more heavily in a larger number of offspring, and by breeding prolifically at the earliest opportunity, while the going is good. Species adapted to these conditions are called r-selected.

In a stable environment the situation is very different, because the population will be finely adjusted to the maximum that the environment can sustain, so competition for food and other resources will be intense. In these circumstances the pressure of natural selection increases in proportion to population density. Heightened competition in a saturated environment puts a premium on the competitive prowess of juveniles, and so parents must invest heavily in each offspring, preparing them for entry into the fray. Species adapted to these conditions have smaller litters, emphasizing the quality rather than quantity of infants born at a more advanced (precocial) stage of development, and infants are given more protracted parental care. Such species are said to be K-selected. Clearly, the slower metabolism of larger mammals will push them towards K-selected life-histories. It also makes them less able to recover from persecution and this is why very many endangered mammals are large, slow-breeding species. All else being equal, K-selected mammals produce fewer young per lifetime than r-selected ones, since not only do they have to invest more in each offspring, but they also have to invest heavily in their own competitive activities, such as territoriality, and in muscle power. The big decision in a mammal's life-history boils down to how to partition energy between reproduction and self-maintenance.

Spendthrifts and Population Explosions
The most dramatic illustration of this association between small size, rapid metabolism and great potential for population

▶ Herbivores in search of pasture: wildebeest and zebras at a river crossing. Like all even-toed hoofed, and some other, mammals, wildebeest are "foregut fermenters": in their foregut, bacteria help break down carbohydrates. Zebras (odd-toed ungulates) and other herbivores are "hindgut fermenters": bacteria at the junction of the small and large intestines fulfill the same role; they are less efficient at digesting cell-wall cellulose, but process food quicker than the ruminating wildebeest, which regurgitate and "chew the cud." Herbivores which need to feed almost continuously, such as the tiny vole with its fast metabolism, or the elephant, cannot "afford" the time to ruminate—they are hindgut fermenters. All the foregut fermenters are medium-sized by comparison.

increase comes from mammals with unexpectedly high metabolic rates for their sizes. Why do microtine rodents, rabbits and weasels spend extra energy on rapid metabolisms when comparably sized marsupials, anteaters and pocket mice maintain homoeothermy without recourse to such fuel-hungry "engines"? The answer is that these energy spendthrifts have apparently shouldered the additional burden of meeting extravagant fuel requirements in order to increase their reproductive potential as an adaptive response to unstable environments. The high "cost of living" of r-selected species such as the lemming, compared to the similarly sized (but K-selected) elephant shrew, is thus a tolerable side-effect of a reproductive rate that enables a female to have 12 offspring by the time she is 42 days old. An elephant shrew at best would have two young in 100 days.

Considering mammals of similar size but different metabolic rate, those species whose populations tend to dramatic fluctuations and cycles (eg microtine rodents and lagomorphs) have more rapid metabolisms than species typified by stable populations (eg pocket mice and subterranean rodents). The Arctic hare has an unexpectedly slow metabolism in comparison to other lagomorphs and its populations do not exhibit the dramatic population cycles typical of the otherwise similar Snowshoe hare. Similarly, Brown lemmings show population cycles with peaks of population density which exceed the troughs 125-fold; the Varying lemming has a lower metabolic rate and shows a maximum of 38-fold variation in numbers. The fluctuations in numbers of voles and lemmings result in huge variation in the availability of prey for weasels. The weasel's small body size and even higher than expected metabolic rate enable it to breed twice a year (fast by carnivore standards), which may be an adaptation allowing them to respond as quickly as possible to such a sudden increase in prey numbers. This gives the weasel an advantage over one of its competitors, the stoat, which is otherwise similar but larger and can only breed once a year.

If small mammals can produce many more young, why are any mammals big? Competition drives mammals into countless niches on land, sea and air and some of these can only be exploited by large species. Large size confers qualities that can be indispensible assets. Such advantages may include (depending on diet and other factors as well as size) the ability to survive on poorer food, to travel farther and faster and hence to exploit widely separated resources, to repel larger predators and to survive colder temperatures. Thus, within an awesome diversity of size, shape and behavior, mammals and their characteristics can be categorized into a series of trends which shimmer elusively through the cloud of adaptation and counter-adaptation.

THE CARNIVORES

CARNIVORES

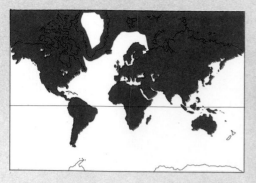

ORDER: CARNIVORA
Seven families; 93 genera; 231 species.

Cat family
Family Felidae—felids
Thirty-five species in 4 genera.
Includes **lion** (*Panthera leo*), **jaguar** *P. onca*),
leopard (*P. pardus*), **tiger** (*P. tigris*), **cheetah**
(*Acinonyx jubatus*), **lynx** (*Felis lynx*), **ocelot**
(*F. pardalis*), **Margay cat** (*F. wiedi*), **Wild cat**
(*F. silvestris*).

Dog family
Family Canidae—canids
Thirty-five species in 10 genera.
Includes **jackals** (*Canis adustus, C. aureus,
C. mesomelas*), **coyote** (*C. latrans*), **wolf**
(*C. lupus*), **Arctic fox** (*Alopex lagopus*), **Red fox**
(*Vulpes vulpes*), **Swift fox** (*V. velox*), **dhole** (*Cuon
alpinus*), **African wild dog** (*Lycaon pictus*).

Bear family
Family Ursidae—ursids
Seven species in 5 genera.
Includes **Polar bear** (*Ursus maritimus*), **Grizzly**
or **Brown bear** (*Ursus arctos*), **Spectacled bear**
(*Tremarctos ornatus*).

Raccoon family
Family Procyonidae—procyonids
Seventeen species in 8 genera.
Includes **raccoon** (*Procyon lotor*), **coati** (*Nasua
narica*), **Giant panda** (*Ailuropoda melanoleuca*),
Red panda (*Ailurus fulgens*).
The Giant panda, and sometimes the Red
panda, are sometimes separated as the family
Ailuropodidae.

Weasel family
Family Mustelidae—mustelids
Sixty-seven species in 26 genera.
Includes **weasel** (*Mustela nivalis*), **Least weasel**
(*M. n. rixosa*), **Black-footed ferret** (*M. nigripes*),

THE Polar bear is up to 25,000 times heavier than the Least weasel; the Giant panda ambles about foraging for bamboo shoots, while the cheetah dashes at up to 60 miles an hour in pursuit of antelope; the aquatic Sea otter and the arboreal Palm civet rarely touch terra firma. Such diversity of form, function and habitat is found throughout the order Carnivora. Represented among the carnivores are the long and thin, the short and fat, the agile and the slow, the powerful and the delicate, the solitary and the sociable, the predatory and the preyed-upon. There is little in the outward appearance of the 231 species, 93 genera and seven families to unite them.

So what does distinguish the Carnivora from other mammals? Ultimately their common lineage rests on one shared characteristic—the possession of the four so-called carnassial teeth. Many species in other orders, past and present, have been meat-eaters, but only members of the Carnivora stem from ancestors whose fourth upper premolar and first lower molar were adapted to shear through flesh. Only the more predacious of the modern species retain this pair of slicing teeth, collectively called carnassials. In species with more vegetarian inclinations, such as pandas, they have reverted to grinding surfaces.

The Ferocious Image
Many living Carnivora are adapted to either mixed (omnivorous) or even largely vegetarian diets, but meat-eating has been their speciality in the past. Although easier to digest than plant material, animal prey is harder to catch, and much of the fascination of carnivores lies in the stealth, efficiency, precision and the almost unfathomable complexity of their predatory behavior.

Prey are killed in various ways. Civets and mongooses (family Viverridae) and weasels and polecats (Mustelidae) are generally "occipital crunchers." They bite into the back of the head and so smash the back of their prey's braincase. Handling prey is dangerous to predators, and in the cases of these two families the victim's armaments are kept well out of harm's way by highly stereotyped behaviour. A weasel, for example, will throw itself on its side or back while delivering the killing bite, pushing away the claws and teeth of the struggling prey with thrusts of its legs. When dealing with small prey, members of the cat family (Felidae—the felids) aim a neck bite which prises apart cervical vertebrae with their sharp-pointed canines. Members of the dog family (Canidae—the canids) generally grab for the nape of the neck, as they tackle small prey, or pinion them to the ground with their forepaws. The grab is followed by a violent, dislocating head shake. However, canids immobilize larger prey through shock, which results from a combination of throat and nose holds, and bites to exposed soft parts that often disembowel the victim.

Carnivores have been dubbed vicious and cruel by people who equate anger and murder in man with social aggression and killing of prey in carnivores; but there is nothing aggressive, let alone vindictive, in a carnivore killing its prey, any more than there is in a herbivore decapitating a plant stem. The lion throttling a zebra is involved in the same function—feeding—as the zebra is in cropping grass.

One predatory phenomenon, more than any other, has resulted in carnivores being unfairly reviled—"surplus killing," that is,

► ▼ **Diet, hunting tactics and habitat** of carnivores vary enormously. In the open grasslands of East Africa, African wild dogs hunt in packs for large prey such as wilderbeest OPPOSITE ABOVE which they rund down, then kill by a combination of nose and tail holds coupled with disemboweling. The bobcat of North America RIGHT inhabits rough terrain, and hunts alone and by stealth for small prey such as rabbits and mice, which it swiftly dispatches by a bite to the neck or throat. The Giant panda BELOW lives in mountainous forests of China, where its placid search for bamboo "prey" lies at one extreme of carnivoran foraging.

ermine or **stoat** (*M. erminea*), **Eurasian badger** (*Meles meles*), **Striped skunk** (*Mephitis mephitis*), **Marine otter** (*Lutra felina*), **Sea otter** (*Enhydra lutris*).

Civet family
Family Viverridae—viverrids
Sixty-six species in 37 genera.
Includes **Palm civet** (*Paradoxurus hermaphroditus*), **genets** (*Genetta* species), **meerkat** (*Suricata suricatta*), **Indian mongoose** (*Herpestes auropunctatus*), **Dwarf mongoose** (*Helogale parvula*), **Banded mongoose** (*Mungos mungo*).
The mongooses are sometimes separated as the family Herpestidae.

Hyena family
Family Hyaenidae—hyenids
Four species in 3 genera.
Includes **Spotted hyena** (*Crocuta crocuta*), **Brown hyena** (*H. brunnea*).

killing more than they can eat in one meal. The farmer who discovers in his coop the slain bodies of a dozen or more chickens, some of them seemingly needlessly decapitated, will vow the fox kills for pleasure.

Many species of carnivores do indeed engage in surplus killing given the opportunity—wolves in a sheep fold, lion among cattle, Spotted hyenas in a herd of gazelle—all do so. But an alternative explanation to "blood lust" is more consistent with the facts. Prey are elusive, almost as well adapted to avoiding predators as their predators are to catching them; so tomorrow's dinner is never assured for a carnivore. However, since many carnivores cache or store portions of their prey or defend an unfinished carcass, natural selection has favored behavior that enables the predator to make the most of any windfall opportunity to kill unwary prey.

In practice, the prey's avoidance of the predator effectively limits the slaughter. Where this does not happen, and so-called surplus killing occurs, it is almost always because human intervention has compromised escape behavior—shut up in their coop, the chickens flutter frantically, but to no avail, as the fox seizes the opportunity to make extra kills.

The Body Plan of a Carnivore
Amongst the carnivores are representatives of almost every variation on the mammalian theme. However, the skeletons of all carnivores, irrespective of whether they walk on the soles of their feet (plantigrade), for example, as bears do, or on their toes (digitigrade) as do canids, share an evolutionarily ancient modification of the limbs—the fusion of bones in the foot (see

BODY PLAN OF A CARNIVORE

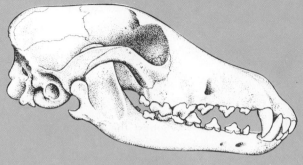

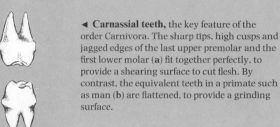

◄ **Carnassial teeth,** the key feature of the order Carnivora. The sharp tips, high cusps and jagged edges of the last upper premolar and the first lower molar (**a**) fit together perfectly, to provide a shearing surface to cut flesh. By contrast, the equivalent teeth in a primate such as man (**b**) are flattened, to provide a grinding surface.

▲ **The skull of a carnivore,** as exemplified by that of the Gray wolf. The "typical" dental formula of carnivores is I3/3, C1/1, P4/4, M3/3 = 44. That is, there are a total of 44 teeth with three incisors, one canine, four premolars and three molars on each side in both the upper and the lower jaw. There are considerable variations on this theme (discussed on those pages introducing the different families). In the case of the Gray wolf one molar is lacking from the "typical" carnivore complement on each side of the upper jaw (indicated by M2/3).

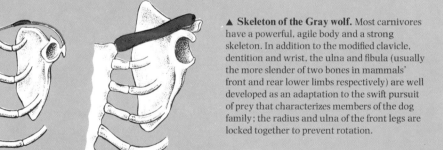

▲ **Skeleton of the Gray wolf.** Most carnivores have a powerful, agile body and a strong skeleton. In addition to the modified clavicle, dentition and wrist, the ulna and fibula (usually the more slender of two bones in mammals' front and rear lower limbs respectively) are well developed as an adaptation to the swift pursuit of prey that characterizes members of the dog family; the radius and ulna of the front legs are locked together to prevent rotation.

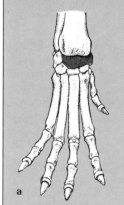

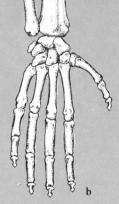

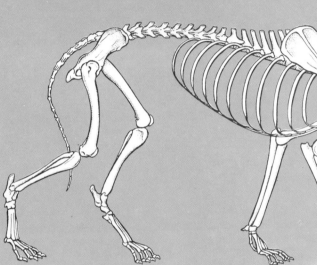

▲ **Fused wrist bones** are typical carnivores (**a**), in which the scaphoid, lunar and centrale bones are fused together to form the scapholunar bone; in a primate (**b**), these bones remain independent.

▲ **The collar bone is reduced** in all carnivores ABOVE RIGHT (**a**) by comparison with other mammals, such as a primate (**b**). Shown here is the collar bone (clavicle) of a wolf, which is reduced to a mere sliver of bone (*red*) suspended on ligaments (*blue*), and of a man.

► **Jaw power** is crucial for the capture and tearing up of prey. Shown here are the lines of force exerted by the jaw-closing muscles of the dog. The massive temporalis (**a**) delivers the power to exert suffocating or bone-splitting pressure, even when the jaws are agape; the rearmost (posterior) fibers of the muscle are most effective when the jaws are open wide. The masseter muscle (**b**) provides the force needed to cut flesh, and for grinding when the jaws are almost closed.

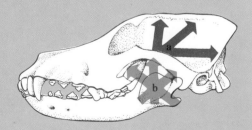

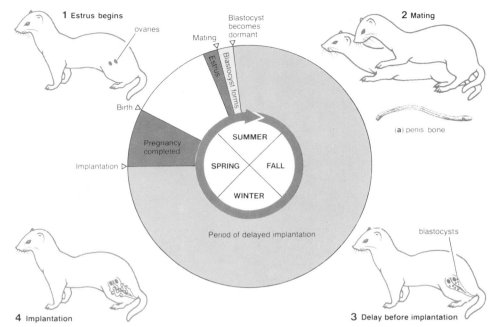

▲ Reproductive cycle of the stoat or ermine (family Mustelidae), one of a number of variations on the normal mammalian cycle displayed by some carnivore species.
(**1**) **Estrus begins.** In early summer, females come into estrus (heat) and up to 10 eggs mature in the ovaries.
(**2**) **Mating** soon occurs and the eggs are released as a result of copulation (*induced ovulation*), through hormonal and nervous stimulation. The prolonged copulation necessary to trigger ovulation is facilitated by the *penis bone* or *baculum* (**a**, shown actual size) which supports the penis of the male.
(**3**) **Delay before implantation.** After fertilization the single-celled eggs travel to the uterus, each developing as it goes into a ball of cells – the blastocyst. Instead of implanting in the uterus wall and continuing to grow into the embryo (as normally happens in most mammals), the blastocysts continue to float free and do not develop further. This *delayed implantation* (or embryonic diapause) lasts for a few days in some species, up to 10 months in the case of the stoat. The delay is maintained by low levels of the hormone progesterone.
(**4**) **Implantation.** In the spring, increased day length, as perceived by the eye, affects the hormone balance, and progesterone levels increase. This allows the blastocysts to implant; pregnancy is completed in 28 days.

OPPOSITE). For members of the dog family, the development of this "scapho-lunar" bone might plausibly be interpreted as providing a firm strut for absorbing the shock of landing at the end of a limb adapted for running. However, the fused bones were present in older, now extinct, forest-dwelling carnivores, so perhaps the scapho-lunar bone originally provided a firm basis for flexion at the mid-carpel joint in carnivores which needed both to climb well and to grapple with prey.

The advantages of a long stride when running may explain the relatively undeveloped collar bone (clavicle), free at both ends and lodged within shoulder muscles (see LEFT). The main function of a large clavicle is to stabilize the lower end of the shoulder blade and to provide attachment for the muscles controlling side-to-side movement of the limbs; neither function is either necessary or desirable for the fore-and-aft swing of the limbs of carnivores, which primarily run down prey.

Once caught, prey must be killed and dismembered. These two quite distinct tasks are served by two sets of jaw muscles, each of which exerts most force at a different phase of the bite. The temporalis muscle runs from the top (coronoid) process of the lower jaw to the side of the braincase behind the eye. This muscle is most effective when the jaws are wide open and is vital for the application of the killing stab of the canine teeth. For those species, such as the big cats, with large canine teeth, more skull surface is required as a base for relatively huge temporalis muscles: this is the function of the so-called sagittal and parietal crests that run

along the top of the skulls of these species. The masseter muscles are used to grind and cut food, when the jaws are virtually closed. The masseter runs from the lower (angular) process of the jaw to the zygomatic arch below the eye. The relative development of these sets of muscles (and the shape of the skull) depend on the species' lifestyle.

The remainder of carnivore anatomy is just as varied as their diverse life-styles would lead us to expect. The retractile claws so typical of cats are not common to all carnivores; apart from cats they are found only amongst the Viverridae (some civets and genets). Canids, by contrast, have digging claws which they use in caching food. The forefeet and hindfeet generally have four and five digits respectively.

A few unusual reproductive traits are found in carnivores. The penis of members of all families, except the hyenas, contains an elongate bony structure known as the baculum or *os penis*. This penis bone functions to prolong copulation, which may be especially important in species where ovulation is induced by copulation. The shape of the baculum is characteristic for each species. The so-called copulatory tie, which "locks" male and female together during copulation, occurs only in canids (see p56).

In most species the cycle of development of the fertilized egg is typical of that found in most mammals—the egg develops continuously from fertilization to birth of the offspring. In some carnivores, principally members of the weasel family, a delay in development occurs (see previous page; also p109).

The senses of the carnivores are all acute. Perhaps most intriguing is their refined ability to use scent not only to find prey (and to escape predators) but as a method of communication. Apart from the signal value of urine and feces which are deployed at strategic locations, most carnivores have several odorous skin glands. Doubtless these odors convey far more complex information than we can yet confirm. It is already known, for example, that one mongoose can recognize the identity and status of another by scent alone and it is likely that most carnivores can recognize individually others of their species from their scent marks.

Distribution

Wild carnivores have a worldwide distribution, with the Arctic foxes of Greenland and the feral cats of Subantarctic Marion Island at the extremes of their latitudinal range. Tundra wolves, rain forest civets, marine otters and desert foxes are among those species which illustrate how carnivores have adapted to every major habitat. Each family is widespread, the dog family most of all. Some species have been introduced by man to areas where they are not native, generally with disastrous consequences; Small Indian mongooses shipped to the Caribbean to control rats spread rabies instead; feral cats imported to remote islands annihilate flightless birds; whereas stoats and Red foxes introduced to control rabbits and to provide sport, in New Zealand and Australia respectively, actually threaten the native faunas.

There is one recent and intriguing move that the carnivores have undertaken voluntarily, and that is into the urban environment. The rubbish tips of the Middle East have provided welcome tidbits for jackals since biblical times, skunks and raccoons forage in the suburbs of North American cities, and the Spotted hyenas that wander the streets of Harer in Ethiopia are widely reported. In the last 20 years carnivores have been knocking at the gates to the capitals of Europe; Eurasian badgers now occupy setts in London and Copenhagen, and Red foxes are seen by lamplight in the streets of Stockholm, Copenhagen, Paris, London and many other towns besides. For hitherto unexplained reasons, urban foxes and badgers are most established in the United Kingdom and, in the case of foxes at least, in the southeast and the Midlands of England especially.

In the built-up districts of Bristol, England, the majority of badger setts are dug in private gardens or isolated strips of woodland. The badgers forage within ranges of 31–81 hectares (77–200 acres) for the varied diet, including earthworms, typical of some rural badgers. However, while rural badgers have so far proven to be rather strictly territorial, the ranges of urban badgers overlap widely (see Societies and Social Behavior, below). Red foxes are common around the university buildings and throughout the city of Oxford. There, the vixen who reared cubs in an automobile factory competes in notoriety with foxes seen in London's Trafalgar Square and Waterloo Rail Station! Oxford's foxes travel ranges that average 86 hectares (213 acres) and encompass every urban habitat from terraced housing to ornamental gardens. They may supplement the rural fox's diet with scraps from bird tables and compost heaps, and with the smaller casualties of road traffic. Only rarely do they raid and overturn dust bins (the culprits are usually dogs).

The Evolution of Carnivores

The early mammals are known largely from their teeth, since the smallness and fragility of their bodies, and also their forest habitats, have not favored the preservation of complete fossil remains. Consequently, we have only fragmentary knowledge of the origins of mammals 190 million years ago in the Tertiary era, and also of the ancestors of modern mammalian orders about 70 million years ago. Among the ancient carnivorous types a specialized pair of shearing carnassials evolved independently several times, for example, in the now extinct order of Creodonts, in which they evolved in different parts of the tooth row from those of modern carnivores.

The most likely forerunners of all living Carnivora are members of the extinct superfamily Miacoidea. These poorly known forest dwellers had spreading paws, probably indicating a tree-dwelling life-style, and carnassials derived from the fourth upper premolar and first lower molar, although the scaphoid and lunar bones were not yet fused. From the miacids the modern carnivore families developed during a fast radiation in the Eocene and Oligocene periods (54–26 million years ago). Doubtless this proliferation of types of predator mirrored a similar evolutionary explosion of potential prey, which in turn developed from the availability of more diverse vegetable food.

Among the more dramatic histories of modern carnivore families is that of the Felidae. All present-day cats are classified within the subfamily Felinae, but their early days were overshadowed by the successful radiation of saber-toothed cats of the subfamily Machairodontinae, which dominated the felid scene from the Miocene to the Pliocene periods (26–2 million years ago). Whereas the lower canines of modern cats are only slightly smaller than their upper ones, the lower canines of saber-toothed cats were reduced to vestiges in order to make room for their massive counterparts in the upper jaw. The extinct genus *Hometherium* had blade-like upper canines, serrated along their inner edge, whereas those of the American Pleistocene genus *Smilodon* were much longer and conical, fashioned more for piercing than for cutting. Probably cats of the *Homotherium* type severed major blood vessels, trachea and esophagi with a rending throat bite to their prey, whereas *Smilodon* was specially adapted to stabbing the throat of thick-skinned victims. It seems unlikely that either type of saber-toothed cat used its long, and hence fragile, fangs to prize apart the vertebrae of

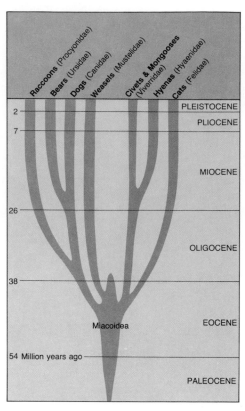

▲ **Evolution of the carnivore families.** Rapid differentiation of mammal, insect and flowering plant species has characterized most of the Cenozoic ("new animal") era of the earth's history. Most of the seven families of the order Carnivora became distinct in the first half of the era, although two appeared later, in the Miocene (bears and hyenas). Saber-toothed cats (see text) were just one example of a tendency to gigantism in the Pliocene and Pleistocene periods. Many large carnivores have died out in relatively recent times, and today smaller species predominate in most families.

▼ **The urban carnivore.** While man disturbs or even destroys their natural habitat many carnivores penetrate our cities in search of food. Prominent among such species in Northern Europe is the Red fox, caught here while on a night-time foray in the suburbs of Oxford, England.

▶ ▼ **Social interactions in the Red fox,** one of several species of carnivore previously supposed to be solitary and which turns out to have a complex social life. The dominant vixen of a Red fox group defers RIGHT to the dominant male (standing) by lying prostrate in his path, yet still manages to intimidate a subordinate female, her sister, who crouches and gapes submissively with ears folded back. BELOW A male solicits play from a vixen by rolling on his back and tugging playfully at her throat. BOTTOM Two adult sisters who have always shared the same home range sit amicably together, one grooming the other.

prey as do the small and medium-sized cats of today. More probably they would bite the victim's throat, as do modern big cats when tackling large prey. The exaggerated size of these teeth presented a severe mechanical problem. If the mouth was to open sufficiently wide to deliver the *coup de grâce*, the action would have involved risk of the predator dislocating its own neck. Consequently, the front neck muscles of Machairodontinae were enormous, and inserted farther beneath the skull than in today's cats, to give optimum mechanical advantage during the stab.

Societies and Social Behavior

Refined though the anatomical specializations of the carnivores may be, and however elegant the details of their behavior, the overwhelming feature of their biology is the subtlety of their societies. The collective strength, coordinated strategy and awesome effectiveness with which the cooperative hunters overpower their prey has captured the human imagination. But there is much more than cooperative hunting, spectacular though it is, to the societies of carnivores who hunt together, and it is increasingly clear that some carnivores have quite different, yet equally complex societies whose origins and maintenance have nothing to do with cooperative hunting.

Traditionally, two ideas were advanced to explain why some carnivores go around in groups: some, such as wolves and lions, it was argued, hunt together only in order to cooperate in the capture of large, dangerous quarry; others, such as some mongooses, were thought to travel together just to enjoy greater vigilance for marauding predators (see pp147, 152), some of which they could collectively repel. Certainly both these are among the chief selective pressures which have fashioned some carnivore societies, but neither is an appropriate explanation of why other species live in groups but travel and hunt alone. There are several species whose shy, nocturnal habits and small prey previously misled people into thinking them strictly solitary or asocial, for example foxes, civets, Brown hyenas, farm cats and Eurasian badgers. The use of radio-tracking and night vision equipment have now revealed that in each of these species (and probably many more) several adults may share roughly the same home range, even if the cohabitants meet only infrequently when foraging, and sometimes even den separately. Such species may be said to live in "spatial groups" whose members' home ranges overlap more than would be expected by chance. Three species which show how other pressures may favor the formation of spatial groups, in the *absence* of concerted hunting or anti-predator behavior are the Eurasian badger and Red and Arctic foxes.

In much of rural Britain the Eurasian badger lives in group territories within which 2–10 animals den together but forage alone, principally hunting for the earthworm *Lumbricus terrestris*. At night this species of worm only crawls from its burrow when the grass temperature is over 2°C (36°F), the air calm and humidity high. The problem for the badgers is that the worms emerge in different places from one night to the next, depending on slight variations in weather conditions. So, to be sure of finding worms, a badger requires access to a territory large enough to accommodate such a variation of climate and therefore worm availability. However, in the night's "good patch" many more worms are often available than one badger can possibly consume, so at no personal cost it can tolerate the presence of others in its territory. From this idea the scientist Hans Kruuk developed a model which correctly predicted that, where patches of earthworms were scattered, badger territories would be bigger, and, independently, that where patches were richer in worms, social groups of badgers would be larger.

The life-styles of Red and Arctic foxes share this feature of foraging for "patchily" dispersed prey, and the "badger model" may apply: territory size is determined by the dispersion of good feeding sites but group size by the amount of food at each feeding patch. For them, as with the badger, there may be little cost to tolerating some additional group members so long as food is plentiful, and, furthermore, in each species positive advantages of group formation have been discovered. Red foxes on the outskirts of Oxford forage in lush gardens where fruit, small mammals, invertebrates and household scraps are abundant. The gardens represent rich patches amidst relatively barren farmland. These suburban foxes live in groups of 3–6 adults which occupy territories varying from 19 to 72 hectares (47–178 acres). Each territory contains a similar number of gardens (about 24) and includes enclaves of housing; where these enclaves are widely dispersed the territories are larger. Similarly, in the fjords of Iceland, Arctic foxes in groups averaging three adults occupy coastal territories of 8.6–18.5sq km (3.3–7.1sq mi). Sixty to 80 percent of their food is obtained by beachcombing, and only beaches favored by the drift of sea currents are bountiful. Each cove thus constitutes a potential foraging patch, into which carrion and driftwood may be swept by the tide. The farmers in this part of the world collect all the driftwood to make fence posts. In each of the fox territories measured, irrespective of the length of coastline it encompassed, the farmers found wood to make roughly 1,900 fenceposts; presumably, therefore, equal supplies of carrion for the foxes were also washed ashore. In both Red and Arctic fox societies a single dog fox forms a spatial group with several related adult vixens of which generally only one, probably the mother of the rest, gives birth to cubs. As the cubs mature a conspicuous advantage of tolerating non-breeding vixens becomes evident: some non-breeders help to feed the cubs, and spend time grooming and playing with them and, presumably, keeping a watchful eye open for danger. This phenomenon of "helping" (alloparenthood) is widespread amongst carnivores (see RIGHT), especially among members of the dog family.

Other carnivores, such as lions, African wild dogs, dholes, wolves, jackals and coyotes also cooperate in the care of young, as well as benefitting from cooperative hunting. Similarly, members of the four genera of mongooses which benefit from group defense against predators also show alloparental behavior. In all cases individuals contribute to, and benefit from, various aspects of group life to different extents: in a pride of lions the males join forces to repel rivals, but hunt less than the lionesses who also suckle each other's cubs (see pp34–35). and within a pack of dholes some individuals may regularly lead the hunt, while others are especially vigilant guards at the den (see pp80–81). The pros and cons of group membership vary also between individuals as their role in the group alters, depending on sex, age and status. In the same way the suite of advantages that makes group living advantageous varies from species to species, and the nature of their societies varies accordingly. The lesson is that no one selective pressure is the sole force for any carnivore species' sociality.

In addition to cooperative hunting, vigilance and infant care, other advantages of group living are becoming apparent: larger groups of coyotes (see pp62–63) and Golden jackals can better defend their prey from rival groups, as can bigger parties of Spotted hyena defend theirs from marauding lions; Dwarf mongooses collaborate in the care of an ailing group member: in the lion and cheetah (see pp42–43) coalitions of males roam together with better chances of usurping resident males than they would have alone; Gray meerkats take it in turns to climb to a vantage point while their companions feed safely; and hunting tricks pass from one generation to another in packs of African wild dogs (see p77) and lion prides.

With variations on these themes, the list is still growing. In all cases, however, ecological circumstances, such as the pattern of food availability, set the limits for what is feasible socially.

Man and Carnivores
Man's relationship with carnivores is one of extremes—the Domestic dog and cat are to

Shared Parenthood

This non-breeding Gray meerkat male is caring for his three-week-old siblings while their mother is away foraging. Both male and female helpers guard the young at the den, a substantial sacrifice since they may not forage all day. Until the babies are weaned their mother neither guards nor provisions them with prey, but puts all her energies into foraging for herself, so as to produce abundant milk. Later, helpers also provision the youngsters with food.

By contrast, in a pack of Banded mongooses, maternal duties are shared among several breeding females, as they are in a band of coatis, and by both females if two Brown hyenas breed together. Lions and domestic cats, but not other felids, commonly live in close-knit groups of related females who share the nursing of each other's cubs.

Within the dog family, although both do happen, joint denning of litters and nursing coalitions are the exception rather than the rule; in most canids reproduction is the prerogative of the most dominant pair within each group. Subordinate animals defer reproduction, perhaps indefinitely, but more often until they accede to dominance within their natal group or disperse to establish a new group. The subordinates' postponement of reproduction results from social suppression, sometimes through direct violence, by the dominant pair. The process can apply to canids which travel and forage as a pack, such as wolves, dholes and African wild dogs, or to those who often travel and forage alone, such as jackals and foxes. In each of these species at least some non-breeders may help tend the breeder's offspring, provisioning them with food. In Red fox groups, whose subadult males emigrate, the helpers are invariably female, while in jackal groups, and probably in those of other members of the genus *Canis* (eg wolves and coyote), males and females are equally likely to be helpers. In the "back-to-front" society of African wild dogs it is young females who emigrate and the majority of helpers are male (see pp78–79).

There are several possible reasons why non-breeding animals may tend the offspring of others: they may be acquiring practice at parenthood, or may benefit subsequently from increased group size or (since groups are often composed of kin) may be investing in infants with which they share almost as many genes as they would with their own offspring (see p66).

▲ ▼ **Oil fields are the last refuge** of the San Joaquin kit fox in Central Valley, California, of which under 7,000 survive. The remainder of its former range has been destroyed by cotton farms. Where oilmen collaborate with conservation agencies to route new roads away from breeding dens, this fox suffers no ill-effects from the increase in industrial activity. Despite the presence of 40–80 wells per square kilometer (100–220 sq mi), breeding adults of this endangered subspecies of Swift fox survive at densities of 0.8–1.1 per square kilometer (2–2.8 sq ml). The survival of other carnivores depends on such acceptance of the shared costs and benefits of integrated land use.

The small black patch visible at the root of the tail BELOW is the site of the violet (or supracaudal) gland—a large scent gland of mysterious function present in most canids.

be found in their millions in all corners of the globe, while some wild species have had their numbers reduced to hundreds and others have been completely annihilated. The dog was one of the first animals to be domesticated, the origins of its close relationship with humans going back some 14,000 years, when man mainly lived in hunter-gatherer societies. It is now generally agreed that the wolf is the ancestor of the Domestic dog, but it is still debated whether dogs were deliberately domesticated to serve as hunters, guards or scavengers, or as sources of food or for warmth at night, or were adopted as pets or companions. The ancestry of the domesticated cats dates back no more than 4,000 years (possibly only 3,500 years) and there is no indication that they were domesticated for any practical purposes.

In common with many groups of mammals, numerous members of the Carnivora are threatened by man either directly through persecution and exploitation or indirectly through destruction of their habitat. Even if in no immediate danger of extinction, almost all carnivores require conservation in the sense of thoughtful management, since their maligned reputations, as much as their predatory behavior, have turned rural people against them. Despite a generally open verdict on

whether predator control is beneficial for either stock protection or disease (rabies) control, more than one Red fox is killed annually per square kilometer (two per square mile) over much of Europe. The onslaught by stockmen on the coyote of North America is notorious (see p63), and in the USSR, following an estimated annual loss of one million cattle to wolves in the 1920s, a precedent was set for killing up to 40,000–50,000 wolves annually. Today wolves are still bountied in the USSR (female plus pups for 200 rubles), with the result that 32,000 were killed in 1979. It is ironic that meanwhile biologists elsewhere struggle to secure the survival of the tiny relict populations of wolves in Italy (about 100 animals), Poland (about 200), Portugal (about 100), Egypt (about 30) and Norway (less than 10 animals).

As their habitats dwindle and populations become more fragile the fate of many species of carnivore is totally in human hands. Our society must decide whether these fascinating and often strikingly beautiful creatures are to survive or not. The problem is illustrated by the fact that the same Red fox, for example, may be seen by different people as aesthetically stunning, as a rabies vector, a noble (if inedible) quarry, a killer of lambs or pheasants, a "useful" predator upon rodents, or a pelt to be harvested. DWM

THE CAT FAMILY

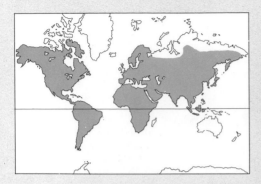

Family: Felidae [*]
Thirty-five species in 4 genera.
Distribution: every continent and major island except Australia, Madagascar and Antarctica. Domestic cat on all continents.

Habitat: very diverse, ranging from desert, through forest to mountain areas.

Size: head-body length from 35–40cm (14–16in) in the Black-footed cat to 2.4–3.1m (7.8–10.2ft) in the tiger; weight from 1–2kg (2.2–4.4lb) in the Black-footed cat to 384kg (845lb) in the tiger.

[*] CITES listed

Big cats
Seven species.
Lion *Panthera leo*
Tiger *P. tigris*
Leopard *P. pardus*
Jaguar *P. onca*
Snow leopard *P. uncia*
Clouded leopard *Neofelis nebulosa*
Cheetah *Acinonyx jubatus*

Small cats
Twenty-eight species of *Felis*, including **lynx** (*F. lynx*), **bobcat** (*F. rufus*), **puma** (*F. concolor*), **Wild cat** (*F. sylvestris*, includes **Domestic cat**), **ocelot** (*F. pardalis*), and **Black-footed cat** (*F. nigripes*).

Felids (family Felidae) are the most carnivorous of the order Carnivora, feeding almost exclusively on vertebrate prey; they sit at the pinnacle of many food pyramids and most have few predators apart from man.

Early forms of modern cats (subfamily Felinae) can be dated to the Miocene (25 million years ago), although the earliest felids evolved in the Eocene (50 million years ago), while the saber-toothed cats (later genera *Homotherium* and *Smilodon*) originated in the intervening Oligocene (38 to 26 million years ago) (see p22). A fundamental distinction between the big cats of the genus *Panthera* and the small cats (genus *Felis*) is that the big cats can roar but cannot purr whereas the small cats can purr continuously but cannot roar. The big cats' ability to roar stems from the replacement of the hyoid bone at the base of the tongue with pliable cartilage allowing greater freedom of movement.

Density of hair, coloring and patterning of the coat vary considerably in relation to habitat. The basic color is usually a shade of brown, gray, tawny or golden-yellow, and this is often patterned with darker circles, stripes, rosettes or spots. Many species have a dark stripe—the tear stripe—running alongside the nose, from the corner of each eye.

Felids have large eyes with binocular and color vision. In daylight, they see about as well as man, but under poor illumination their sight is up to six times more acute than ours. Their eyes adapt quickly to sudden darkness by rapid action of the iris muscles that control pupil diameter. The image is further intensified by a reflecting layer, the *tapetum lucidum*, which lies outside the receptor layer of the retina. Any light that passes through the receptor layer without being absorbed is reflected back again and may stimulate the receptors a second time.

The outward sign of this is the "eyeshine" seen when light is shone into cats' eyes at night.

Felids have large ears which funnel sound waves efficiently to the inner ear. The small cats are particularly sensitive to high frequency sound. The felid sense of smell is less well developed than in canids, although it is still important.

As well as smell and taste, there is a third

▼ **The big cats – some characteristic activities.** (1) Snow leopard (*Panthera uncia*) scent marking a rock by projecting urine backward. (2) Clouded leopard (*Neofelis nebulosa*) sharpening its claws on a tree. (3) Lions (*Panthera leo*)—lionesses head-butt in greeting. (4) Cheetahs (*Acinonyx jubatus*) – two subadults play-chasing. (5) Tiger (*Panthera tigris*) roaring, a call that warns other tigers it is in residence. (6) Jaguar (*Panthera onca*) covering prey with leaf litter. (7) Leopard (*Panthera pardus*) caching prey up a tree.

Skulls of Felids

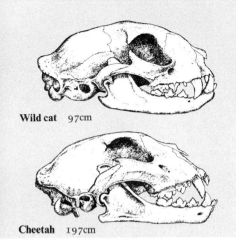

Wild cat 97cm

Cheetah 197cm

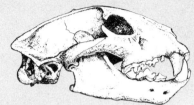

Clouded leopard 230cm

Felid skulls are small, with a short face resulting from reduction in the nasal cavity and jaw length. The dental formula (see p20) is I3/3, C1/1, P3/2, M1/1 = 30, except for the lynx and Pallas's cat, which lack the first upper premolars and hence have 28 teeth. The molars and premolars are adapted as gripping and tearing carnassials. The upper carnassial tooth (premolar 3) has a dual purpose: it has a sharp cutting edge but its anterior cusp is relatively broad and is used to crush bones. The canines are large (particularly so in the Clouded leopard) and used for grabbing and killing prey. Jaw mobility is restricted to vertical movements with the powerful masseter muscle giving a vice-like grip. To compensate for the lack of chewing molars, the tongue is coated with sharp-pointed papillae which retain and lacerate food and rasp flesh off a carcass. Each genus has its own arrangement of papillae.

sense, which utilizes the vomeronasal or Jacobson's organ sited in the roof of the mouth. The use of Jacobson's organ is associated with a distinctive facial gesture, an open-mouthed lip curl known as the Flehmen reaction. This is most commonly seen in a sexual context, possibly helping the two sexes to find one another.

The facial whiskers are long, stiff and highly sensitive; they are especially useful when hunting at night. Like a fingerprint, each cat's whiskers form a unique pattern.

Over three-quarters of cat species are forest dwellers and agile climbers, with a renowned reflex ability to fall on their feet: the vestibular apparatus of the inner ear, which monitors balance and orientation, acts in conjunction with vision to provide information relayed to the brain on the falling cat's orientation. The neck muscles rotate the head to an upright horizontal position, with which the rest of the body rapidly aligns so that the cat lands upright.

The majority of felids are solitary, extremely secretive and live in inaccessible, remote areas. The only real threat to their survival comes from man, notably the trade in spotted skins, which has brought species such as the tiger, leopard and ocelot near to extinction

GK

LION

Panthera leo
One of 5 species of the genus *Panthera*.
Family: Felidae.
Distribution: S Sahara to S Africa, excluding
Congo rain forest belt; NW India (a remnant
population only in Gir Forest Sanctuary).

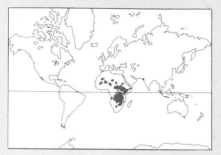

Habitat: varied, from rich grasslands of E Africa
to sands of Kalahari Desert.

Size: male head-body length
2.6–3.3m (8.5–10.8ft); tail
length 60–100cm (2–3.3ft);
shoulder height 1.2m (4ft);
weight 150–240kg
(330–530lb). Female head-
body length 2.4–2.7m
(8–9ft); tail length
60–100cm (2–33ft);
shoulder height 1.1m
(3.6ft); weight 122–182kg
(270–300lb).

Coat: light tawny; white on abdomen and
inner side of legs; back of ears black; mane of
male tawny through reddish-brown to black.
Coat of immature animals has a rosette pattern
which fades as they mature, although vestiges
may remain on lower abdomen and legs of
adults.

Gestation: 100–119 days.

Longevity: about 15 years (to 24 in captivity).

Subspecies: 7. **Angolan lion** Ⓔ (*P. l. bleyenberghi*),
Zimbabwe, Angola, Katanga (Zaire). **Asiatic lion** Ⓔ
(*P. l. persica*), Gir Forest, NW India; coat thicker than
African lions with a longer tail tassel, a more
pronounced belly fringe and a more prominent tuft
of hair on its elbows, mane smaller. **Masai lion**
(*P. l. massaieus*), E Africa. **Senegalese lion** Ⓔ
(*P. l. senegalensis*), W Africa. **Transvaal lion** Ⓔ
(*P. l. krugeri*), Transvaal. **Barbary lion** Ⓔ𝕏 (*P. l. leo*),
N Africa. **Cape lion** Ⓔ𝕏 (*P. l. malanochiata*), Cape to
Natal.

Ⓐ CITES listed.   Ⓔ Endangered.   Ⓔ𝕏 Extinct.

▷ **Two lionesses prepare to hunt together.**
It is the pride's females that do most hunting.

▶ **A battle-scarred lion** rests in the midday
heat. The main role of males is to protect the
pride from other marauding males. This one has
clearly experienced several such encounters.

BECAUSE of its strength and predatory
habits, the lion has been considered for
many centuries to be the "King of Beasts."
The myth of the supernatural powers of the
lion survives today: by consuming or wear-
ing parts of a lion it is believed that one can
revive lost powers, cure illness and win
immunity from death. The powerful image
of the creature still lures hunters to Africa
from all parts of the world to demonstrate
their prowess and courage by shooting one;
a trophy bestows social prestige on its
owner. Fortunately, most people are now
content merely to watch or to photograph
this magnificent animal.

Lions were once far more widely distributed than they are today. Cave paintings
and archaeological finds testify to their
widespread presence in Europe some
15,000 years ago. The writings of Aristotle

mention lions in Greece as recently as 300 BC, and the Crusaders frequently encountered lions on their journeys through the Middle East. Lions could still be found in much of the Middle East and northern India up to the turn of the century.

Like other members of the cat family, the lion has a lithe, compact, muscular and deep-chested body. Its head is rounded and shortened and bears prominent whiskers. The skull is highly adapted to killing and eating prey, and the jaws are short and powerful. Backward-curved horny papillae cover the upper surface of the tongue; these are useful both in holding onto meat and in removing parasites during grooming. Vision and hearing are of greater importance than sense of smell in locating prey. As in most other cats, adult male lions are considerably larger than adult females (20–35, sometimes 50, percent heavier). The males' greater size gives them a marked advantage at feeding sites, where they are able to crowd in or even to steal carcasses for themselves. Indeed, pride males may survive almost exclusively on kills made by females.

The male's chief role in the pride is to defend the territory and the females from other males and size is obviously an advantage here too. The evolutionary pressure on males towards increased size is balanced by the penalty of an increased requirement for food. This double-edged aspect of size may explain the luxuriance of the male mane. The mane gives the appearance of great size without the drawbacks of increased weight. Confrontations between rival males are often settled before fighting takes place, the smaller of the two animals perceiving its disadvantage and withdrawing before coming to blows. The mane has other functions as well, such as protecting its owner against the claws and teeth of an opponent should fighting actually occur.

The bulk of a lion's diet comprises animals weighing 50–500kg (110–1,100lb), although it is an opportunistic feeder known to eat rodents, hares, small birds and reptiles. On the open plains, where cover is sparse, hunting primarily takes place at night but, where vegetation is thick, it may also occur during the day. Adult males rarely participate in hunts, probably because their mane makes them too conspicuous. When several lions stalk, they usually fan out and partially encircle the prey, cutting off potential escape routes. Although they can reach 58km/h (36mph) some of their prey can attain speeds of up to 80km/h (50mph), so lions must use stealth to approach to within about 30m (100ft) of their prey. From this distance they can

charge the prey and either grab or slap it on the flank before it outruns them. Lions do not take wind direction into account when hunting, even though they are much more successful when hunting upwind. Typically, only about one in four of lion charges end successfully. Once knocked down, the prey has little chance of escape. Large animals are usually suffocated either by a bite to the throat or by clamping the muzzle shut.

The prey is usually eaten by all members of the group. When several lions feed together, or when the carcass is small, squabbles are frequent, but are usually brief and serious injuries are rare. Adult females require about 5kg (11lb) of meat per day and adult males 7kg (15.4lb).

Lions share their ranges with a variety of other carnivores such as leopards, cheetahs, wild dogs and spotted hyenas, each of which may feed on many of the same prey species as lions. But although all five species hunt animals weighing less than 100kg (220lb), only the lion regularly kills prey larger than about 250kg (550lb). Lions are also more likely to kill healthy adult prey than are the other carnivores. Hyenas are potentially the strongest competitors, being large-bodied noctural hunters. But by running down their prey, rather than stalking it as cats do, hyenas tend to kill calves and old and sick animals. Lions may actually benefit from the presence of hyenas, for in a study in the Ngorongoro Crater region of the Serengeti, in Tanzania, some 81 percent of all carcasses fed on by lions had been killed by hyenas.

Sexual maturity may be attained as early as 24–28 months in captivity and 36–46 months in the wild—a difference which may be due to nutritional factors. Females are sexually receptive more than once in a year, the receptive period lasting 2–4 days. The interval between cycles is highly irregular and may be between two weeks and several months. Ovulation is induced by copulation.

Gestation is short for such a large mammal—100–119 days. As a result, cubs are very small at birth and weigh less than one percent of the adult weight. Reproduction occurs throughout the year, although several females in a pride may give birth in the same month. Females rear their young together and will suckle cubs other than their own. Litter sizes vary from 1 to 5, with an average of 2 or 3. Cubs are weaned gradually and start eating meat at three months of age while continuing to nurse for up to six months from the female's four nipples. Mortality of cubs is high—as many as 80 percent may die before two years of

▲ **Lions mating.** While consorting, the adult male remains close to the receptive female TOP; other pride males may follow the pair from a distance. Either of the pair may initiate copulation by rubbing heads or by sniffing the other's groin. Copulation CENTER usually lasts about 20 seconds, during which the male usually emits a low growl and licks or bites the female's neck. The male usually dismounts abruptly as the female is likely to turn quickly and threaten with a snarl BELOW, or slap out. A pair may copulate up to 50 times in 24 hours.

◄ **Alert to any approach** – a group of lionesses, aroused while resting on a rocky outcrop in the heat of the day.

age. An adult female will produce her next litter when her cubs are two years old. If the entire litter dies, she will mate soon after the death of the last cub.

The lion is the most social of all the felids. Its social organization is based on the pride, which usually consists of 4–12 related adult females, their offspring and 1–6 adult males. Lions spend most of their time in one of several groups within the pride (see BELOW). Pride males may be related to each other, but are usually not related to the females. Both sexes defend the territory, although the males are more active in doing so. Territorial boundaries are maintained by roaring, urine marking and patrolling. Intruders usually withdraw at the approach of a resident, although males may fight and occasionally kill each other.

A pride will range over an area of between 20 and 400sqkm (8–155sqmi), depending on the size of the pride and the amount of game locally available. Large ranges may overlap with those of neighboring prides, although each pride has a central area for its exclusive use.

The varied environments in which lions can live profoundly affect their social behavior and ecology. Several studies of lions in Africa have shown that the lower the abundance of prey, the larger the territory must be. This relationship is clearest when measured during the season of lowest prey abundance. Factors such as rainfall, which govern the movements of prey, help to determine the severity of the lean season. The maximum size of a territory is deter-

▲ **Settled into a good meal,** three lions share a zebra carcass. As is usual, the actual kill was made by lionesses within their pride.

▶ **Straining every muscle,** a lion drags his kill to cover. This stray domestic horse was probably at a double disadvantage: on the one hand alone and ill adapted to its surroundings, and on the other made all the more conspicuous and attractive because of its differentness.

The Size of Groups Within the Pride

The members of a lion pride are normally scattered in several groups throughout the pride's range. The size of these groups—sometimes called "companionships" or "subprides"—is influenced by a number of ecological and social factors and is not merely a reflection of pride size: two prides, one of 7 and one of 20 animals, studied in Uganda, each had an average group size of 3 animals. Many factors favor the formation of larger groups: success in hunting large prey is increased and more kills can be stolen from other large carnivores. They also have fewer kills stolen by hyenas. One group of 2 lions studied had 20 percent of kills stolen by hyenas while larger groups of 6 or more lions lost only about 2 percent.

Other factors, however, restrict group size. If the available prey is small, few lions will be able to feed off one kill; and when prey is both scarce and small aggression among individuals at the kill increases, so that cubs

and juveniles may get little food. Lions feeding primarily on zebra can live in much larger groups than those killing small prey such as warthogs. Areas where prey is abundant throughout the year can support larger numbers of lions than areas where the supply of prey is low and irregular, but the sizes of groups found in each area are similar; there are simply more groups where prey is abundant. Whereas, for example, one area in Ruwenzori National Park supported some 14,000kg of prey per sqkm (350 tons/sqmi) and one lion per 2.5sqkm (1sqmi), another area with 2,800kg of prey per sqkm (70.5 tons/sqmi) supported only one lion per 11sqkm (4.3sqmi). But because lions in each area fed on animals of about 100kg (220lb), the average group size in the two areas was identical. Apparently, while the average number of lions in a given area is affected by the relative abundance of prey, group size is affected little, if at all.

mined by the pride's ability to defend it and by the point at which social cohesion would otherwise break down.

Because they are poor competitors at kills, cubs can easily starve during their first year of life. Adult females may even prevent their own offspring from feeding during periods of food shortage. Even in times of abundant prey, cubs may die of starvation if only small animals are killed, because of the dominance of adults at the kill. By 18 months cubs are better able to secure food at kills, and by two years the survival of cubs is no longer related to the abundance of prey.

Instances of humans falling victim to lions are common. The Romans used lions imported from North Africa and Asia Minor as executioners, a practice which continued in Europe in medieval times. Attacks by man-eaters are also well known in the wild, although they are often perpetrated by injured or aged animals unable to kill their normal food; man is an easy prey, being neither swift nor strong. Many cases of man-eating have followed upon the extermination of the lions' normal supply of game. However, this has not always been the case. Towards the end of the last century, for example, two apparently healthy lions preyed regularly on the laborers of the Uganda–Kenya railway—so successfully that construction was halted.

While lions are not immediately threatened with extinction, their long-term survival is far from assured. In the past, local populations of lions were considerably reduced in numbers by hunters, who regularly killed up to a dozen per hunting trip. Today, hunting is regulated, but many lions are still killed illegally, trapped in snares set for other animals. A more significant threat comes from the fact that the game on which lions depend need large areas of land—a resource that is rapidly diminishing. As agriculture spreads, lions are quickly eliminated, either shot for their attacks on cattle or forced out as the game is destroyed.

KGVO

Blood Relatives

Kin selection in a lion pride

A lioness suckles the cubs of a female relative alongside her own; a male newcomer to the pride kills her cubs, but subsequently tolerates the boisterous play of the cubs he fathers. These and other unusual features of lion society can only be explained when it is known which lion is related to which.

Blood relationships among lions are discovered by keeping careful records of known individuals in a pride over a number of years. At the core of a lion pride are 4–12 related females. They are related because they grew up in that pride, as the offspring of related females. On average they are about as closely related as cousins. A pride probably persists for many generations, and if it grows larger than its optimum size, surplus subadult females (2½–3 years old) are driven out. These are not normally allowed to join other prides and as nomads will have a shortened life span and a reproductive success less than a quarter that of resident females.

Young subadult males are also driven out at 2½–3 years old, if they do not leave of their own accord. They go as a group, with the other young males with whom they have grown up. Some of them may be brothers, littermates from the same lioness, but on average the adult males within a pride are about as closely related as half-brothers. Some are more distant relatives. The young male group remains together over the next year or two until, still as a group, they manage to take over as the breeding males of a pride. It is not likely to be the pride they grew up in, so they are not related to the females. Males may maintain tenure of a pride for periods as short as 18 months, or as long as 10 years, depending on the degree of competition from rival groups of males, and on the number of males in the coalition in possession.

A lioness will allow cubs which are not hers to suckle from her—cubs of four different mothers have been observed suckling at the same time from one lioness. This is most unusual among mammals—in most species a mother will not nurse offspring other than her own. The cubs which a lioness feeds, if they are not her own, are the offspring of her relatives. When she feeds any cubs, she is feeding young lions which carry a proportion of genes identical to her own. That proportion is a half if the cubs are her own offspring and the proportion is lower if the cubs are the offspring of a distant relative. But, in either case, by helping them with a supply of milk, she is helping to rear lions with some of her own genes.

Evolution has favored good parental behavior because that increases the number of the parents' genes which are passed on directly to future generations. Similarly, through the process known as kin selection, evolution also favors behavior which increases the number of an animal's genes which are passed on indirectly, via the offspring of relatives. This does not imply, or require, the tolerant lioness to be conscious of kin selection; evolution has merely made her behave tolerantly towards her pride companions' offspring because they are related to her.

The males in a pride are surprisingly close companions: they fight fiercely and cooperatively against strange males, but they do not fight each other for receptive females. Instead they operate a kind of gentleman's agreement whereby the first male to encounter a female in heat is usually accepted as being dominant over other males.

▶ **Lion pride at rest,** showing the relationships to the lioness marked (1). She is suckled by three cubs, one her own (i), the others the offspring of the two females 3 and 6. (2) Her half sister. (3) Her first cousin who has two cubs (iii). (4) Her second cousin. (5) Her elderly mother. (6) Her daughter who has two cubs (vi). (7) Her daughter who has three cubs (vii). (8), (9) Adult males who are half brothers to each other but not related to any of the pride females.

▷ **Lions and cubs.** An adult lion ABOVE with a cub he has just killed. Whenever a coalition of males takes over a pride they are liable to kill cubs sired by the ousted males. The new pride males soon have their own offspring to which they are extremely tolerant BELOW.

▼ **Close companions,** these males are related as are most pride males. Social bonds formed during grooming such as this show clear benefits when the males have to make a coordinated defense of the pride against intruding males.

Lions have good reason not to fight in such cases. Firstly, the chances are very low of any one mating resulting in a reared cub. Secondly, and more important, if a male lets his related companion mate instead, some of his own genes are nevertheless still passed on to any cubs fathered.

It is also not in the lion's long-term interest to fight with his companions, because a male needs companions to defeat the rival groups of males waiting to take over his pride. The biggest groups of males which take over a pride, those of 4–6, manage to keep possession of prides for 4–8 years, much longer than pairs can. The teamwork needed is possible only among companions who do not quarrel.

An established adult male in a pride is usually friendly towards the females and toward the cubs fathered by him or by his related companions. A member of a newly arrived male group behaves very differently. He is liable to kill at least some of the cubs in the pride when he takes it over. This violent and apparently unadaptive behavior was at first puzzling—most mammals do not ordinarily kill the young of their own species. However, from records of the life histories of lions in prides over several years, it is now clear that if males kill cubs when they take over prides, they probably leave more descendants of their own. A male is not related to the cubs he kills, but by killing them he can make their mothers produce his own offspring sooner (by becoming receptive to him soon after the death of her last infant). His cubs will also survive better if there are no older competing cubs present. Thus, killing cubs in such circumstances is adaptive and, like other lion behavior, is an aspect of the process of kin selection at work.

BCRB

TIGER

Panthera tigris [E]
One of 5 species of the genus *Panthera*.
Family: Felidae.
Distribution: India, Manchuria, China, Indonesia.

Habitat: Varied, including tropical rain forest, snow-covered coniferous and deciduous forests, mangrove swamps and drier forest types.

Size: Male Indian: head-to-tail-tip 2.7–3.1m (8.8–10.2ft); shoulder height 91cm (3ft); weight 180–260kg (396–573lb); female: head-to-tail-tip 2.4–2.8m (7.8–9.4ft); weight 130–160kg (287–353lb). Male Javan and Sumatran: head-to-tail-tip 2.2–2.7m (7.2–8.9ft); weight 100–150kg (220–380lb).

Gestation: 103 days.

Longevity: about 15 years (to 20 in captivity).

Subspecies: 8 (see p38).

[E] Endangered

FEW animals evoke such strong feelings of fear and awe as the tiger. For centuries its behavior has inspired legends, and the occasional inclusion of man in its diet has intensified the mystique.

Tigers are the largest living felids. Siberian tigers are the largest and most massively built subspecies; the record was a male weighing 384kg (845lb).

Like that of other big cats, the tiger's physique reflects adaptations for the capture and killing of large prey. Their hindlimbs are longer than the forelimbs as an adaptation for jumping; their forelimbs and shoulders are heavily muscled—much more than the hindlimbs—and the forepaws are equipped with long, sharp retractile claws, enabling them to grab and hold prey once contact is made. The skull is foreshortened, thus increasing the shearing leverage of the powerful jaws. A killing bite is swiftly delivered by the long, somewhat flattened canines.

Unlike the cheetah and lion, the tiger is not found in open habitats. Its niche is essentially that of a large, solitary stalk-and-ambush hunter which exploits medium- to large-sized prey inhabiting moderately dense cover (see OVERLEAF).

The basic social unit in the tiger is mother and young. Tigers have, however, been successfully maintained in pairs or groups in zoos and are seen in groups (normally a female and young, but sometimes a male and female) at bait kills in the wild, indicating a high degree of social tolerance. The demands of the habitat in which the tiger lives have not favored the development of a complex society and instead we see a dispersed social system. This arrangement is well suited to the task of finding and securing food in an essentially closed habitat where the scattered prey is solitary or in small groups. Under these circumstances, a predator gains little by hunting cooperatively, but can operate more efficiently by hunting alone.

In a long-term study of tigers in Royal Chitawan National Park, in southern Nepal, it was found, using radio-tracking techniques, that both males and females occupied home ranges that did not overlap those of others of their sex; home ranges of females measured approximately 20sqkm (8sqmi) while males had much larger ones, measuring 60–100sqkm (23–40sqmi). Each resident male's range encompassed those of several females. Transient animals occasionally moved through the ranges of residents, but never remained there for long. By comparison, in the Soviet far East, where the prey is scattered and makes large seasonal movements, the density of tigers is low, less than one adult per 100sqkm (40sqmi).

Tigers employ a variety of methods to maintain exclusive rights to their home range. Urine, mixed with anal gland secretions, is sprayed onto trees, bushes and rocks along trails, and feces and scrapes are left in conspicuous places throughout the area. Scratching trees may also serve to signpost. These chemical and visual signals convey much information to neighboring animals, which probably come to know each other by smell. Males can learn the reproductive condition of females, and intruding animals are informed of the resident's presence, thus reducing the possibility of direct physical conflict and injury, which the solitary tiger cannot afford as it depends on its own physical health to obtain food. The importance of marking was evident in the Nepal study, when tigers which failed to visit a portion of their home range to deposit these "occupied" signals (either due to death or confinement with young) lost the area in three to four weeks to neighboring animals. This indicates that boundaries are continually probed and checked and that tigers occupying adjacent ranges are very much aware of each other's presence.

The long-term exclusive use of a home range confers considerable advantages on the occupant. For a female, familiarity with an area is important, as she must kill prey

▲ **A tiger drinks frequently** during a meal, and in the wild will often drag its dead prey into cover in the vicinity of water.

◄ **The striking "white tiger"** was once not unusual in north and east central India, where the forbear of this zoo-bred animal originated.

► **Land tenure systems** of tigers in Chitawan National Park, Nepal. Each male's range encompasses those of several females. There is little or no overlap between individuals of the same sex in Chitawan. In other places female ranges may overlap.

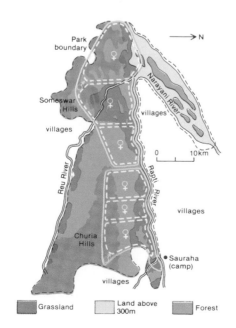

with some regularity to raise young. When the young are small and unable to follow she must obtain food from a small area, as she has to return to suckle them at regular intervals. Later, when her young are larger and growing rapidly she must be able to find and kill enough prey to feed herself and the young.

Territorial advantages for males seem to be different; they maintain ranges three or four times larger than those of females, so food is not likely to be the critical factor. What matters is access to females and paternity of cubs. Males are not directly involved in the rearing of young. Although there is not as much evidence as for lions (see p35), several instances have been reported of male tigers killing cubs. These are usually associated with the acquisition of one male's home range by another. By killing the offspring of the previous male, the incoming male ensures that females in his

newly acquired range come into heat and bear his offspring.

Tigers living in areas of prime habitat raise more young than can find openings, so large numbers of animals, usually young adults, live on the periphery. There is no clear picture of the social organization in these marginal areas, but ranges are certainly larger and probably overlapping, and there is little successful reproduction.

This outlying segment of the population is important, as it promotes genetic mixing in the breeding population and ensures that there are enough individuals to fill any vacancies that may arise. Unfortunately, it is usually these tigers that come into conflict with humans, as the habitat they occupy is, more often than not, heavily exploited by man and his livestock.

Sexual maturity is reached by 3–4 years of age. Breeding activity has been recorded in every month for tigers from tropical regions, while in the north breeding is restricted to the winter months. A female is only receptive for a few days and mating may take place as many as 100 times over a period of two days. Three to four cubs, weighing about 1kg (2.2lb) each, are born blind and helpless. The female rears them alone, returning to the "den" site to feed them until they are old enough to begin following her, at about eight weeks of age. The cubs remain totally dependent on their mother for food until they are approximately 18 months old and may continue to use their mother's range until they are $2–2\frac{1}{2}$ years old, when they disperse to seek their own home ranges.

All the surviving subspecies are endangered. Its broad geographical distribution, which encompasses such a variety of habitat types, creates the illusion that the tiger is an adaptable species. In fact, it is a highly specialized large predator with very specific ecological requirements and is much less adaptable than, say, the leopard. Once found across much of Asia, the tiger's present distribution and reduced numbers indicate that the requirements for large prey and sufficient cover are becoming more difficult to meet as areas suitable for large wild hoofed mammals, and consequently tigers, are being appropriated for agricultural purposes. As most tiger reserves are relatively small, less than 1,000sqkm (390sqmi), and isolated, the effective population-size is small and there is little or no inter-breeding between populations.

Tigers only rarely become man-eaters; indeed they normally avoid contact with man. Some man-eaters may be old or disab-

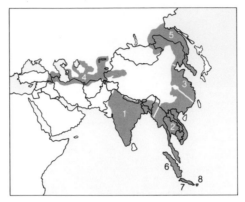

led but there are also many cases of healthy, young adult tigers acquiring the habit. This behavior may begin with an accident—a sudden close encounter that ends with the person being killed. Sometimes a single episode may be all that is required for a tiger to learn to kill a man. Whether or not a tiger takes the next step and becomes a deliberate man-eater may depend on the opportunity. There is also some suggestion that "aversive" encounters with people over the first human kill may discourage further incidents. The availability of other prey may also be a factor.   MS

◄ **Original distribution of the eight subspecies** (second half 19th century). (1) Indian tiger (*Panthera tigris tigris*): reddish-yellow to rust brown, underside whitish; stripes black; ears black with white spots on outside, white within; only 2,000–3,000 remain. (2) Indochinese tiger (*P. t. corbetti*): darker than Indian, lighter than South Chinese. (3) South Chinese tiger [EX?] (*P. t. amoyensis*): reddish-ocher; light belly colors do not extend far up flanks. (4) Caspian tiger [EX?] (*P. t. virgata*): stripes less wide, more brownish on sides; winter hair and belly mane long, nape mane short. (5) Siberian tiger (*P. t. altaica*): largest living felid; coat long, thick, yellowish without red in winter but reddish in summer; belly white extends onto flanks; tail white and black; only 200 in wild. (6) Sumatran tiger (*P. t. sumatrae*): smaller than Indian; stripes closer set; cheek hair long; short neck mane. (7) Javan tiger (*P. t. sondaica*): stripes narrower; only 3–4 in wild. (8) Balinese tiger [EX] (*P. t. balica*): the smallest tiger.

3

4

Hunting Technique

Tigers hunt alone, actively searching for prey more often than waiting in ambush. An individual will typically travel 10–20km 6–12mi) during a night of hunting. Tigers do not easily catch their prey—probably only one in 10 or 20 tries is successful.

Having located the quarry, a stalking tiger then uses sight. The tiger makes maximum use of cover for concealment to move closer to the prey (**1**). It must approach to within 20m (66ft) or less if the final rush is to be successful. The approach is extremely cautious, with the tiger placing each foot carefully on the ground and pausing from time to time to assess the situation. It assumes a semi-crouch or crouch, with the head up, during the stalk. Having made use of the distance and position of the prey, the tiger gathers itself up and suddenly rushes its victim (**2**), covering the intervening distance in a few bounds. When contact is made, the momentum of the charge may knock the animal off its feet, or if the prey is in flight a slap with a forepaw may serve to throw it off balance. A tiger's attack is usually from the side or from the rear; it does not launch itself into the air or spring on its prey from a distance. While it is seizing the prey about the shoulder, back or neck (**3**) with its claws, the tiger's hind feet usually do not leave the ground. At this point, the prey is jerked off its feet, if it hasn't happened earlier in the attack. A bite to the throat or neck may be delivered upon contact or while the tiger brings the victim to the ground (**4**).

When the prey weighs more than half as much as the tiger, the throat bite is commonly used and death is most likely caused by suffocation. (See p45 for description of physical adaptations to hunting large prey.) The grip may be retained for several minutes after death. Kills are carried or dragged into dense cover and tigers usually commence feeding on the rump. It is not unusual for a tiger to consume 20–35kg (44–77lb) of meat in a night, but the average eaten over several days is less, about 15–18kg/day (33–40lb).

Tigers stay near their kill and continue to feed at their leisure until only skin and bones remain—the average time in the Chitawan National Park was three days at each kill. Small prey, such as Barking deer, are eaten in one meal, whereas the larger sambar, elk and bison provide food for several days unless several tigers (usually females and young) are feeding on the carcass.

A tigress with young has to kill more often to provide food—an estimated once every 5–6 days, or 60–70 animals per year, for a female with two young. This compares with a kill every 8 days or 40–50 kills per year for a female in the same area without dependent young.

A tiger will eat whatever it can catch, but the larger hoofed mammals (prime adults, as well as young or aged animals) in the 50–200kg (110–440lb) range form the bulk of their diet. Typical prey are thus sambar, chital, Swamp deer, Red deer, Rusa deer and Wild pigs. Tigers occasionally take very large prey such as rhino and elephant calves, water buffalo, moose, wapiti and gaur. In many areas, agricultural stock are also readily taken, especially where wild prey is depleted.

▲ **Sumatran tiger in stream.** During the hot season tigers spend much of the daytime resting near streams or other water courses and often lie or stand in water to keep cool.

◀ **Camouflage of tigers.** A tigress in tall grass illustrates the advantage of the cryptic coat coloration. The stripes disrupt the outline of the body as the hunter stalks or lies in ambush for its prey.

CHEETAH

Acinonyx jubatus [V]
Sole member of genus.
Family: Felidae.
Distribution: Africa, S Asia, Middle East.

Habitat: most habitats in Africa except rain forest.

Size: head-body length 112–135cm (44–53in); tail length 66–84cm (26–33in); weight 39–65kg (86–143lb). Males usually slightly larger than females.

Coat: tawny with small round black spots. Face marked by conspicuous "tear stripes" running from the corner of the eyes down sides of nose; cubs under three months old blackish, with a mantle of long blue-gray hair on top of the back and neck.

Gestation: 91–95 days.

Longevity: up to 12 years (17 in captivity).

Subspecies: 2 **African cheetah** (*A. j. jubatus*) and **Asiatic cheetah** [E] (*A. j. venaticus*). (**King cheetah**, a mutant form occuring only in S Africa, was once incorrectly described as a separate species, *Acinonyx rex*. Coat: spots along spine joined together in stripes, with small splotches on the body.)

[E] Endangered. [V] Vulnerable.

THE fastest animal on land, the cheetah can sprint at up to 96 kilometers an hour (60mph) for a brief part of its chase. It still occurs over most of Africa, but very few now remain in southern Asia (where it probably evolved) and the Middle East.

The cheetah is easily distinguished from other cats, not only by its distinctive markings, but also by its loose and rangy build, small head, high-set eyes and small, rather flattened ears. The usual prey consists of gazelles, impala, wildebeest calves and other hoofed mammals up to 40kg (88lb) in weight. In some areas, hares are also an important food. The prey is hunted by stalking from a few seconds up to several hours, until the prey is within 30m (100ft), before chasing. About half the chases are successful and an average chase is 170m (550ft) and lasts 20 seconds, rarely exceeding one minute. The prey is suffocated by biting the underside of the throat. On average, an adult eats 2.8kg (6.2lb) of meat per day. Drinking is seldom more frequent than once every four days and sometimes as infrequent as once in 10 days.

Sexual maturity occurs at 20–23 months old. Courting females and males probably already know each other because their home ranges overlap. Females in heat squirt urine on bushes, tree trunks and rocks to attract males which, when they discover the scent, hurriedly follow the trail, calling with yelps. The receptive female responds to the yelps by approaching the male. Mating sometimes occurs immediately, with copulation lasting less than one minute. They stay together for a day or two and mate several times. The males have a hierarchy and apparently it is usually only the dominant male that mates, while his companions wait nearby.

There is no regular breeding season and cubs are born in all months. The litter size is 1–8, but the average is three. Newborn cubs weigh 250–300g (8–11oz) and are up to 30cm (12in) long from the nose to the root of the tail. Their eyes open at 2–11 days old. Cubs remain hidden under bushes or in dense grass, but their mother carries them to a new hiding place every few days. By 5–6 weeks old, cubs are able to follow their mother and begin eating from the prey their mother catches. Males do not help to raise

▲ **A rate of acceleration** comparable to that of a high-powered sports car enables the cheetah to outrun all other animals over short distances.

▲ **A solitary hunter,** the cheetah uses a stalk-and-rapid-chase technique. This female has spotted her quarry and is about to begin stalking.

▶ **A strangling throat bite** killed this Thomson's gazelle; the carcass is now dragged away to cover.

◀ **Mantle of blue-gray hair** indicates that these cubs, feeding with their mother, are under three months old.

The Cheetah's Niche

Where cheetahs are found so also are other large carnivores such as lions, leopards, hyenas, wild dogs and jackals—and other meat-eaters such as vultures. But if different species are to coexist in the same area they must exploit available resources in ways that minimize the likelihood of direct competition and open conflict. One way of achieving this is to evolve an anatomy that is highly specialized for a particular method of hunting.

A slender build and highly flexible spine enable the cheetah to make astonishingly long and rapid strides; and, unlike other cats, the cheetah's claws when retracted are not covered by a sheath but are left exposed to provide additional traction during rapid acceleration. However, with great sprinting prowess comes limited endurance and this means that the cheetah can only hunt effectively in open country where there is enough natural cover for stalking.

A sure method of killing prey is also important. The small upper canine teeth have correspondingly small roots bounding the sides of the nasal passages, permitting an increased air intake that enables the cheetah to maintain a relentless suffocating bite.

The cheetah usually hunts and eats later in the morning and earlier in the afternoon than other large carnivores, which tend to sleep in the heat of the day; its less-developed whiskers suggest less nocturnal activity than other cats.

Greater daytime activity, however, brings the cheetah into contention with vultures—soaring on daytime thermals. Vultures sometimes drive a cheetah away from its kill and their descent also attracts other carnivores who may then appropriate the cheetah's meal. The problem is minimized by the cheetah's stealth as a hunter and by its habit of dragging its prey to a hiding place before eating.

the cubs. Weaning occurs at about three months of age. Fewer than one-third of the cubs, on average, survive to adulthood.

Adult females are solitary, except when they are raising cubs. They rarely associate with other adults, and when they do, it is likely to be for only a few hours following a chance encounter with a sister or when found by territorial males. Males are more gregarious than females and often live in permanent groups, which are sometimes composed of littermates.

In the 16th century, cheetahs were commonly kept by Arabs, Abyssinians and the Mogul emperors to hunt antelopes. More recently, cheetahs have been in demand for their fur, which is used for women's coats. In the wild, cheetahs are widely protected, but so long as the trade in skins in many European countries and Japan remains legal, widespread poaching will continue to occur. An estimated 5,000 cheetah skins were traded annually in recent years.

A more substantial threat to the cheetah's survival is the loss of habitat, which deprives it of suitable prey, reduces its hunting success, causes more cubs to die of starvation and fall victim to predators, increases the proportion of kills stolen by other large carnivores, and causes conflict with man through increased attacks on domestic livestock. Captive breeding, although successful, is not a suitable alternative to preserving the natural habitat. The total surviving cheetah population in Africa is probably only about 25,000   GWF

Cheetahs of the Serengeti
Male–female differences in habitat exploitation

Spacing behavior among cheetahs shows how they exploit their habitat and prey. In areas such as the Serengeti in East Africa, where prey species are migratory, adult female cheetahs (with or without cubs) migrate annually over a home range of about 800sqkm (310sqmi). Each adult female travels her home range in an annual cycle and appears to use the same area year after year.

Cheetah litters separate from their mother when they are adult size, at 13–20 months old. The siblings usually remain together for several months longer. One by one the females, when 17–23 months old, leave their littermates.

Female cheetahs, although not territorial, avoid each other. Adult females are not aggressive to other females or to males, but if they see another cheetah nearby their usually walk farther away or hide. Their mutual avoidance means that non-related or distantly related females, as well as close relatives, have home ranges that overlap each other, but in which they rarely interact.

Young adult male cheetahs leave their mother's home range as a group. Apparently they are chased away by older and stronger territorial males. The young males disperse about 20km (12mi), and probably sometimes much farther, beyond their mother's home range. Adult male littermates often remain together for life and non-littermates sometimes join together in groups of 2–4.

Territorial males defend a well-defined area throughout which they regularly mark prominent trees, bushes and rocks with urine, feces and scratch marks. Territories of males in the Serengeti cover about 30sqkm

▲ **A vigilant female** sits aloft on a termite mound for a better view of her surroundings, while her cubs frolic nearby.

◄ **Scent-marking its territory,** a male cheetah sprays urine backward onto a conspicuous landmark, one of many similarly marked by the same animal in its territory.

► **In defense of their territory,** males close in on one of three intruding males; this one was subsequently killed. It is now known that male cheetahs, often close relatives, sometimes work together to hold and defend a territory. Previously it was supposed that a territory was always held and defended by one dominant animal.

▶ **Home ranges** of members of three cheetah families observed on the Serengeti Plains, Tanzania, over the same period. Home ranges of other families overlapped these. TOP The home ranges of two female cheetah littermates partly overlap each other and the ranges (not shown) of their mother, other females, territorial males and nomadic males. The home ranges of these sisters are large because they follow the migratory prey. Each home range shown represents the limit of movement in a full year: for several weeks, the cheetah remains in one locality within her range, making zig-zag and circular movements in search of prey. When hunting becomes poor, she moves on a few kilometers to a new locality.
CENTER In this typical cheetah family two young adult daughters (white) remain near and overlap their mother's home range (blue), while the young adult males (dotted yellow line) probably left because of aggression by territorial males in their mother's area, and they remain nomadic until they are able to defend a territory. About half the males remain in groups, whereas females are always solitary. Some male groups consist of littermates, some consist of males who were born to different mothers and some groups are a mixture of both. Male group size is 2–4.
BOTTOM The home ranges of this mother (blue) and daughter (white) are entirely in the grasslands. Cover is, however, available in drainages with tall dense herbs and in rocky outcrops with bushes. In this case the two sons (dotted yellow line) emigrated more than 18km (11mi) from their mother's home range, ousted two territorial males from a woodland territory and established themselves there.

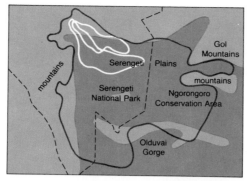

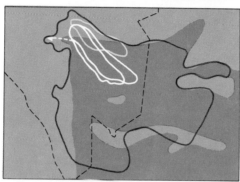

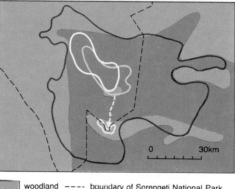

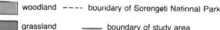

woodland   ---- boundary of Serengeti National Park
grassland   —— boundary of study area

(12sqmi). Territorial males do not migrate 50–80km (30–50mi) to follow the prey, as the females do, but when there is no food or water within the territory they temporarily leave to feed and drink nearby. Lone males and groups of males are known to hold their territories for at least four years, but eventually they are ousted or killed by stronger males, either another lone male, or a group of males in coalition.

The males' tendency to live in small groups, as well as to hunt and eat together, is most probably due to an increased success in establishing and defending a territory compared with the chance they would have as solitary males. The males hold territories in places of moderate vegetative cover, such as woodlands and bushed drainages (see movements of emigrating males, LEFT).

Not all male cheetahs are territorial; some males seem to be nomadic. These nomads frequently encounter territorial males, who respond aggressively to them. One fight observed between a group of three territorial males and a group of three intruding males began when the territorial males chased and caught one of the intruders. All three territorial males fought with the intruder, biting him repeatedly all over his body and pulling out mouthfuls of fur. Eventually one of the territorial males inflicted a suffocating bite on the underside of the neck, the same bite that is used in killing prey.

Immediately after killing the first intruder, the territorial males walked towards the other two intruders, who were watching from about 275m (300yd) away. They fought briefly, then one territorial male chased an intruder at least 1km (1,100yd). Soon after, all three fought with the remaining intruder, but eventually left him alone. The result of this territorial encounter was one intruder lying dead, one injured and one chased away. The defenders were unharmed except for one bloody lip.

The social system of male territoriality in itself restricts the density of cheetahs. When the cheetah population increases, more of the available habitat is claimed by territorial males, leading to increased conflict and more deaths. Females, too, are affected through increased harassment from the sexually motivated males. Sometimes, territorial males intent on mating virtually hold a mother cheetah captive for a day or two, which prevents her from tending her cubs. This probably leads to a greater number of cub deaths, by making cubs more conspicuous in their behavior and therefore vulnerable to predators, and by reducing the mother's ability to feed them.   GWF

LEOPARD

Panthera pardus
One of 5 species of the genus *Panthera*.
Family: Felidae.
Distribution: Africa S of the Sahara, and S Asia;
scattered populations in N Africa, Arabia, far
East.

Habitat: most areas having a reasonable
amount of cover, a supply of prey animals and
freedom from excessive persecution; from
tropical rain forest to arid savanna; from cold
mountains almost to urban suburbs.

Size: head-body length
100–190cm (40–75in); tail
length 70–95cm (28–37in);
shoulder height 45–80cm
(18–32in); weight 30–70kg
(66–155lb). Males are about
50 percent larger than
females.

Coat: highly variable, essentially black spots on
a fawn to pale brown background. Typically,
the spots are small on the head, larger on the
belly and limbs, and arranged in rosette
patterns on the back, flanks and upper limbs.

Gestation: 90–105 days.

Longevity: up to 12 years (20 in captivity).

Subspecies: 7. **Amur leopard** E
(*P. p. orientalis*), Amur-Ussuri region, N China,
Korea; coat long and thick, light-hued in
winter, reddish-yellow in summer; spots large.
Anatolian leopard E (*P. p. tulliana*), Asia
Minor; coat brighter and tanner, often with
some gray hues. **Barbary
leopard** E (*P. p. panthera*), Morocco, Algeria,
Tunisia. **North African leopard** (*P. p. pardus*),
Africa except extreme N, Asia; coat yellowish-
ocher. **Sinai leopard** E (*P. p. jarvis*), Sinai;
coat light with large spots. **South Arabian
leopard** E (*P. p. nimr*). **Zanzibar leopard** EX?
(*P. p. adersi*), Zanzibar; spots very small.

E Endangered.   EX? Probably extinct.   V Vulnerable.

► **A North African leopard** licking a paw
clean, rather like a big domestic cat. The coat
spots provide excellent camouflage, especially
in trees; and the prominent, extremely sensitive
whiskers are those of an animal that hunts at
night.

CONFUSION surrounds leopards. Even the name "leopard" originates from the mistaken belief that the animal was a hybrid between the lion (*Leo*) and the "pard" or panther. And only just over a century ago it was still disputed whether leopards and "panthers" were separate species. In fact the words "pard" and "panther" are vague, archaic terms that have been used for several large cats, especially the leopard, jaguar and puma. With luck, the confusing term "panther" will die out before the single species, best called the leopard, does.

About 30 subspecies have been named, but only about seven are still accepted today. The commonest form is the North African leopard, which occurs over most of the leopard's range. The other subspecies are small or geographically isolated populations.

In form the leopard is average among the large cats—slender and delicate compared with the jaguar, but sturdy and stolid compared with the cheetah. There are various aberrant coat patterns. One of the commonest and most striking is melanism, the leopard being totally black. It is caused by a recessive gene, which is apparently more frequent in leopard populations in forests, in mountains and in Asia. In the Malay peninsula as many as 50 percent of leopards may be black; elsewhere the proportions are much lower. The name "Black panther" is sometimes erroneously applied to such animals in the belief that they are a distinct species. Several other cat species, including the jaguar and serval, also exhibit melanism.

The leopard is the most widespread member of the cat family, and this is largely due to its highly adaptable hunting and feeding behavior. Leopards catch a great variety of small prey species—mainly small mammals and birds—and they do so by a combination of opportunism, stealth and speed. They hunt alone, generally at night, and either ambush their prey or stalk to within close range before making a short fast rush. Adept tree climbers, leopards often drag their prey up trees, out of reach of scavengers. Because of the variety and small size of their prey, leopards avoid strong competition with such carnivores as lions, tigers, hyenas and African wild dogs, which depend on larger prey.

Over most of their range, leopards have no particular breeding season. Females are sexually receptive at 3–7 week intervals, and the period of receptivity lasts for a few days, during which mating is frequent. Most litters consist of usually three (range 1–6) blind, furred cubs weighing 430–570g (15–20oz).

The cubs are kept hidden until they start to follow the mother at 6–8 weeks old. Only the mother cares for the young. She does so until her cubs are about 18–20 months old, whereupon she mates again. Sexual maturity is probably achieved in leopards at about $2\frac{1}{2}$ years.

▲ **The legendary "black panther"** was once thought to be a distinct species. It is now known to be a black-coated form of the leopard. The way the light falls on this individual clearly reveals the familiar leopard spots against the black fur.

HOW LEOPARDS USE TREES

◄ **Resting.** Safely aloft and shaded from the midday sun, a leopard dozes in the branches of an acacia tree.

▼ **Hunting.** Ready to leap, a leopard surveys its surroundings for potential prey. Occasionally a leopard will drop directly onto a passing animal from the cover of a tree.

► **Conserving food.** Leopards often drag their kills – in this case a topi calf – up trees, where they can eat and store them out of reach of most scavengers.

The leopard is almost entirely solitary. Females occupy territories of 10–30sqkm (4–12sqmi) or more which overlap little with those of other females. Superimposed on these is another mosaic of similar but larger male territories. These areas are defended in fights and are marked throughout by urine sprayed onto logs, branches and tree-trunks in the course of the leopard's extensive travels around its territory. The main vocalization is a rough rasping sound—like that of a saw being used on coarse wood; it is used both to proclaim the territory-holder's presence and to make contact between separated individuals. When in heat a female rasps to attract a male and a mother rasps to call her cubs. When 2–3 years old, male cubs disperse and settle elsewhere, while female cubs probably take over part of their mother's territory.

Leopard numbers are declining almost everywhere, partly from hunting for their fur, which is highly prized for decorating affluent women. In many areas, too, leopards are persecuted because of their attacks on domestic livestock. Numbers will continue to decline, but despite the likely loss of some subspecies, the adaptable leopard will probably continue to thrive in many areas where human population pressures are low. There are still well over 100,000 left.

Leopards are a highly popular attraction for visitors to National Parks. Elsewhere, relations with man are mutually hostile. In Asia, very occasionally, leopards become man-eaters and individuals have been known to kill over one hundred people. As well as killing them for profit and to reduce loss of livestock, man also kills leopards for sport—in Africa the leopard is one of the "Big Five" most highly rated prey of the Western sport hunter, the other favored species being the lion, buffalo, elephant and rhinoceros.   BCRB

OTHER BIG CATS

Three species in 2 genera
Family: Felidae.

Jaguar   Snow   Clouded
       leopard   leopard

▶ **The rare Snow leopard** patrols large territories in its remote Asian homeland. A superb jumper, the Snow leopard may ascend above 6,000m (19,000ft) in summer in pursuit of prey.

▼ **The jaguar climbs well** but usually stalks its prey on the ground. Larger than the Old World leopard it somewhat resembles, the jaguar has a more compact body, more reddish coloration, a broader head and more powerful paws.

THE jaguar, Snow Leopard and Clouded leopard occur in quite different regions of the world, but all live in mostly forested wilderness habitats. Their numbers are low and diminishing, partly as a result of the demand for their attractive pelts by the fur trade—a practice that is now banned. All three species are illustrated on pp26–27.

The **jaguar** is the only member of the genus *Panthera* (big cats) to be found in the Americas, where it is considered to be the New World equivalent of the leopard.

Although the jaguar is classified with the big cats, which can roar, it does not seem to do so, a characteristic it shares with the Snow leopard. It grunts frequently when hunting and will snarl or growl if threatened. The male also has a mewing cry used in the mating season. The jaguar has a compact body with a large broad head and powerful paws.

Jaguars prefer dense forest or swamps with good cover and easy access to water, although they will hunt in more open country if necessary. They swim and climb very well, but usually stalk prey on the ground. Prey species include peccary, deer, monkeys, tapir, sloths, agouti, capybara, birds, caymen, turtles, turtle eggs, frogs, fish and small rodents. They will also take domestic stock if it is easily available. The prey is often cached by burying.

It is quite widely believed, particularly among the Amazonian Indians, that jaguars catch fish which they deliberately lure to the surface by twitching their tail in the water, flicking the fish onto the bank with a forepaw. It seems more likely that as the jaguar crouches in ambush on the bank, its tail occasionally hits the surface of the water, by which it may inadvertently attract fish.

Jaguars are solitary, except during the breeding season, and maintain a territory which varies from 5 to 500sqkm (2–200sq mi), depending on prey density. They are occasionally known to travel up to 800km (500mi) but why they undertake such a journey is unknown.

Two to four young, each weighing 700–900g (25–32oz), are born at a time. They are blind at birth, but open their eyes after about 13 days and remain with their mother for two years. Sexual maturity is achieved at three years.

The shy, nocturnal and virtually unknown **Snow leopard** or **ounce** is classified with the big cats, but shares some small cat characteristics, for example it does not roar and it feeds in a crouched position.

The Snow leopard has to contend with extremes of climate and its coat varies from fine in summer to thick in winter. The surfaces of its paws are covered by a cushion of hair which increases the surface area, thus distributing the animal's weight more evenly over soft snow and protecting its soles from the cold.

Prey density is usually very low and territories are therefore large, probably up to 100sqkm (38sqmi). Snow leopards move to different altitudes along with migrating prey, which include ibex, markhor, wild sheep, Musk deer, as well as marmots, Piping hare, bobak, tahr, mice and birds; in winter, deer, wild boar, gazelles and hares form a major part of their diet. Snow leopards usually stalk their prey, springing upon it, often from 6–15m (20–50ft) away.

Snow leopards are solitary except during the breeding season (January to May), when male and female hunt together, or when a female has young. One to four young are born in spring or early summer in a well-concealed den lined with the mother's fur. Initially, the spots are completely black. The young open their eyes at 7–9 days, are quite active by two months and remain with their mother through their first winter.

Snow leopards are extremely rare in many parts of their range due to the demand for their skins by the fur trade. Although in many countries it is now illegal to use these furs, the trade continues and the species remains under threat.

Neither truly a big cat nor a small cat, the **Clouded leopard** provides a bridge between the genera *Panthera* (lion, tiger etc) and *Acinonyx* (cheetah) on the one hand and the genus *Felis* (small cats) on the other, sharing

characteristics of both groups. It differs from the big cats in having a rigid hyoid bone in its vocal apparatus, which prevents it roaring, and from the small cats by the low level of grooming and by its posture when at rest, lying with its tail directed straight behind and its forelegs outstretched.

The Clouded leopard is heavily built, with short legs and a long tail. It has the usual felid complement of 30 teeth but the upper canines are relatively long and, in conjunction with the incisors, are used to tear meat from prey as the leopard jerks its head upwards. The snout is rather broad, although the head is quite narrow. The retina is most often yellow and the pupils contract to a spindle.

The Clouded leopard is an arboreal cat preying mainly upon monkeys, squirrels and birds, which it often swats with its broad, spoon-shaped paws. It is an adept climber and can run down trees head-first, clamber upside down on the underside of branches and swing by a single hindpaw before dropping directly onto deer or wild boar, which are its main terrestrial prey. The Clouded leopard is active at twilight, resting and sleeping in the treetops for the rest of the day and night.

Two to four blind and helpless young are born; their coloration and coat patterning differs from the adult's in that the large spots on the sides are completely dark. Cubs open their eyes after 10–12 days and are quite active by five weeks. The young Clouded leopard probably achieves independence by nine months.

Clouded leopards are elusive, and there is no information about the social behavior of this species in the wild.   GK

Abbreviations: HBL = head-body length; TL = tail length; wt = weight. Approximate measure equivalents: 10cm = 4in; 1kg = 2.2lb.
V Vulnerable.   E Endangered.

Jaguar V
Panthera onca

SW USA to C Patagonia. In tropical forest, swamps and open country, including desert and savanna. HBL 112–185cm; TL 45–75cm; shoulder height 68–76cm; wt 57–113kg. (Females on average 20% smaller.) Coat: basically yellowish-brown but varying from almost white to black, with a pale chest and irregularly placed black spots on belly; back marked with dark rosettes; lower part of tail ringed with black; a black mark on the lower jaw near the mouth; outer surface of ear pinnae black. Gestation: 93–110 days. Longevity: up to 20 years in captivity. Subspecies: 8. **Yucatán jaguar**

(*P. o. goldmani*), SW Yucatán (Mexico), N Guatemala. **Panama jaguar** (*P. o. centralis*), C America, Colombia. **Peruvian jaguar** (*P. o. peruviana*), Ecuador, Peru, Bolivia. **Amazon jaguar** (*P. o. onca*), forests of Orinoco and Amazon basins. **Paraná jaguar** (*P. o. palustris*), S Brazil, Argentina. **Arizona jaguar** (*P. o. arizonensis*), USA to NW Mexico. *P. o. veracrucensis* and *P. o. harnandes*, Mexico, very rare.

Snow leopard E
Panthera uncia

The Altai, Hindu Kush, and Himalayas. In mountain steppe and coniferous forest scrub at altitudes between 1,800 and 5,500m. HBL 120–150cm; TL about 90cm. Coat: soft gray, shading to white on belly; head and lower limbs marked with

solid black or dark brown spots arranged in rows; body covered with medium brown blotches ringed with black or dark drown; a black streak along the back; tail round and heavily furred; ear pinnae black edged; winter coat lighter. Gestation: 98–103 days. Longevity: up to 15 years in captivity.

Clouded leopard V
Neofelis nebulosa

India, S China, Nepal, Burma, Indochina to Sumatra and Borneo, and Taiwan. In dense forest at altitudes up to 2,000m. HBL 60–110cm; TL 60–90cm; shoulder height about 80cm; wt 15–20kg. Coat: short, from dark brown or gray to brownish or ocher-yellow, patterned distinctively with black stripes, spots and blotches;

forehead and top of head lack spots, but six lines extend lengthwise across nape of neck, the outer ones much wider than the central ones; two stripes along the back which reduce to spots near the head; flanks with oblong to roundish blotches, each comprising a ring of pale fur outside a dark brown or grayish ring enclosing a paler center that is spotted; legs, throat and belly with black blotches shading to white on the underparts; ear pinnae rounded, black on outside and white on inside with a buff spot; tail long and bushy, ringed and tipped with black. Gestation: 85–90 days. Longevity: up to 17 years in captivity Subspecies: 2. **Formosan Clouded leopard** (*N. n. brachyurus*) from Taiwan, with tail not so long. All others included in *N. n. nebulosa*.

SMALL CATS

Genus *Felis* [*]
Twenty-eight species.
Family: Felidae.
Distribution: N and S America, Eurasia, Africa.

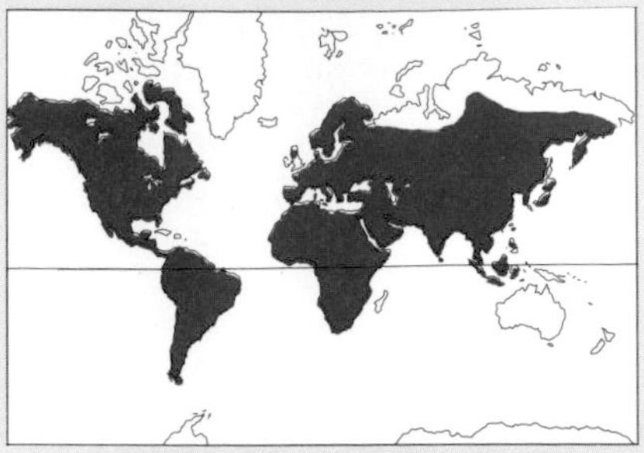

Habitat: from arid regions with sparse cover (Desert cat), through steppe, bush and savanna (African wild cat) to cool-temperate forest (European wild cat).

Size: head-body length from 35–40cm (14–16in) in the Black-footed cat to 105–196cm (41–77in) in the puma; weight from 1–2kg (2.2–4.4lb) to 103kg (227lb).

Coat: most often spotted or striped, sometimes uniform; face markings often striped with a black tear stripe from the eye.

Gestation: from about 56 days in the Leopard cat to 90–96 days in the puma.

Longevity: 12–15 years in the European wild cat.

Species include the **Wild cat** (*F. sylvestris*), W Europe to India (includes **European wild cat**), and subspecies **African wild cat** (*F. s. lybica*), Africa, and **Domestic cat** (*F. s. catus*), worldwide. **Leopard cat** (*F. bengalensis*), E and SE Asia. **Lynx** (*F. lynx*), Europe to Asia, N America. **Puma** (*F. concolor*) or **cougar,** Canada to Patagonia. **Bobcat** (*F. rufus*), Canada to Mexico. **Ocelot** [V] (*F. pardalis*), Arizona to Argentina. **Margay cat** [V] (*F. wiedi*), Mexico to Argentina. **Geoffroy's cat** (*F. geoffroyi*), S America.

[*] CITES listed. [V] Vulnerable.

Although most have never been properly studied, the 28 species of "small cats" are generally known to be similar in anatomy, morphology, biology and behavior to the better known "big cats."

Distinguishing characteristics of the genus *Felis* include: a fully ossified (bony) hyoid bone in the vocal apparatus which prevents them from roaring; claws that can be withdrawn (except in the Flat-headed cat) into sheaths which are longer on the outer side (of equal length in big cats); and a hairless strip along the front of the nose (furred in the big cats). When resting, they tuck their forepaws beneath their body by bending them at the wrist joint, and the tail is wrapped round their body; big cats at rest place their paws in front of their bodies and extend their tails straight behind them. Small cats feed in a crouched position whereas big cats lie down to feed.

The classification of small cats is controversial: here we have grouped the European wild cat, the African wild cat and the Domestic cat together as one species, *F. silvestris*. In the table overleaf the facts presented for *F. silvestris* are those for the European wild cat, which is taken to be representative of the group.

The Domestic cat (*F. s. catus*) is thought to be a descendant of the African wild cat (*F. s. lybica*), which was domesticated in Ancient Egypt, probably about 2000 BC. Controversy rages over the issue but, whatever its origins, the Domestic cat is certainly the most successful and widespread felid, being found worldwide in human settlements, often leading a wild (feral) existence.

There is little information to allow comparison of the behavior of the species and subspecies of small cats. However, in one recent study in Scotland, the social organization and feeding behavior of the European wild cat and the Domestic cat were compared. This revealed that the society of feral Domestic cats varied considerably: from solitary individuals to groups of up to 30 members, or a mixture of the two lifestyles, depending on the availability of food and its dispersal in time and space. It was found that feral Domestic cats that depend on dispersed rabbit prey in an open habitat hunt alone, while those exploiting a clumped food resource, such as food put out at human dwellings, live in groups. The social organization of European wild cats was found to be very similar to solitary feral Domestic cats, although their ranges were on average larger at 176 hectares (435 acres) for an adult male compared to an average of 35 hectares (87 acres) for Domestic cats. This was due to more widely

▶ **A serval stalks through long grass.** This slender long-legged African savanna cat prefers to live near water. The small head with large rounded ears and the long neck are also characteristic.

▶ **Surprised by night,** a Scottish Wild cat puts on an impressive threat display.

1

2

Bobcat and Lynx: habitat and physique

Although very similar in basic form, different small cats species show a wide range of physical adaptations to their habitats. The lynx (1) and the bobcat (2) are two North American felids of similar size—5–30kg (11–66lb)—which occupy different habitats.

The plain brownish-gray coat of the lynx enables it to be inconspicuous against a background of dense, moss-laden coniferous forests and swamps—the typical vegetation from which it stalks its main prey, the Snowshoe hare. The black-spotted brown coat of the bobcat blends in well with the background of rocks, brush and other dense vegetation where its main prey—cottontails—feed. Because of the denser cover, sound may be more important than sight in locating prey for the lynx than the bobcat, and hence its ear tufts, which are thought to help hearing, are longer than those of the bobcat.

Lynx live in cold northern latitudes where snow lies deep for much of the year. As adaptations to the lower temperatures (to $-57°C/-70°F$) they have shorter tails than the bobcats and their foot pads are well protected with a dense covering of fur, while those of the bobcat are bare. The longer legs of the lynx are also an adaptation to traveling through deep snow, where the bobcat is at a disadvantage.   TNB

dispersed food resources; for example, rabbit prey were more sparsely distributed in the high altitude, young forest and scrub of scottish wild cats' habitat than in the farmland habitat of the feral domestic cats. The basic hunting technique in dense habitats with defended territories where prey was scarce, small and widely dispersed, was solitary stalking. However, where prey was abundant, relatively large and patchily distributed, cats often lived in groups to defend and exploit this food. This detailed study of the wild and domestic subspecies of *F. silvestris* exemplifies the functional relationship between grades of social organization and feeding ecology, where both abundance and dispersion of food are important.

The most serious threat to small cats is the fur trade, which continues to demand large numbers of spotted cat skins, despite considerable adverse public opinion. The resulting pressure on wild populations of these rare, beautiful and little understood creatures is pushing many of them to the brink of extinction. To take an example, the ocelot is particularly vulnerable, its skin being in great demand by the fur industry. Widespread, and also easily trapped or shot, it is consequently the most frequently hunted small cat in Latin America. In 1975, Britain alone imported 76,838 ocelot skins. It is now rare and threatened in parts of its range, and populations everywhere are seriously reduced in number.

The bobcat, lynx and puma are suffering similar fates, and the situation is often exacerbated by their persecution as pests and by destruction of their habitat. In North America alone, during 1977–78 over 85,000 bobcat skins and 20,000 lynx skins were harvested, together worth over $16 million.

The situation with many of the smaller cats is even worse: for example, over 20,000 pelts of the rare Geoffroy's cat are taken each year. Similarly, both the Margay cat and Leopard cat have beautifully marked coats that are much in demand by the fur trade, and both are in consequence subject to intense hunting.

Enormous numbers of felid skins are required because of the intricate matching procedure required for each garment. When a species becomes too scarce to provide the minimum number of skins demanded by the trade, another more common one is exploited by the illegal hunters. Thus, species by species, the small spotted cats are being hunted to a point where the remaining populations are so small and widely dispersed that they may never recover.   GK

THE 28 SPECIES OF SMALL CATS

Abbreviations: HBL = head-body length; TL = tail length; wt = weight.

Approximate measure equivalents: 10cm = 4in; 1kg = 2.2lb.

[V] Vulnerable.   [R] Rare.   [E] Endangered.   [I] Threatened, but exact status indeterminate.

Genus *Felis*

Mostly forest-dwellers preying on small mammals, but opportunistically taking any small vertebrate prey. Coat variable in density and length, most often spotted or striped, but sometimes uniform. Face markings variable but often striped; black "tear" stripes normally present. Tail tapered or rounded at tip, often with dark rings. Ear pinnae vary in size and degree of roundness, with tufted tips in some species. Color of iris of eyes varies from rich orange, through yellow to green; pupils contract to a circle, slit or spindle shape. Skull normally rounded. The anatomy, morphology and biology of wild members of the genus is poorly understood. (The following table cites features where they are known.)

African golden cat
F. aurata

Senegal to Zaire and Kenya. Forest and dense scrubland. Prey: small mammals and birds. HBL 70–95cm; TL 28–37cm; wt 13.5–18kg. Coat: chestnut-brown to silver-gray; patterning variable in type and extent; eyes brown; tail tapered at tip; ears small and rounded.

Asiatic golden cat [I]
F. temmincki
Asiatic golden or Temminck's golden cat.

Nepal to S China and Sumatra. Forest. Prey: rodents, small deer, game birds. HBL 75–105cm; TL 40–55cm; wt 6–11kg. Coat: uniform golden-brown with head typically striped with white, blue and gray (much variation). Litter 2–3.

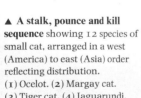

(Black-footed cat continued)
on underside of feet; legs with wide black rings on upper parts; skull broad; ears large; pupils contract to slit; hair on soles of feet. Gestation 63–68 days; litter 2–3.

Bobcat
F. rufus
Bobcat or Red lynx.

S Canada to S Mexico. Rocky scree, rough ground, thickets, swamp; Prey: rodents, small ungulates, large ground birds; active at twilight. HBL 62–106cm; TL 10–20cm; wt 6–31kg. Coat: barred and spotted with black on reddish-brown (very variable) basic color: underside white, tail tip black; heavily built with a short tail and short ear tufts. Gestation 60–63 days; litter 1–4.

Caracal
F. caracal
Caracal, lynx or African lynx.

Africa and Asia from Turkestan, NW India to Arabia. Wide habitat tolerance. Prey: rodents and other small mammals including young deer, which are either run down or pounced on; mainly active at twilight but will hunt during the night in hot weather or by day in the winter. HBL 55–75cm; TL 22–23cm; wt 16–23kg. Coat: reddish-brown to yellow-gray; underside white; ears tufted; legs very long; eyes yellow-brown; pupils contract to a circle. Gestation 70–78 days; litter 1–4.

Chinese desert cat
F. bieti

C Asia, W China, S Mongolia. Steppe and mountain. HBL 70–85cm; TL 30–35cm; wt about 5.5kg. Coat: brownish-yellow with dark spots merging into stripes; underside paler;

Flat-headed cat [I]
F. planiceps

Borneo, Sumatra, Malaya. Forest and scrub; prefers proximity to water. Prey: small mammals, birds, fish, amphibians; nocturnal. HBL 41–50cm; TL 13–15cm; wt 5.5–8kg. Coat: plain reddish-brown, underside white; dark spots on throat, belly, inner sides of legs; ears black with ocher spot at the base; tear streaks white; head slightly flattened; legs short; paws small; ears small and rounded; claws not fully retractile.

Geoffroy's cat
F. geoffroyi
Geoffroy's cat/Geoffroy's ocelot.

Bolivia to Patagonia. Upland forests and scrub. Prey: birds and small mammals; climbs and swims well. HBL 45–70cm; TL 26–35cm; wt 2–3.5kg. Coat: silver-gray, through ocher-yellow to brownish-yellow with small black spots. Litter 2–3.

Jaguarundi [I]
F. yagouaroundi
Jaguarundi, jaguarondi, eyra, Otter-cat.

Arizona to N Argentina. Forest, savanna, scrub. Prey: birds, rabbits, rodents, frogs, fish, poultry; active at twilight. HBL 55–67cm; TL 33–61cm; wt 5.5–10kg. Coat: either uniform red or uniform gray, lighter underneath; newborn dark spotted; legs very short; body long and slender; ears small, round; eyes brown; pupil contracts to a slit. Gestation 63–70 days; litter 2–4.

Iriomote cat [E]
F. iriomotensis

Iriomote Islands, Ryukyu Islands, Sub-tropical rain forest, always near water. Prey: waterbirds, small

---

▲ **A stalk, pounce and kill sequence** showing 12 species of small cat, arranged in a west (America) to east (Asia) order reflecting distribution.
(1) Ocelot. (2) Margay cat. (3) Tiger cat. (4) Jaguarundi. (5) and (6) European and African Wild cat. (7) Black-footed cat. (8) Sand cat. (9) Jungle cat. (10) Leopard cat. (11) Asiatic golden cat. (12) Fishing cat.

Bay cat [R]
F. badia
Bay or Bornean red cat.

Borneo. Rocky scrub: Prey: small mammals and birds. HBL about 50cm; TL about 30cm; wt 2–3kg. Coat: uniform bright reddish-brown; lighter colored on underside; head short and rounded.

Black-footed cat
F. nigripes

S Africa, Botswana, Namibia. Steppe and savanna. Prey: rodents, lizards, insects. HBL 35–40cm; TL 15–17cm; wt 1–2kg. Coat: light brown with dark spots on body and black patches

red tinge on the back; tail ringed; skull broad; ears large; soles of the feet padded with fur.

Fishing cat
F. viverrina

Sumatra, Java, to S China to India. Forest, swamps, marshy areas (dependent on water). Prey: fish, small mammals, birds, insects and crustacea. HBL 57–85cm; TL 20–32cm; wt 5.5–8kg. Coat: short and coarse, light brown with dark brown or black spots; tail ringed with black; paws slightly webbed and claws not fully retractile. Gestation 63 days; litter 1–4.

rodents, crabs, mud-skippers; nocturnal and strictly territorial with ranges up to 2km².

Jungle cat
F. chaus

Egypt to Indochina and Sri Lanka. Dry forest, woodland, scrub, reed beds, often near human settlements. Prey: rodents and frogs, occasionally birds; most active in day. HBL 60–75cm; TL 25–35cm; wt 7–13.5kg. Coat: sandy-brown to yellow-gray, sometimes with dark stripes on face and legs and with a ringed tail; young have distinct close-set striped pattern which disappears in the adult, tail short; legs

(Jungle cat continued)
long; ears tapered and tufted with a light spot at the base. Gestation 66 days; litter 2–5.

Kodkod
F. guigna
Kodkod, huiña.

C and S Chile, W Argentina. Forest; prey birds and small mammals; probably nocturnal. HBL 40–52cm; TL 17–23cm; wt 2–3kg. Coat: gray varying to ocher-brown, with dark spots and ringed tail; underside whitish; prominent dark band across the throat, but few markings on the face.

Leopard cat
F. bengalensis
Leopard or Bengal cat.

Sumatra, Java, Borneo, Philippines, Taiwan, Japan. Forest, scrubland, particularly near water. Prey: rodents, small mammals, birds, which it drops on from above; active at night and at twilight; good swimmers and climbers. HBL 35–60cm; TL 15–40cm; wt 3–7kg. Coat: background color varies from ocher-yellow to ocher-brown with underside paler; covered with black spots; prominent white spot between the eyes; eyes yellow-brown to greenish-yellow; ears rounded and black with a white spot on the outer surface. Gestation about 56 days; litter 2–4.

Lynx
F. lynx (F. pardina)
Lynx, Northern lynx.

W Europe to Siberia; Spain and Portugal; Alaska, Canada, N USA. Coniferous forest and thick scrub. Prey: rodents, small ungulates;

crepuscular. HBL 67–110cm; TL 5–17cm; wt 5–29kg. Coat: light brown with dark spots; tail black-tipped (coloration and patterning very variable); ear tufts long and black; two tassels on throat; tail short; paws large with thick fur padding; pupils contract to a circle; 28 teeth. Gestation 60–74 days; litter 1–5.

Marbled cat
F. marmorata

Sumatra, Borneo, Malaya to Nepal. Forest. Prey: rodents, birds, small mammals, insects, lizards, snakes; nocturnal and arboreal. HBL 40–60cm; TL 45–54cm; wt about 5.5kg. Coat: soft, long fur, light-

(Marbled cat continued)
brown with striking patterns of dark brown blotches and spots all over.

Margay cat V
F. wiedi
Margay cat, "tigrillo".

N Mexico to N Argentina. Forest, scrubland. Prey: rats, squirrels, opossums, monkeys, birds; excellent climber. HBL 45–70cm; TL 35–50cm; wt 4–9kg. Coat: yellow-brown with black spots and stripes; tail ringed; eyes large, dark brown. Litter 1–2.

Mountain cat R
F. jacobita
Mountain or Andean cat.

S Peru to N Chile. Mountain steppe. Prey: small mammals and birds. HBL 70–75cm; TL about 45cm; wt 3.5–7kg. Coat: brown-gray with dark spots, a ringed tail and white belly; long- and thick-haired especially on the tail, which appears perfectly round.

Ocelot V
F. pardalis

Arizona to N Argentina. Forest and steppe. Prey: small mammals, birds, reptiles; excellent climber and swimmer; may live in pairs. HBL 65–97cm; TL 27–40cm; wt 11–16kg. Coat: ocher-yellow to orange-yellow in forested areas, grayer in arid scrubland; black striped and spotted; underside white; tail ringed; eyes brownish; hair curls at the withers to lie forward on upper neck. Gestation 70 days; litter 2–4.

Pallas's cat
F. manul
Pallas's cat, manul.

Iran to W China. Mountain steppe, rocky terrain, woodland. Prey: mainly rodents. HBL 50–65cm; TL 21–30cm; wt 3–5kg. Coat: long, orange-gray with black and white head markings; belly light gray; ears small and rounded, widely separated on a broad head with a low forehead; pupil contracts to a circle; front premolar teeth missing, giving 28 teeth; eyes face almost directly forward. Litter 1–5.

Pampas cat
F. colocolo

Ecuador to Patagonia. Grassland, forest, scrub. Prey: small- to medium-sized rodents, birds, lizards large insects; probably nocturnal. HBL 52–70cm; TL 27–33cm; wt 3.5–6.6kg. Coat: long, soft, gray-brown with brown spots (very variable) and with reddish-hue; ears tapered and tufted; eyes yellow-brown; pupil contracts to a spindle. (Previously called *F. pajeros*, derived from the Spanish "paja," meaning straw, because it lives in reed beds.)

Puma
F. concolor
Puma, cougar, Mountain lion, panther.

Includes Eastern cougar E (*F. c. cougar*), E N America, and Florida cougar E (*F. c. coryi*), S Canada to Patagonia. Forest to steppe, including conifer, deciduous and tropical forests, grassland and desert. Prey: from small rodents to fully grown deer; mainly active at twilight. HBL 105–196cm; TL 67–78cm; wt 36–103kg. Coat: plain gray-brown to black (very variable); cubs initially dark spotted; head round and small; body very slender; eyes brown; pupils circular; tail black-tipped. Gestation 90–96 days; litter 3–4.

Rusty-spotted cat
F. rubiginosus

S India and Sri Lanka. Scrub, forest, around waterways and human settlements. Prey: small mammals, birds, insects. HBL 35–48cm; TL 15–25cm; wt 1–2kg. Coat: rust colored with brown blotches and stripes.

Sand cat
F. margarita

N Africa and SW Asia (Sahara to Baluchistan). Desert. Prey: small rodents, lizards, insects; nocturnal. HBL 40–57cm; TL 25–35cm; wt 2–2.5kg. Coat: plain yellow-brown to gray-brown; tail ringed, with a black tip; kittens born with distinct coat markings which usually fade in adulthood; hair covers paw pads; head very broad; eyes large and forward on the head; ears tapered.

Serval
F. serval

Africa. Savanna, normally near water. Prey: game birds, rodents, small ungulates; good climber. HBL 70–100cm; TL 35–40cm; wt 13.5–19kg. Coat: orange-brown with black spots (very variable); slender build with long legs, small head, rather long neck and large, rounded ears; eyes yellowish; pupils contract to a spindle. Gestation about 75 days; litter 1–3.

Tiger cat V
F. tigrinus
Tiger or Little spotted or Ocelot cat, oricilla.

Costa Rica to N Argentina. Forest. Prey: small mammals, birds, lizards, large insects; good climber. HBL 40–55cm; TL 25–40cm; wt 2–3.5kg. Coat: light brown with very dark brown stripes and blotches; underparts lighter; white line above the eyes. Gestation 74 days; litter 1–2.

Wild cat
F. silvestris
(Includes Domestic cat, *F. s. catus*, and African wild cat, *F. s. lybica*)

W Europe to India; Africa (*F. s. catus* worldwide—introduced by man). Open forest, savanna, steppe. Prey: small mammals and birds; nocturnal. HBL 50–80cm; TL 28–35cm; wt 3–6kg; (slightly smaller for *F. s. lybica*). Coat: medium brown, black-striped; *F. s. lybica* is light brown with stripes; *F. s. catus* shows many color forms; females generally paler than males; tail black-tipped. Gestation 68 days; litter 3–6.

GK

North America's Secretive Cats

Flexible land use in the lynx, bobcat and puma

Three main species of small cats inhabit the wilderness areas of North America. Distribution of the lynx, in the coniferous forest and thick scrub of Alaska, Canada and the northern USA, barely overlaps with that of North America's most common felid, the bobcat, which extends south across the USA including most habitats (except those without sign of tree or shrub). The much larger puma, cougar or mountain lion inhabits mostly rocky terrain ranging from forest to desert from southern Canada south to Patagonia in southern South America.

Adapting to a wide range of habitats, climate and degrees of prey availability, the solitary individuals of each species display great flexibility of behavior. (See also the physical adaptaions described on p51.) Their success in breeding and survival is based on land tenure—the maintenance of more or less exclusive access to prey within a defined home area. Generally, older resident cats which occupy distinct areas year after year have the greatest breeding success. Others, usually younger individuals, are not as successful because they fail to occupy areas in prime habitat permanently, unless a vacancy occurs or they settle in less favorable habitats.

Of the many influences on the land-tenure system of cats, abundance, population stability and distribution and mobility of prey are especially important. Abundant prey allows cats to survive on smaller areas at higher densities. Stable prey populations permit long-term familiarity with hunting areas and neighbors, so prompting stable tenure; scattered, fluctuating prey may force overlap and the sharing of limited resources. Finally, highly mobile prey may demand seasonal shifts of hunting areas. To adapt to all these factors requires a flexible land-tenure system.

The puma, largest of all the "small cats," demonstrates this flexibility. In the rugged mountains of northwestern North America, individual pumas shift between large summer ranges (which vary from 106 to 207sqkm/41–80sqmi for females and up to 293sqkm/113sqmi for males) and smaller winter ranges averaging 107sqkm (42sqmi) and 126sqkm (49sqmi) for females and males, respectively. Locations of seasonal ranges are determined by the immigration patterns of their main prey, Mule deer and elk. Winter snow at higher altitudes forces hoofed mammals, and consequently the pumas, from higher summer ranges into lower valleys, but pumas maintain approximately the same distance from each other in both their summer and winter ranges. The home ranges of adult male pumas overlap the least, those of adult females overlap more, sometimes completely, and one male's range may overlap those of several females. Sometimes a female's

▲ **Puma surveying its territory.** The puma is the largest of North American cats and it may travel through summer ranges of over 200–300sqkm (77–116sqmi).

Warning Off Intruders

North American cats advertise land occupancy largely by scent and visual signals. The means used to warn off intruders include the depositing of urine, feces, and anal gland secretions, and making scrapes in the ground. Vocalizations play little part.

Bobcats frequently squirt urine (**1**) along common travel routes (which in females may also indicate whether they are receptive or approaching receptivity), deposit feces (**2**) in latrine sites (middens) which if near dens may indicate that they are being used by females with offspring, and (**3**) scrape with or without defecating or urinating along trails, trail intersections and other important places in their home ranges; scraping also adds to the conspicousness of other scent marks. Intruding cats coming across such marks (**4**) usually respect the prior rights of other cats, as newcomers seldom succeed in permanently settling in areas already occupied by residents. Body posture and facial expressions are probably effective close-range signals when two animals meet, as in (**5**) a defensive threat, and (**6**) an attack threat.

Some of the bobcats travelled at least 30km (20mi) away in search of more prey. Young bobcats dispersed up to 158km (99mi) from their place of birth. Adult bobcats, like adult pumas, avoid encounters except when mating.

Less is known about the land-tenure system of the lynx. The availability of their main prey, Snowshoe hares, appears to determine the spatial organization of lynx. Where hares are abundant, lynx may have a system similar to the bobcat's, with males using ranges up to 50sqkm (19sqmi) and females using ranges up to 26sqkm (10sqmi). However, when hare populations crash, a periodic occurrence in the north, home ranges enlarge and overlapping increases as lynx seek out remaining concentrations of hares. When hares suddenly decline over a vast area, lynx have been known to disperse up to 480km (300mi) and areas of use become large, up to 122sqkm (47sqmi) and 243sqkm (94sqmi) for females and males, respectively. Long-term stable land tenure is unlikely to occur among fluctuating lynx populations because long-lived neighboring residents familiar with each other and stable prey populations are needed, and these conditions occur only periodically in many harsh northern environments.

Land tenure in the ocelot and jaguarundi, which occur in the southern USA at the northern limit of their ranges, has not been intensively studied, but one early account suggests that an ocelot territory never contains more than one male and one female. Because their tropical environment is more stable than northern environments, and because they feed on a wide variety of prey (mice, rats, pacas, agoutis, coatis, monkeys and peccaries), ocelots should have relatively stable home ranges.

Systems of land tenure serve many functions. Some maintain densities of breeding adults below levels set by food supplies and thus regulate populations. Where deer and elk increased from 2.6–3.3 and from 1.5–2.5 per sqkm respectively, puma densities remained constant at 1 puma per 35sqkm (14sqmi) throughout a five-year period. Land-tenure systems also ensure reproductive success by maximizing the number of females bred by individual males. In one area, there were 1.7 resident females for each resident male bobcat. Survival is probably enhanced because residents familiar with locations of prey and cover have lower death rates and produce more young than individuals who are unable to occupy land permanently.   TNB

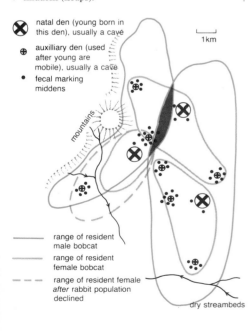

▼ **Homes ranges of the bobcat.** The size of home ranges in bobcats varies seasonally with prey availability. In this area, following a decline in the local rabbit population, one female bobcat extended her range. Overall, male ranges overlap very little with those of other males, (one overlap area shown shaded), but partially embrace the ranges of several females. Dens in active use are marked with fecal middens (heaps).

⊗ natal den (young born in this den), usually a cave

⊕ auxilliary den (used after young are mobile), usually a cave

• fecal marking middens

1km

mountains

——— range of resident male bobcat

——— range of resident female bobcat

- - - range of resident female *after* rabbit population declined

dry streambeds

range may be partially overlapped by more than one male, but which male mates with the female is not known. Where ranges overlap, pumas seldom use the same localities at the same time. Avoidance of other pumas, a frequent but little understood behavior pattern, also reduces fighting between these powerful predators to rare events. Young pumas disperse up to at least 45km (28mi) from their natal areas.

The land-tenure system of bobcats appears to be highly flexible, varying with different habitats and prey—mainly hares or rabbits. In one area where rabbits were relatively abundant but protective cover limited, adult male bobcats occupied partially overlapping ranges up to 108sqkm (42sqmi), while adult females occupied smaller, more exclusive areas up to 45sqkm (17sqmi). A natal den and up to five auxiliary dens which were used to rear young formed focal points of activity within each female's range. Less than one percent of the average area used by adult females was shared with other resident females and about two percent of the area used by males were shared with other resident males.

Like those of male pumas, the home ranges of resident male bobcats overlap those of one or more resident females. This permits them to mate with as many females as possible, while keeping other males away. If rabbit populations remain stable, bobcats roam the same ranges year after year, but if rabbits decline, resident bobcats have to enlarge or abandon their familiar ranges.

THE DOG FAMILY

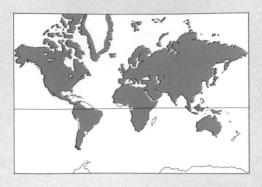

Family: Canidae
Thirty-five species in 10 genera.
Distribution: worldwide, excluding a few areas (eg Madagascar, New Zealand) in most of which Domestic dog introduced.

Habitat: evolved in open grasslands but now adapted to an exceptionally wide range of habitats.

Size: ranges from the Fennec fox—minimum adult head-body length 24cm (9.5in), tail 18cm (7in) and weight 0.8kg (1lb)—to the Gray wolf, up to 200cm (6ft 7in) in overall length and 80kg (175lb) in weight. Other fox species weigh between 1.5 and 9kg (3.3-20lb), all other species between 5 and 27kg (11-60lb).

Gray wolf *Canis lupus*
Red wolf *Canis rufus*
Coyote *Canis latrans*
Dingo *Canis dingo*
Domestic dog *Canis familiaris*
Jackals Four species of *Canis*

Vulpine foxes Twelve species of *Vulpes*
South American foxes Seven species of *Dusicyon*
Arctic fox *Alopex lagopus*
Bat-eared fox *Otocyon megalotis*

African wild dog *Lycaon pictus*
Dhole *Cuon alpinus*
Maned wolf *Chrysocyon brachyurus*
Raccoon dog *Nyctereutes procyonoides*
Bush dog *Speothos venaticus*

Canids evolved for fast pursuit of prey in open grasslands and their anatomy is clearly adapted to this life. Although the 35 species and 10 genera vary in size from the tiny Fennec fox to the powerful Gray wolf, all but one have lithe builds, long bushy tails, long legs and digitigrade four-toed feet, tipped with non-retractile claws. The Bush dog is the single exception. A vestigial first toe (pollex) is found on the front feet in all save the African wild dog. The dingo and the Domestic dog also have vestigial first claws (dew claws) on their hind legs. Other adaptations to running include fusion of wrist bones (scaphoid and lunar) and locking of the front leg bones (radius and ulna) to prevent rotation.

Male canids have a well-developed penis bone (baculum) and a copulatory tie keeps mating pairs locked together, facing in opposite directions for a time lasting from a few minutes to an hour or more. Its function is unknown, although people speculate loosely that it serves to "cement the pair bond." The mechanism involves a complex arrangement of blood vessels and baculum, combined with the reversed body position, so that blood is trapped in the engorged penis, impeding withdrawal.

Gestation lasts about nine weeks in most species and one litter is born annually. The pups' eyes generally open at about two weeks and the young begin to take solid food from 2–6 weeks of age. Solid food is regurgitated by *Canis* species, African wild dogs, dholes and probably Maned wolves but carried to cubs by vulpine and Arctic foxes.

Canids originated in North America during the Eocene (54–38 million years ago), from which five fossil genera are known. Two forms, *Hesperocyon* of North America and *Cynodictis* of Europe, are ancient canids, with civet-like frames. They share this long-bodied, short-limbed physique with the Miacoidea from which all Carnivora evolved (see p22). As modern canid features evolved, the family blossomed: 19 genera in the Oligocene (38–26 million years ago), 42 in the Miocene (26–7 million years ago), declining to the 10 genera recognized today.

The heel of the carnassial teeth in most canids has two cusps, but in the Bush dog, African wild dog and dhole only one, and this has led some taxonomists to group these genera together as the subfamily Simocyoninae, distinct from the subfamily Caninae, containing all other species except the Bat-eared fox, classified alone in the Otocyoninae. Members of the three largest genera, *Canis*, *Vulpes* and *Dusicyon*, are generally more similar to members of their own genus than to members of others, but the distinctions between genera are often minimal. In descending order of atypicality

► **Members of the genus *Canis*,** whose breeding plasticity (especially in the Gray wolf, *Canis lupus*) is the source of all today's breeds of Domestic dog (*C. familiaris*). (1) Coyote (*C. latrans*) showing "play" face; 16kg (35lb). (2) Red wolf (*C. rufus*) in submissive greeting posture; 23kg (50lb). Subspecies of Gray wolf: (3) Arabian wolf in defensive threat posture; 23kg. (4) Mexican wolf in offensive threat posture; 32kg (70lb). (5) European wolf howling; 25kg (55lb). (6) Tibetan wolf cocking leg (therefore, a dominant individual) to urinate. (7) Gray wolf/Husky cross, a common wolf/Domestic dog hybrid; 54kg (120lb).

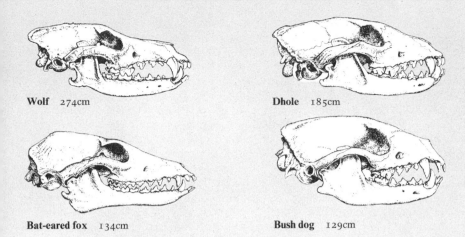

Wolf 274cm

Dhole 185cm

Bat-eared fox 134cm

Bush dog 129cm

Skulls of Canids

Canids have long muzzles, well-developed jaws and a characteristic dental formula (see p20) of I3/3, C1/1, P4/4, M2/3 = 42, as exemplified by the Gray wolf. Three species depart from this pattern, the Bat-eared fox (= 48), the dhole (= 40), and the Bush dog (= 38). Shearing carnassial teeth (P4/M1) and crushing molars are well developed and, except in the Bat-eared fox, are the largest teeth.

5

6

7

the most unorthodox canids are the African wild dog, Bush dog, Bat-eared fox, Raccoon dog, dhole, the Maned wolf and the Arctic fox. These seven are placed in single-species genera, but as none is any more closely related to any other than to the bulk of canids, it seems prudent to abandon the division into subfamilies.

The most striking feature of the canids is their opportunistic and adaptable behavior. This is most conspicuous in the flexible complexity of their social organization. Remarkably, in this respect there is as much variation within as there is between species. Although African wild dogs, and possibly dholes and Bush dogs, almost always hunt in packs, wolves, coyotes and jackals feed on prey ranging from ungulates to berries. Partly as a consequence, they lead social lives that vary from solitary to sociable—some wolf populations comprise monogamous pairs, whilst elsewhere packs may have up to 20 members. These species, and some others like Red and Arctic foxes, live in groups even where large prey does not abound and where they hunt alone. Apart from hunting, there are many other reasons for group living—cooperative defense of territories or large carcasses, communal care of offspring ("helping," as in jackals, see p66), rivalry with neighboring groups.

Selective breeding has emphasized canid plasticity in creating the Domestic dog. Various origins have been proposed for Domestic dogs and doubtless many canids have been partly domesticated at one time or another, but the wolf is generally accepted as ancestor of today's Domestic dogs. The earliest Domestic dog is either the so-called Starr Carr dog of Yorkshire, England, which lived 9,500 years ago, or, perhaps, the specimen found by Coon in Iran, dating back over 11,000 years.

With all their adaptability, members of the dog family cannot escape the indirect threat of habitat destruction. The Small-eared dog and the Bush dog are seen so rarely that there is very little information on either. The Simien jackal numbers less than 500 individuals in the highlands of Ethiopia, and the Maned wolf only 1,000–2,000 in its Argentinian and Brazilian strongholds. These species, and perhaps the African wild dog, are probably endangered. DWM

WOLVES

Two of 9 species of the genus *Canis*
Family: Canidae.
Distribution: N America, Europe, Asia.

Gray wolf ⓋV

Canis lupus
Gray wolf, wolf, Timber or White wolf.

Distribution: N America, Europe, Asia, Middle East.

Habitat: forests, taiga, tundra, deserts; plains and mountains.

Size: head-body length 100–150cm (40–58in); tail length 31–51cm (13–20in); shoulder height 66–81cm (26–32in); weight 12–80kg (27–175lb).
Males larger than females.

Coat: usually gray to tawny-buff, but varies from white (in N tundra) through red and brown to black; underside pale.

Gestation: 61–63 days.

Longevity: 8–16 years (to 20 in captivity).

Subspecies: up to 32 have been described. Surviving subspecies include the **Common wolf** (*C. l. lupus*), forests of Europe and Asia, medium-sized with short, dark fur. The **Steppe wolf** (*C. l. campestris*), steppes and deserts of C Asia, small, with a short, coarse gray-ocher coat. The **Tundra wolves** of Eurasia (*C. l. albus*) and America (*C. l. tundarum*), large, with coat long and light-colored. **Eastern timber wolf** (*C. l. lycaon*), once the most widespread in N America, but now only in areas of low human population density; smaller, usually gray in color. The **Great Plains wolf** ⓔ EX or Buffalo wolf (*C. l. nubilus*), white to black in color, once followed the great herds of bison on the North American plains.

Red wolf Ⓔ

Canis rufus

Distribution: SE USA (now probably extinct in wild).

Habitat: coastal plains, forests.

Size and weight—15–30kg (33–66lb)—intermediate between Gray wolf and coyote (pp46–47); gestation and longevity same as Gray wolf.

Coat: cinnamon or tawny with gray and black highlights.

Ⓥ Vulnerable.   Ⓔ Endangered.   EX Extinct.

No animal is more enshrined in the myths and legends of the peoples of the North than the wolf. For thousands of years it has competed with man for game and killed his farm animals. Stories of attacks on humans are rife, but very many are exaggerated, and most are fantasy. There are few substantiated cases of a healthy wolf attacking a man and even today a sturdy stick is all that shepherds in Italy's Abruzzi mountains require to fend off a threatening wolf. Many legends probably originated at times of war, famine or epidemic, when wolves scavenged corpses. Wolves can, however, wreak havoc on farm stock—there are still occasions in Italy when over 200 sheep may be killed by a pack in one night.

Two species of wolf remain today. The Gray wolf is the largest member of the dog family. It was once the most widespread mammal, apart from man, outside the tropics (the Red fox has that distinction today). Now it is restricted to a few large forests in eastern Europe, some isolated mountain refuges in the Mediterranean region, mountains and semidesert areas of the Middle East, and wilderness areas throughout Asia and North America. This decline appears to be largely the result of human persecution and habitat destruction. The extremely rare Red wolf was once found throughout the southeastern USA but is now thought to be extinct in the wild, the result largely of hybridization with eastward-moving coyotes (see p62).

The immense former geographic range and ecological adaptability of the wolf are reflected in wide variations of form and behavior. The smallest and lightest-colored wolves inhabit semidesert areas. Forest-dwelling wolves tend to be of medium size and grayish. Tundra wolves are among the largest, their coat color ranging from white through gray to black.

Wolves will take a wide range of food. In wilderness areas, typical prey are moose, deer and caribou, which weigh up to 10 times as much as a wolf and are hunted by

An Annual Cycle of Stability and Aggression

Two wolves meet nose to nose, others lie sleeping, or observing pups at play. The wolf pack appears calm, friendly, harmonious. Only the informed observer (and wolves!) will notice the signs indicating the hierarchy and tension: a tail kept somewhat lower and ears held back as a subordinate wolf greets a more dominant pack member (1), the non-aggressive play face of one pup as it is grabbed by another (2), a stiff-legged shove as one pup tries to exert authority over one of its contemporaries (3).

From late fall to late winter, when breeding starts, such interactions become more frequent and purposive. Only one female usually mates and females may fight vigorously for that right. Even if the dominant female is not challenged, fights may break out among low-ranking females seeking a higher place in the hierarchy. Juveniles and pups may join fights and some pack members may be driven out. Males may also fight to become the pack sire. Eventually, the dominant pair copulate, generally two or three times a day for approximately 14 days. After that, calm is restored. With the hierarchy fixed for several months, some subordinate pack members may decide to leave.

▲ **Lone Gray wolf on the move.** Most wolves live in packs. Lone wolves are generally younger animals in search of their own territory and mate. The lone wolf skirts the territories of others and rarely howls or scent marks.

► **Hierarchy within a wolf pack** is well defined among both males and females. Changes in leadership result in social turmoil as pack members gang up on deposed dominants. At other times a gaping threat, as illustrated, suffices to maintain everyday relationships.

packs. Young and old or otherwise debilitated animals are most likely to be taken. Smaller mammals such as beaver and hares may be important prey, for example in summer. When domestic animals are available, wolves often turn to them because they have poor defenses. Wolves will on occasion take carrion and plant material, and even when wild prey is available will scavenge at trash cans and refuse dumps.

To find enough food, wolf packs require extensive home ranges, from 100sq km or less to areas in excess of 1,000sq km (40–400sq mi), depending mainly on prey density. Scent marking and vocalizations (the long, deep "mournful" howls that together with yips, barks, growls and whines make up the wolf vocabulary) help to define and defend these territories (see pp60–61). Most packs in forested areas occupy stable, year-round territories. In northern tundra regions, packs are usually nomadic as they follow the migrations of caribou and saiga antelope, but even they may return each year to established summer denning areas.

The nucleus of the wolf pack is the breeding pair (wolves usually mate for life). Body postures are an important part of the "language" that creates and reinforces hierarchy in the pack. Pack size depends on the size and availability of prey. In moose country, packs of up to 20 individuals occur, but this declines to about 7 where the main prey are deer. In the Italian Abruzzi, where most natural prey has been exterminated, wolves subsist on human garbage, supplemented by the odd sheep, goat or dog. There, wolves mostly travel alone.

Breeding occurs in late winter and some 4–7 blind and helpless pups are born in a den. After about a month, the pups emerge, to receive food and attention from their parents and other pack members. If the food supply is ample, these "helpers" can assist the pups to be fit and large enough to travel with the pack at 3–5 months; if food is scarce, their presence may reduce the pups' chances of survival. Some pups leave the pack during the following breeding season, while others remain as "helpers." Wolves are sexually mature at two years old.

It is a paradox that the wolf, once so feared and hated, now finds its own destiny in man's hands. It is ironical, too, that today the wolf should be so outnumbered by its descendant, the domestic dog. The battle for survival has been won by man and only if man provides suitable refuges and accepts a small loss of livestock will the wolf survive.

EZ

To Howl or Not to Howl?

How wolves keep their distance

On occasion, wolf packs meet. When they do, a fight may develop, with the common outcome a dead wolf, lying where it fell victim to the other pack, a snarl on its face as testimony to its violent death.

Such encounters, although rare, have over the past decade been the primary natural cause of death among adult wolves in the Superior National Forest of Minnesota, USA. The likelihood of such disastrous encounters is reduced by each pack restricting its movements to a relatively exclusive territory of 65–300sq km (25–115sq mi). The territory may be 10–20km (6–12mi) across, but only the outer kilometer or so is shared with neighboring packs or lone wolves. This periphery is visited much less often than the rest of the territory, presumably because of the danger of accidentally running into hostile neighbors. How do wolves recognize this periphery and thus avoid it and their neighbors?

Scent marking provides part of the answer. The dominant animals of each pack urinate on objects or at conspicuous locations about once every three minutes as the pack travels about its territory. The density of scent marks in the border regions is twice as high as elsewhere, the reason for which is not fully understood. However, wolves are known to increase their rate of scent marking after they encounter scent marks left by strangers, as they do much more frequently on the occasional visits to the edges of their pack territory. This higher density of scent marks, both its own and those of strangers, appears to enable a pack to recognize the periphery and keep from trespassing into even more dangerous areas beyond.

However, scent marks only inform a pack of where its neighbors *were*, and approximately *when* they passed through, not about where they are now. If the neighboring pack is traveling in the border area along the same trail but in the opposite direction, then whatever the density of scent marks they alone will not prevent an accidental meeting. Wolf packs need a more instantaneous spacing mechanism, and howling appears to fill this requirement.

When a pack howls, all members usually join the chorus. Under ideal conditions, this chorus can advertise a pack's location over distances as great as 10km (6mi). Thus a pack can broadcast its whereabouts over much of its territory in an instant. When two packs are approaching one another along a common border the chances of hearing howling continue to improve: the more likely an encounter becomes, the better the chance of hearing the neighbor pack's howling, and when they do so wolves normally avoid the meeting.

We might expect a pack to howl frequently as it travels about its territory and to reply immediately upon hearing strangers howl nearby. In fact, howling occurs only sporadically (in one study, only once every 10 hours), and as often as not a pack declines to answer a stranger's howling. The reasons for this apparent reluctance lie in another type of encounter between packs. On several occasions, packs in Superior National Forest have been observed to invade a neighbor's territory, follow a trail straight to the residents' location, and then attack them. In at least two of these "deliberate" encounters, resident wolves died and, in one case, the resident pack apparently disbanded after the attack and its territory was usurped by the intruders. Thus, a reply may incite an attack.

Although these deliberate encounters are

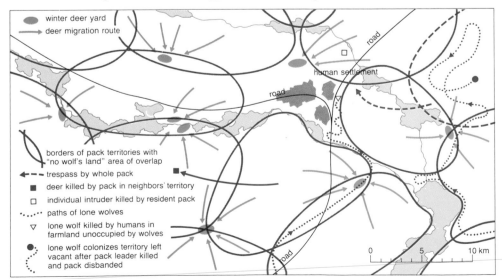

- ⬤ winter deer yard
- → deer migration route
- borders of pack territories with "no wolf's land" area of overlap
- ◀--- trespass by whole pack
- ■ deer killed by pack in neighbors' territory
- □ individual intruder killed by resident pack
- ···· paths of lone wolves
- ▽ lone wolf killed by humans in farmland unoccupied by wolves
- ● lone wolf colonizes territory left vacant after pack leader killed and pack disbanded

road

human settlement

road

road

0   5   10 km

the need to defend a valuable resource appears to outweigh the relatively small risk of attack. Older pups, which can retreat with the pack, and already exploited kills are not sufficient cause to run this risk; reply rates of 30 percent have been observed in these conditions.

This resource-based decision is further modulated by pack size and season. A pack of 7–10 wolves replied on 67 percent of the nights when the observers howled to them, whereas a pack of 3–5 replied on only 40 percent; and during the breeding season, when interpack aggression reaches its zenith, reply rates increase for all packs.

There are two other reasons why failing to reply to strangers' howling may benefit a pack. If the pack desires to seek out its neighbors, it may be best to do so unannounced. And because a pack fails to reply about as frequently as it replies, neighbors are kept uncertain of the pack's whereabouts, and may refrain from entering an area despite their howls being unanswered.

A lone wolf keeps a lower profile than a pack. Loners—mostly younger animals that have left their natal pack—travel areas 10–20 times greater than does a pack. In this search for a place to settle, find a mate and start its own pack, the lone wolf rarely scent marks or howls. Many loners never reach their goal, but fall victim to hunters, trappers or hostile wolf packs. Once in possession of a vacant area, however, the lone wolf begins to scent mark and will howl readily in response to strangers, ready to defend its territory.   FHH

less frequent than accidental ones, they confront the pack with the dilemma "to reply, or not to reply." If a pack seeks to avoid an encounter, it solves this dilemma by applying a simple rule. When the pack can do so with little loss, it usually slips silently away from the strangers. The silence offers no clues to strangers seeking a deliberate encounter, while any scent marks left by the pack during the retreat can help to prevent an encounter desired by neither pack. But, if to move off means that a pack risks losing an important resource, then it usually stays where it is and replies. The most important resources for the wolf pack are young pups and fresh prey kills: neither can be abandoned without a potentially great loss to the pack. Packs at fresh kills have replied to neighbors' howls in more than four out of every five cases observed. The pack's answering howls prevent any accidental meeting, and although they could assist strangers intent on an attack

COYOTE

Canis latrans
Coyote or Prairie wolf or Brush wolf.
One of 9 species of the genus *Canis*.
Family: Canidae.
Distribution: N Alaska to Costa Rica;
throughout Mexico, continental US and much
of W and C Canada.

Habitat: open country and grassland; may also
occupy deciduous, mixed coniferous and
mountain forests.

Size: head-body length 70–97cm
(28–38in); tail length 30–38cm
(12–15in); shoulder height
45–53cm (18–21in); weight
11.5–15kg (25–33lb).

Coat: grizzled buff-gray; muzzle, outerside of
ears, forelegs and feet dull brownish-yellow;
throat and belly white; prominent black stripe
down middle of back; black patches on front
forelegs and near base and tip of tail.

Gestation: 63 days.

Longevity: up to 14.5 years (18 in captivity).

THE stark image of a solitary coyote is
familiar to many, thanks to its use in
countless Westerns. It has been a persistent
image, and for long the coyote was considered to be a solitary animal. But recent
studies have shown that in some situations
coyotes live cooperatively in a way similar to
wolves.

The coyote—whose name derives from
the original Aztec word for the species,
coyotl—is a medium-sized canid with a
rather narrow muzzle, large pointed ears
and long slender legs. Size varies between
populations and from one locale to another,
and adult males are usually heavier and
larger than adult females.

While the geographic ranges of most
predators are shrinking, that of the coyote is
increasing. A northerly and, particularly,
an easterly expansion from the central Great
Plains began in the late 19th century, as
local populations of the larger canids, the
Gray wolf (*Canis lupus*) and the Red wolf (*C.
rufus*), were decimated by man.

Coyotes can interbreed with the Domestic
dog, the Red wolf and, probably, the Gray
wolf (the so-called Eastern coyotes are now
thought to be fertile coyote–Gray wolf hybrids). The coyote–Domestic dog hybrid
("coydog") can reproduce at one year old
and has two litters a year. Coydogs are even
more liable to attack farm and domestic
animals than are coyotes.

Like jackals and wolves, the coyote is an
opportunistic predator. Mammals, including carrion, generally make up over 90
percent of its diet. Ground squirrels, rabbits
and mice predominate, but larger animals
such as the Pronghorn antelope, deer and
Rocky mountain sheep are included.
Coyotes also eat fruit and insects. Small prey
are hunted singly, but larger animals are
hunted cooperatively. Coyotes normally
stalk small prey from a few meters, but
occasionally from as far as 50m (165ft) and
for as long as 15 minutes. Two or more
coyotes may chase larger prey for up to
400m (1,300ft).

▲ **A foraging coyote** follows intently the
progress of its prey, probably a small rodent or
insect.

▶ **The familiar howl** of the coyote, heard so
often in Western movies, is only one in an
elaborate repertoire of calls.

▲ **A solitary coyote** pauses while out hunting in Banff National Park, Alberta, Canada.

▲ **A coyote pack defends a carcass** on the edge of its territory. Three pack members (**1**) are feeding while the dominant male (**2**) aggressively threatens (tail bushy and almost horizontal, ears erect and slightly forward, fur erect on neck and shoulders, mouth open to expose canines) an intruder (**3**), who assumes a defensive threat posture (tail between legs, ears pressed back on head, mouth open to expose all teeth, back arched and hair erect along entire length of back and neck). Another male (**4**), backing up his dominant partner, shows less intense aggression. (**5**) Another trespasser watches for the outcome of the encounter. Other coyotes (**6**) wait in their own territory for the resident pack to leave the carcass.

The basic social unit in most coyote populations is the breeding pair; and the size of the home range varies from 14 to 65sq km (5.5 to 25sq mi) for males, with an average of 25sq km (9.9sq mi) for females. Coyotes are now known to form packs similar to wolf-packs, in certain situations. Such packs are formed by delayed dispersal of the young, who remain as "helpers" in a pack; a typical pack consists of about six closely related adults, yearlings and young. It is usually the dominant male and female that breed.

Pack members sleep, travel and hunt larger prey together and cooperate in territorial disputes and defense of carrion. In general, coyote packs are smaller than wolf packs and associations between individuals less stable. The reasons for this may be the early expression of aggression, which is found in coyotes but not in wolves, and the fact that coyotes often mature in their first year whereas wolves do so in their second.

Variation in social organization enables the coyote to thrive on diverse prey and this flexibility is probably the reason for the wide, and expanding, geographic range of the species. Coyotes living in packs are more effective predators of large animals, and where such prey (eg deer, elk) is available, packs of 3–8 coyotes are found. Where the principal prey is small mammals, the pups disperse early, packs are not formed, and most sightings are of solitary coyotes. Seasonal variation in social structure also occurs: when Ground squirrels and the young of large mammals are available as prey, coyotes spend less time together.

Coyotes use urine marking and calls to define their territory, to communicate with each other, and to strengthen social bonds. The coyote's howl is unique and consists of a series of high-pitched staccato yelps followed by a prolonged siren wail. Their vocalizations also include barks, bark-howls, group yip-howls and group howls.

During the last 150 years, coyotes have been responsible for large economic losses to US agriculture, especially sheep farming. Some ranchers have lost up to 67 percent of their lambs and 20 percent of their sheep to coyotes in a single year; others lose very few. In fact, there is evidence that attempts to control coyotes by poisoning may also deplete the numbers of their natural prey and lead to increasing attacks by coyotes on farm animals. Although the species is not endangered, it is now totally protected in 12 states and the coyote harvest is regulated by a hunting or trapping season in most of the remaining states and Canada.   WDB

Both sexes attain sexual maturity during the first breeding season (January to March) following birth. Females produce one litter a year, averaging six pups per litter. The young are born blind and helpless in a den and are nursed for a period of 5–7 weeks. At three weeks pups begin to eat semisolid food regurgitated by both parents and other pack members of both sexes. Most young disperse in their first year and may travel up to 160km (100mi) before settling down.

JACKALS

Four of 9 species of the genus *Canis*
Family: Canidae.
Distribution: Africa, SE Europe, S Asia to Burma.

Size: head-body length
65–106cm (26–42in); tail length
20–41cm (8–16in); shoulder
height 38–50cm (15–20in);
weight 7–15kg (15–33lb),
averaging 11kg (24lb).

Gestation: 63 days.

Longevity: 8–9 years (to 16 years in captivity).

Golden jackal
Canis aureus
Golden or Common jackal.

N and E Africa, SE Europe, S Asia to Burma.
Arid short grasslands. Coat: yellow to pale gold,
brown-tipped.

Silverbacked jackal
Canis mesomelas
Silverbacked or Blackbacked jackal.

E and S Africa. Dry brush woodlands. Coat:
russet, with brindled black-and-white saddle;
fur finer than *C. aureus*.

Simien jackal E
Canis simensis
Simien or Ethiopian jackal, Simien fox.

Bale and Simien regions of Ethiopia. High
mountains. Coat: bright reddish with white
chest and belly.

Sidestriped jackal
Canis adustus

Tropical Africa. Moist woodlands. Coat: grayer
than *C. aureus* with distinctive white stripe from
elbow to hip and tail white-tipped.

E Endangered.

THE jackal has a bad name: the word can
also mean "one who performs menial
tasks for others, especially of a base nature."
But the facts about jackals are rather more
edifying than the popular image of a co-
wardly scavenger. Jackals are much less
dependent on carrion than is commonly
supposed, and their family life is noted for its
stability: partnerships between male and
female are unusually durable for a mammal.

Jackals are small slender dog-like omnivores with long sharp canines and well-
developed carnassial teeth used for shearing
tough skin. Like most other canids, jackals
are lithe muscular runners with long legs
and bushy tails. They have large erect ears
and an elaborate repertoire of ear, muzzle
and tail postures. The average weight of
11kg (24lb) applies to all species except the
South African Silverbacked jackal, where in
some populations the male is usually 1kg
(2.2lb) heavier than the female.

Of the four species, the Golden jackal has
the widest distribution (East Africa to
Burma); the others are limited to Africa. In
East Africa, distribution of Golden, Silverbacked and Sidestriped jackals overlaps; but
each species occupies a different habitat.
Skeletal remains of Silverbacked jackals in
Bed I (1.7 million years old) of the Olduvai
Gorge provide the earliest fossil record of a
present-day *Canis*; the species still lives in
the brush woodland nearby the gorge.

Coat color and markings also distinguish
the species, the coat of the Simien jackal

being the most colorful. In the Golden
jackal, coat color varies with season and
region: on the Serengeti Plain in north
Tanzania it is brown-tipped yellow in the
rainy season, changing to pale gold in the
dry season.

Jackals are opportunistic foragers for their
very varied diet. They eat fruits, invertebrates, reptiles, amphibia, birds, small
mammals—from rodents to Thomson's
gazelles—and carrion. In the Silverbacked
jackal's diet, rodents and fruit are the most
important items, and the fruit of the tree
Balanites aegyptiaca, which is highly nutritious and often favored, may even function
as a natural "wormer" to alleviate infestation by parasites. In the Serengeti, scavenging usually contributes less than 6 percent of a jackal's diet.

Cooperative hunting is important for
Golden and Silverbacked jackals. In both
species, pairs have been observed to be three
times more successful than individuals in
hunting Thomson's gazelle fawns. Members
of the same family will also cooperate in
sharing larger food items, ranging in size
from hares to perhaps a wildebeest carcass,
and will transport food in their stomachs for
later regurgitation to pups or a lactating
mother. Food is also cached.

Both sexes mature at 11 months,
although they may not breed at once. Some
yearlings stay on as "helpers" to assist their
parents in raising the next litter. Serengeti
Golden jackals court at the end of the dry

▶ **Mutual grooming** of these two adult
Silverbacked jackals indicates their close family
ties. Jackal family groups are tightly knit, and
cubs are tended by parents and helpers of both
sexes.

▲ **The four species of jackal** depicted in typical play postures. (1) Golden jackal cub attacking the twitching ear of an adult; (2) Silverbacked jackal juveniles in a tail-pulling game, the victim's arched back and laid-back ears revealing its unease; (3) two Simien jackal near-adults play-chasing; and (4) a Sidestriped jackal playing with a dead mouse.

▲ **A jackal pounces** onto a small animal. The steeply arched trajectory, stiff tail, forward ears and close-gathered front paws of this Silverbacked jackal characterize the hunting pounce of many canids.

▶ **The den of a jackal** may be a natural hole or crevice, a den built by another animal, or a new excavation – seldom more than 3m (10ft) long; sometimes jackals may simply hide in thickets. The present occupant of this rock-sheltered den is a Golden jackal.

Jackal Helpers

This typical Silverbacked jackal family group comprises the breeding female (1) and her pups (two shown suckling and one begging her to regurgitate food), and a "helper" (2) in submissive posture towards its father, the breeding male (3). Why some juveniles stay to live with their parents, apparently delaying their own reproduction by a year, and, instead, help raise their younger brothers and sisters is an intriguing question, and attempts to answer it have provided insight into how and why family bonds develop in a hunting and gathering mammal.

In many ways jackals have to contend with conditions not unlike those probably experienced by early man in Africa. In much the same environment, they, too, live in small close-knit families that share food and care for dependent young; and, when they mate, they probably mate for life. Mated pairs of Silverbacked jackals in the Serengeti have been observed to produce pups for at least six years; Golden jackals, for at least eight.

In a recent six-year study in the Serengeti, 12 of 19 litters of Silverbacked jackals, and 6 of 8 Golden jackal litters, had "helpers." Within the family, these helpers were subordinate to parents, and male and female alike assisted in guarding and feeding the pups.

When a jackal pair raises a litter unaided, pups will often be left on their own for up to 40 percent of the time—that is, after the first three weeks of virtually constant attention. But with a helper present, the pups are seldom left undefended. The presence of a single adult at the den provides considerable protection. Not only will an adult "rumble growl" or "predator bark," warning the pups to take refuge and threatening the predator, but a single adult can successfully drive off large predators. A jackal will not hesitate to chase and bite a hyena, even though the latter may be five times its own weight. Adult jackals are quick, and can close in and dart away before a hyena can turn and defend its rear.

Helpers also regularly bring food to the lactating mother, and there are more regurgitations of food, and more nursing sessions by the mother, in families with helpers. Helpers may also improve the provisioning of pups indirectly by allowing the parents to spend more time foraging alone or hunting as a pair. Also, larger families (families with helpers) may be able to defend and exploit a carcass more successfully than an individual. A single jackal, instead of feeding, may spend most of its time threatening vultures—and then often in vain.

Survival rates for Silverbacked jackals confirm the genetic advantage of helpers to members of this species. Silverbacked parents with no helpers raise on average only one pup; with just a single helper, three pups may survive, and a family with three helpers is known to have reared six pups. On average, the reproductive success of families observed increased by 1.7 pups with the addition of each helper. Moreover, since their parents are monogamous, jackal helpers are as closely related to their full siblings as they would be to their own offspring. In the short term, therefore, helpers can do more to ensure the survival of their own genes by caring for their brothers and sisters than they could by starting their own families.

There are of course other benefits to jackals from staying on the territory where they were born and extending their experience at home. They may live longer and may in time raise their own pups more successfully than they would otherwise. In a few cases helpers may actually inherit part of their parents' territory and benefit from long familiarity with it. The precise contribution of factors such as these to the evolution of helping behavior is, however, difficult to evaluate; and the fact that a one-year-old jackal can emigrate and yet still benefit genetically (more siblings survive), as long as one litter-mate does stay and help, is a typical complication.

Among Golden jackals, pup survival does seem to improve in the presence of helpers, but not as markedly as with Silverbacked jackals. Goldens whelp during the rainy season (December–January), when food on the shortgrass plains is most abundant. However, the rains that bring the wildebeest and zebra also flood dens, and pups die of exposure and illness. Thus, any long-term gains may, in the short term, be offset.

season (October) and produce pups in the rainy season (December–January). Thus whelping occurs during the period of greatest food abundance on the shortgrass plains. Silverbacked jackals whelp in July–October, which coincides with a peak in rodent numbers and with fruiting of the balanites tree. Most jackal species have a maximum litter size of nine, but a pregnant Sidestriped jackal has been found with 12 fetuses, so reabsorption of fetuses, or other early mortality, may occur. The number of pups which reach maturity varies; in Serengeti Silverbacked jackal litters without a helper, only one pup survives on average; with one helper, three or more may live.

Evidence of helping behavior has emerged in all members of the dog family that have been studied in detail. The jackal helper (see LEFT) is fully mature (jackals reach sexual maturity at 11 months), and while subordinate to its parents, is an important member of the family.

Young jackal pups remain in the den—a natural shelter or simple excavation—for some three weeks, during which time the mother spends about 90 percent of her time with them, perhaps to keep them warm. She nurses the pups until they are about eight weeks old. The female initiates all den changes, which may be as frequent as every two weeks. When Silverbacked jackal pups are three months old they stop using a den. Pups are fed regularly by regurgitation until about five months old, and may occasionally be fed until they leave their parents, at one or two years of age.

Jackal pairs hold territories of 0.5–2.5sq km (0.2–1sq mi) throughout the year. They forage and rest together and all their behavior is highly synchronized. They tend to scent mark their territory in tandem, with either male or female making the first mark, probably advertising to intruders that both members of the pair are in residence. The males are strictly monogamous, perhaps because divided paternal care might reduce the number of cubs that survive. Females reserve their aggression for female intruders, thus preventing the sharing of the male and his paternal investment. Since females may be able to produce litters with several sires, the male needs to ensure that he alone copulates with his mate, if a wasted investment in pups that he has not sired is to be avoided. It is not surprising therefore that the male of a pair fiercely threatens and attacks any male intruder on the territory. Both members of a pair have important roles in maintaining their territory and in raising the young. When one parent dies, the rest of the family is unlikely to survive.

In addition to posture and scent, each jackal species communicates through its own repertoire of calls. These may include howls, yelps, barks and other vocalizations. Silverbacked and Golden are more vocal than Sidestriped jackals. In the Serengeti Goldens locate each other by howling, while the contact call of the Silverbacked jackal is a series of yelps.

In agricultural areas jackals tend to be persecuted by man; and jackals are also killed for their fur. In Ethiopia the Simien jackal's numbers have been so reduced that this is now an endangered species, with only an estimated 500 left in the wild.   PDM

▼ **Carrion,** though important, forms a very much smaller part of a jackal's diet than has been traditionally supposed. This group of Silverbacked jackals deters vultures which would almost certainly succeed in driving away a solitary jackal.

FOXES

Twenty-one species in 4 genera
Family: Canidae.
Distribution: Americas, Europe, Asia, Africa.

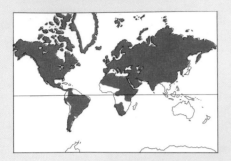

Habitat: very wide-ranging, from Arctic tundra to city center.

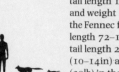

Size: ranges from head-body length 24–41cm (9.5–16in), tail length 18–31cm (7–12in) and weight 1.5kg (3.3lb) in the Fennec fox to head-body length 72–100cm (28–39in), tail length 25–35cm (10–14in) and weight 9kg (20lb) in the Small-eared dog.

Gestation: between 50 days (Fennec fox and others), and 60–63 days (Red fox).

Longevity: up to 6 years (13 in captivity).

Vulpine foxes

Twelve species of the genus *Vulpes*.
N and S America, Europe, Asia, Africa.
Coat: mostly grays to red-browns, but white, silver, cream, buff-yellow and black also.
Species include: the **Red fox** (*V. vulpes*) or Silver or Cross fox; the **Gray fox** (*V. cinereoargenteus*) or Tree fox; the **Swift fox** (*V. velox*) or Kit fox; the **Fennec fox** (*V. zerda*); and the **Indian fox** (*V. bengalensis*).

South American foxes

Seven species of the genus *Dusicyon*.
Coat: mostly grays with tawny grizzling, often with black markings.
Species include: the **Argentine gray fox** [*] (*D. griseus*); the **Colpeo fox** [*] (*D. culpaeus*); and the so-called **Small-eared dog** [?] (*D. microtis*).

Arctic fox

Alopex lagopus
Arctic or Polar or White or Blue fox.
N polar regions.
Coat: very thick, either white (gray-brown in summer) or blue (chocolate-brown in summer)

Bat-eared fox

Otocyon megalotis
Bat-eared fox or Delandi's fox.
E and S Africa.
Coat: gray to buff; face markings, tips of ears, feet and dorsal stripe all black.

[*] CITES listed. [?] Threat suspected.

IN Aesop's fable the cunning fox outwits the stork; and in the Uncle Remus stories Br'er Fox is the chosen adversary of Br'er Rabbit. That foxes figure as the wily character in the popular tales of many lands reflects both their distribution and their resourceful behavior. The largest genus of foxes, *Vulpes*, is also the most widespread of canid genera, and one of its members, the Red fox, is the most widely dispersed and arguably the most adaptable of all carnivores.

Foxes are small canids with pointed muzzles, somewhat flattened slender skulls, large ears and long bushy tails. All species are opportunistic foragers, using hunting techniques which vary from stealth to dash-and-grab. Apart from the Bat-eared fox (see p73) which eats mainly termites, there are no proven differences in species' diets other than those imposed by the limits of available prey. Arctic foxes will take sea birds, ptarmigan, shore invertebrates, fruits and berries, together with carrion found while methodically beachcombing. They time their shore visits to coincide with the receding tide when fresh debris is stranded. Red foxes have similarly diverse diets, ranging from small hoofed mammals, rabbits, hares, rodents and birds to invertebrates such as beetles, grasshoppers and earthworms. Red foxes have been observed to fish, wading stealthily through shallow marshes. In season, fruit such as blackberries, apples and the hips of the Dog rose can form as much as 90 percent of the diet.

All vulpine foxes catch rodents with a characteristic "mouse leap," springing a meter off the ground and diving, front paws first, onto the prey. This aerial descent may be a device literally to squash the vertical jump used by some mice to escape predators. Red foxes catch earthworms that leave their burrows on warm moist nights by criss-crossing pastures at a slow walk and listening for the rasping of the worms' bristles on the grass. Once a worm is detected, the fox poises over it before plunging its snout into the grass. Worms whose tails retain a grip in their burrows are not broken but gently pulled taut after a momentary pause—a technique foxes share with bait-collecting fishermen.

The few fox species that have been studied in several different habitats have been found to eat whatever food was locally available. Nevertheless, foxes may have some preferences. For example Red foxes, if given the choice, will prefer rodents of the family Microtinae, such as field voles, to members of the family Muridae, such as field mice. However, being true opportunists, they will cache even unfavored prey for future use, and have a good memory for the location of these larders.

The similar foraging behavior of different fox species may affect their geographical distribution, as it leads to severe competition for food. Arctic and Red foxes were once thought to be separated by the Arctic species' remarkable tolerance to cold temperatures—its metabolic rate does not even start to increase until −50°C, in contrast to the Red fox's, which increases at −13°C. However, Red foxes are sometimes found in even colder places than Arctic foxes, so they are probably separated by food

▲ **Unmistakably vulpine.** the mask of the Red fox, with its prominent ears, eyes and whiskers, fine muzzle and sensitive nose, epitomizes the species' alertness – often unfairly portrayed in fables as sly cunning.

▶ **The coat of the northern Red fox** occurs in three color forms, here represented in a group of foxes scavenging from a carcass in a northern forest. (**1**) Two individuals with the vivid flame-red coloring typical of most high latitude Red foxes; (**2**) the melanistic ("Silver") form; and (**3**) the intermediate so-called Cross fox. The different forms are probably under complex control of two different genes.

◀ **South American foxes** of the genus *Dusicyon*. (**1**) the Small-eared dog (*D. microtis*): (**2**) the Colpeo fox (*D. culpaeus*); (**3**) the Argentine gray fox (*D. griseus*); (**4**) Azara's fox (*D. gymnocercus*); and (**5**) the Crab-eating fox (*D. thous*).

▲ **Smallest of all canids,** the Fennec fox, fully grown, weighs scarcely 1.5kg (3.3lb). With its large ears and pale fur, it is well adapted to the desert conditions of Northern Africa, Sinai and Arabia where it lives.

▼ **Eight vulpine species,** depicted in a dash and swipe after a bird, shown in west-to-east order of distribution (only Gray and Corsac, and occasionally Red foxes climb trees). (**1**) Gray fox (*Vulpes cinereoargenteus*); (**2**) Swift fox (*V. velox*); (**3**) Cape fox (*V. chama*); (**4**) Fennec fox (*V. zerda*); (**5**) Rüppell's fox (*V. rüppelli*); (**6**) Blanford's fox (*V. cana*); (**7**) Indian fox (*V. bengalensis*); (**8**) Corsac fox (*V. corsac*).

competition: the Red is up to twice as heavy, needs correspondingly more food, and thus in the far north, where prey is sparse, cannot match energy gains with expenditure in the way that the Arctic fox can. However, in areas where both species can subsist, the Red fox's greater size enables it to intimidate the Arctic fox and in effect determine the southern limit of the latter's range. The ranges of these species doubtless fluctuated as Ice Ages came and went.

Direct competition may also have affected the distribution and sizes of *Dusicyon* species. In central and southern Chile both the Colpeo fox and the Argentine gray fox eat rodents, birds, birds' eggs and snakes in comparable quantities. However, these two species vary in size with latitude throughout their range. Average body length of the Colpeo fox increases from 70 to 90cm (28–35in) and that of the Argentine gray decreases from 68 to 42cm (27–17in) with change in latitude from 34°S to 54°S. Where the two species are of similar size (34°S), the Colpeo inhabits higher altitudes of the Andes, so reducing competition. Further south, where the altitude of the Andes decreases, bringing the species into apparently direct competition, the much smaller size of the Argentine gray fox predisposes it to hunting smaller prey than the Colpeo fox, and so, again, competition is reduced.

Foxes breed once a year. Litter sizes are normally from one to six, the average for the Red fox varying with habitat between four and eight. The maximum number of fetuses found in a Red fox vixen is 12. Vixens have six mammae, or teats. Known gestation periods are 60–63 days for the Red fox and 51 for the Fennec fox. Cubs are generally born in burrows (either dug by the vixen or appropriated from other species) or rock crevices. Litters of Red foxes have been found in hollow trees, under houses or simply in long grass. Foxes have generally been considered as monogamous, but communal denning has now been recorded for the Indian fox and the Red fox, and "helpers" at the den occur in both Arctic

and Red foxes (see below). Among Red foxes the proportion of vixens which breed varies greatly between areas, from 30 percent to almost all.

Foxes have been characterized as solitary carnivores, foraging alone for small prey for which cooperative hunting would be a hindrance rather than an advantage. In this respect their social behavior has been contrasted with that of pack-hunting canids such as wolves. However, with modern radiotracking studies and with night-vision equipment, it has become clear that fox society is complex. In some areas foxes are monogamous; in others, as with Red and Arctic foxes, they may live in groups, generally composed of one adult male and several vixens. So far, the maximum proven adult group size for Arctic foxes is three and for Red foxes six. There is no evidence of successful immigration of vixens into such groups, so the female members are probably relatives, whereas all male offspring emigrate. Dispersal distance varies with habitat and records of over 200km (125mi) exist. Males invariably disperse farther than females.

Although their paths may cross many times each night, foxes within a group may

▲ **Gray fox in a tree.** Not surprisingly this tree-climbing species of the Americas is also known as the Tree fox. Although tree climbing is most common in Gray foxes, Red foxes also occasionally climb – in some places even sleeping in bushy trees.

◄ **Recently reclassified** as a subspecies of the Swift fox, the prairie-dwelling Kit fox of the southwestern United States and northwestern Mexico is smaller yet has larger ears than other North American foxes. Eight of the 10 subspecies of Swift fox share the common name Kit fox.

that of strangers. Foxes have paired anal sacs on either side of the anus. These can be evacuated voluntarily, or the secretion may be coated onto feces. Foxes also have a skin gland, 2cm (0.8in) long, on the dorsal surface of the tail, near the base. This "supracaudal gland," or "violet gland," is covered in bristles and appears as a black spot on the tails of all vulpine foxes. Its function is unknown. There are yet more glands between their toes. Both males and females may "cock their legs" when urine marking.

Territory sizes are probably determined by the availability of food and by the mortality rate, which is mainly dependent on man and rabies. Where mortality through hunting is high few Red foxes survive three years. The oldest vixen known from the wild was the nine-year-old matriarch of a group of four occupying a 40-hectare (100-acre) territory in Oxfordshire, England.

Like other canids, foxes communicate by means of sound as well as by means of scent marking and postural signals. The Arctic fox calls quite often—for example when an enemy approaches, or during the breeding season. The vocalizations of the Red fox include aggressive yapping and a resonant howl used by young foxes in winter and, more often, in the mating season. Barks, soft whimpers (between vixen and pups) and screams are also part of the repertoire of the Red fox.

Despite their fabled cunning, foxes, too, have their endangered species. Both the little-known Small-eared dog of tropical South America and a subspecies of the Swift fox, the Northern Swift fox (*V. velox hebes*), are listed as threatened by the IUCN. The latter, a small 2kg (4.4lb) North American prairie-dwelling fox, was rarely seen in the northern Great Plains between 1900 and 1970, and seems to have been completely

forage mainly in different parts of the territory, with dominant animals monopolizing the best habitat.

Range sizes for Red foxes have been found to vary between 10 and 2,000 or more hectares (25 and 5,000 acres), those of Arctic foxes between 860 and 6,000 hectares (2,100 to 15,000 acres). Territory area and group size are unrelated. Feces and urine are left on conspicuous landmarks, like tussocks of grass. These scent marks are distributed throughout the foxes' range, but especially in places visited often. Dominant animals scent mark with urine more than subordinates do, and individuals can distinguish the scent of their own urine from

5   6   7   8

◀ **White form of the Arctic fox** in its smoky gray summer coat. The short, rounded ears and short muzzle are heat-saving adaptations to the polar climate, as is the fur that lines the soles of its feet. Arctic foxes are often observed following Polar bears in order to scavenge from their kills.

▶ **The coat of Arctic foxes** occurs in two color forms, each with a different summer and winter coloration. (1) A white, or Polar, form in winter coat attacks a ptarmigan; (2) the same form in summer coat; (3) a steel-gray to brown, or Blue, form beachcombs for carrion, again in winter; and (4) a Blue fox vixen "helper" in brown summer coat with her year-younger siblings. This litter contains both color forms – the light gray cubs have the summer coat of the white form, while the dark gray cub is a further variant of the summer coat of the Blue form. The two color forms are genetically determined by a single gene, the white form being recessive. The ratio of white to blue varies: in mainland Alaska, Canada and Eurasia less than 1 percent are blue, but on small islands like the Pribilofs more than 90 percent are blue. The extent of snow cover in the habitat seems to influence which form predominates.

▼ **Very large ears** of these Bat-eared foxes leave little doubt as to why the species is so named. The ears are an adaptation to locating insect prey by sound and also assist heat loss in their hot environment.

exterminated by hunting in Canada. In 1928 it disappeared from Saskatchewan and in 1938 from Alberta. However, Swift foxes seem to have reappeared recently within the range previously occupied by the Northern Swift fox, although they may be the Southern form, *V. v. velox.*

The management and conservation of foxes turn on three main issues: killing for sport or predator control; hunting for pelts; and rabies control. The past decade has witnessed a revival of the prewar vogue for fox skins and has resulted in huge harvests. In the 1977–78 season, 388,643 Red foxes, 264,957 Gray foxes and 37,494 Arctic foxes were taken in North America. In 1978, nearly one million skins of the Argentine gray fox were reputedly exported from Argentina. The risk of over-harvesting has prompted several of the midwestern states of the United States to limit fur licenses severely and to extend closed seasons. Outside North America there is little control of the trade in canid skins. The new market for pelts has transformed Britain and Ireland, where there are no monitoring systems, into fur-trapping nations for the first time in recent history, and it is estimated that 50,000 to 100,000 Red fox skins were exported in 1980, with prices in 1979 averaging $60 (£30).

All genera of foxes are liable to spread,

and to suffer from, rabies, the virus disease that causes hydrophobia in humans. Millions of foxes have been slaughtered in unsuccessful attempts to control the disease, but foxes have such resilience that populations can withstand about 75 percent mortality without further declining. The best hope for eliminating rabies may lie in oral vaccination—accomplished by air-dropping fox baits containing anti-rabies vaccine. Preliminary trials in Switzerland and Canada have shown that up to 74 percent of foxes will eat the bait. However, an effective killed vaccine suitable for oral administration has yet to be perfected.

DWM

The Bat-eared Fox—An Insect Eater

Besides the ears (among foxes only the Fennec fox's are larger in relation to its body), it is teeth and diet that set this African species apart from all other foxes. Although usually found near large herds of hoofed mammals, such as zebras, wildebeest and buffalo, the Bat-eared fox is the only canid to have largely abandoned mammalian prey.

The teeth of the Bat-eared fox are relatively small, but it has between four and eight extra molars (see p57). On the lower jaw a step-like protrusion anchors the large digastric muscle that is used for rapid chewing. The diet includes fruits, scorpions and the occasional mammal or bird, but 80 percent is insects, and of these most are termites, particularly the Harvester termite (*Hodotermes*) and dung beetles (Scarabidae).

These insects abound only where large ungulates are numerous—the Bat-eared fox remains dependent on mammals for provision of its food, despite the insectivorous nature of its diet. Colonies of Harvester termites (which can make up 70 percent of the fox's diet) live underground, but large parties surface to forage for small blades of grass, from which they are taken by the foxes, and such grass occurs mainly where large ungulates feed. Dung beetles eat the dung of ungulates and lay their eggs in dung balls, which the female beetles bury. Bat-eared foxes eat both adults and larvae, which they locate by listening for the sound of the grub as it gnaws its way out of the dung ball. In this, the large ears, up to 12cm (5in) long, serve the fox well.

Bat-eared foxes usually breed in self-dug dens in pairs, but there are records of a male with two breeding females (and one record of communal nursing). The pups (usually 2–5) are born after a 60-day gestation. Juveniles achieve full adult size at four months and, when accompanying adults, may account for reported group sizes of up to 12. Foraging is usually done on an individual basis.

Extensive overlap of foraging areas has been reported. Interaction between groups varies from peaceful mingling to overt aggression. Two or three breeding dens are sometimes clustered within a few hundred meters—probably a response to locally suitable soil or vegetation. Reported home range sizes vary from 0.5 to 3sq km (0.2–1.1sq mi). Population density may reach 10 per square kilometer (26/sq mi), but 0.5–3 per square kilometer (1.3–7.8/sq mi) is more usual.

JM

THE 21 SPECIES OF FOXES

Genus *Vulpes*

N and far north of S America, Europe, Africa and Asia. Muzzle pointed; ears triangular and erect; tail long and bushy; skull flattened, by comparison with *Canis*. Tail tip often different color from rest of coat (eg black or white); black triangular face marks between eyes and nose.

Indian fox
Vulpes bengalensis
Indian or Bengal fox.

India, Pakistan and Nepal. Steppe, open forest, thorny scrub and semidesert up to altitudes of 1,350m. Regarded anatomically as the "typical" vulpine fox. HBL 45–60cm; TL 25–35cm; wt 1.8–3.2kg. Coat: sandy-orange with legs tawny-brown; tail black-tipped.

Blanford's fox *
Vulpes cana
Blanford's or Hoary or Baluchistan fox.

Afghanistan, SW USSR, Turkestan, NE Iran, Baluchistan. Mountainous regions. HBL 42cm; TL 30cm; wt 3kg. Coat: as Indian fox, but blotchy with dark mid-dorsal line and brown chin.

Cape fox
Vulpes chama
Cape or Silverbacked fox.

Africa S of Zimbabwe and Angola. Steppe, rocky desert. Anatomy, especially skull, similar to Indian fox and Pale fox. HBL 45–61cm; TL 30–40cm; wt 3.6–4.5kg. Coat: rufous-agouti with silvery-gray back; tail tip black; dark facial mask lacking; ears elongate.

Gray fox
Vulpes cinereoargenteus
Gray or Tree fox.

Central USA to the prairies, S to Venezuela, N to Ontario. Able to climb trees. Formerly separated as *Urocyon*, partly because of longer tail gland. HBL 52–69cm; TL 27–45cm; wt 2.5–7kg. Coat: gray-agouti; throat white; legs and feet tawny; mane of black-tipped bristles along dorsal surface of tail. Canine teeth shorter than average for *Vulpes*.

Corsac fox
Vulpes corsac

SE USSR, Soviet and Chinese Turkestan, Mongolia, Transbaikalia to N Manchuria and N Afghanistan. Steppe. HBL 50–60cm; TL 22–35cm; wt unknown. Coat: russet-gray with white chin. Subspecies: 3.

Tibetan fox
Vulpes ferrilata
Tibetan or Tibetan sand fox.

Tibet and Nepal. High steppe (4,500–4,800m). Although the most *Dusicyon*-like of *Vulpes* species, probably descended from Corsac fox. HBL 67cm; TL 29cm; wt not known. Coat: pale gray-agouti on body and ears; tip of tail white. Head long and narrow; canines elongate.

Island gray fox
Vulpes littoralis

Islands of W USA. Smaller than Gray fox but otherwise identical. HBL 59–79cm; TL 11–29cm; wt not known.

Pale fox
Vulpes pallida

N Africa from Red Sea to Atlantic, Senegal to Sudan and Somalia. Desert. HBL 40–45cm; TL 27–29cm; wt 2.7kg. Coat: pale fawn on body and ears; legs rufous; tail tip black; no facial marks; fur short and thin; whiskers relatively long and black.

Rüppell's fox
Vulpes ruppelli
Rüppell's or Sand fox.

Scattered populations between Morocco and Afghanistan, NE Nigeria, N Cameroun, Chad, Central African Republic, Gabon, Congo, Somalia, Sudan, Egypt, Sinai, Arabia. Desert. HBL 40–52cm; TL 25–35cm; wt 1.7kg. Coat: pale, sandy color; conspicuous white tail tip and black muzzle patches; whiskers relatively long and black. Subspecies: 6.

Swift fox
Vulpes velox
Swift or Kit fox.

NW Mexico and SW USA, N through prairie states to Alberta, Canada. Arid steppe and prairies. Kit foxes (8 of subspecies) formerly classified as *V. macrotis*. HBL 38–50cm; TL 22–30cm; wt 1.8–3kg. Coat: buff-yellow; limbs and feet tawny; black tip to very bushy tail. Subspecies: 10.

Red fox
Vulpes vulpes
Red or Silver or Cross fox.

N Hemisphere from Arctic Circle to N African and C American deserts and Asiatic steppes. Wide-ranging: Arctic tundra to European city centers. Natural S limit in Sudan. Introduced into Australia. (The N American subspecies *V. v. fulva* was formerly considered a separate species *V. fulva*.) Male HBL 68cm; TL 44cm; wt 5.9kg. Female HBL 66cm; TL 42cm; wt 5.2kg. (*V. v fulva*: HBL 55–62cm; TL 35–40cm; wt 4.1–5.4kg.) Coat: rust to flame-red above (with silver, cross and color phases); white to black below; tip of tail often white. Subspecies: 48.

Fennec fox
Vulpes zerda

N Africa, throughout Sahara, E to Sinai and Arabia. Sandy desert. Formerly separated as *Fennecus* because of large ears, rounded skull and weak dentition. HBL 24–41cm; TL 18–31cm; wt 0.8–1.5kg. Coat: cream with black-tipped tail; soles of feet furred; ears very large, up to 15cm long; dark bristles over tail gland; whiskers relatively long and black. The smallest fox.

Genus *Dusicyon*

Restricted to S America. Anatomy intermediate between *Vulpes* and *Canis*, with the extinct *D. australis* (Falkland Island wolf) most dog-like and *D. vetulus* most vulpine. Coat: usually gray with tawny grizzling. Skull long and thin; ears large and erect; tail bushy. Biology poorly known.

Colpeo fox *
Dusicyon culpaeus.

Andes from Ecuador and Peru to Tierra del Fuego. Mountains and pampas. (*D. culpaeolus* found in Uruguay is similar, but smaller, whereas *D. inca* from Peru is larger; both may be better considered subspecies of *D. culpaeus*, as indeed may be Azara's fox.) HBL 60–115cm; TL 30–45cm (see p70); wt 7.4kg. Coat: back, shoulders grizzled gray; head, neck, ears, legs tawny; tail black-tipped. Subspecies: 6.

Argentine gray fox *
Dusicyon griseus
Argentine gray or Gray or Pampas fox.

Distribution as Colpeo fox but lower altitudes in Ecuador and N Chile. Plains, pampas and low mountains. HBL average 42–68cm (see p78); TL 30–36cm; wt 4.4kg. Coat: brindled pale gray; underparts pale. Subspecies: 7.

Azara's fox
Dusicyon gymnocercus
Azara's or Pampas fox.

Paraguay, SE Brazil, S through E Argentina to Rio Negro. Pampas. Perhaps same species as Colpeo fox. HBL 62cm; TL 34cm; wt 4.8–6.5kg. Coat: uniform grizzled gray. Subspecies: 2.

Small-eared dog ?
Dusicyon microtis
Small-eared dog, Zorro negro, Small-eared zorro.

Amazon and Orinoco basins, parts of Peru, Colombia, Ecuador, Venezuela, Brazil. Tropical forests. Formerly considered sufficiently distinct to be placed in separate genus *Atelocynus*. Ears short (5cm) and rounded; has long, heavy teeth and enlarged second lower molar; gait reputedly cat-like. HBL 72–100cm; TL 25–35cm; wt 9kg. Coat: dark.

Sechuran fox
Dusicyon sechurae

N Peru and S Ecuador. Coastal desert. HBL 53–59cm; TL about 25cm; wt about 4.5kg. Coat: pale agouti without any russet tinges; tail black-tipped.

Crab-eating fox
Dusicyon thous
Crab-eating fox or Common zorro.

Colombia and Venezuela to N Argentina and Paraguay. Savanna, llanos and woodland. Formerly considered sufficiently distinct to be placed in separate genus *Cerdocyon*. HBL 60–70cm; TL 28–30cm; wt 5–8kg. Coat: gray-brown; ears dark; tail with dark dorsal stripe and black tip; foot pads large; muzzle short. Subspecies: 7.

Hoary fox
Dusicyon vetulus
Hoary fox or Small-toothed dog.

S central Brazil: Minas Gerais, Matto Grosso. Previously allocated to *Lycalopex* on basis of small teeth. HBL 60cm; TL 30cm; wt 2.7–4kg. Dark line present on dorsal surface of tail. A small *Dusicyon*, with short muzzle, small teeth and reduced upper carnassials.

▶ **Crab-eating fox,** with the grizzled gray coat, long pointed skull and large ears typical of the South American genus *Dusicyon*.

Genus *Alopex*

Similar to *Vulpes* but distinguished on basis of skull characters and adaptations to polar climate.

Arctic fox

Alopex lagopus
Arctic or Polar or Blue or White fox.

Circumpolar in tundra latitudes. Tundra and intertidal zone of seashore. Male: HBL 55cm; TL 31cm; wt 3.8kg. Female: HBL 53cm; TL 30cm; wt 3.1kg. Coat: very thick with two dichromatic color forms: "white" which is gray-brown in summer; and "blue" which is chocolate-brown in summer; 70% of fur is fine, warm underfur. Has remarkable tolerance to cold and only starts shivering at −70°C. Subspecies: 9.

Genus *Otocyon*

Distinguished from other genera on the basis of unusual dentition.

Bat-eared fox

Otocyon megalotis
Bat-eared fox or Delandi's fox.

Two populations, one from S Zambia to S Africa, the other from Ethiopia to Tanzania. Open grasslands. HBL 46–58cm; TL 24–34cm; wt 3–4.5kg. Coat: gray to buff, with face markings, tips of ears, feet and dorsal stripe all black. Ears large (to 12cm); teeth weak but with extra molars to give 46–50 teeth in all; lower jaw with step-like angular process to allow attachment of large digastric muscle used for rapid chewing of termites. Subspecies: 2.

Fox Classification

The classification of foxes is complicated by similarities between imperfectly distinguished species and by fragmentary knowledge of their behavior. The arrangement adopted here is already contracted, but even so it could probably be further simplified. The genera are mainly distinguished by the fact that the "brows" formed by the frontal bones above and between the eyes are slightly indented or dished in the genus *Vulpes* and flat in *Dusicyon* (as opposed to convex in *Canis*). Familiarity with the widespread Red fox has lured some people into considering it as the "typical" vulpine fox, whereas it is perhaps the least typical—for example in being the largest. On the basis of morphology, the Indian fox is the "average" *Vulpes*, and even the Gray fox and the Fennec fox—species once placed in the separate genera *Urocyon* and *Fennecus*—conform to that average more closely than does the Red fox. Similarly, the South American Azara's fox and the Argentine gray fox are typical of *Dusicyon*; and the Small-eared dog (once classified as *Atelocynus microtus*) and the Crab-eating fox (once *Cerdocyon thous*) are so similar to them that to split them off from *Dusicyon* seems an unnecessary complication.

In both *Vulpes* and *Dusicyon* some geographically close species may be related, as in the case of the mountain-dwelling Tibetan fox and the similar but larger Corsac fox of lower altitudes in central Asia, from which the former is probably descended. In contrast, the Cape fox of southern Africa is morphologically most similar to the geographically distant Indian fox, which inhabits similar steppe country. Those species which in a north–south arc separate the Indian fox and the Cape fox, namely Rüppel's fox, the Fennec fox and the Pale fox, are close relatives whose differences are adaptations to various arid landscapes. The distribution of Blanford's fox falls within this arc, but its small size—head-body length only 42cm (16.5in)—is probably an adaptation to a mountainous rather than a desert existence.

The desert foxes are the smallest, the lightest-colored and have the largest whiskers and external ears. This trend culminates in the very small 1.5kg (3.3lb) Fennec fox, whose heavily furred paws and large ears are adapted to life on hot sand dunes. Another fox specifically adapted to an extreme environment is the Arctic fox, whose species name (*Alopex lagopus*), indicates the resemblance of the long fur of the paws to that of a hare. Although very similar to, and sometimes classified within, *Vulpes*, the Arctic fox is sufficiently distinct (for example, in coloration) to merit generic status. Recent field studies have highlighted considerable similarities in the behavior of Red and Arctic foxes, and the two probably share a common ancestor, *Vulpes alopecoides*, from which they diverged in the Pleistocene Ice Ages, 1–2 million years ago.

Like the Arctic fox, the Bat-eared fox of Africa is placed in its own genus. *Otocyon* is separated on the basis of its dentition, unique among canids, which has evolved as an adaptation to an insectivorous diet.

The South American *Dusicyon* foxes are intermediate in appearance between the popular images of foxes and that of canids such as wolves and coyotes; indeed, in 1868 the taxonomist J. E. Gray called them Fox-tailed wolves. The Falkland Island wolf (*D. australis*) became extinct in 1880. It was first described by Darwin, who noted that it fed on the goose *Chloephaga picta*. In their skull and teeth these wolf-like foxes were more similar to *Canis* than *Dusicyon*, but their extermination by pelt-hunters has sadly relegated them to the status of a biological mystery. Some maintain that *D. australis* was descended from a domestic canid and not from a *Dusicyon* ancestor, pointing out that it has a white-tipped tail in contrast to the black one of all surviving *Dusicyon* species. Another South American mystery is *D. hagenbecki*, a fox-like canid known from a single skin collected in the Andes.

AFRICAN WILD DOG

Lycaon pictus [E]
African wild dog or Cape hunting dog or
Tri-colored dog or Wild dog.
Sole member of genus.
Family: Canidae.
Distribution: from the Sahara to S Africa.

Habitat: from semidesert to alpine; savanna
woodland probably preferred.

Size: head-body length 75–100cm
(30–40in); tail length 30–40cm
(12–16in); shoulder height 75cm
(30in); weight 20–27kg
(44–60lb). No variation between
sexes and little variation between
populations.

Coat: short, dark with a unique pattern of
irregular white and yellow blotches on each
individual; muzzle dark; tail white-tipped.

Gestation: 70–73 days.

Longevity: about 10 years.

[E] Endangered.

▼ **Impressive shearing teeth** displayed, as a
male African wild dog interrupts his midday
rest to yawn and to urinate: the posture
indicates a subordinate status in the pack of
which he is a member – only the dominant
male and female cock a hind leg while
urinating.

AFTER a chase of some three kilometers, a
gazelle suddenly swerves. The African
wild dog at its heels fails to follow the jink,
but the second dog a few meters behind has
to run only one side of a triangle to the
gazelle's two, and is able to intercept and
seize the tiring prey. In the face of a cooperative hunter like the African wild dog,
the evasive action that would have foiled a
solitary cheetah seals the gazelle's fate.

The African wild dog is the least typical
canid. It is exclusively carnivorous and has
a short powerful muzzle that houses an
impressive array of shearing teeth, but with
the last molar poorly developed; unlike
other canids it has lost the fifth digit on the
front feet. The large rounded ears are used in
signals to other wild dogs and in controlling
body temperature.

Although savanna woodland is probably
the preferred habitat, wild dogs have been
recorded in the Sahara and in the snows of
Mount Kilimanjaro at 5,600m (18,500ft).
They are seldom numerous and densities as
low as one pack per 2,000sq km (770sq mi)
are not uncommon.

African wild dogs hunt, rest, travel and
reproduce in packs which average 7 or 8
adults but vary from 2 to 20 in number.
With pups a pack may contain over 30
individuals. Packs have a home base only
when young pups are present. At other
times the pack crisscrosses its range in the
course of seeking and catching prey, covering from 2 to 50km (1–30mi) each day. The
home ranges of packs studied on the
Serengeti Plain (north Tanzania) average
1,500sq km (580sq mi). The ranges of
different packs overlap extensively. If packs
meet, the larger group usually chases away
the smaller.

Wild dogs rely mainly on sight when
hunting, which usually takes place in the
cool hours around dawn and dusk, only
occasionally at night. Packs hunt at least
once a day, and large packs, particularly
when taking smaller prey, at least twice.

The chief prey species varies, with impala
in southern Africa, puku in parts of Zambia,
and Thomson's gazelle in most of East
Africa. All of these weigh between 20 and
90kg (44–200lb), but herbivores as small as
Cane rats (5kg/11lb) and as large as Greater
kudu (about 310kg/680lb) have been reported in the diet.

Hunting success depends on the ability to
choose young or weak animals, often selected from among a herd, that can be
overhauled in a straight chase. African wild
dogs can run at about 60km/h (37mph) for
5km (3mi) or more. Normally all adults
present share the kill, but adults will stand
aside to let any pups present eat first.

The adult males and adult females in a
pack have separate dominance hierarchies.
The dominant male and female usually stay
close to each other. About once a year—
often at a time of relative food abundance,
the dominant female is mated by the dominant male. The female selects a den, usually
a preexisting hole, and pups are born blind
and weighing about 400g (14oz). At about
three weeks of age their eyes open, and the
pups emerge above ground when they start
to eat solid food regurgitated by all the
adults. Once they are weaned, at about 10
weeks, the pups rely on food (and protection) provided jointly by the pack until they
can fend for themselves at about 14 months.
When the pups are about three months old,
they start to roam with the pack. Sexual
maturity is attained between 12 and 18
months.

Most males born in a pack will remain
there through their 10 years or so of life.
Females between 14 and 30 months of age
leave their natal pack in groups of littermate
sisters, and emigrate to a different male kin
line (see pp78–79).

The African wild dog is listed by the IUCN
as threatened by extinction and probably
the world population does not exceed
10,000. They have been persecuted by man,
are susceptible to epidemic diseases, such as
distemper, and their habitat is shrinking as
human populations expand. However, wild
dogs are able to survive in places that are of
marginal use to man, such as semidesert
and swamps, and they breed successfully in
zoos.   JM

A Hunting Tradition

A zebra stallion trots away from his group of mares and foals as the pack of dogs approaches. With head lowered, teeth bared and nostrils flaring he charges at the leading dogs, who turn and flee.

This is usually what happens when African wild dogs and zebras meet. But not always. A minority of wild dog packs will attack zebras. When they do, it is they who charge first, to cause a stampede before the stallions can take the initiative. Then they mount a closely coordinated attack (see drawing), one dog grabbing the chosen victim's tail and another its upper lip, while the rest disembowel it.

Of 10 wild dog packs recently studied on the Serengeti Plain in Tanzania, only two had the ability to turn the tables on an adult zebra— eight times a dog's weight—and kill it. These two zebra-hunting packs were large, with eight or more adult members, but pack size

was not the crucial factor: three other packs of similar size ignored zebras and, on one occasion, just four dogs from a zebra-hunting pack were observed to kill a zebra.

Why then do not all African wild dog packs hunt zebras? A clue to the answer seems to lie in the fact that one of the two zebra-hunting packs was known to have hunted zebras for at least 10 years, over three generations. For this pack, zebra-hunting was a tradition, learned by each generation from its predecessor. Other packs studied did not exhibit any such hunting tradition, although some did show a preference for Grant's gazelles over Thomson's gazelles.

Not only zebra hunting but also such knowledge as the location of water, prey concentrations and range boundaries may be passed on as a tradition. Studies of African wild dogs (and also of some monkeys) indicate that man's previously supposed unique reliance on cultural as against genetic inheritance should rather be viewed as a dramatic extension of a pattern that exists in other social animals.

▲ **The chase.** A pack of African wild dogs hard on the heels of a wildebeest, which has probably been selected because it is young or weak. The two leading dogs, about to seize the prey, are almost certainly the dominant individuals within the pack, as these take the most dangerous role in the hunt.

▼ **The kill.** Once caught, prey is rapidly disemboweled – here the fate of a Thomson's gazelle.

A "Back-to-front" Social System

Parent role-reversal in African wild dogs

In a strange tug-of-war, one adult female African wild dog holds a puppy by the head, another has the pup's hind-quarters in her mouth, and the two are pulling in opposite directions. Pups are often injured and may even die in these struggles, which are part of a protracted conflict over possession of pups when two females try to raise litters at the same time. Such macabre behavior is just one example of the strange social organization of this species, in which only one female per group normally breeds successfully.

The social arrangements of African wild dogs are extraordinary because they are the exact opposite of those in most other social mammals, such as coatis, baboons, lions and elephants. Within the wild dog pack all the males are related to each other, and all of the females to each other but not to the males. Females migrate into the pack, whereas males stay with their natal pack. Before entering a pack, female littermates live in friendly coexistence, but once they start to compete to breed aggression breaks out. Males in the pack outnumber females by two to one—more males are born (59 percent of young born in one study) than females, and aggression between females often leads to the disappearance, and probably the death, of the loser. Only the dominant male and female normally breed, but should another female produce a litter few if any will survive because of harassment by the dominant female.

Why have African wild dogs evolved such a "back-to-front" social system? The evolutionary success of any species and of its individual members can be measured by the number of young successfully reared. However, the number that can be reared is limited by the amount of effort that can be expended by parents in raising young—the parental investment. Each sex must maximize its parental investment if it is to be reproductively successful. In most social mammals the female has a major, often exclusive, role in rearing offspring, and her ability to provide adequate food and protection is limited to a few young. In such systems the males provide only a single sperm cell; so to achieve maximum reproductive success males mate with many females. The capacity of parental investment of the females is the limiting resource, over which the males fight. The overall result is that the maximum number of young is reared within the limits of parental investment.

The African wild dog achieves the same results, but with a reversal of roles. Since

males help raise young and there are more of them than females, the number of offspring reared is controlled by their parental investment, not the females'—this time males are the limiting resource and it is the females that fight to ensure that it is their young that the males help to rear, not another female's.

The question can now be asked, How did this system come about? It seems likely that African wild dogs evolved from a jackal-like ancestor which showed some degree of parental care (as do jackals today—see p66). Later, African wild dogs became specialist cooperative hunters of large hoofed animals, so that individuals could only survive in a pack. However, to prevent the adverse effects of inbreeding, one sex has to disperse. In this case it is the females that do so; but

▲ ▶ **Aggression breaks out** when females compete to breed. Simple gestures (as with the female threatening a throat bite to her sister BELOW RIGHT) help establish which female should breed. If the dominance hierarchy breaks down, and a second female breeds, the dominant female will fight over pups of the other litter ABOVE, which often results in death for the pups.

Comparison of breeding systems

African wild dogs and lions are cooperative hunters which inhabit the same regions of Africa and rear young communally. The pattern seen in lions is typical of most social mammals.

Lion	African wild dog
Stable groups composed of related females: daughters stay with mothers, aunts etc.	Stable groups composed of related males: sons stay with fathers, uncles etc.
Males usually leave natal group and try to breed elsewhere.	Females usually leave natal group and try to breed elsewhere.
Aggression more intense between males than females.	Aggression more intense between females than males.
More females survive to maturity than males.	More males survive to maturity than females.

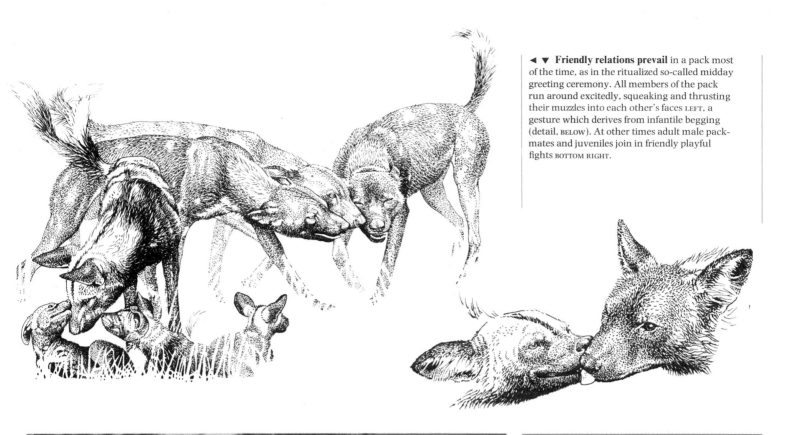

◄ ▼ **Friendly relations prevail** in a pack most of the time, as in the ritualized so-called midday greeting ceremony. All members of the pack run around excitedly, squeaking and thrusting their muzzles into each other's faces LEFT, a gesture which derives from infantile begging (detail, BELOW). At other times adult male pack-mates and juveniles join in friendly playful fights BOTTOM RIGHT.

why not males? Even though all adults help to rear the young, the pack still only has the capacity to raise one litter. If more are produced the pack will be over-extended and few if any pups survive. Thus in such circumstances only one female has reproductive potential; the only chance for a second female to produce young is to migrate to another pack, where she might achieve dominance.

It is interesting that competition between females has also been reported to be more severe than between males in wolves and coyotes, both species with considerable male investment in pup-rearing and anatomically similar to the ancestor of the African wild dog. The prolonged conflicts seen today between two would-be breeding African wild dog females may be a vestige of the original agent of natural selection that first led this species to evolve its peculiar breeding system.   JM

DHOLE

Cuon alpinus [v]
Dhole or Asian wild dog or Red dog.
Sole member of genus.
Family: Canidae.
Distribution: W Asia to China, India, Indochina to Java; rare outside well-protected areas.

Habitat: chiefly forests.

Size: head-body length 90cm (35in); tail length 40–45cm (16–18in); shoulder height 50cm (20in); weight: average 17kg (37lb). USSR populations some 20 percent longer.

Coat: sandy russet above, underside paler; tail black, bushy; pups born sooty brown, acquiring adult colors at 3 months; distinct winter coat in dholes in USSR.

Gestation: 60–62 days.

Longevity: not known.

Subspecies: 10, including the **East Asian dhole** (*C. a. alpinus*), and the smaller **West Asian dhole** (*C. a. hesperius*), both listed by IUCN as threatened. Three Indian subspecies, of which only *C. a. dukhunensis*, found S of Ganges, is fairly common; *C. a. primaevus* (Kumaon, Nepal, Sikkim and Bhutan) and *C. a. laniger* (Kashmir and Lhasa) verge on extinction.

[v] Vulnerable.

BRANDED as cruel and wanton killers because they often kill by disemboweling their prey, dholes are persecuted by man throughout their range. Until recently, little was known of these secretive animals, but is has now been established that they are group-living, with cooperative hunting and group care of young at the heart of their societies. In many respects their life style resembles that of the African wild dog (see pp76–79).

The dhole differs from most canids in having one fewer molar teeth on each side of the lower jaw and in having a thick-set muzzle, both adaptations to an almost wholly carnivorous diet. They feed on wild berries, insects, lizards and on mammals ranging in size from rodents to deer. They eat fast: a fawn is dismembered within seconds of the kill. At a kill, dholes compete for food chiefly through speed of eating, rather than by fighting. A dhole can eat 4kg (8.8lb) of meat in 60 minutes, and it is common to see dholes running from the carcass with pieces of meat to eat undisturbed by other pack members. Heart, liver,

rump, eyeballs and any fetus are eaten first. When water is nearby, dholes drink frequently as they eat. If water is distant, they make for it soon after eating. Dholes will often lie in water even in the cool of the day. They do not cache food, but they often scavenge their own kills and those of leopards and tigers.

A dhole pack is an extended family unit, usually of 5–12 animals, and rarely exceeding 20. In a pack observed in Bandipur Tiger Reserve, southern India, the average number of adults was 8, rising to 16 when there were pups; there were consistently more males than females. Packs are territorial and numbers are regulated by social factors affecting reproduction (only one female breeds) and by emigration or deaths in both adults and young.

Dholes are sexually mature at about one year. Whelping occurs between November and April and the average litter size is eight. Before giving birth the bitch prepares a den, usually in an existing hole or shelter on the banks of a streambed or among rocks. In the Bandipur pack more than three adults took

Hunting Strategies

Dholes are active chiefly during the day, although hunts on moonlit nights are not uncommon. Most hunts involve all adult members of a pack, but solitary dholes often kill small mammals such as a chital fawn or Indian hare. Prey is often located by smell. If

tall grass conceals their prey, dholes will sometimes jump high in the air or stand briefly on their hind legs in order to spot it.

Dholes have evolved two strategies to overcome the problems posed by hunting in thick cover, both depending heavily on cooperation in the pack. In strategy 1, the pack moves through scrub in extended line abreast, and any adult capable of killing when it locates suitable prey may begin the attack. If the prey is small it will be dispatched by one dhole. When the prey is larger—for example a chital stag—the sound of the chase and the scream of the prey attract other pack members to assist. It is rare for two large animals to be killed in one hunt in the scrub.

In strategy 2 (LEFT) some dholes remain on the edge of dense cover to intercept fleeing prey as it is flushed out by the other pack members. In thick jungle the chase seldom lasts more than half a kilometer (0.3mi).

Larger mammals are attacked from behind, usually on the rump and flank, and immediately disemboweled. The resultant severe shock and loss of blood kills the prey—dholes seldom use a throat bite. Small mammals are caught by any part of the body and killed with a single head shake by the dhole. Even before their prey is quite dead, dholes start eating. In general they are efficient killers—two or three dholes can kill a deer of 50kg (110lb) within two minutes. Interference at this stage by human observers will prolong the death throes, thus fueling the prejudice that dholes are cruel hunters.

▲ **Dholes feeding on a chital stag.** Pack members normally feed peaceably at kills, but individuals may sometimes, as here, remove portions to consume undisturbed at a distance.

▼ **Before the morning hunt** a pack of adult dholes, calling intermittently to one another, gather in a forest clearing. The hunting strategies of dholes depend on close cooperation between pack members (see box).

part in feeding both the lactating mother and the pups, which eat regurgitated meat from the age of three weeks. At this time the hunting range of the Bandipur pack was some 11sq km (4sq mi), much smaller than its normal range of 40sq km (15sq mi). Sometimes a second adult (the so-called "guard dhole") stays by the den with the mother while the rest of the pack is away hunting.

Pups leave the den at 70–80 days; if the site is disturbed earlier the pups will be moved to another den. The pack continues to care for the pups by regurgitating meat, providing escorts, and allowing pups priority of access at kills. At five months pups actively follow the pack and at eight months they participate in kills of even large prey such as sambar, a species of large deer.

Dhole calls include whines, growls, growl-barks, screams and whistles, and squeaks by the pups. The whistle is a contact call most often used to reassemble the pack after an unsuccessful hunt. The "latrine sites"—communal defecation sites at the intersection of trails and roads—may be a major means of communication by smell, serving to warn off neighboring packs at the edge of the home range and to mark how recently an area has been hunted, thus ensuring efficient use of all parts of the home range.

Hunters consider dholes as rivals, jungle tribesmen pirate their kills, and until recently others tried to eliminate them by poisoning their kills and offering bounties. Today the main threat to the dhole comes from habitat destruction and decimation of prey species by man. In India the creation of many tiger reserves and national parks has helped to conserve the subspecies *C. a. dukhunensis.*   AJTJ

MANED WOLF

Chrysocyon brachyurus [v]
Maned wolf, *lobo de crin*, or *lobo guará* or
boroche.
Sole member of genus.
Family: Canidae.
Distribution: C and S Brazil, Paraguay,
N Argentina, E Bolivia, SE Peru.

Habitat: grassland and scrub forests.

Size: head-body length 105cm
(41in); tail length 45cm (18in);
shoulder height 87cm (34in);
weight 23kg (51lb). No variation
between sexes or different
populations.

Coat: buff-red, with black "stockings," muzzle
and "mane"; white under chin, inside ears and
tail tip. Pups born black but with white-tipped
tail.

Gestation: about 65 days.

Longevity: unknown in wild (12–15 years in
captivity).

[v] Vulnerable.

Iɴ Brazil, the cry of the Maned wolf at
night is believed to portend changes in
the weather and its gaze is said to be able to
fell a chicken. These are two of the myths
that shroud South America's largest and
most distinctive canid. Although considered
endangered throughout its range, it remains one of the least studied of wild dogs.

The Maned wolf is so named for the patch
of long black erectile hairs across the shoulders and for its wolf-like size. But it is not a
true wolf (see p58), and most closely resembles in general form and coloring a long-
legged Red fox. The tail is relatively short,
the ears are erect and about 17cm (7in) in
length, and the coat is softer in texture than
that of many canids and lacks underfur.

It has been suggested that its long legs are
an adaptation for fast running. In fact,
Maned wolves, which have a characteristic
loping gait, are not particularly swift runners and their long legs are most likely an
adaptation to tall grassland habitats. The
foot pads are black and the two middle toe
pads are joined at the base. To increase the
area of contact with marshy ground, the
foot can be spread laterally.

Maned wolves are opportunists, taking
small vertebrate prey up to the size of pacas,
which weigh about 8kg (18lb). Rabbits,
small rodents, armadillos and birds are the
most common prey, with occasional fish,
insects and reptiles. Seasonally available
fruits make up about half the diet, the most
frequent being *Solanum lycocarpum*, known
as "fruta do lobo"—wolf's fruit, which may
have therapeutic properties against the
Giant kidney worm (*Dioctophyma renale*)
common in the Maned wolf. Foraging is
usually done at night, but sometimes occurs
in the day in areas less disturbed by man.
Individuals hunt alone and may cover
32km (20mi) during the course of a night.
They catch small vertebrates by using a slow
stalk followed by a stiff-legged pounce
similar to that of Red foxes.

Although sexually mature after about
one year, Maned wolves probably do not
breed until nearly two years old. Females
produce one litter (2–5 pups) per year,
usually in June–September. They reach
adult size by about one year. Maned wolves
make their dens in available cover, for
example, tall grass or a thicket. The extent to
which males take part in raising the young
is not known for free-living individuals but
males in captivity have been observed to
care for pups and feed them by regurgitation. Females probably also regurgitate
food to young. The breeding of this species in
captivity has rarely been successful.

Little is known about the social organization of free-living Maned wolves. However,
one study suggests that two adjacent, but
nonoverlapping, territories of about 30sq
km (11sq mi) were each occupied by a
monogamous pair. Although the male and
female of each pair shared the same range,
they were rarely found in close association
except during the breeding season. In captivity, serious fighting often occurs when
individuals of the same sex are placed in the
same enclosure. Maned wolves in the wild
have been seen to deposit feces at intervals
along major pathways and to renew this
marking periodically. Special defecation
sites are used near favorite resting places

and dens, where feces are deposited at an average height of 40cm (16in) above surrounding ground level.

The Maned wolf is classified by the IUCN as "vulnerable" and by the Brazilian government as "endangered." The species' range has diminished considerably during recent decades. Maintaining these animals in captivity is complicated by the need for enclosures of at least several hundred square meters. In addition, Maned wolves are subject to a variety of diseases including parvovirus as well as Giant kidney worm infestation. About 80 percent of captive and sampled wild-caught individuals suffer from cystinuria, an inherited metabolic disease known to be fatal in some cases.

Maned wolves are only occasionally hunted for sport, but are frequently captured for sale to South American zoos. Individuals may take farm stock up to the size of a lamb and the species is shot or trapped as a result. Although these canids are shy and usually avoid man, female Maned wolves have been known to defend pups aggressively against capture by humans. In Brazil, parts of the Maned wolf's body, even its feces, are supposed to have medicinal value, or to work as charms. For example, the left eye removed from a live Maned wolf is said to bring luck.   JMD

▲ **Unexpectedly long legs,** attractive red coat and rarity value of the Maned wolf make it a popular exhibit at zoological gardens fortunate enough to have one.

◄ **Sizing each other up,** two Maned wolves, here in captivity, circle each other warily. The animal on the right, with its arched back, erect hair and turned head is giving an impression of greater size, probably in an effort to outface the other.

◄ **Surveying its native wilderness,** a Maned wolf displays itself on the skyline. Maned wolf numbers are dwindling and the species is now regarded as threatened.

Evolution of the Fox-on-stilts

A poor fossil record has obscured the origin of the Maned wolf. However, it has been suggested that one or more waves of small primitive canids may have invaded South America from North America some 2 million years ago, and that these early savanna canids were probably faced with two locomotion options. They would have to go either through the tall grass, or over the top of it. Apparently only the Maned wolf took the latter route. With long legs and height came large body size and a heavy additional energy requirement. Opportunistic foraging, large mutually exclusive territories, and a tendency to pair with a single mate may all be adaptations to a scarce and evenly distributed food supply. In a tropical climate, a large body also brings with it the problems of temperature control. The pups' black fur, lack of underfur in adults and the nocturnal activity of the Maned wolf may all have evolved in response to this problem.

As in other large carnivores of the

grasslands, such as the lion, the Maned wolf has evolved simple methods of long-distance communication. When wanting to be conspicuous, an individual turns broadside, erecting the hair across its shoulders and along its back (see ABOVE); the back is arched and the head turned to the side to display the white patches on the ears and throat. The cry of the Maned wolf is a deep-throated extended bark repeated at intervals of about seven seconds. These signals may have evolved in part as aids to maintaining a certain level of dispersal among individuals of the species.

OTHER DOGS

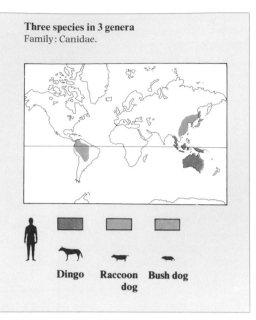

Three species in 3 genera
Family: Canidae.

Dingo   Raccoon   Bush dog
         dog

▼ **Wild dog of Australia. The dingo** is descended, like the Domestic dog, from the wolf and lives as a completely wild dog in Australia; similar forms inhabit many Southeast Asian islands.

THE **dingo** may be descended from the earliest tamed members of the genus *Canis*. Its origins remain obscure although it has lived unchanged in Australia for at least 8,000 years. The dingo's history has always been loosely associated with the Aborigines who probably colonized Australia some 20,000 years before it did. Perhaps Australian Aborigines used the dingo for warmth at night or as food or a guard, since they probably did not use it for hunting. The flexibility of dingo social behavior parallels that of the coyote or wolf (see pp58–61); indeed, the dingo is probably descended from the Indian wolf *C. lupus pallipes*. Its diet varies between small mammals, especially European rabbits, lizards and grasshoppers caught by one individual to large ungulates, especially feral pigs and kangaroos, devoured as carrion or hunted by a pack.

Although the name dingo is most commonly applied to the wild canid of Australia, we use it to describe also the suite of little-known "dingo-like" dogs, members of which have been variously called the New Guinea singing dog, Malaysian wild dog, Siamese wild dog, Filipino wild dog etc. The term pariah dog is sometimes loosely used to cover both wild dingoes and feral domestic

dogs. Some taxonomists argue that all dingoes are feral domestic dogs (*C. familiaris*). Here we opt for the other view, that dingoes are sufficiently distinct from domestic dogs, anatomically and reproductively, to merit species status.

The New Guinea singing dog, found in mountains above 2,130m (7,000ft), is sometimes known as *C. hallstromi*, and may be descended from the ancient Tengger dog of Java (a fossil ancestor of dingoes). It howls rather than barks, and is used by Papuan natives as food, for hunting and as a guard.

There is a risk that these small populations of "dingo" will be outbred to oblivion with village curs before they can be studied. This is sad because not only are they interesting in their own right, but they are important for unraveling the history of domestication of the dog and of primitive man's migrations.

In Australia the dingo is economically important, directly because of attacks on sheep and thus indirectly due to the costs of poisoning, bounties and dingo-proof fencing. Aerial poisoning with baits has greatly reduced dingo numbers, but their populations are generally robust in Australia, except in Queensland where remnants of "pure dingo" are likely to be swamped to extinction by feral dog genes.

Raccoon dogs, as their name suggests, look rather like raccoons (family Procyonidae). Although the natural distributions of the two species are widely separated, in Europe confusion can occur since both species have been introduced there. Some taxonomists regard Raccoon dogs as primitive canids, but their affinities with other living species are unknown.

Raccoon dogs are omnivores, with a diet which varies with the seasonal availability of fruits, insects and other invertebrates, occasional vertebrates and, where available, marine invertebrates caught while beach-combing. Apparently they prefer to forage in woodland with an abundant understory, especially of ferns. In the 1920s they were introduced into western Russia for fur farming (furriers call them Ussuri raccoons); they subsequently spread throughout much of eastern Europe and north to Finland. Outside the fur trade this range expansion has been viewed as undesirable, since the Raccoon dog carries rabies and its arrival has further complicated the control of Red fox rabies in eastern Europe. There is some evidence that during their winter hibernation—itself a unique feature amongst canids—Raccoon dogs may incubate the rabies virus and hence cause the disease to

▲ **Barely resembling a dog, the Bush dog** of Central and South America has short legs, a compact body, short snout and small ears.

▲ **Dingos live in packs,** like coyotes or wolves, and may hunt cooperatively.

▼ **Looking more like a raccoon than a dog,** the Raccoon dog of Eastern Asia has been introduced to parts of Europe.

persist from one season to the next, in places where fox densities are so low that rabies might otherwise die out.

Although they are the only members of the family reputed not to bark, the behavior of Raccoon dogs is otherwise recognizably canid. Like Bat-eared foxes, they occasionally hold their tails aloft in inverted-U positions during social interactions. Subordinate animals apparently do not wag or lash their tails, unlike other canids. However, following mating there is a copulatory tie.

Raccoon dogs are reported to live in pairs or temporary family groups, with males contributing to pup care. Preliminary radio-tracking studies suggest that the home ranges of several Raccoon dogs may overlap widely and when food is clumped, such as at a fruiting bush, they may feed together amicably. In two study areas in Japan home ranges averaged about 10 and nearly 50 hectares (25 and 123 acres), whereas one estimate from Europe is of 100–200 hectares (250–500 acres). All these figures indicate relatively small ranges, considering the species' body size. Raccoon dogs defecate at latrine sites, each dog using several, but not all, of the latrines within its home range. Animals feeding at the same place do not necessarily use the same latrines. These latrines are clearly a form of scent marking. The highest rates of marking occur in summer. Although the mated pair is thought to be the basic social unit, there is no firm evidence on the ties between animals that share all or part of their home ranges.

The **Bush dog** is one of the least known of canids and one of the least "dog-like" in appearance. It is a stocky, broad-faced animal with small, rounded ears, squat legs and a short tail.

Bush dogs are elusive and very little is known of their behavior in the wild. They are, however, listed as vulnerable by the IUCN.

Packs of up to 10 animals have been reputed to hunt together, often seeking prey considerably larger than themselves, for example capybaras and rheas (to 45kg/100lb and 25kg/55lb respectively). Packs are said to pursue amphibious prey into the water, where the dogs swim and dive with agility. Their teeth are sturdy and highly adapted to their carnivorous way of life. The dental formula ($I3/3$, $C1/1$, $P4/4$, $M1/2 = 38$) is not shared by any other American canid.

Studies in captivity have shown that males feed their nursing mates and that littermates squabble very little over food in comparison with, say, young foxes. This is probably related to their cooperative hunting in later life—wolf pups are similarly amicable over food. Adults are said to keep in contact with frequent whines; this may be an adaptation favorable to maintaining group cohesion whilst foraging in forest undergrowth where visibility is poor. When scent marking, males urinate by cocking their legs at 90 degrees, but females reverse up to trees and urinate on the trunk from a handstand position. **DWM**

Abbreviations: HBL = head-body length; TL = tail length; wt = weight. Approximate measure equivalents: 10cm = 4in; 1kg = 2.2lb. ⓥ Vulnerable.

Dingo
Canis dingo

Australasia, including Indonesia (part), also Malaysia, Thailand, Burma. Ubiquitous, from tropical forest to semiarid regions. HBL 150cm; shoulder height 50cm; TL 35cm; wt 20kg. Coat; largely reddish-brown with irregular white markings. Gestation: 63 days. Longevity: up to 14 years in captivity; widely subject to bounty schemes in wild.

Raccoon dog
Nyctereutes procyonoides

E Asia, in Far East, E Siberia, Manchuria, China, Japan and N Indochinese Peninsula. Introduced in Europe. In woodland and forested river valleys. HBL 50–60cm; shoulder height 20cm; TL 18cm; wt up to 7.5kg. Coat: long brindled black-brown body fur with black facial mask, sleek black legs and black stripe on tail. Gestation: 60–63 days. Longevity: not known. Subspecies: 5.

Bush dog ⓥ
Speothos venaticus
Bush dog or Vinegar fox.

Panama to Guiana and throughout Brazil. In forests and forest-edge marshland. HBL 66cm; shoulder height 26cm; TL 13cm; wt 5–7kg. Coat: dark brown; lighter fawn on head and nape; chin and underside may be cream-colored or dark. Gestation: reportedly 80 days or more. Longevity: not known. Subspecies: 3.

THE BEAR FAMILY

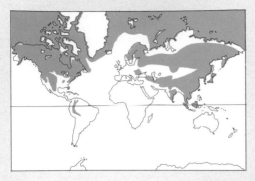

Family: Ursidae
Seven species in 5 genera.
Distribution: Arctic, N America, Europe, Asia and S America.

Habitat: from Arctic coasts to tropical jungle, chiefly forests.

Size: ranges from 1.1–1.4m (3.6 4.6ft) in overall length and weighing 27–65kg (60–143lb) in the Sun bear to 2–3m (6.6–9.8ft) and 150–650kg (220–1,430lb) in the Polar bear, fat-laden males reaching 800kg (1,760lb) or more.

Grizzly or **Brown bear** *Ursus arctos*
Polar bear *Ursus maritimus*
American black bear *Ursus americanus*

Asian black bear *Selenarctos thibetanus*

Sun bear *Helarctos malayanus*

Sloth bear *Melursus ursinus*

Spectacled bear *Tremarctos ornatus*

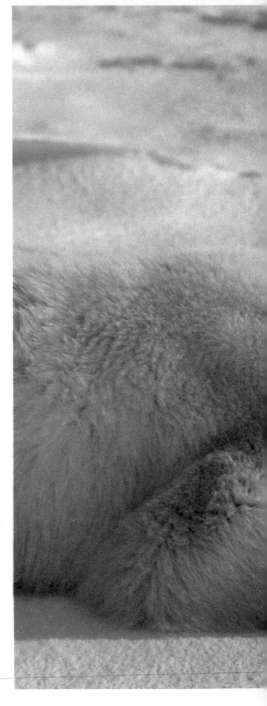

THE bears (family Ursidae) include the world's largest terrestrial carnivores—the Grizzly and Polar bears. Most bears are found in small concentrations in temperate and subtropical regions; they are seldom numerous, but their size and activities command man's attention.

The four genera that contain single species are more southerly in distribution than the three *Ursus* species. The Sun bear is the smallest, with the Sloth bear, Asian black bear and Spectacled bear similar in size. *Ursus* species increase in size from the American black bear through the Grizzly bear to the Polar bear, males of which may weigh over 800kg (1,760lb). In species reported to have only one mate (Sun and Sloth bears), males are only 10–25 percent larger than females, but in species whose males may compete for access to several females they are 20–100 percent heavier.

Bears have large, heavily built bodies, thick, short, powerful limbs and short tails (rarely over 12cm/4.7in long). Their eyes and erect rounded ears seem small in comparison to their large heads. Hearing and sight are less developed than their acute sense of smell. Bears walk on the soles of their feet (plantigrade gait) which are broad, flat and armed with five long, curved nonretractile claws, used while foraging or for climbing. Apart from the Polar bear and grizzly, most species climb well, but the Sun bear is the most adept, helped by its naked soles. In other bears the soles are well furred, especially in the Polar bear. Bears can run fast over a short distance. The coat is long, shaggy and predominantly one color—black, some shade of brown, or white. The four smaller species have lighter chest markings.

Bears are largely herbivorous, as their build and the arrangement of their teeth suggests, although they may take meat occasionally. The one exception is the Polar bear, which feeds primarily on seals. Sloth and Sun bears apart, bears generally forage by day. Unlike canids, bears use few vocalizations in communication and few facial expressions. (It is a matter of controversy whether pricked or lowered ears presage a change.) Scent marking is known to be used by, for example, the grizzly (see box, p90).

Births relate to seasons in temperate and arctic regions but not in the tropics. Most species are promiscuous, with male home ranges overlapping many female home ranges. True gestation is short, although implantation of the fertilized egg is delayed, so that apparent gestation is long, up to 265 days in the Polar bear. The young (usually 1–3) are born in seclusion, near-naked (except the Polar bear), helpless and very small (200–700g/7–25oz).

Bears from colder regions (*Ursus* species and some Asian black bears) enter a period of winter dormancy or lethargy, during which time the cubs are born. This behavior is not true hibernation as body temperature and pulse rate do not drop. However, the bears do not eat during this time but live off fat built up during a period of enormous appetite in the fall. The reasons for this winter lethargy are two-fold. Firstly, the bears' chief food (succulent vegetation) is not available in the cold northern winters. Secondly, the cubs are so small at birth (0.25–1 percent of the mother's weight) that they cannot regulate their own body temperature; the snug environment of the den provides the warmth necessary to prevent death. The exceptions to "hibernation" highlight these reasons; among Polar bears (which eat meat and therefore do not rely on seasonal vegetation) only pregnant females den, and in southern populations of Asian and American black bears, where food is available throughout the year, the males remain active in winter.

Bears evolved more recently than other carnivores. They can be traced back 20 million years to the Miocene era when the Dawn bear (*Ursavus elmensis*) first appeared—a small carnivore about the size of a

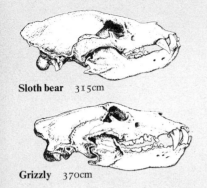

Sloth bear 315cm

Grizzly 370cm

Skulls of Bears

The skulls of bears are the longest and most massive among the carnivores. Bears' teeth show how the family has evolved from being chiefly carnivorous to largely herbivorous animals. The Grizzly bear has the typical bear arrangement of unspecialized incisors, long canines, reduced or absent premolars (the carnassial teeth undeveloped), and broad, flat molars with rounded cusps for crushing the vegetable matter that makes up much of the diet. The wide variation in number of teeth between individuals (I3/3, C1/1, P2–4/2–4,

M2/3 = 34–42) indicates that a reduction in the number of cheek teeth is in mid-evolution.

However, the Polar bear, which is the most recent of the *Ursus* line, has a purely carnivorous diet (chiefly seal meat) and appears to be evolving flesh-shearing carnassials again.

The Sloth bear has an unusual dental formula for a bear. It lacks the inner pair of upper incisors (I2/3)—a specialized modification for sucking up termites. The smaller molars are an adaptation to a diet of fruit and insects.

fox. Gradually, in later species, the skull became more massive, the carnassial teeth lost their shearing function, the molars became square with rounded cusps, weight increased, the tail was reduced to a mere stub, legs and feet became heavy, the feet relatively shorter, and the gait plantigrade. *Ursus minimus* appeared about 5 million years ago and probably gave rise to the Asian and American black bears. Brown bears first appeared in Asia and then spread to Europe some 250,000 years ago, where they confronted the Cave bear (*U. spelaeus*). Later (70,000–40,000 years ago) they reached North America. Before then, however, the grizzly gave rise to the Polar bear, the most recent of the *Ursus* line, with no fossil record before 70,000 years ago.   FB

▲ **Grizzly bears at a salmon run.** The bears only congregate in numbers at such sites of food concentration.

◄ **Growing to be the largest of the bears,** Polar bear cubs are only 0.25 percent of the weight of their mother at birth.

GRIZZLY BEAR

Ursus arctos
Grizzly or Brown bear.
One of 3 *Ursus* species.
Family: Ursidae.
Distribution: northwest N America;
Scandinavia to E USSR; Syria to Himalayas;
Pyrenees, Alps, Abruzzi and Carpathian
mountains.

Habitat: chiefly forests.

Size: variable, depending
on locality and nutrition;
adult females with access
to salmon weigh
120–205kg (265–453lb),
inland females 80–180kg
(176–397lb). Males
20–80 percent heavier,
largest recorded from
British Colombia and
Alaska 386 and 443kg
(850 and 975lb); head to
tail-tip length 2.0–2.8m
(6.6–9.2ft); shoulder
height 1.2–1.5m (4–5ft).

Coat: long, coarse, usually brown and
frequently white-tipped (grizzled) but color
variable from cream to black.

Gestation: 210–255 days.

Longevity: to 25–30 years in wild (47 recorded
in captivity), but usually less.

Subspecies: 2 or 3. **Grizzly bear** (*U. a.
horribilis*) or **Brown** or **Eurasian brown bear**—
males rarely over 275kg (600lb)—over whole
of range except that of Kodiak bear. **Kodiak
bear** (*U. a. middendorffi*) restricted to Kodiak,
Afognak and Shuyak islands. **Eurasian
brown bear** sometimes considered separate
subspecies (*U. a. arctos*).

▶ **Lord of his domain,** this massive Grizzly
bear need fear no other animal apart from man.
When surveying their surroundings or out to
intimidate, grizzlies often assume such an
upright, totem-like posture; otherwise they
travel on all fours.

GRIZZLIES may weigh nearly half a tonne,
can shear off 12-millimeter steel bolts
and can charge at 50 kilometers an hour;
but these largest of land animals are also one
of the most vulnerable species on earth.

The Grizzly bear (or Brown bear as it is
mostly known in Europe) once ranged
throughout North America, most of Europe,
and northern Asia. Today, although it remains the most widely distributed bear,
large populations remain only in Alaska and
Canada and in the USSR. Today's population of 1,000 or more in the southern USA
has declined from perhaps 100,000 in 180
years. There are some isolated populations
in Europe, amounting to fewer than 30
individuals.

In America the largest individuals are in
the far Northwest (Kodiak bears). In Eurasia
size increases from west to east (Kamchat-
kan brown bear). But size is notably related
to available food, and subspecies distinctions
also appear to be more related to nutrition
than to geographic isolation.

▲ **The size and power** of the Grizzly bear are fully expressed in the massive proportions of this bear's head. The prominent nose and diminutive ears reflect a reliance on smell rather than hearing.

▼ **Grizzlies love water.** Here a satiated adult relaxes in the shallows of a salmon stream.

The fur is extremely variable in color, from cream through cinnamon and brown to black. In gross form the Grizzly bear has a concave outline to the head and snout, ears that are inconspicuous on a massive head, and high shoulders which produce a sloping backline. Its sense of smell is much more acute than its hearing or sight.

During the 4–7½ months spent outside their den (much more in southern populations) grizzlies consume large amounts of food—12–16kg (26–35lb) a day. Grizzlies cannot digest fibrous vegetation well and they are highly selective feeders. The diet shows dramatic shifts as they move from alpine meadows to salmon streams to avalanche chutes and riverside brushlands. Grizzlies are omnivorous, with flattened cheek teeth and piercing canines 30mm (1.2in) or more in length (see p87). Their large claws often exceed 6cm (2.4in) in length; they are used to dig up tubers and burrowing rodents. The diet is dominated by vegetation, primarily succulent herbage,

tubers and berries. Insect grubs, small rodents, salmon, trout, carrion, young hoofed mammals (deer etc) and livestock are all taken as the opportunity arises.

Breeding occurs in May or June, when males search for receptive females. Ovulation is induced by mating, after a brief courtship of 2–15 days. Implantation of the fertilized egg is delayed until October or November, when the female dens in a self-made or natural cave, in a hollow tree or under a windfall. The young (usually 2–3) are born in January–March; they weigh only 350–400g (12.5–14oz), are nearly naked, and are quite helpless. They remain denned until April–June, then accompany the mother for 1½–4½ years. The age at which a female first gives birth, the litter size and the interval between litters are controlled by nutritional factors (see box, p95). Population numbers are largely independent of population density among females but density-dependent among males. Because reproduction is under nutritional

▲ **Adept salmon fishers,** Grizzly bears catch their prey with teeth or claws and usually take it ashore before delicately stripping off the flesh, first on one side, then the other, leaving behind the head, bones and tail.

▶ **The bear hug.** Apparently locked in vicious combat, two juvenile males practice their fighting skills. Later in life such fights are for real, possibly with a fatal outcome.

control, females tend to establish exclusive access to forage and mutually exclusive home ranges, although limited overlap may occur. The range sizes of adult females can vary enormously from region to region; for example, 14.3sq km (5.5sq mi) on an Alaskan island and 189sq km (73sq mi) in northern Alberta. Comparable figures for adult males are 24.4sq km (9.4sq mi) to 1,054sq km (406sq mi). Young females may remain in the mother's range after leaving her care—three generations of females have been known in the same range. Adult males are solitary, and their ranges encompass those of several adult females, as well as overlapping with other adult males. Young males may travel up to 100km (62mi) after leaving their mothers and spend much of their time avoiding risky contact with adult males.

The Grizzly bear has been wiped out over much of its range and is endangered in many areas. Hunting and loss of habitat are the major causes. Legal hunting can be controlled, but bears that venture into man's expanding domain are killed because of the threat (actual or feared) to livestock. The use of incinerators and bear-proof disposal units in parks, rather than dumps, can reduce available food. Townsites and livestock are simply incompatible with bears.

FB

Why Bears Are Aggressive

Every year big bears maul or kill other bears—and sometimes people. Bears *are* aggressive. Why? The reason, true for both males and females, lies in the drive to achieve reproductive success. Female Grizzly bears in northern inland populations are unlikely to produce more than 6–8 young during their lives; and even the healthiest American black bear female is unlikely to produce more than 12–13. Thus, each young bear is crucial to a female's reproductive success and is vigorously defended. Other bears or people who stray close enough to appear as a threat to young bears are charged and may be wounded or killed.

Males fight to ensure they sire as many cubs as possible, and thus perpetuate their own genes. As receptive females are rare, scattered, and only available for breeding every few years, at which time they are promiscuous and likely to conceive young sired by different males, the male has to decide whether to defend a single female from the attention of other males or to mate with as many females as possible. Bears take the latter option. Defending a female from all comers would bring a male into conflict with other equally mature males—something to be avoided, as such fights, when they do occur, often result

in the death or severe wounding of one combatant.

Males reduce potential competition by evicting from their home ranges (or even killing) subadult males that might compete for females in later seasons. Out of the breeding season, mature males also establish a dominance hierarchy of access to females; this occurs particularly when mature males gather at sites of food concentration—for example, at waste dumps or salmon runs.

Marking probably serves to advertise the presence of a dominant male and thus to reduce the risk of dangerous encounters. In areas of stable air currents, bears mark by scraping the bark off trees and rubbing against the surface, leaving scent. Where air currents are unstable, bears often mark the ground with regularly spaced depressions or scrapes.

Bears' eyesight is poor; a myopic bear may not distinguish between humans and subadult bears so most attacks on man are probably cases of mistaken identity. Although human body odors are generally repellent to them, bears living near waste dumps without incinerators generally associate human odor with food—often with tragic consequences. Such human victims are rarely eaten.

POLAR BEAR

Ursus maritimus [v]
One of 3 *Ursus* species.
Distribution: circumpolar in northern hemisphere.

Habitat: sea ice and waters, islands and coasts.

Size: body length of males 2.5–3m (8.2–9.8ft), females 2–2.5m (6.6–8.2ft). Weight of males 350–650kg (770–1,430lb) or more in fat-laden individuals, females 175–300kg (385–660lb).

Coat: white, or yellowish from staining and oxidation of seal oil.

Gestation: about 8 months.

Longevity: 20–25 years.

[v] Vulnerable.

▶ **Four-square, the largest carnivore on land,** a Polar bear is captured in statuesque pose. Atop its back is an immobilizing dart, fired in order to tag the bear for conservation purposes.

▼ **Arctic sun silhouettes four bears.** Usually solitary, Polar bears may congregate in ice-free conditions or by major food sources.

THE Polar bear inhabits a cold and hostile environment that most of us never see. Yet Polar bears, part of the culture of arctic coastal peoples, are of special interest to increasing numbers worldwide who wish to see this species preserved.

Not only is the Polar bear the largest carnivorous quadruped, it is also unique in its combination of great size, white color and adaptations to an aquatic way of life. Polar bears are as big as or bigger than the large Brown bears, but less robustly built, with a more elongated head and neck, and are adapted to a sea ice environment. A thick winter coat and fat layer protect them against cold air and water. They are completely furred except for the nose and the foot pads; short ears are another adaptation to cold. Polar bear milk has a high fat content (31 percent) and enables cubs to maintain their body temperature and to grow rapidly during the four months before they leave the den. The white coat color serves as camouflage and the claws are extremely sharp, providing a secure grasp on the bears' seal prey. Their acute sense of smell is an essential aid to hunting. Polar bears can, if necessary, swim steadily for many hours to get from one piece of ice to another. Apart from their build, the water-repellent coat and feet that are partially "webbed" are also adaptations to swimming.

The Polar bear was first described as a distinct species in 1774. It shares with the Brown bear a common ancestor (*Ursus etruscus*) from which both stemmed (see also p87). That they are still closely related is evident from the successful raising of fertile hybrids in captivity. Recent mark-and-recapture studies show that Polar bears have a seasonal preference for specific geographic areas, with only limited exchange of bears between adjacent areas. The size of Polar bear skulls increases from east Greenland west to the Chukchi Sea, from 37 to 41cm (14.5–16in). It is likely therefore that this genetic variation results from the existence of several more or less distinct subpopulations.

Among the ice floes of the Arctic the Polar bear is at the top of the food chain. Polar bears feed primarily on Ringed seals, Bearded seals being the secondary prey species. They also eat Harp seals and Hooded seals and scavenge on carcasses of walrus, Beluga whales, narwhals and Bowhead whales. On occasion Polar bears may kill walrus or attack Beluga whales. They occasionally eat small mammals, birds, eggs and vegetation when other food is not available. Polar bears catch seals in various ways. In late April and May they break into Ringed seal pupping dens excavated in the snow overlying the sea ice. During the rest of the year, seals are taken mostly by waiting at a breathing hole or at the edge of open water. Bears also sometimes stalk seals that are hauled out on the ice in late spring and summer.

Most female Polar bears first breed at five years of age, a few at four; most breeding males are probably older. The maximum breeding age is not known, but reproductively active females 21 years old have been reported. Polar bears mate in April, May and June. One male may mate with several females in a season, or with one. The males locate females in heat by following their scent. Implantation of the fertilized egg in the uterus and its subsequent development are delayed, resulting in a relatively long gestation period of 195–265 days. The pregnant females seek out denning areas in November and December, and excavate maternity dens, generally in drifted snow along coastlines. The cubs are born in December and January, the number varying from 1 to 3, with estimates of average litter size varying between 1.6 and 1.9 cubs. At birth cubs weigh 600–700g (21–25oz). In most areas, the females and cubs leave the dens in late March and April, by which time the cubs weigh 8–12kg (17–24lb). The young usually remain with the mother for 28 months after birth, and the female can breed again at about the time the young leave her. Thus the mimimum breeding interval is usually three years.

Polar bears may travel 20km (43mi) or more in a day; one bear that was monitored off the coast of Alaska traveled 1,119km

Conservation of a Species

The cooperation between the six countries concerned with the management and conservation of Polar bears is widely viewed as a model for conserving other species and even other natural resources.

Public concern for the Polar bear increased during the 1960s at a time of increasing human activity in the Arctic, particularly in petrochemical exploration and development. Hunting pressures also increased at this time.

The 1973 Agreement on Conservation of Polar Bears created a *de facto* high seas sanctuary by banning the hunting of bears from aircraft and large motorized boats, and in areas where they had not been previously taken by traditional means. The agreement states that nations shall protect the ecosystems of which Polar bears are a part, emphasizes the need for protection of denning and feeding areas and migration routes, and states that countries shall conduct national research, coordinate management and research for populations that occur in more than one area of national jurisdiction, and exchange research results and data. Appended resolutions request establishment of an international hide-marking system, protection of cubs, females with cubs, and bears in dens. The Convention on

International Trade in Endangered Species requires its 50-plus signatory countries to maintain records of Polar bears, or parts of bears that are exported.

The existence of more or less separate subpopulations has facilitated the management of Polar bears at a national level. Limits on hunting vary according to country. Canada allows about 600 bears to be taken annually, mainly by coastal Eskimos for meat, personal use and the sale of skins; included are a few bears (less than 15 a year) taken by licensed sport hunters guided by Eskimos. The US Marine Mammal Protection Act of 1972 transferred management authority for Polar bears from the State to the Federal government and restricted hunting to Alaskan Eskimos, who take about 100 bears each year. In Greenland (where the government shares responsibility with Denmark) Eskimos or long-time residents take 125–150 bears each year for subsistence and sale of skins. Norway has stopped nearly all hunting in the Svalbard island group because current population estimates are lower than previous ones; this bear population is shared with the USSR, where hunting has not been allowed since 1956, and the only bears taken are a few cubs (under 10 a year) for zoos.

(694mi) during a year. Being closely associated with sea ice, most Polar bears move south in the winter as the ice extends, and north in summer as it recedes. They are most numerous in places where wind and currents keep the ice in motion, resulting in a mix of heavy ice, newly frozen ice and open water. In these conditions seals are more available to the bears. Such areas are mostly within 300km (186mi) of the coast. In some areas, bears also spend time on land, including females who use traditional maternity dens on land, and other bears who spend summer on land where ice leaves the coast or large bays.

Apart from breeding pairs and females with young, Polar bears are usually solitary. However, they occasionally congregate, and show tolerance for one another, for example at exceptionally good food sources such as a whale or a walrus carcass, where 30–40 bears have been observed, or where bears are forced ashore by ice-free conditions. Adult males are aggressive towards one another during the breeding season and also occasionally kill cubs. Some Arctic foxes that spend the winter on sea ice feed almost exclusively on the remains of seals killed by Polar bears. JWL

AMERICAN BLACK BEAR

Ursus americanus
American black or North American black bear,
or Kermodes or Glacier bear.
One of 3 *Ursus* species.
Family: Ursidae.
Distribution: N Mexico and N California to
Alaska and across to Great Lakes,
Newfoundland and Appalachians; isolated
populations include Florida–N Gulf coast.

Habitat: forest and woodland.

Size: very variable depending
on locality and nutrition; east
of 100°W, where energy-rich
acorn and beech nut mast is
available, adult females
average 90kg (200lb) in a
70–120kg (155–265lb)
range; to the west, females
weigh 45–90kg (100–200lb),
with an average of 65kg
(145lb). Males 10–50 percent
heavier; largest recorded
males from E USA 264 and
272kg (582 and 600lb); head
to tail-tip length 1.3–1.8m
(4.3–5.9ft); shoulder height
80–95cm (31–37in).

Coat: color uniform, with wide geographical
variation (see below); sometimes a white chest
patch; black phases throughout range.

Gestation: 210–215 days.

Longevity: maximum recorded 32 years in wild
(not known in captivity).

Up to 18 subspecies recognized. Greatest
variation in coat color in W, particularly along
Pacific coast. **Kermodes bear** (*Ursus americanus
kermodei*), central coast of British Columbia;
coat can be pure white. **Blue** or **Glacier bear**
(*U. a. emmonsii*), N British Columbia coast to
Yukon; coat bluish. *U. a. altifrontalis*, SW
British Columbia; coat black and forehead high.
Cinnamon bear (*U. a. cinnamomum*), SW
Canada and W USA; coat reddish brown to
blond. *U. a. carlottae*, Queen Charlotte Islands;
large form with massive skull and black coat.
U. a. vancouveri, Vancouver Island; massive
skull, black coat. Eastern populations typically
black, eg **Eastern black bear** (*U. a. americanus*),
E and Central N America; **Newfoundland black
bear** (*U. a. hamiltoni*), with enlarged skull.

Subspecies status (especially those on
mainland) debatable; best considered races.
Differences in island races due to geographic
isolation and in mainland races due to
nutrition.

WHITE, blue and brown (and black) they
are all American black bears. The
geographical variation in coat color is very
great but because most of the range is
continuous, few clear distinctions can be
made (see BELOW LEFT).

The American black bear is much like a
small Grizzly bear. It once inhabited most
forested areas of North America, including
northern Mexico. As it is adaptable, it has
maintained much of that range in areas
where forests have been spared by man. In
extensive forested areas black bears may
overlap with the Grizzly bear, though they
are less likely to venture into the open.
Otherwise their niches are similar—both
prefer forests and are largely omnivorous,
but may take prey. Although a grizzly may
occasionally kill a black bear, there seems
to be little direct competition.

The black bear has a shorter coat (usually
without whitish hair tips) than the grizzly, a
convex outline to the head and snout, a less
sloping backline, and shorter claws that
seldom exceed 6cm (2.4in). Both young and
adults climb well.

The black bear feeds on almost any succulent, nutritious vegetation (tubers, bulbs,
berries, nuts and young shoots) and also on
grubs, carrion, fish, young hoofed mammals
or domestic stock. The search for energy-
rich food often creates conflict with bee- and
orchard-keepers. The food requirement is
some 5–8kg a day (11–18lb/day).

denned with the mother until April or May, then accompany her for 1½ (sometimes for 2½) years. Weaning occurs usually from July through September of their first year. Few American black bears approach the greatest ages recorded in the wild—23, 27 and 32 years. Sport hunting is the major cause of death, as it is with Grizzly bears. The influence of food availability on breeding is as significant as in grizzlies (see Life in the Slow Lane, BELOW).

Lone females and mother-plus-young groups often establish mutually exclusive home ranges of 2.5 to 94sq km (1–36sq mi); male home ranges overlap and are 5–6 times larger. Black bears are promiscuous. The female vigorously defends her litter, which may have more than one sire. As in grizzlies, a female may abandon a singleton cub—a female that carries on caring for a single cub for two years in the end rears fewer cubs than if she abandons the cub, breeds the next year and produces three young.

The American black bear suffers persecution and hunting pressures like the grizzly, but its intelligence, more secretive nature and better reproductive potential have allowed it to survive over a wider range and in greater numbers than the North American grizzly. No subspecies is endangered, although the Glacier bear and Kermodes bear are rare.   **FB**

EATING HABITS

◀ **Mainly herbivorous,** as are most bears, the American black bear will eat meat when the chance arises, and anything else it can find. Here a bear takes the beaver it has just caught ashore to eat.

▲ **Feeding from a carcass,** in this case a steer killed in a storm.

▼ **Scavenging at a waste dump.** Scarcity of food often drives North American bears to sites where they may encounter man.

Northern populations den for 5–7½ months each year, after which they roam large areas, foraging selectively on the richest food to regain the weight they have lost in the winter. Southern males may not den.

Black bears breed in May–July. One to three near-naked cubs are born in January or February; they weigh only 220–295g (7.8–10.4oz). The cubs remain

---

Life in the Slow Lane

Apart from an occasional dash to catch prey, the pace of life for the big North American bears is slow; their growth rate is slow, lifespan long (up to 30 years) and reproductive potential low (as few as 6–8 cubs in a lifetime).

For many bears, particularly northern populations, food is scarce and slow-growing; female American black bears have to range over areas of up to 94sq km (36sq mi) to meet their needs. The winter is long and the period of activity short. Without sufficient food a female will not reproduce: if a berry crop fails, few females will produce young that year— failed implantation of the egg at the start of denning is an "efficient" means of abortion if the female is not fat enough.

Females from eastern populations of black bear become reproductive at 3–5 years, have 2–4 cubs in a litter and may reproduce every two years. Western females, with poorer forage, do not become reproductive until 4–8 years, have litters averaging 1.7 cubs and usually wait 3–4 years between litters. Potential rates of increase of black bear numbers are thus only 12–24 percent per year. For the Grizzly bear the situation is even worse: females in northern inland areas,

where forage is very poor, range over areas of up to 200sq km (77sq mi), they do not mature until 8–10 years of age, and average litter size is 1.7, with 4–5 years between litters. Better-fed coastal females mature at 4–6 years, have litters averaging 2.2 cubs and conceive every 3–4 years. Reproductive potential is thus as low as 6–16 percent per year for grizzlies.

For males, the consequences of food scarcity are equally significant. To find enough food and locate the few females available for mating, adult male black bears search vast areas up to 600sq km (grizzlies range over 400–1,100sq km).

Adult males may kill young males still accompanying their mothers if the female is receptive (in estrus). Aggression results as both male and female try to maximize reproductive success (see p99).

With food scarce, yet critical for reproduction, black bears and grizzlies are attracted to dumps, beehives, livestock, or the bait stations of hunters, which makes them more vulnerable to man. With such low rates of reproduction, these populations can sustain only a very low rate (0–5 percent per year) of additional "unnatural" deaths. Each bear killed by man is a significant loss.

SMALL BEARS

Four species in 4 genera
Family: Ursidae.

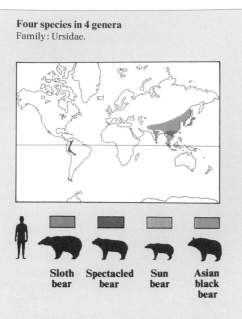

Sloth bear   Spectacled bear   Sun bear   Asian black bear

THE four smaller bears are more southerly in distribution than the *Ursus* species. Each is placed in a separate genus.

The **Sloth bear** differs markedly from other bears. With its long curved claws it can hang sloth-like upside down. Its naked and flexible lips and long snout, nostrils that can be closed, hollowed palate, and lack of two inner upper incisor teeth are specialized feeding adaptations unique in the bear family. The coarse coat is usually black, but often mixed with brown, gray or rusty-red.

Sloth bears are primarily nocturnal. They are omnivorous, eating insects, grubs, sugarcane, honey, eggs, carrion, fruits and flowers. When feeding on termites, a Sloth bear breaks open a termite mound with its claws, and uses its lips and long tongue as a tube, first to blow away dust, then to suck up the prey. The claws are equally useful when foraging in trees for fruits and flowers.

Northern populations breed in June, southern populations all year round. Seven months later 1–3 (usually 2) young are born in a ground shelter. The Sloth bear does not become dormant, but dens for seclusion and protection. Cubs leave the den after 2–3 months but accompany the mother for two, possibly three, years. Sloth bears are reported to have only one mate.

The **Spectacled bear** of South America is descended from ancestors which entered the continent from North America some 2 million years ago. The markings around each eye vary considerably between individuals. The thick coat is otherwise of uniform color.

The Spectacled bear lives in a variety of habitats and altitudes from 200 to 4,200m (650–14,000ft). Although it prefers humid forests, it makes use of grasslands above 3,200m (10,500ft) and lower lying scrub deserts—all habitats threatened by human encroachment.

It is a good climber, commonly foraging in trees in search of succulent bromeliad "hearts," petioles of palm fronds, and fruits such as figs in the forests and cactus in the desert. Fruit-bearing branches, broken while foraging, may be pulled together as a platform or nest which is sometimes used as a day-bed. Although primarily herbivorous, the Spectacled bear also feeds on insects, carrion, occasionally domestic stock and, reportedly, young deer, guanacos and vicuñas. The Spectacled bear appears to be active throughout the year. Litters comprise 1–3 (usually 2) small cubs of 300–325g (10.5–11.5oz).

The **Sun bear** or Malayan sun bear is the smallest member of the bear family. It is also the one with the shortest and sleekest coat—perhaps an adaptation to a lowland equatorial climate.

Although it inhabits both lowlands and highlands, the Sun bear is primarily a forest dweller, resting and feeding in trees in tropical to subtropical regions of Southeast Asia (Borneo, Sumatra, Malay Peninsula, Kampuchea, Vietnam, Laos, Burma, and possibly southern China).

Relatively low weight, strongly curved claws, and large paws with naked soles help to make the Sun bear an adept climber. It is primarily nocturnal, frequently resting or sunbathing during the day on a platform of broken branches several meters above ground level. It is omnivorous, eating tree fruits, succulent growing tips of palm trees, termites, small mammals and birds, and can cause significant damage in cocoa and coconut plantations.

Sun bears may mate at any time of year. They do not become dormant. The young,

▲ **The four smallest bears** all occur in the tropics. (1) The shaggy-coated Sloth bear makes good use of its long curved claws and flexible snout to forage, either on the ground for termites and grubs or in trees. The Sun bear in the foreground (2) is the smallest bear; here it licks termites from the mound it has broken open. The Spectacled bear (3), shown climbing a tree in search of fruit, is the only South American bear. The Asian black bear (4) is mainly herbivorous but may, as here, take carrion.

◄ **Performing bears,** once common, are a rare sight today. This Indian Sloth bear must be one of the last "trained" members of what is a threatened species.

usually two, each weighing 300–340g (10.5–12oz), are born in seclusion on the ground. Sun bears are thought to have only one mate. Their cautious nature and small size make them, for man, the least dangerous of bears, and for this reason locals sometimes keep them as pets.

The **Asian black bear** inhabits forest and brush cover (in places, together with the Brown bear) from Iran through the Himalayas to Japan.

The Asian black bear is somewhat smaller than the American black bear which it resembles in habits and with which it may share a common ancestor (see p87). In addition to the typical jet black coloration, brown and reddish brown individuals also occur. The generic name *Selenarctos*, meaning "moon bear," derives from the white

chest mark. There is often a "mane" of longer hairs at the neck and shoulders. The very prominent ears are rounded.

The species is omnivorous, feeding mainly on plant material, especially nuts and fruit, but also ants and larvae. It is a good climber and frequently forages in trees and on succulent vegetation on avalanche slopes. In summer it sleeps or rests on tree platforms built of branches broken while feeding.

Asian black bears may seek out cultivated crops or domestic livestock, although they tend to avoid human contact. In Japan they cause serious damage to forest plantations by feeding on the living tissue of tree bark. Only northern populations den consistently in winter. Females with their young (usually one or two) leave the den in May and stay together about two years. FB

Abbreviations: HTL = head-to-tail-tip length; HT = height; TL = tail length; WT = weight. Approximate measure equivalents: 10cm = 4in; 1kg = 2.2lb.
ı Threatened, status indeterminate.
v Vulnerable. * CITES listed.

Sloth bear ı
Melursus ursinus

E India and Sri Lanka; lowland forests. HTL 1.5–1.9m; shoulder ht 60–90cm; wt 90–115kg, occasionally up to 135kg; males larger than females. Coat: long and shaggy, usually black, with white to chestnut U- to Y-shaped chest mark. Gestation: about 210 days. Longevity: to 30 years in captivity (not known in wild).

Spectacled bear v
Tremarctos ornatus

Andes, from W Venezuela to Bolivia; various habitats, but prefers humid forests. HTL (males) 1.3–2.1m; shoulder ht 70–90cm; wt commonly 130kg but up to 200kg; females much smaller, 35–65kg. Coat: black or brown-black, with white to tawny "spectacles" sometimes extending to chest. Gestation: 240–255 days. Longevity: to 20–25 years in captivity (not known in wild).

Sun bear *
Helarctos malayanus
Sun bear or Malayan sun bear.

SE Asia; primarily forests. HTL (males) 1.1–1.4m; shoulder ht 70cm; wt 27–65kg, females about 20 percent less. Coat: deep brown to black, often a whitish or orange chest mark; light fur (usually grayish or orange) on the short, mobile muzzle. Gestation: about 96 days. Longevity: not known.

Asian black bear *
Selenarctos thibetanus
Asian black bear or Himalayan black bear.

Iran to Japan; forests and brush cover. HTL 1.4–1.7m; wt: (males) 50–120kg, (females) 42–70kg. Coat: long, jet black with purplish sheen; white crescent on chest, some white on chin. Gestation: not known. Longevity: to 24 years in wild (not known in captivity).

THE RACCOON FAMILY

Family: Procyonidae
Seventeen species in 8 genera.
Distribution: N, C and S America; pandas in Asia.

Habitat: very diverse, from cool temperate to tropical rain forest; Common raccoon in urban and agricultural areas.

Size: head-body length from 31–38cm (12–15in) in the ringtail to 150cm (59in) in the Giant panda; weight from 0.8–1.1kg (1.8–2.4lb) in the ringtail to 100–150kg (220–330lb) in the Giant panda.

Raccoons and coatis
(subfamily Procyoninae)
Fifteen species in 6 genera.
Raccoons Six species of *Procyon*.
Coatis Three species of *Nasua*, 1 *Nasuella*.
Olingos Two species of *Bassaricyon*.
Ringtail and **cacomistle** Two species of *Bassariscus*.
Kinkajou *Potos flavus*

Pandas (subfamily Ailurinae)
Two species in 2 genera.
Giant panda *Ailuropoda melanoleuca*
Red panda *Ailurus fulgens*.

THE raccoon family contains just 17 species, but its members show a remarkable diversity in form and ecology. This diversity is reflected in the scientific debate about its classification, which still rages today. Here we take the view that there are two subfamilies, the Ailurinae (the herbivorous pandas) and the Procyoninae (the other 15 omnivorous species). Most controversy surrounds the position of the two panda species. Some consider them so distinct as to belong to a separate family, the Ailuropodidae, while others retain the Red panda alone in the Ailurinae and place the Giant panda in the Ailuropodidae or even with the bear family, Ursidae.

The raccoon family is descended from the dog family, Canidae. Recognizable fossil *Bassariscus* have been found from 20 million years ago, a time when Europe and North America were one continent. When the continents separated, the family split, with procyonines remaining in the New World and the ailurines, resembling the Red panda, in the Old World.

Procyonids, except the Giant panda, are small, long-bodied animals with long tails. The kinkajou is uniformly colored, but the others have distinctive markings, ringed tails (except the Giant panda) and facial markings that vary from the black mask of the raccoons to white spots in the coatis and

▶ **Feeding techniques** and other features of members of the family Procyonidae. (1) Coati grubbing for insects. (2) Ringtail eating a lizard. (3) Head of a cacomistle. (4) Kinkajou licking nectar from a flower while holding on with its prehensile tail. (5) Tail of olingo, which is bushy not prehensile. (6) Giant panda eating bamboo shoots.

▼ **The unmistakable fox-like face** and markings of a Common raccoon at the entrance of its den. Like most procyonids, raccoons are generally active at night.

Skulls of Procyonids

The teeth of procyonids are generalized, as befits omnivores. The typical dental formula (see p20) is l3/3, C1/1, P4/4, M2/2 = 40 but this varies with species. The kinkajou has only three premolars above and below. The Red panda has three premolars above and four below; and the Giant panda three or four above and three below plus an extra molar below. Only the cacomistle has well-developed carnassials. In raccoons the carnassials are unspecialized and the molars flat-crowned. In coatis the molars and premolars are high-cusped as adaptations to a more insectivorous diet: the canines are long and blade-like and may be used for cutting roots while digging.

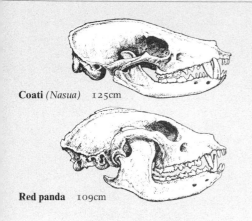

Coati *(Nasua)* 125cm

Red panda 109cm

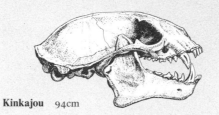

Kinkajou 94cm

cacomistle. The Giant panda is white, with black legs, shoulders, ears and eyepatches. The Red panda is red with a white face.

The feet of procyonids have five toes and the animals walk partly or wholly on the soles of their feet (plantigrade gait). The Giant panda has an extra digit that functions like an opposable thumb, as does the Red panda, although the digit is much smaller. Claws are nonretractile, except that ringtails and Red pandas have semi-retractile claws on their forepaws. Kinkajous have a prehensile tail and long tongue used in feeding. The muzzle is usually pointed, although the kinkajou has a short muzzle and coatis a long, flexible snout. The cacomistle has unusually large ears to help it locate prey.

The small procyonids can live 10–15 years in captivity, but rarely more than seven in the wild. Females usually breed in the spring of their first year, males from their second year on. Gestation varies from 63 days in raccoons to five months in Giant pandas. The young weigh about 150g (5.3oz) and are poorly developed at birth, even in the Giant panda. In most species there are 3–4 young in a litter, but Red pandas have only one or two and Giant pandas and kinkajous usually only one. Females bear their litters in dens or nests and provide all of the parental care.

All the procyonids are nocturnal, except coatis, which are active by day, and the Giant panda, active at twilight. Except possibly ringtails, they are solitary but not territorial. Neighbors sometimes fight, but usually simply avoid each other. Kinkajous are tolerant of each other and of olingos in fruit trees. Females are accompanied by their young for a few months to a year. Coati females, unlike the others, live in social groups.

Most procyonid species are thriving, with exception of the Barbados raccoon, which may be extinct, and the Giant panda.   JKR

RACCOONS

All six species of the genus *Procyon*
Family: Procyonidae.
Distribution: N, C and S America.

Size: head-body length 55cm
(22in); tail length 25cm (10in).
Weight usually 5–8kg (11–18lb),
sometimes up to 15kg (33lb),
females being about 25 percent
smaller than males.

Gestation: 63 days.

Longevity: not known in wild (over 12 years
recorded in captivity).

Common raccoon
Procyon lotor
S Canada, USA, C America; introduced in parts
of Europe, Asia. Commonest species, occupying
diverse habitats. Coat: usually grizzled gray but
sometimes lighter, more rufous (albinos also
occur); tail with alternate brown and black
rings (usually 5); black face mask accentuated
by gray bars above and below, black eyes and
short, rounded, light-tipped ear pinnae.

Tres Marías raccoon
Procyon insularis
María Madre Island, Mexico. Coat shorter,
coarser, lighter-colored than *P. lotor*.

Barbados raccoon
Procyon gloveranni
Barbados. Coat darker than *P. lotor*. Very rare.

Crab-eating raccoon
Procyon cancrivorus
Costa Rica south to N Argentina. Coat shorter,
coarser, more yellowish-red and with less
underfur than *P. lotor*; hair on nape of neck
directed forward. Tail longer than *P. lotor*.

Cozumel Island raccoon
Procyon pygmaeus
Cozumel Island, Yucatán, Mexico. Coat lighter
than *P. lotor*. The smallest raccoon, often only
3–4kg (6.6–8.8lb).

Guadeloupe raccoon
Procyon minor
Guadeloupe. Coat paler than *P. lotor*.

R ACCOONS are mischievous animals, notorious as crop marauders, garbage bandits and escape artists. Physically, they are quite unmistakable: a fox-like face with a black mask across the eyes, a stout cat-like build and a ringed tail. Young "coons" make enchanting pets, but when adult their insatiable curiosity, destructive nature and general untrustworthiness can try the most devoted of owners.

The popular name "raccoon" originated from a North American Indian word *aroughcan* or *arakun* (roughly translated as "he who scratches with his hands"). The species epithet *lotor* refers to this species' habit, in captivity, of apparently "washing" food and other items. The term "washing" is in fact a misnomer. In the wild, similar actions of rubbing, feeling and dunking, using their highly dextrous and sensitive front paws, are associated with location and capture of aquatic prey, such as crayfish and frogs. Whether these actions are simply investigative or intended to rid the prey of distasteful skin secretions is not known. However, the behavior is innate, and captive animals unable to give vent to their tendencies naturally will relieve their frustration by simulating the actions on any prey-like object, even in the absence of water.

In most areas raccoons forage at night near streams or marshy areas, where frogs, crayfish, fish, birds and eggs are sought. However, upland areas are also frequented in search of fruit, nuts and small rodents. They also consume insects and are even known to eat earthworms. Fresh corn appears to be a particular delicacy and since raccoons harvest corn before farmers, they are considered a nuisance in many areas. Raccoons have no aversion to living near humans and sometimes seek shelter in barns, sheds and other buildings. They occur in many urban areas, especially near parks or ravines, and night raids on garbage bins often annoy people.

The Common raccoon has been extending its range northwards in recent years

▲ Begging for food. Common raccoons normally forage on their own for prey, but where food is potentially abundant they will congregate. This group is begging beside a road, where they know passers-by will give them scraps.

◄ Peacefully suckling her young, a Common raccoon uses her dextrous paw to control one of her cubs. Raccoons den in ground burrows and in or near human habitation as well as in trees.

▼ The Crab-eating raccoon from South America is a good climber, like other species, with a longer tail and shorter, coarser and yellower hair than the Common raccoon. Crabs form only a minor part of its diet.

coincident with increasing land clearance for agriculture and a gradually warming climate. It has been successfully introduced to Europe and Asia, where there are wild populations in some areas. The other species are restricted in distribution. Most unusual is the semiaquatic Crab-eating raccoon, which was once placed in a separate genus, *Euprocyon*. Crabs are not its principal food, but it does prey on several types of animal found in or near its aquatic habitat.

In the northern United States and southern Canada, the Common raccoon becomes very inactive during the winter months, although it is not a true hibernator. They will remain in the same den for a month or more unless temperatures rise above freezing at night. Communal denning is common and a female and her offspring of the year often hunt independently but den together. Up to 23 raccoons have been reported in a single den, but more than one adult male in a den is rare. As far as is known most raccoons that den together are relatives. Since the Common raccoon is an excellent climber and is often seen in trees when pursued, many people consider that large hollows in trees are the preferred dens for raccoons. Although females may prefer arboreal protection for their young in the spring, recent radio-tracking studies in Ontario and the northern prairies have shown that raccoons often use ground burrows. Even when there were many tree dens available, raccoons had more dens in the ground and spent more time in such sites.

Similar ground dens were also used by Red foxes, Striped skunks, porcupines, and their likely originators, woodchucks. Other den sites are brush and log piles, barns, and even the attics of old houses.

In Common raccoons, the mating season is late January and early February. Raccoons are probably polygynous, with one male searching the ranges of, and visiting, two or three females. Home ranges of adult females overlap, but adult males seldom occur in the same range except seasonally abundant food supplies. More than one male may be found in different parts of a female's range; scars seen on adult males suggest that aggressive encounters may occur in the competition to find a mate. Year-round ranges of raccoons vary from 50–5,000 hectares (125–12,350 acres) depending on population density and the abundance of prey, but most raccoons regularly forage over about 800 hectares (2,000 acres). Movements by adult females are quite restricted in April, when 3–7 young are born. There are records of raccoons born during the late summer months, which suggests that some raccoons can mate much later than midwinter. This may occur when severe weather, preventing traveling, coincides with a female's first menstruation and mating occurs during a later period in heat. Juveniles generally forage with or near their mother for the first year. In southern areas, dispersal (if any) of juveniles occurs in the autumn, but in northern areas not until the spring when the next litter arrives. Males disperse more frequently and over longer distances than females. Northern raccoon populations also have individuals with longer and thicker coats, heavier weights, fewer breeding yearlings, larger litters, mutually exclusive territories among males, and winter denning.

The sport of "coon hunting" is prevalent during September to December each year, especially in eastern North America. High fur prices ($25–$50 each) during the 1970s intensified the interest in trapping and hunting raccoons, although night-time hunting with specially bred hounds has a long tradition, second only, perhaps, to that of English fox hunting. Over four million raccoons are harvested annually either this way or by trapping, and many others die each year on roads. Parasites, diseases (such as distemper) and malnutrition after severe winters also cause mortality. The Common raccoon is the major rabies vector in the southeastern United States, and in recent years raccoon rabies has spread northward to Virginia and Maryland.   DRV

COATIS

Four species in 2 genera
Family: Procyonidae.
Distribution: Southern N America, C and
S America.

Habitat: wide-ranging, including tropical
lowlands, dry high-altitude forests, oak forests,
mesquite grassland and on the edge of forests.

Gestation: 77 days.

Longevity: 7 years (to 14 years in captivity).

Ringtailed coati
Nasua nasua
Forests of S America, E of Andes, S to
N Argentina and Uruguay.

Size: head-to-tail-tip length
80–130cm (32–50in), somewhat
more than half being tail; weight
4.0–5.6kg (8.8–12.3lb) (male);
3.5–4.5kg (7.7–9.9lb) (female).
Coat: tawny-red with black face; a
small white spot above and below
each eye and a large one on each
cheek; white throat, belly; black
feet, black rings on tail.

White-nosed coati
Nasua narica
SE Arizona, Mexico, C America, W Colombia
and Ecuador.
Size: as Ringtailed coati. Coat: gray or brown
with silver grizzling on sides of arms and a
white band round the end of the muzzle; other
facial markings, throat, belly, feet and tail as in
Ringtailed coati.

Island coati
Nasua nelsoni
Cozumel Island, near Yucatan Peninsula,
Mexico.
Size: head-to-tail-tip length 70–80cm
(28–32in), tail shorter than body. Coat:
shorter, softer and silkier than the White-nosed
coati, otherwise similar.

Mountain coati
Nasuella olivacea
Mountain forests of Ecuador, Colombia and
W Venezuela.
Size: head-to-tail-tip length 70–80cm
(28–32in), tail shorter than the body. Coat:
olive brown, with black muzzle, eye rings and
feet; tail with black rings.

A long, ringed tail, often held erect above the body, and a highly mobile, upturned and elongated snout are characteristic physical features of coatis. Socially, they are also very distinctive—the males are solitary, while females live in highly organized groups, with individuals often caring for each other's young. Unlike their relatives, they are mainly active in the daytime.

Coatis have strong forelimbs and long claws. They can reverse their ankles and descend trees head first. Their long tail is used as a balancing rod while climbing.

Coatis are primarily insectivorous, but are also fond of fruit. They forage with their nose close to the ground, sniffing in leaf litter and rotting logs on the forest floor for beetles, grubs, ants and termites, spiders, scorpions, centipedes and land crabs, which are excavated with their forepaws. They also occasionally catch frogs, lizards and mice, and unearth turtle and lizard eggs. They eat

When Is a Coati a Coatimundi?

Female coatis and their young associate in bands of 5–12 individuals, but adult males are solitary. This difference at first confused biologists, who described the solitary males as a separate species. The use of the name "coatimundi"—meaning "lone coati" in Guarani—for this "species" reflects the same error.

The social bonds between adult females, often shown by mutual grooming (1), bring benefits to all the members of a coati band, but mostly to the juveniles. The adults and subadults surround the juveniles, and also watch for predators (2). Adults will cooperate to chase a predator away vigorously. Juveniles also get nearly as much grooming (3) from their mother's allies as they do from her and are even allowed to nurse. They also spend much time playing together (4).

One theory to explain this behavior was that allied females must be genetically closely related in order to have any interest in caring for each other's young. However, recent fieldwork shows that normal cooperative relationships occur frequently among unrelated females. The term "reciprocal altruism," essentially a formal description of friendship, is used to describe these relationships. They take time to develop, but once established they allow "friends" reciprocally to protect and tend each other's offspring. As a result, females can safely bring their young down from the nest 6–10 weeks earlier than can other procyonid mothers and can devote more of their attention to searching for food than they could if they had to protect their young themselves. During the nesting season, lone females devote about 18 percent of their foraging time to vigilance, whereas after rejoining the band the proportion is only about 10 percent.

▲ **Tail-up posture** of the White-nosed coati which is often displayed when excavating food items.

◀ **Long, mobile snout and strong front claws** are tools of the trade for the Ring-tailed coati, which snuffles around in the litter on the forest floor for insect prey and excavates the surface soil to grub out lizards and spiders from their burrows.

ripe fruits both on the ground and high in trees. Males forage quietly alone, and catch more lizards and rodents than females and young, who forage in groups.

In the larger species, females mature in their second year, males in their third. Females chase males away during most of the year, because they sometimes kill juveniles, but in February and March they become more tolerant. Usually, a single male, normally the most dominant one at the center of the band's range, breeds with each band of females. He gradually wins his way into the band by grooming its members and behaving submissively. Mating occurs in a tree. Soon afterwards the male is expelled from the band by the females, who again become aggressive. About 3–4 weeks before giving birth, females separate from their bands to build nests in trees. Platform nests may be assembled from sticks, but often a large palm tree is chosen, the crown of which makes a natural nest with little modification. Coatis bear litters of 3–5 poorly-developed young weighing only 100–180g (3.5–6.4oz) and keep them on the nest for 5–6 weeks, leaving only for brief periods to forage. By late May, when the young weigh about 500g (18oz), mothers bring them down from the nest and they rejoin bands. Soon afterwards the male that bred with the band often joins it for a few minutes on several successive days and grooms with all its members, including the new juveniles. These encounters apparently allow males to recognize their own offspring in order to avoid preying on them later.

The home ranges of bands are about 1km (0.6mi) in diameter and each band's range is completely overlapped by the peripheries of its neighbors' ranges, although in any area one band is encountered much more often than any other. Bands usually tolerate each other when they meet, sometimes even foraging or grooming together. Each band's range includes the ranges of several adult males. New bands usually come about through the splitting of a band and the friendly relationships between neighbors reflect a continuation of earlier social bonds. Nonetheless, each band's membership is stable and distinct. Males mark their ranges by dragging their abdomens on branches and often fight when they meet, but their ranges do overlap.

Coatis interact little with humans, except for occasionally raiding crops planted near forest.   JKR

GIANT PANDA

Ailuropoda melanoleuca [R]
Giant panda, Panda, Panda bear or Bamboo bear.
Sole member of genus.
Family: Procyonidae.
Distribution: Szechuan, Shensi and Kansu provinces of C and W China.

Habitat: cool, damp bamboo forests at altitudes of 2,600–3,500m (8,500–11,500ft).

Size: shoulder height 70–80cm (27–32in); can measure about 170cm (67in) when standing; weight 100–150kg (220–330lb), males being about 10 percent larger than females.

Coat: ears, eye patches, muzzle, hind limbs, forelimbs and shoulders black, the rest all white.

Gestation: 125–150 days.

Longevity: unknown in the wild (over 20 years in captivity).

[R] Rare.

▼ **Boldly marked,** "cuddly" and "human," the Giant panda is at the same time one of the rarest and one of the best known of animals.

THE Giant panda's rise to fame has been rapid. It was discovered only in 1869 and the first captive animal was not brought to the West until 1937. In recent years they have become precious diplomatic gifts, presented to only a few fortunate and highly favored countries. The attraction derives not only from their scarcity, but also from their unique combination of endearing traits, such as apparent cuddliness, short face, bold color pattern and human-like ways of sitting and eating. The Giant panda's scarcity and popularity led to its adoption as the symbol of the World Wildlife Fund.

The Giant panda is often referred to simply as "the panda" and sometimes misleadingly as the Panda bear or Bamboo bear. Its taxonomic position is debatable (see p98). Giant pandas are difficult to observe in their natural habitat, so little is known about them in the wild.

Giant pandas are bear-like in shape with striking black and white markings. They have what is in effect an extra digit on their forepaws. One of the wrist bones, the radial sesamoid, is much enlarged and elongated; it is used like a thumb to oppose the rest of the digits. This enables the Giant panda to grip slender pieces of food in its forepaws—notably the bamboo that is by far the largest item of the diet. Much of the bamboo stem ingested is passed out relatively unchanged in the many large feces about 10 hours later and digestion of food is clearly inefficient. The animal usually sits upright while feeding, holding the food in a forepaw. Small food items may be eaten directly off the ground. Pandas in the wild also eat bulbs, grasses and occasional insects and rodents.

Full sexual maturity is reached at 4–5 years old for females and probably a couple of years later for males. The female is apparently receptive to the male for only one period in the year, in April–May. It is not known how male and female find one another at this time, but voice and scent are probably important—both calling and scent marking increase around the time of mating. Mating itself is brief and unelaborate. The litter size is one, two or occasionally three, but apparently only one cub can be reared, for they are small and helpless, weighing 100–150g (3–5oz), and blind at birth. They are born in a sheltered den. The eyes open at $1\frac{1}{2}$–2 months, the cub is mobile at three months, is said to be weaned at six months and may be independent at twelve.

Giant pandas are largely solitary in the wild and probably have a territorial system like that of the leopard (see pp46–47). Scent marking is common, especially in males, by

rubbing the anal glands against large objects. There are a few simple vocal signals, used at short range. A louder whinny-like bleating carries a few hundred meters.

Giant pandas are one of the rarest of mammals—there are probably fewer than 1,000 in the wild, perhaps even less than 500. They are not persecuted, and indeed they are protected by sentiment and tradition, and by law in mountain forest reserves. These areas are generally both inaccessible and inhospitable, so there should be little human pressure on them for cultivation or settlement. The Giant panda is listed as rare in the IUCN Red Data Book, rather than as endangered. In recent years, there has been a widespread increase in mortality following the flowering, seeding and dieback of the bamboo *Sinarundinaria nitida*, which takes place only about every 100 years. Obviously the species has encountered and overcome this phenomenon over the centuries, and certainly Giant pandas are able to supplement their bamboo

▲ **A hidden "thumb"** provided by the enlargement of one of the wrist bones allows the Giant panda to grip bamboo stems. Mostly leaves and slender stems are eaten, but Giant pandas can also cope with stems up to about 40mm (1.5in) in diameter. The carnassial teeth are adapted to both slicing and crushing and there is also an extra lower molar.

diet with other foods if necessary and if these are available. But the increase in human population and settlement around the areas of Giant panda habitat mean that the animals can no longer move to and restock other isolated patches of suitable habitat. Human intervention to protect the species may become necessary.

Small isolated populations are always at risk, so a breeding captive population is a vitally important backup. Although a few Giant pandas have been kept in captivity for many years, breeding has been poor. The first cub actually reared was born in 1963 in Peking Zoo, and since then there have been only a dozen other successes. The fundamental problem is that captive Giant pandas are so rare and highly prized. Most nations or zoos have only a pair or a single animal, and are not prepared to send them to places where they might breed better. There have been a variety of problems; they include a female too accustomed to humans to accept a male panda (London), a male who does

not adopt the right mating posture (Washington), a sick female (London), a sick male (Madrid), a pregnant female who died (Tokyo), and males who either are aggressive towards or not aroused by females.

One solution to the problem of incompatibility between the sexes is artificial insemination. The technique has produced a few results in China since 1978, but it is difficult to determine the success rate. It is of value only in cases where the female becomes fully fertile but where natural mating cannot take place. The method depends on reliable ways of immobilizing Giant pandas, and on development of techniques to store semen.

The survival rate of Giant panda cubs in captivity is low, as it probably is in the wild. A high proportion of litters consists of twins; the mother only attempts to rear one of them, and ignores the other. In principle, the reproduction rate in captivity could be considerably increased if methods could be developed for handrearing these abandoned cubs; attempts so far have failed.   BCRB

OTHER PROCYONIDS

Five species in 3 genera
Family: Procyonidae.

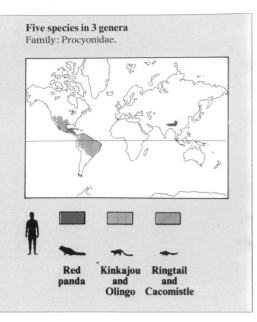

Red
panda

Kinkajou
and
Olingo

Ringtail
and
Cacomistle

▼ **The Red panda** is fairly nocturnal, as indicated by the well-developed whiskers. The soft, deep-red fur and white face markings are distinctive.

Among the least known of procyonids are the nocturnal species of Central and South America, and the Red panda of Asia. Although now overshadowed by the fame of the Giant panda, the **Red panda** was for 50 years the only panda known to man. It has distinctive red fur and is more widespread than the Giant panda. Like its much larger relative, the Red panda has an extra "thumb" (the enlarged radial sesamoid), although it is less well developed.

Red pandas have a varied, mainly vegetarian diet—fruit, roots, bamboo shoots, acorns and lichens are reportedly eaten. In captivity, they readily consume meat, so it is likely that in the wild they eat some insects or carrion. They are excellent climbers and probably forage mostly in trees.

The birth season is from mid-May to mid-July. Although Red pandas normally have a single period in heat, there are suggestions that either they have several or they exhibit delayed implantation of the fertilized egg. One to four young (commonly two) are born, fully furred but blind and helpless, in a hollow tree. They are weaned at around five months and become sexually mature at 18–20 months. Males take no part in rearing their young.

Adult Red pandas are fairly nocturnal, are believed to be solitary and are probably territorial. Males in particular scent mark using their anal glands. They also use regular defecation sites, which may serve as territorial markers. Both subspecies of Red panda are scarce and are declining. A small amount of illegal hunting takes place, but much more serious is the extensive deforestation which has accompanied the increase in local human populations. *A. f. styani* is reasonably well protected in reserves in China. There are about 140 Red pandas in captivity, about half of them captive-bred.

The **kinkajou** and the **olingos** are strikingly similar in external appearance and habits. All have long bodies, short legs, long tails and are nocturnal fruit-bearers; the species are sometimes even found foraging together, usually several kinkajous and one or two olingos—but they are difficult to tell apart.

A closer examination reveals important differences. Kinkajous are slightly larger than olingos, have foreshortened muzzles

Abbreviations: HBL = head-body length; TL = tail length; wt = weight. Approximate measure equivalents: 10cm = 4in; 1kg = 2.2lb.
[*] CITES listed.

Red panda [*]

Ailurus fulgens
Red or Lesser panda.

Himalayas to S China. Favors remote, high-altitude bamboo forests. HBL 50–60cm; TL 30–50cm; wt 3–5kg. Coat: soft, dense, rich chestnut-colored fur on the back; limbs and underside darker; variable amount of white on face and ears. Gestation: 90–145 days. Longevity: up to 14 years. Subspecies: 2; *Ailurus fulgens fulgens*, Himalayas from Nepal to Assam. *Ailurus fulgens styani*, N Burma and S China.

Kinkajou

Potos flavus

S Mexico to Brazil, in tropical forest. HBL 42–57cm; TL 40–56cm; wt 1.4–2.7kg. Coat: short, uniformly brown. Gestation: 112–118 days. Longevity: up to 23 years in captivity.

Olingo

Two species of *Bassaricyon*.

Bassaricyon gabbii in C America and northwestern S America; *B. alleni* in Amazonia. In tropical rain forest at about 1,800m. HBL 42–47cm; TL 43–48cm; wt about 1.6kg. Coat: gray-brown, long, loose hair with blackish hues above, yellowish below and on insides of the limbs; yellowish band across neck to back of ears; tail with 11–13 black rings, often indistinct. Gestation: 73–74 days. Longevity: more than 15 years in captivity. *Bassaricyon lasius* (Costa Rica) and *B. pauli* (Panama) are probably subspecies of *B. gabbii*, and *B. beddardi* (British Guiana) a subspecies of *B. alleni*.

Ringtail

Bassariscus astutus
Ringtail, Civet cat, Miner's cat, or Ring-tailed cat.

W USA, from Oregon and Colorado south and throughout Mexico. Dry habitats, especially rocky cliffs. HBL 31–38cm; TL 31–44cm; wt 0.8–1.1kg. Coat overall gray or brown; white spots above and below each eye and on cheeks.

Cacomistle

Bassariscus sumichrasti

C America. Dry forests. HBL 38–50cm; TL 39–53cm; wt 0.9kg. Coat as above.

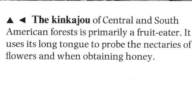

▲ ◀ **The kinkajou** of Central and South American forests is primarily a fruit-eater. It uses its long tongue to probe the nectaries of flowers and when obtaining honey.

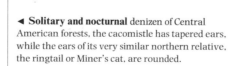

◀ **Solitary and nocturnal** denizen of Central American forests, the cacomistle has tapered ears, while the ears of its very similar northern relative, the ringtail or Miner's cat, are rounded.

and short-haired prehensile tails; olingos have long muzzles and bushy non-prehensile tails. Kinkajous also have a long extrudable tongue, possibly used to reach nectar and honey, and lack one premolar. They also lack anal sacs, instead of which they have scent glands on the chest and belly. Kinkajous eat only fruit and other sugary foods, while olingos also eat large insects, small mammals and birds. In all, the olingos are normal procyonids, while kinkajous are considered by some to merit subfamily status.

Very little is known about the life-style of these elusive animals. Kinkajous breed throughout the year; they produce a single young each year. Large numbers will congregate in fruiting trees, but whether these groups remain together is doubtful.

The **ringtail** is a graceful carnivore which was often reared as a companion and mouser in prospectors' camps in the early American West—hence the name Miner's cat. Although one of the smallest procyonids, it is the most carnivorous. Both the ringtail and its slightly larger relative the **cacomistle** have dog-like teeth which also reflect their predatory nature. The cacomistle spends much more time in trees than the ringtail. Both species have long legs, lithe bodies and long, bushy, ringed tails. They have fox-like faces, and their ears are larger than in other procyonids: the ringtail's are rounded while the cacomistle's are tapered. The ringtail has semiretractile claws, the cacomistle's are nonretractile.

Both prey heavily on lizards and on small mammals up to the size of rabbits, but they also eat large insects, fruit, grain and nuts. They are strictly nocturnal and although fairly common are rarely seen. Both are solitary and have home ranges of more than 100 hectares (250 acres). Generally, only one male and one female are found in any area.

JKR

THE WEASEL FAMILY

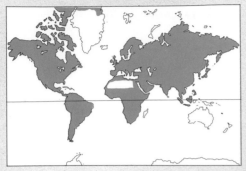

Family: Mustelidae
Sixty-seven species in 26 genera.
Distribution: all continents except Antarctica and Australia (but introduced into New Zealand).

Habitat: from Arctic tundra to tropical rain forest, on land, in trees, rivers and the open sea.

Size: smallest is the Least weasel: head-body length 15–20cm (6–8in), tail length 3–4cm (1–1.5in), weight 30–70g (1–2.5oz). Many species under 1kg (2.2lb). Giant otter head-body length 96–123cm (38–48in), tail length 45–65cm (18–26in), up to 30kg (66lb); the Sea otter may reach 45kg (100lb). Males larger than females, often considerably so.

Weasels and allies (subfamily Mustelinae)
Thirty-three species in 10 genera, including **European common weasel** and **Least weasel** (*Mustela nivalis*), **ermine** (*M. erminea*), **European polecat** (*M. putorius*), **Long-tailed weasel** (*M. frenata*), **kolinsky** (*M. sibirica*), **American mink** (*M. vison*), **Stone marten** (*Martes foina*) or Beech or House marten, **Pine marten** (*M. martes*), **sable** (*M. zibellina*), **fisher** (*M. pennanti*), **wolverine** (*Gulo gulo*).

Skunks (subfamily Mephitinae)
Thirteen species in 3 genera, including **Spotted skunks** (*Spilogale*) and **Striped skunk** (*Mephitis mephitis*).

Otters (subfamily Lutrinae)
Twelve species in 6 genera, including the **North American river otter** (*Lutra canadensis*), **Eurasian otter** (*L. lutra*), **Spot-necked otter** (*Hydrictis maculicollis*), **Oriental small-clawed** and **Cape clawless otters** (*Anonyx cinerea* and *A. capensis*), **Giant otter** (*Pteroneura brasiliensis*) and **Sea otter** (*Enhydra lutris*).

Badgers (subfamily Melinae)
Eight species in 6 genera, including the **Eurasian badger** (*Meles meles*), **American badger** (*Taxidea taxus*) and **Ferret badgers** (*Melogale*).

Honey badger (subfamily Mellivorinae)
One species, *Mellivora capensis*.

A small brown blur streaking across a road; a striped snout peering cautiously out of a dark hole at dusk; a widening V-shaped ripple speeding away across still water; a rare glimpse of a graceful, brown cat-like creature in a tree: these are all that most people will ever see of a wild mustelid. Yet some of these shy animals (weasels, badgers, mink, skunks) are surprisingly common in north temperate farmland. Mustelids are also common in Africa and South America.

The mustelids are a large, widely distributed and rather mixed group. They occupy nearly every habitat, including fresh and salt water, in all continents except Australasia (though they have been introduced into New Zealand) and Antarctica. Many are small, under 1kg (2.2lb)—the smallest carnivores are mustelids—have a long body with short legs, and are skillful climbers. All have five toes on each foot, with sharp, nonretractile claws. Males are larger than females, particularly in weasels and polecats, where male skulls are some 5–25 percent longer, and body weights up to 120 percent greater (see p111). Sexual dimorphism is much less pronounced in badgers, otters and skunks. Mustelids have 28–38 teeth (see OPPOSITE).

As well as terrestrial weasels and polecats, the family includes the semiarboreal martens, amphibious otters, semiaquatic mink and burrowing badgers. The range of body weights is exceptional—the Giant otter and the wolverine may outweigh the Least weasel a thousand times. The basic short-leg, long-body plan also occurs with a variety of adaptations in form and diet fitted to life as a carnivore in very different habitats.

The anal glands are an important feature of the anatomy of most mustelids. They consist of two groups of modified skin glands, each emptying into a storage sac, which opens by a sphincter into the rectum near the anus. Discharge of the sacs is under voluntary control. The glands produce a thick, oily, yellow, powerful-smelling fluid called musk, the chemical composition of which is probably slightly different in each individual. A little musk is secreted with the feces, which are then carefully placed where other individuals can find them. Pine martens and sable often deposit them on conspicuous stones in the middle of a track; otters leave their spraints (feces) on the same riverbank sites for generation after generation. A secondary function of the glands is defense. When severely frightened most mustelids will discharge musk, probably as a reflex action. Perhaps from such beginnings, the musk glands of the New World skunks and some of the Old World polecats evolved into effective defense weapons, supported by unmistakable warning displays in their behavior and striking color patterns in their coats.

The reproductive habits of mustelids are remarkable for several unusual features. In most species the sexes live separately for much of the year; they rarely meet and are hostile when they do. During the temporary truce in the mating season the male seizes the female by the scruff of the neck and may drag her about vigorously before mounting. Copulation is repeated and very prolonged—up to one to two hours even in the weasels. The penis is stiffened by a bone, the baculum, which facilitates the long copulation. The whole procedure seems calculated to thoroughly arouse the female and is associated with induced ovulation. So far as is known, all female mustelids can be

▼ **Representative species,** illustrating the great variety of habitat and prey. (1) American mink with rabbit. (2) European polecat hunting in rabbit burrow. (3) Eurasian badger in tunnel of its sett. (4) Wolverine following scent trail across the ground. (5) Pine marten hunting birds. (6) Spotted skunk in threat posture which precedes spraying. (7) European weasel dragging mouse along a snow tunnel. (8) Cape clawless otter, using forepaws to hold down fish. (9) Pacific Sea otter about to crack shell of crustacean prey on stone lying on its chest.

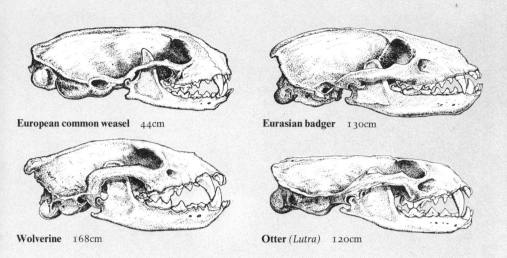

European common weasel 44cm

Eurasian badger 130cm

Wolverine 168cm

Otter *(Lutra)* 120cm

Skulls of Mustelids

Mustelid skulls tend to be long, flattened, and more or less triangular or wedge-shaped, tapering to the muzzle. Skull size, and numbers and adaptations of teeth vary widely. Most members of the largest subfamily, the Mustelinae, for example the European common weasel, have a dental formula I3/3, C1/1, P3/3, M1/2 = 34, with prominent, sharp canines and cutting carnassial teeth; in the wolverine (I3/3, C1/1, P4/4, M1/2 = 36) the heavy premolars and powerful jaws can crush even thick bones. The dental formula of the Honey badger is I3/3, C1/1, P3/3, M1/1 = 32, while in the Eurasian badger it is I3/3, C1/1, P4/4, M1/2 = 38—the largest number of teeth in the family. In otters of the successful genus *Lutra* the arrangement is I3/3, C1/1, P3–4/3, M1/2 = 34–36.

induced to produce eggs (ovulate) only by vigorous copulation. Prolonged mating may expose the pair to dangers from larger predators, but this risk is outweighed by the advantage of virtually certain fertilization.

After mating, the fertilized egg travels to the uterus, as is usual in mammals, developing, as it goes, into a ball of cells called a blastocyst. In most mammals, the blastocyst implants into the uterus wall within a few days and development of the embryo proceeds. But in the 16 or more mustelid species with delayed implantation, it floats free in the uterus, for periods from a few days up to 10 months, and implants only when certain conditions are met. These are not the same for all species; for example, in New Zealand ermine implantation occurs once the lengthening days of spring reach a ratio of about 11 light to 13 dark hours. In Eurasian badgers, however, implantation occurs while they are semidormant in December. (See illustration on p21.)

Two puzzling aspects of delayed implantation in mustelids are its uneven distribution and its evolutionary advantage. So far as is known, extended delay occurs in all marten species and in the wolverine, but in none of the polecats; in the Eurasian and American badgers, but not in the Honey badger; in the North American river otter, but not in the closely related Eurasian river otter; in western forms of the Eastern spotted skunk, but not in eastern forms, nor in the Striped skunk; in ermine and Long-tailed weasels, but not in the Common weasel. There is no explanation as to why delayed implantation should benefit some species of river otters, spotted skunks and weasels but not similar species in the same or comparable habitats.   CMK

WEASELS AND POLECATS

Twenty-one species in 7 genera
(including 14 of 16 species of *Mustela*)
Family: Mustelidae.
Subfamily: Mustelinae.
Distribution: widespread from tropics to Arctic,
in Americas, Eurasia, Africa; introduced in
New Zealand.

Habitat: very varied, from forests to mountains,
farmland, semidesert, steppe and tundra.

Size: ranges from head-body
length 15–20cm (6–8in), tail
length 3–4cm (1–1.5in) and
weight 30–70g (1–2.5oz) in
males of the Least weasel, to
head-body length 47–55cm
(18–22in), tail length 16cm
(6.5in) and weight 1.4–3.2kg
(3–7lb) in the grison.

Coat: weasels brown above, white or yellow
below in summer, entirely white in northern
populations in winter; polecats various colors,
often with bold black and white markings,
never brown and white.

Gestation: 35–45 days, extended by delayed
implantation in 2 species.

Longevity: average less than 1 year in
European common weasel, perhaps more in
other species.

Species include: the **European common weasel**
(*Mustela nivalis nivalis*), Eurasia and **Least
weasel** (*M. n. rixosa*), N America. **European
polecat** (*M. putorius putorius*), Europe and
ferret (*M. p. furo*). **Ermine** or **stoat**
(*M. erminea*), N America and Eurasia. **Long-
tailed weasel** (*M. frenata*), N and S America.
Steppe polecat (*M. eversmanni*), USSR to China.
Black-footed ferret [E] (*M. nigripes*),
N America. **Marbled polecat** (*Vormela
peregusna*), Eurasia. **Zorilla** (*Ictonyx striatus*),
Africa.

[E] Endangered.

► **"Giant" among predators,** a European
polecat with its rabbit prey. Though smallest
among the carnivores, members of the weasel
and polecat group differ from most other
members of the order in their ability to catch
and kill, single-handed, prey much larger than
themselves.

THE Least weasel has been described as
"the Nemesis of Nature's little people."
The identification with the goddess of retri-
bution is very apt for this formidable hunter,
the smallest of a group of carnivores of
different sizes but similar shape and habits.
The seven genera of weasels and polecats
comprise 21 of the 33 species of the subfamily Mustelinae.

Most weasels and polecats weigh less than
2kg (4.4lb), some much less, and there are
pronounced differences in size between
males and females (see RIGHT). Knowledge
of the group is very uneven; the Northern
Hemisphere (Holarctic) weasels—the European common weasel, the ermine or stoat,
and the Long-tailed weasel—are known in
much greater detail than any other species;
for some of the tropical species there is no
reliable information at all. As a group, these

are among the most widespread carnivores
in the world.

The Holarctic weasels have long, slim
bodies and short legs, a flat-topped, sharp-
faced, almost triangular head, and short,
rounded ears. Coat color (see RIGHT) distinguishes them from the polecats, which in
general are stockier in build and less agile,
but have a similarly shaped face and ears.
All species have the habit of sitting up on
their haunches for a better view than they
can get from on all fours.

All weasels and polecats are terrestrial
hunters, taking whatever small rodents,
rabbits, birds, insects, lizards and frogs are
locally available. Most are purely carnivorous; their teeth are highly adapted to
killing and cutting up prey (see p109). They
do not feed indiscriminately—each species
chooses, from the range of potential prey, a
different menu. The choice is determined by,
among other things, their own size and the
size, relative number and catchability of
possible food items. The small Common and
Least weasels are hunters of mice and voles,
especially Field voles; they can kill young
rabbits, but it is probably not worth their
while to try if they can still find enough
small rodents and birds. The larger weasels,
such as the ermine and Long-tailed weasel,
catch any rodents that expose themselves
above cover, but gain a better return in
energy from concentrating on larger prey
such as rabbits and water voles.

A natural experiment in Britain, started
in 1953, illustrated the dependence of the
Common weasel and ermine on different
prey. The virulent introduced disease myxo-
matosis suddenly removed about 90 percent
of the previously abundant rabbits. Hedges

COAT COLOR IN ERMINE

◄ **An ermine or stoat in summer coat,** chestnut colored with a white bib.

▼ **A transitional stage in the fall,** with white extending upward.

▽ **All-white winter coloration,** excepted only the black tip to the tail, not seen here.

The ermine is an opportunistic feeder, as these pictures demonstrate. Rabbits and voles may be the usual prey, but birds (here jay and Wood pigeon) and, near human habitation, domestic fowl eggs will eagerly be seized upon.

Why Are Male Weasels Bigger than Females?

Male mustelids are often larger than females. This is specially evident in the smaller species, such as the European common weasel (see RIGHT), where the female is half the weight of the male. The reason for this remarkable sexual dimorphism has perplexed scientists for generations, and a number of theories have been proposed.

The simplest explanation is that the size difference enables males and females to eat different prey and so avoid competition with each other, particularly when food is scarce. An individual will always try to prey on the largest animal possible, to get the best return for its effort; males are able to catch prey too big for females to handle.

An alternative, but not incompatible, explanation reflects the adaptation of males and females to quite different roles in reproduction. Males are promiscuous and territorial—they compete with other males for access to females and for the best territories. For them, fighting ability, actual or threatened, increases with size—the largest is often the most successful breeder and dominant individual, so sexual selection has favored the development of large males. For a female, who raises young on her own, small size has benefits; she can enter rodent

burrows inaccessible to other, larger predators (including male weasels), needs to eat less of her catch herself, and therefore need not travel so far from her young in the search for food.

and banks became flushed with vegetation, a home for many voles and mice. Throughout Britain the ermine population was drastically reduced, while that of the European common weasel increased. Since 1970 the slow recovery of the rabbits has accelerated and many field edges are close-cropped again. The ermine is now increasing, while the weasel declines.

Most of the larger polecats are more generalized feeders, eating anything they meet and can catch, most often rodents, but also insects, worms and carrion. One, the rare Black-footed ferret of the western prairies of the USA, is a true specialist, depending entirely on Prairie dogs. Where Prairie dogs are controlled by man, as they are over most of their range, Black-footed ferrets have died out. This is the only member of the weasel–polecat group listed as an endangered species by the IUCN.

The breeding habits are known in detail for only a few species. In the ermine and the Long-tailed weasel, implantation of the fertilized egg is delayed, but in other species apparently not. The young are born blind and thinly furred, in a secure nest, often borrowed from a prey species and lined with fur from previous meals. The eyes open at 3–4 weeks in the European common weasel,

5–6 weeks in the larger weasels and polecats. The young chew on meat at 3–5 weeks, although lactation lasts about 6–12 weeks and the family stays together some weeks after weaning. The larger species and males of the ermine and Long-tailed weasels first breed as one-year-olds; females of these species mate, when still nestlings, with the male currently holding the territory in which their mother resides. Both sexes of the European common and Least weasel may mature at 3–4 months if food is abundant.

Weasels hunt largely underground or under snow, and are active day and night. Some larger species are more often nocturnal. Usually, males and females have separate home ranges; these may overlap with the range of a member of the opposite sex, but not with the range of one of the same sex. Residents avoid each other whenever possible; females are subordinate to males, except when with young. Home ranges are smaller in habitats rich with prey, in the nonbreeding season, and in the smallest species. Male European common weasels in Britain have ranges of 1–25 hectares (2.5–62 acres); male ermine in Europe have ranges of 20–40 hectares (50–100 acres) and in Russia up to 100 hectares (250 acres); European polecats in Russia range over 100–2,500 hectares (250–6,200 acres). Grisons, and possibly the African striped weasel, may be more sociable, as they are reputedly seen in groups (of unknown composition) and, in captivity, one male and one female or two male grisons may be kept in one cage for long periods. However, four grisons observed together in captivity showed no evidence of the mutual grooming characteristic of social animals. Most mustelids, sociable or not, may be seen in parties of females and young just before the dispersal of the litters.

Some people persecute small mustelids as pests of game and poultry. The extinction of

◀ **Variations on a theme.** These chiefly more southerly species share the same body plan as the ermine or Common weasel but tend to have black, not brown as the predominant dark coloration, or to be larger. (**1**) North African banded weasel (*Poecilictis libyca*). (**2**) African striped weasel (*Poecilogale albinucha*). (**3**) Marbled polecat (*Vormela peregusna*). (**4**) The skunk-like zorilla (*Ictonyx striatus*), which appears to threaten to stink-spray. (**5**) Little grison (*Galictis cuja*) and (**6**) European polecat (*Mustela putorius*) in winter coats, both in upright sniffing/looking-out stance. (**7**) Patagonian weasel (*Lyncodon patagonicus*) in typical flattened weasel posture. (**8**) Black-footed ferret (*Mustela nigripes*) at Prairie dog burrow.

◀ **Gamekeeper's gibbet.** A dozen ermine (stoats) bear witness to the ruthless extermination of small mustelids as threats to game birds and poultry.

▼ **Trapper and marten** (see box).

Mustelids as Furbearers

Mustelids are the commonest of the small predators of the northern forests. In the vast snowy regions of Canada, Scandinavia and Siberia, sable and other martens, mink, kolinsky and ermine, otters and wolverines are active throughout the winter. These species have solved the problem of conserving the heat of their small bodies during the months of sub-zero temperatures by developing long, dense, water-repellent coats, which man greatly prizes.

Wild mustelids contributed substantially to the vigorous fur trade of the 18th and 19th centuries. At that time, wild-caught furs were important to the economy of northern lands. In the 16th to early 19th centuries, fur trappers and traders were among the first to explore and develop newly discovered North America. The furs of many wild mustelids were much sought after for their beauty and practical value. Furs such as Russian sable became a badge of wealth and rank; mink was, and still is, a byword for luxury; wolverine was prized as a trimming for parka hoods, because rime frost does not condense on it. Ermine was traditionally worn by British justices and peers—50,000 ermine pelts were sent from Canada for George VI's coronation in 1937—but nowadays the price of labor is so high that the tiny ermine pelts (300 for a coat) are not considered worth handling, especially as larger, equally fine, white pelts can be taken from other sources.

When the exploitation of furbearers was regulated only by an apparently insatiable market, the rapid price rises during the 19th century were bound to be followed by overtrapping. Populations of the larger and slower-breeding mustelids such as sable and fisher were greatly reduced by 1900. The possible disappearance of these economically important species stimulated much ecological research, especially in the USSR, where now (as elsewhere) fur trapping is carefully controlled by closed seasons and quotas adjusted annually to the estimated population densities of furbearers. (BELOW Trapper and marten.)

Some furs are now produced largely or entirely on farms, for example, American mink. The advent of acceptable synthetic fur fabrics, and changes in fashions, have reduced the demand for pelts. These developments ensure that what remains of man's exploitation of the wild furbearing mustelids is now more rational and sustainable. An exception is the Giant otter, still illegally poached in Brazil (see p125).

the European polecat in England was probably due to intensive gamekeeping. Others hail weasels and polecats as useful exterminators of rodents. Both opinions are exaggerated.

All weasels and polecats eat large numbers of voles, mice, rats and rabbits—in one year a single family may consume thousands of such prey. Farmers have always hoped (and as often assumed) that small mustelids could help rid their houses and farms of rodents—or at least prevent outbreaks. This was the attitude in Europe before the introduction of the domestic cat in the 9th century. It was still regarded as evident truth in 1884, when the European common weasel, ermine and ferret were deliberately introduced to New Zealand to control the European rabbits over-running the new sheep pastures. Unfortunately, they did not succeed, and neither did the Small Indian mongooses taken to Hawaii to clear sugar plantations of rats (see p148).

Small herbivores such as rabbits and rodents normally reproduce in greater numbers than their predators. If conditions become favorable for the rodents, they will increase rapidly, and the mustelids cannot reproduce fast enough to catch up. The mustelids will increase, but only after some delay, by which time the rodents are already abundant. Predation is usually heaviest when rodent numbers are declining for some other reason (for example, the increased age of maturity, shorter breeding season and more extensive dispersal which is characteristic of peak-year vole populations). In such circumstances mustelids can accelerate, even prolong, a decrease in rodent numbers.

In the extreme case of a small, isolated prey population with no safe refuges, mustelids can achieve impressive results. On an island off Holland, a few ermine introduced in 1931 increased rapidly and by 1937 had exterminated a plague of water voles. In an 8.5 hectare (21 acre) enclosure on a New Zealand farm, ferrets and feral Domestic cats together almost eliminated an entire dense population of rabbits in three years (up to 120 per hectare or 48 per acre). But out in the open fields, although mustelids may influence the way populations of voles fluctuate, they cannot "control" them, either by greatly reducing their numbers or by preventing new outbreaks. CMK

THE 21 SPECIES OF WEASELS AND POLECATS

Abbreviations: HTL = head-to-tail-tip length; HT = height; TL = tail length; WT = weight. Approximate measure equivalents; 10cm = 4in; 1kg = 2.2lb.
E Endangered.

Five species are sufficiently distinct to be placed in separate genera, and there are just two species of grison (*Galictis*). All others are *Mustela*, although some authorities recognize fewer species. Two distinct forms each of *Mustela nivalis* and *M. putorius* are here listed separately. For **European mink** (*M. lutreola*) and **American mink** (*M. vison*) see p116. Figures for size and breeding are mostly very approximate, or unknown (indicated by ?). Males of most species are considerably heavier than females (see p111).

European common weasel
Mustela nivalis

Europe from Atlantic seaboard (except Ireland), including Azores, Mediterranean islands, N Africa and Egypt, E across Asia N of Himalayas; introduced in New Zealand. Very large variation in size, from small form similar to Least weasel (see below) in N Scandinavia and N USSR—in Sweden HBL (male) 17–21cm; TL 3–6cm, WT 40–100g—to largest in S beyond range of ermines—eg Turkmenia: HBL (male) 23–24cm; TL 5–9cm; WT to 250g. Coat brown above, white below, turning entirely white in winter except in W Europe and S USSR; no black tip to tail. Gestation 34–37 days; Litter size 4–8; may produce 2, even 3, litters a year in vole plagues. (In Sweden two subspecies are recognized: *M. n. nivalis* in N and C Sweden is smaller, shows less sexual dimorphism, normally has white winter fur (but not always) and has more white on underside when compared to *M. n. vulgaris* in S Sweden, which retains summer coat in winter and also has a brown spot on cheek.)

Least weasel
Mustela nivalis rixosa

N America, S to about 40°N. HBL (male) 15–20cm; TL 3–4cm; WT 30–70g. Coat brown and white in summer, turning white in winter. Breeding as for European common weasel. (Some scientists regard the Least weasel as a separate species, distinct from the European common weasel, even though they have interbred in captivity. Here it is considered a subspecies of *M. nivalis*.)

Ermine
Mustela erminea
Ermine, stoat or Short-tailed weasel.

Tundra and forest zones of N America and Eurasia, S to about 40°N, including Ireland and Japan, but not Mediterranean region, the semideserts of USSR and Mongolia, or N Africa; introduced in New Zealand. Very large variation in body size especially in N America; largest in N—HBL (male) 24cm; WT 200g—smallest in Colorado (where Least weasel is absent)—HBL (male) 17cm; WT 60g; Russian races 130–190g; British and New Zealand races up to 350g. Coat brown and white; prominent black tip to tail, even in winter white. Delayed implantation of 9–10 months, from early summer mating to whelping in spring, which is not shortened by abundance of food; active gestation about 28 days; litter size 4–9, sometimes up to 18.

Long-tailed weasel
Mustela frenata

N America from about 50°N to Panama, extending through northern S America along Andes to Bolivia. HBL (male) 23–35cm; TL 13–25cm; WT (male) 200–340g, (female) 85–200g. Coat and breeding as in *M. erminea*; S races have white facial markings and yellow underparts.

Tropical weasel
Mustela africana

E Peru, Brazil. HBL (male) 31–32cm; TL 20–23cm; WT ? Coat reddish-brown above, lighter below with median abdominal brown stripe; black tail tip indistinct; foot soles naked. Formerly placed by some in separate genus *Grammogale*.

Mustela felipei

A new species first described in 1978, from highlands of Colombia. HBL of 2 males 21–22cm; TL 10–11cm; WT ? Coat blackish-brown above, orange-buff below; no black tail tip; short ventral brown patch (not stripe); feet bare and webbed. Formerly placed by some in separate genus *Grammogale*.

European polecat
Mustela putorius putorius

Forest zones of Europe, except most of Scandinavia, to Urals. HBL (male) 35–51cm; TL 12–19cm; WT 0.7–1.4kg. Coat buff to black with dark mask across eyes. Gestation 40–43 days; litter 5–8.

Ferret
Mustela putorius furo

Domesticated form of *M. putorius* (or possibly of *M. eversmanni*). Albinoes and white or pale fur common. Introduced and feral in New Zealand.

Steppe polecat
Mustela eversmanni

Steppes and semideserts of USSR and Mongolia to China. HBL (male) 32–56cm; TL 8–18cm; WT about 2kg. Coat reddish-brown, darker below and on feet and face mask; ears and lips white. Gestation 36–42 days; litter 3–6, occasionally up to 18.

Black-footed ferret E
Mustela nigripes

W prairies of N America, only within range of Prairie dogs (*Cynomys*); rare and endangered; derived from *M. eversmanni* invading N America during Pleistocene (2 million to 10,000 years ago). HBL (male) 38–41cm; TL 11–13cm; WT 0.9–1kg. Coat yellowish with dark facial mask, tail tip and feet. Gestation of one female in 2 seasons 42 and 45 days; litter 3–4.

Mountain weasel
Mustela altaica

Forested mountains of Asia from Altai to Korea and Tibet. HBL (male) 22–29cm; TL 11–15cm; WT 350g. Coat dark yellowish to ruddy-brown, with creamy-white throat and ventral patches; paler in winter, but not white; white upper lips and chin shading to adjacent darker areas (cf *M. sibirica*). Gestation 30–49 days; litter usually 1–2 but up to 7–8.

Kolinsky
Mustela sibirica
Kolinsky, Siberian weasel.

European Russia to E Siberia, Korea and China, Japan and Taiwan (see also *M. lutreolina*). HBL (male) 28–39cm; TL 15–21cm; WT 650–820g. Coat dark brown, paler below; may have white throat patch; paler in winter, but not white; dark facial mask with white upper lips and chin sharply contrasting with surrounding darker fur; tail thick and bushy. Gestation 35–42 days; litter 4–10.

Yellow-bellied weasel
Mustela kathiah

Himalayas, W and S China, N Burma. HBL (male) 23–29cm; TL 16–18cm; WT ? Coat deep chocolate-brown (rusty-brown in winter), yellow below; may have white spots on forepaws and whitish throat patch, chin and upper lips; tail long-haired, at least in winter.

Back-striped weasel
Mustela strigidorsa

Nepal, E through N Burma to Indochinese Peninsula. HBL (female) about 29cm; TL 15cm; WT ? Coat deep chocolate-brown (paler in winter), with silvery dorsal streak from base of skull to tail root and yellowish streak from chest along abdomen; upper lip, chin and throat whitish to ocherous; tail bushy; feet naked at all seasons.

Barefoot weasel
Mustela nudipes

SE Asia, Sumatra, Borneo. Coat uniform bright red with white head; feet naked at all seasons.

Indonesian mountain weasel
Mustela lutreolina

High altitudes of Java and Sumatra. The few known specimens are similar in size and color to European mink (*M. lutreola*) (russet-brown, no face mask, variable white throat patch); but skull similar to *M. sibirica*. Probably derived from *M. sibirica* stranded on the islands at the end of the Pleistocene. Some authorities consider *M. lutreolina* and *M. sibirica* as one species.

Marbled polecat
Vormela peregusna

Steppe and semidesert zones from SE Europe (Rumania) E to W China, to Palestine and Baluchistan. HBL (male and female) 33–35cm; TL 12–22cm; WT about 700g. Coat black, marked with white or yellowish spots and stripes, face like European polecat, *M. putorius*. Gestation 56–63 days; litter 4–8.

Zorilla
Ictonyx striatus
Zorilla, African polecat.

Semiarid regions throughout Africa S of Sahara. HBL (male and female) 28–38cm; TL 20–30cm; WT 1.4kg. Coat black, strikingly marked with white; hair long and tail bushy. Gestation 36 days; litter 2–3.

North African banded weasel

Poecilictis libyca

Semidesert fringing the Sahara from Morocco and Egypt to N Nigeria and Sudan; closely related to *Ictonyx*, possibly same genus. HBL (male and female) 22–28cm; TL 13–18cm; wt (male) 200–250g. Coat black, marked with variable pattern of bands and spots. Gestation unknown; litter 1–3.

African striped weasel

Poecilogale albinucha

Africa S of Sahara. HBL (male and female) 25–35cm; TL 15–23cm; wt 230–350g. Coat black with 4 white and 3 black stripes down back; tail white. Gestation 31–33 days; litter 1–3.

Grison

Galictis vittata
Grison or huron.

C and S America from Mexico to Brazil, up to 1,200m. HBL (male and female) 47–55cm; TL 16cm; wt 1.4–3.2kg. Face, legs and underparts black; back and tail smoky-gray with white stripe across forehead; feet partly webbed. Gestation unknown; litter probably 2–4.

Little grison

Galictis cuja

C and S America, at higher altitudes than *G. vittata*. HBL (male and female) 40–45cm; TL 15–19cm; wt about 1kg. Coat as *G. vittata*, but back is yellowish-gray or brownish.

Patagonian weasel

Lyncodon patagonicus

Pampas of Argentina and Chile. HBL (male and female) 30–35cm; TL 6–9cm; wt ? Top of head creamy-white; back grayish; underparts brown. Only 28 teeth.

▲ **European polecat.** The blond head and white feet of this animal indicate that it probably is a hybrid between a wild polecat and a domesticated ferret.

MINK

Two of 16 species of the genus *Mustela*
Family: Mustelidae.
Subfamily: Mustelinae.
Distribution: N America, France, E Europe to
NW Asia

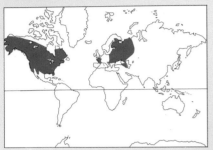

Habitat: margins of waterways and lakes, rocky
coasts.

Gestation: 34–70 days.

Longevity: up to 6 or more years (to 12 in
captivity).

American mink
Mustela vison
American or Eastern mink.

Size: head-body length of males
34–54cm (13.5–21.5in), females
30–45cm (12–18in); tail length of
males 15–21cm (6–8.5in), of
females 14–20cm (5.5–8in).
Weight: 0.5–1.5kg (1.1–3.3lb).
Coat: thick, glossy, brown; winter
coat darker; white patch usually
lacking on upper lip. Fourteen
subspecies.

European mink
Mustela lutreola
Size: slightly smaller than American mink—
head-body length of males 28–43cm
(11–17in), females 32–40cm (12.5–15.5in);
tail length in males 12–19cm (4.7–7.5in),
females 13–18cm (5.1–7in). Weighs slightly
less than American mink. Coat similar to that
of American mink but with white patch on
upper lip. Seven subspecies, decreasing in size
from *M. l. turovi* (Caucasus) to *M. l. lutreola*
(northernmost form).

▶ **An American mink emerges** from its
waterside den. Mink are opportunistic hunters
and cache surplus prey in their dens. One
mink's cache was found to contain 13 freshly
killed muskrats, 2 mallard ducks and 1 coot.

A mink, to most people, is an expensive fur coat. In reality, mink are two species of lively carnivores which might be said to cloak the shoulders of the Northern Hemisphere, only the less fortunate ending their days in the wardrobes of society ladies.

The American mink and the smaller and less common European mink live predatory lives along the margins of waterways. As a result of escapes from fur farms, the American mink is now naturalized in many parts of Europe and has in places supplanted the native species.

These close relatives of the weasels and polecats are semiaquatic and have partly webbed feet which assist in underwater hunting. Mink are somewhat serpentine in shape. They have small ears and long bushy tails. The coat provides insulation against low northern temperatures. The fur has two components: long guard hairs each surrounded by 9–24 underfur hairs that are one third or half the length. There are two molts each year: the thick, dark winter coat is shed in April, to be replaced by a much flatter and browner summer coat. The summer molt occurs in August or September and the winter coat is in its prime condition by late November. Northern subspecies have darker fur than southern forms.

Mink originally evolved in North America. The European species is a late migrant to Eurasia across the Bering Land Bridge during the last glacial phase of the Pleistocene. The two species have only been geographically isolated for some 10,000 years and are, in consequence, very similar in appearance, although there are skeletal differences, and American mink grow to a greater size (as do the males of each species).

Mink are truly carnivorous and take a wide variety of prey from aquatic and bank-side habitats. Their eyesight is not particularly well adapted to underwater vision, and fish are often located from above before the mink dives in pursuit. Mink rely heavily upon sense of smell when foraging for terrestrial prey.

Mink are solitary and territorial. Individuals defend linear territories of 1–4km (0.6–2.5mi) of river or lake shore by scent marking and overt aggression. Each territory contains several waterside dens, and a "core" area where the occupant forages most intensively. Marshland territories cover up to 9 hectares (22 acres), while those on a rocky coastline, such as Vancouver Island, are only 0.7km (0.4mi) long, reflecting the replenishment of rockpool resources by tides. Female mink ranges

◀ **Distinguishing two species.** The European mink BELOW always has a white patch on its upper lip. American mink ABOVE, now naturalized in Europe, are larger, and most lack the white patch. However, 10–20 percent not only possess the patch, but it may be as large as that of the European species. In such animals only study of the skeleton can guarantee correct identification.

The Versatile Mink

The carnivorous diet of mink includes crayfish, crabs, fish (**1**), small burrowing mammals (**2**), muskrats and rabbits, and birds (**3**). This range of prey—hunted in water, on land in swamps and down burrows—is considerably greater than that of more specialized mustelids, such as otters and weasels.

For mink, the so-called "broad niche" which they occupy carries both costs and benefits. The costs arise when mink compete with a more specialized predator. Since a "specialist" is better adapted than a "generalist" to exploiting certain prey, the generalist fares the worse when those prey become the object of competition. For example, at times of absence or scarcity of other prey groups, mink may depend heavily on fish, bringing them into direct competition with otters. Such competition only limits mink populations when otter population density is high. Even then direct competition is normally restricted by other factors, such as differential selection of fish prey on a size basis and exploitation of different parts of the habitat (for example, on a lake, the open waters by otters, and marsh and reedbeds by mink). On the benefit side, mink have such a wide choice of prey that they can normally turn to alternatives if one type of prey becomes scarce; such an option is closed to specialists.

In other respects mink are also at an advantage in a waterside habitat. Their small size, allowing access to many diverse refuges and better use of available cover, and tolerance of human disturbance give them the edge on, for example, otters, which are intolerant of humans and require dense riverside cover and larger holt sites.

The adaptability of minks is reflected in the variety of habitats in which they thrive—from the arctic wastes of Alaska, to the steaming swamps of the Florida Keys; from inland lakes and rivers to wave-battered rocks of the Atlantic coastline.

are about 20 percent smaller than those of males quoted above. Mink scent mark with feces coated by secretion from glands at the end of the gut (proctodeal glands), by an "anal drag" action, and by secretions from glandular patches on the skin of the throat underside and chest, deposited by "ventral rubbing."

As the mating season (February to March) approaches, males leave their territories and travel long distances in search of females. One male may mate with several females and each female may be mated by several males. How, with promiscuous mating, do the fittest individuals contribute the most offspring to the next generation? It appears that the roving existence of the rutting male is very demanding, thus ensuring that stronger animals travel farther and mate with more females than weaker ones. Experiments in mink farms have shown that when a female is mated by several males during her three weeks on heat, it is the last mating which produces most of the kits. In the wild, therefore, the males which father the most kits are the stronger ones which are still mating at the end of the season. Fighting is common between rutting males.

Seven to 30 days may elapse between fertilization and implantation of the egg; gestation proper lasts 27–33 days. After the resulting five- to ten-week pregnancy four to six blind and naked young are born. The female rears the kits alone and weans them at 8–10 weeks. They disperse from her territory at 3–4 months of age, males to a greater distance, often 50km (31mi) or more. Sexual maturity is reached at 10 months.

The American mink is widely regarded as a pest and a possible threat to native species in countries where it is now naturalized. The European mink may be one of those threatened species; already declining as a result of intensive hunting, it may fail in competition with its more vigorous American relative. Although it is protected in some countries, the European mink's conservation may be further hampered by problems of identification and hybridization where the two species occur together.

Mink have been trapped for their fur for centuries. The American species has a superior coat and has been bred in fur farms since 1866. Its hardiness and variety of mutant fur colors make it especially suited to this purpose. In 1933 the Russians started a program of release into the wild in order to establish a superior source of "free range" fur; by 1948 3,700 had been released.   JDSB

MARTENS

All 8 species of the genus _Martes_
For tayra (_Eira barbata_) see opposite.
Family: Mustelidae.
Subfamily: Mustelinae.
Distribution: Asia, N America, Europe.

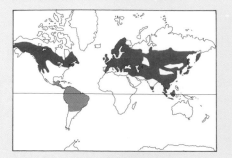

Martens		**Tayra**

Habitat: forests, chiefly coniferous but also deciduous and tropical mountain forests; Stone marten in urban areas.

Size: head-body length 30–75cm (12–30in); tail length 12–45cm (4.7–18in); weight 0.5–5kg (1–11lb). Males 30–100 percent heavier than females in all species.

Coat: generally soft, thick, brown, with feet and tail darker, sometimes black, and often a pale throat patch or bib; tail bushy; soles of feet furred.

Gestation: 8–9 months (including 6–7 month delay in egg implantation) in most N species.

Longevity: to 10–15 years in most species.

▲ **A Pine marten in its hollow-tree nest** with a captured mouse. Pine marten numbers have been much reduced in many parts of Europe. At the western limit of its range it crosses with sable, producing a hybrid called the "kida."

THE North American porcupine would seem to have the perfect defense against predators – sharp quills. But the fisher, one of eight marten species, has evolved a unique technique to kill porcupines and thus is the only animal for whom this porcupine is an important prey item. Foraging both in trees and on the ground, the fisher, like all martens, is a highly adapted, efficient predator.

Martens are medium-sized carnivores, only moderately elongated in shape, with wedge-shaped faces and rounded ears that are larger than in some mustelids. While the bushy tail serves as a balancing-rod, the large paws with haired soles and semiretractile claws are also great assets to these semiarboreal animals. Martens seem to leap from branch to branch effortlessly, and are among the most agile and graceful of the weasel family. Pathways, in trees or on the ground, may be marked with scent from the anal glands and with urine.

The Stone, Beech or House marten inhabits coniferous and deciduous woodlands from Europe to Central Asia and is often found near human habitation. Its large white throat patch extends onto its forelegs and underside. It is very similar to those species restricted to northern coniferous forests—the Pine marten, sable, Japanese marten and North American marten, which have smaller bibs. Differences between these four (which some authorities classify as one species) are graded from Europe eastward to North America: for example, the Pine marten is the largest and the North American marten the smallest. Two species from southern Asia, the Yellow-throated marten and Nilgiri marten, have striking yellow bibs and are again sometimes considered one

species. The fisher, from coniferous and mixed woodlands of North America, is the largest species and lacks the throat patch of other martens.

Martens are opportunistic hunters whose main foods are small vertebrates, especially mice, squirrels, rabbits and grouse. Carrion is also important in their diet, as are fruits and nuts when abundant. Martens inspect likely prey hiding places and if they sight prey, attempt a short rush to catch and kill it with a bite to the back of the neck.

Fishers are typical martens in most respects. They are not named for skill at catching fish or "fishing" bait out of traps as is commonly supposed. More likely, the name derives from old English ("fiche"), Dutch and French words for the European polecat and its pelt. Fishers are best known for their unique technique for preying on porcupines. The arrangement of quills on a porcupine protects it from an attack to the

The Tayra—a South American Marten?

The tayra (*Eira barbata*) inhabits forests from Mexico to Argentina and in Trinidad, where it searches for birds, small mammals and fruits—sometimes causing substantial damage to banana crops.

Tayras are similar in size and form to fishers. Head-body length is 90–115cm (35–45in), tail length 35–45cm (14–18in) and weight 4–6kg (8.8–13lb). Their coat is shorter, dark brown to black in color, with the head gray, brown or black and a yellow to white throat patch. Litters average three kits and are born in May after a 63–67 day gestation without the delayed egg implantation that occurs in most martens.

The comparison of the tayra with the North American fisher is a common one. But a correlation of typically mustelid features (elongation in shape, difference in size between sexes, carnivorous diet, and intolerance of other members of the same species) shows that the fisher and other martens (and also the small weasels) are at one end of a spectrum, and the tayra (and perhaps the badgers) closer to the other.

Tayras are less elongate in shape, have longer legs and are less sexually dimorphic in body size than are the martens. Tayras are fairly tolerant of other members of their

species and are often found in pairs and larger, probably family, groups, while martens are intolerant of other members of their species and are territorial toward members of their own sex. Vegetable matter, especially fruits, is more important in the diet of the tayra than in that of martens.

Finally, the tayra has a metabolic rate that is lower than might be expected for a mammal of its size, while the fisher is known to have a slightly elevated metabolic rate.

No good explanations of these correlations have yet been presented, although rates of energy expenditure may be part of the explanation. Species that are more elongate and live in a cooler climate expend energy more rapidly and thus have higher energy requirements than does the more compact tayra with its tropical distribution.

◄ **The Beech marten primarily hunts in trees** ABOVE, but may hunt rats and mice around farms, even denning in attics, and also inhabits rocky areas—hence the alternative names House marten and Stone marten.

◄ **American marten foraging in winter snow.** This species prefers continuous coniferous forest. Although populations were decimated in the first half of the 20th century, the species is now making a comeback.

back of the neck, where most carnivores attack, but its face is not protected. Fishers stand low to the ground and can thus direct an attack to a porcupine's face, yet are big enough to inflict damaging wounds. A fisher circles the porcupine on the ground, taking advantage of any chance to bite its face. The porcupine attempts to keep its well-quilled back and tail toward the fisher and to seek protection for its face against a log or tree. If the fisher delivers enough solid bites to the porcupine's face, the porcupine suffers

shock or is unable to protect itself. The fisher then overturns the porcupine and begins feeding on its unquilled belly.

Killing a porcupine is long, hard work and a successful kill may take over half an hour. Depending on how many scavengers share the kill, the fisher may have enough food for over two weeks. Where porcupines are common, they may make up a quarter of a fisher's diet.

Martens are generally solitary. They are polygamous, and mating normally occurs in late summer (early spring in the fisher). During early spring, litters of 1–5 sparsely furred, blind and deaf kits are born. Around 2 months of age the kits are weaned. They are able to kill prey by 3–4 months, shortly before they leave their mothers. Martens become sexually active when between one and two years old, depending on species and sex, and it is probably at this time that they try to establish territories.

Martens were a distinct group within the weasel family by the Pliocene (7–2 million years ago). Skeletal characteristics of these ancestral martens show that the three present-day groups of martens—Pine martens, Yellow-throated martens and the fisher—were already distinguishable. Evolution of the distinct species within the former two groups began during the Pleistocene only 2 million years ago.

Because several of the martens, especially the sable and fisher, have been valued for their fur, hunting and trapping pressure on marten populations has sometimes been very high. This pressure, in combination with the destruction of the conifer and conifer-hardwood forests preferred by these species, has led to a decline in some populations. At present, however, none of the martens is considered endangered. **RAP**

Abbreviations: HBL = head-body length; TL = tail length; wt = weight. Approximate measure equivalents: 10cm = 4in; 1kg = 2.2lb.

Pine marten
Martes martes

C and N Europe, W Asia. HBL 40–55cm; TL 20–28cm; wt 0.9–2kg. Coat chestnut-brown to dark brown, bib creamy-white.

American marten
Martes americana

Northern N America to Sierra Nevada and Rockies in Colorado and California. HBL 30–45cm; TL 16–24cm; wt 0.5–1.5kg. Coat golden-brown to dark brown, bib cream to orange.

Japanese marten
Martes melampus

Japan, Korea. HBL 30–45cm; TL 17–23cm; wt 0.5–1.5kg. Coat yellow-brown to dark brown, bib white/cream.

Fisher
Martes pennanti
Fisher or pekan or Virginian polecat.

Northern N America to California (Sierra Nevada) and W Virginia (Appalachians). HBL 47–75cm; TL 30–42cm; wt 2–5kg. Coat medium to dark brown; gold to silver hoariness on head and shoulders; legs and tail black; variable cream chest patch. Gestation 11–12 months (implantation delayed 9–10 months).

Sable
Martes zibellina

N Asia, N Japanese islands. HBL 35–55cm; TL 12–19cm; wt 0.5–2kg. Coat dark brown, yellowish bib not always clearly delineated; tail short. Egg implantation and gestation 1 month longer than above species.

Stone marten
Martes foina
Stone, Beech or House marten.

S and C Europe to Denmark and C Asia. HBL 43–55cm; TL 22–30cm; wt 0.5–2kg. Coat chocolate-brown, underfur lighter than previous species, white bib often in 2 parts.

Yellow-throated marten
Martes flavigula

SE Asia to Korea, Java, Sumatra, Borneo. HBL 48–70cm; TL 35–45cm; wt 1–5kg. Coat yellow-brown to dark brown, bib yellow to orange, legs and tail dark brown to black. Gestation variable, 5–6 months with some 3–4 months' delayed implantation.

Nilgiri marten
Martes gwatkinsi
Nilgiri or Yellow-throated marten.

Nilgiri mountains of S India. Smaller than *M. flavigula*, but coat similar.

WOLVERINE

Gulo gulo
Wolverine or glutton.
Sole species of the genus.
Family: Mustelidae.
Subfamily: Mustelinae.
Distribution: circumpolar, in N America and Eurasia.

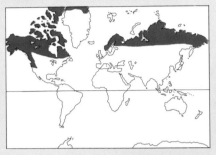

Habitat: arctic and subarctic tundra and taiga.

 Size: in Alaska, head-body length up to 83cm (33in); tail length 20cm (8in); weight up to 25kg (55lb); in Alaska males average. 15kg (33lb), females 10kg (22lb).

Coat: long, dark brown to black; lighter band along flanks to upperside of bushy tail.

Gestation: about 9 months.

Longevity: to 13 years (18 in captivity).

The 2 subspecies are the **European wolverine** (*Gulo gulo gulo*) and the **North American wolverine** (*Gulo gulo luscus*).

▶ **Over soft, deep snow** RIGHT, ABOVE the large feet of the wolverine enable it to catch its reindeer prey, which is handicapped by a weight load 8–10 times greater.

▶ **Somewhat bearlike in outward appearance,** the powerful wolverine is occasionally killed by packs of wolves (and probably also by Grizzly bears and pumas where they occur with wolverines). But a solitary wolf would find a wolverine a fearsome combatant.

▷ **The wolverine's remote habitat** has not protected it from persecution: it is hunted by fur trappers in North America and in Scandinavia. In consequence, its range and numbers have decreased during the past 100 years, though some expansion of range is occurring where the wolverine is protected or its harvest regulated.

BECAUSE it is rare and inhabits remote areas, the wolverine has been poorly understood for centuries. The first description of the "glutton"—in 1518—tells of "an animal which feeds on carcasses and is highly ravenous. It eats until the stomach is tight as a drumskin then squeezes itself through a narrow passage between two trees. This empties the stomach of its contents and the wolverine can continue to eat until the carcass is completely consumed." This fable was still widespread during the 18th century. At that time even the famous Swedish taxonomist Carl Linnaeus was uncertain whether the European wolverine belonged to the weasel family or to the dog family; in the first edition of his *Systema naturae* (1735) the wolverine was even omitted.

The wolverine is heavily built, with short legs. However, because its feet are large they bear a weight load of only 27–35g/sq cm (0.4–0.5lb/sq in). In consequence, although an adult reindeer can elude a wolverine on bare ground, or even on snow if the crust is thick enough, the wolverine has the advantage in soft snow. In winter the wolverine feeds mainly on reindeer and caribou, which are either killed or scavenged. The wolverine's skill in scavenging indicates that it has a particularly well developed sense of smell. While it will kill a small mammal by a neck bite and usually eat it immediately, a wolverine drags down larger prey by jumping on its back and holding on with its powerful claws until the animal collapses to the ground. The wolverine's powerful jaw and chewing muscles enable it to break even thick bones. A carcass, although often completely utilized, is not immediately consumed by a wolverine but dismembered and hidden in widely dispersed caches, in crevices or buried in marshes or other soft ground. These provisions may be used, as much as six months later, by a wolverine female to feed herself and her newborn kits. The more diverse summer diet includes birds, small and medium-sized mammals, plants and the remains of reindeer calves or other prey killed by predators such as lynx, wolves and Grizzly bears.

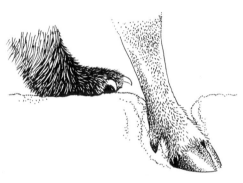

The mating season extends from April to August, but implantation of the fertilized egg is delayed so that births take place during late January to early April, when 1–4 (average 2.5) kits are born blind, in a den that is usually dug in a deep snowdrift. The kits stay in and around the den until early May, but litters may be moved to new sites. Such moves are believed to be triggered by meltwater entering the den or by direct disturbance. Moves may also be an adaptation to avoid human persecution, since the accumulation of tracks around the den makes it easier for hunters to locate it. Females reach reproductive maturity in their second year, but reproduction is suppressed when food is scarce, whereas when prey is bountiful females breed annually.

The young are accompanied by their mother throughout the summer and thereafter remain, living within her home range at least into late fall. Male kits generally disperse by the onset of the next breeding season, but some female kits may remain in or near their mother's home range indefinitely. The adult female maintains, by scent marking and aggression, a territory of 50–350sq km/(19–135sq mi), which is exclusive from April to September. Male territories span up to 600–1,000sq km (230–390sq mi) and overlap the areas of several females as well as other males. Scent marking is usually in the form of urination, defecation or a scent secretion from the abdominal or ventral gland. In the latter case, a wolverine traveling over tussocky tundra will periodically stop while straddling a tussock and rub the scent gland on it. Willow shrubs may be similarly marked as individuals clamber over branches.

The distribution of wolverines has contracted during the past 100 years, for example from eastern Canada and the prairie provinces, and their numbers have also declined over large areas. These reductions are most marked where human populations are densest. The wolverine is not endangered, but it may be considered as vulnerable over most of its range.

Wolverines are shot and trapped where they are still regarded as big game, as a predatory pest or as furbearers, although the toll is modest (recently 800 pelts per year from Alaska, each with a value of $150–250) compared to that during the 16th and 17th centuries, when wolverine pelts were so valuable that the city of Turinsk in Siberia reputedly incorporated a wolverine in its coat of arms as the symbol of local commerce.   AB/AJM

SKUNKS

Subfamily: Mephitinae
Thirteen species in 3 genera.
Family: Mustelidae.
Distribution: N, C and S America.

Size: overall length ranges from 40cm (16in) to 68cm (27in), weight from 0.5kg (1.1lb) to 3kg (6.6lb).

Longevity: to at least 7 years (to 8–10 years in captivity).

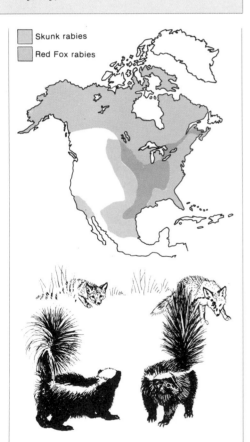

☐ Skunk rabies
☐ Red Fox rabies

▲ **Skunks and rabies.** Over much of the USA skunks are the chief vector (carrier) of rabies. Where both skunks and Red foxes are carriers, rabies is often transmitted when a rabid fox attacks a skunk despite the threat display and squirting tactics ABOVE that usually deter a healthy predator.

▶ **The Pygmy spotted skunk,** a rare species of western and southwestern Mexico, showing the silkier coat that is characteristic of all Spotted skunks.

SKUNKS are best known for their odorous defense and their role as a transmitter (vector) of rabies. Although all mustelids possess anal glands, the ability to expel a fine spray of foul-smelling liquid at an intruder is most pronounced in skunks, in which it develops at less than one month old. Most species of skunk forewarn predators by stamping their front feet, raising their tail and walking stiff-legged. Spotted skunks will occasionally bluff by handstanding without spraying. If that fails, they will drop onto all fours and spray. The spray is aimed at the face and causes intense irritation, even temporary blindness, if it reaches the eyes. The odor (a sulfurous smell) persists in the area for days and absorbent clothing that has been "sprayed" is probably best discarded. Although most animals avoid skunks, a notable exception is the Great horned owl, which does not appear to be deterred by skunk spray while foraging at night.

Skunks are intermediate between weasels and badgers in build. There can be considerable variation in coat pattern even within species: for example in the Hooded skunk the white-backed form has two bands of white on its back narrowly separated by a black line, whereas in the black-backed form the white stripes are widely separated and are situated on the sides of the animal. The distinctive black and white markings help advertise their presence to intruders and, together with threat postures that make use of the tail covered with extra-long hairs, forewarn them that they may be sprayed. Skunks can spray up to 4–7m (13–23ft) in a favorable wind—although they are usually only accurate for up to about 2m (6.5ft). Normally skunks and skunk dens do not smell "skunky." During aggressive encounters between skunks, however, they will spray one another.

All skunks are largely carnivorous, with insects and small mammals as major prey, but they also eat grubs, birds' eggs and fruit seasonally. They are found in a wide variety of habitats, and are common in many urban areas, but prefer open or forest edge areas, where they forage at night, using their long front claws for rooting out food.

Inactive denning periods (not true hibernation) occur during the winter months if weather conditions are severe. In some areas several species occur together, but each uses different portions of the area more effectively than the others. This habitat partitioning allows coexistence, although the Striped skunk—the most common species—is invariably dominant where it overlaps with others. Except for Spotted skunks, which are mainly active at twilight, skunks are chiefly nocturnal. For example, stripped skunks, normally forage only at dusk, dawn and during the night, ambling in search of prey at a leisurely pace and avoiding contact with people and domestic animals.

Skunks are the major vectors of rabies in much of the continental United States, with over 4,000 cases diagnosed in skunks during some years—in other words over two-thirds of all cases in wildlife. Whereas the role of the Red fox in rabies outbreaks has been declining recently, the role of skunks is increasing. The skunk's role in carrying rabies in some areas led early homesteaders to name it the "Phoby cat" or "Hydrophobia skunk." Rabid skunks may attack virtually anything that moves. All species carry rabies, but the Striped skunk is most often involved as it is more widespread. Skunk rabies cases are most prevalent in the midwestern USA and recently have been the most important source of human exposure to rabies in Texas and California. Rabid skunks have high levels of virus in the saliva, and as they have long incubation periods they are important reservoirs of the disease, which might otherwise be easier to control among foxes. Skunk spray is not known to carry rabies virus.

Skunks coexist with foxes, raccoons and coyotes, groups of skunks often using the same burrows as these species, but at different times of the year. Since skunks are in frequent contact with man's domestic animals, such as cattle, horses, pigs, dogs and cats, there is a great deal of potential for interspecies rabies transmission. Rabies outbreaks occur when skunks' movements are most extensive, during the fall and spring months. Transmission between skunks may occur during winter communal denning when territories overlap, and also through

▲ **Species of skunks.** (1) Western spotted skunk in a handstand threatening posture characteristic of the genus *Spilogale*. (2) Hooded skunk. (3) Hog-nosed skunk foraging with its long naked snout. (4, 5) Two forms of the Striped skink, the commonest species.

the aggressive behavior of some males towards females with litters. Since rabies reduces population density and contact between individuals, outbreaks often occur 3–4 years apart when populations are high.

During most of the year females occupy home ranges of 1–2sq km (0.4–0.8sq mi), each overlapping at least partially with other females. The territory of one male will encompass those of several females, but rarely that of other males. Males have no role in raising young. In fact, aggressive behavior by adult males toward females and their young can result in deaths.   DRV

Abbreviations: HTL = head-to-tail-tip length; wt = weight. Approximate measure equivalents: 10cm = 4in; 1kg = 2.2lb.
⊡ CITES listed.

Striped skunk
Mephitis mephitis

S Canada, USA, N Mexico. Commonest species; diverse habitats include suburban areas; dens in burrows and even under buildings. Overall length 68cm, weight 1.5–3kg. Coat black with forking white stripes of varying length on back and tail; white patch on head; black and white hairs not mixed. Mates in February; true gestation 62–66 days; 3–9 young born in May–June.

Hooded skunk
Mephitis macroura

SW USA. Rare, more secretive than

M. mephitis. Coat black with white back; 1–3 white stripes may be present; black and white hairs mixed. Mates in February; true gestation 63 days; 3–5 young born in May.

Hog-nosed skunk
Seven species of the genus *Conepatus*

Hog-nosed skunk (*C. mesoleucus*), S USA, Nicaragua; **Eastern hog-nosed skunk** (*C. leuconotus*), E Texas, E Mexico; **Amazonian skunk** (*C. semistriatus*), S Mexico, Peru, Brazil; **Andes skunk** (*C. rex*), Peru; *Conepatus castereus*, Argentina; *C. chinga*, Chile, Argentina, Paraguay; **Patagonian skunk** ⊡ (*C. humboldti*), Patagonia.

Diverse habitats, but prefer rugged terrain; den in rocky crevices and burrows. Overall length 60cm, weight 1.5–2kg. Coat black with large white band on back and white tail; color may be similar to *M. mephitis* where the two do not overlap; distinguished by lack of white head stripe and by bare elongated snout; large claws another adaptation for digging. Mate in February; true gestation 42 days; 2–4 young born in May–June.

Spotted skunks
Four species of the genus *Spilogale*

Western spotted skunk (*S. gracilis*), W USA to C Mexico. **Eastern spotted skunk** (*S. putorius*), SE and C USA to E

Mexico. **Southern spotted skunk** (*S. angustifrons*), C Mexico to Costa Rica. **Pygmy spotted skunk** (*P. pygmaea*), W and SW Mexico. All readily climb trees, den in crevices, burrow and use low buildings. All some 40cm in overall length, weighing 0.5kg. Coat black with 4–6 broken white stripes or spots; hair silkier than in other genera. All bear 2–6 young.
S. angustifrons, *S. putorius* and *S. pygmaea* mate February–March; true gestation 42 days; young born in May in *S. putorius* true gestation may be delayed 2 weeks. *S. gracilis* mates in late summer; with delayed implantation young are born in April–May.

OTTERS

Subfamily: Lutrinae ⬚
Twelve species in 6 genera.
Family: Mustelidae.
Distribution: widespread in subpolar regions excluding Australasia and Madagascar, the Sahara, part of E USSR, W China, W Asia, S North America, SW South America.

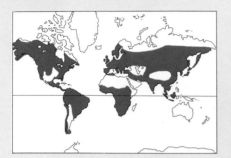

Habitat: aquatic (including marine), and terrestrial.

Size: ranges from the Oriental short-clawed otter with head-body length 41–64cm (16–25in), tail length 25–35cm (10–14in), weight about 5kg (11lb), to the Giant otter of S America with head-body length 96–123cm (38–48in), tail length 45–65cm (18–26in), weighing up to 30kg (66lb). The shorter Sea otter may attain 45kg (88lb).

Coat: browns and grays; darker above, chest, throat and underside usually lighter.

Gestation: mostly 60–70 days, but up to 12 months with delayed implantation in some species.

Longevity: up to 12 years in wild (Giant otter), and 21 years in captivity.

Six species of the genus *Lutra*: the **North American river otter** (*L. canadensis*), N America; **European river otter** or **Eurasian otter** (*L. lutra*), Eurasia, N Africa; **Marine otter** ⬚ (*L. felina*), S America; **Southern river otter** (*L. provocax*), S America; **Neotropical river otter** (*L. longicaudis*), C and S America. **Hairy-nosed otter** ⬚ (*L. sumatrana*), SE Asia.

Spot-necked otter (*Hydrictis maculicollis*), Africa.

Indian smooth-coated otter (*Lutrogale perspicillata*), Asia.

Oriental short-clawed otter (*Aonyx cinerea*), Asia; **Cape clawless otter** (*A. capensis*), Africa.

Giant otter ⬚ (*Pteronura brasiliensis*), S America.

Sea otter (*Enhydra lutris*), N America.

⬚ CITES listed. ⬚ Vulnerable.
⬚ Known to be threatened, status indeterminate.

ALTHOUGH all are rather similar in appearance, otters exhibit striking behavioral and social variations; in most species numbers are rapidly declining, through direct persecution by man, and indirectly because of loss of habitat.

Otters are the only truly amphibious members of the weasel family. They largely forage in water, but are equally at home on land, except for the Sea otter, which rarely comes ashore in California. Otters' tightly packed underfur and long guard hairs are water-repellent, and the body is elongated, sinuous and lithe, built for vigorous swimming. The limbs are short and the paws are webbed in most species. The forefeet are shorter than the hindfeet. The tail is fully haired, thick at the base and tapering to a point, flattened on the underside and in some species on the upper surface. There are numerous stiff whiskers (vibrissae) around the nose and snout, and in tufts on the elbows. These tactile hairs are sensitive to water turbulence and are used in searching for prey. The ears are small and round, and like the nostrils are closed under water, an indication that sound is not important in the location of prey. Most otters have claws, but those without them (and also the Sea otter) use their acute sense of touch and their manual dexterity to find and seize prey.

Otters' diets are varied, but most species eat frogs, crayfish, crabs and fish—usually sluggish non-game species such as roach, sticklebacks or eels. Otters consume their catch immediately. Bones are crushed with well-developed premolars (see p109 for dentition of otters). Very occasionally a rogue will enter a hatchery and kill large numbers of fish. Like most carnivores, otters prey on what is readily available and the easiest to catch: in Europe lethargic frogs and eels in winter, coots and ducklings in spring, spawning crayfish, perch or roach in summer.

Otters use different tactics to catch their prey; the Oriental short-clawed and Cape clawless otters (both *Aonyx* species) are hand-oriented and will invariably grab an octopus or a crayfish with outstretched forepaws; on the other hand, the six *Lutra* species and the Giant otter are mouth-oriented like most carnivores, so chase their fish prey underwater, catching it in their jaws. These successful predators can quickly hunt down and eat their daily quota of food, which may be about 1kg (2.2lb) for *Lutra*.

An otter will have several hunting sessions a day, swimming and feeding for an hour or more before hauling out to rest on the bank. Otters have a very rapid metabolism and a meal will pass through their digestive tract in a few hours—giving them boundless energy on the one hand, but forcing them also to eat at frequent intervals, often four times a day. The Giant otter and Indian smooth-coated otter, which often hunt in pairs or groups, remain in the vicinity of their still-feeding partners, waiting for them to finish before moving on.

▲ **The hydrodynamic form** of this Small-clawed otter exemplifies the perfect adaptation of all otters to an amphibious way of life.

▼ **Stiff whiskers and manual dexterity** are adaptations to catching prey in muddy or dark waters. Here a Cape clawless otter eats a fish.

The otters of the genus *Lutra* are probably the most numerous and are certainly the most widespread otters. The four New World species range from Alaska to Tierra del Fuego. The three Central and South American species are so similar in size and shape that they can only be distinguished by the shape of the nose pad (see p127). Four previously separated species (*L. annectens, L. platensis, L. enudris, L. incarum*) have recently been lumped together under the heading *L. longicaudis*; it is even suggested that all South American otters, while showing geographic variation in size and color, are really subspecies of the North American river otter or Canadian otter (*L. canadensis*). One New World species, the Marine otter, inhabits the rough waters of the western coast of South America from Peru to Cape Horn. Its fur is coarse and the skull is similar to that of the Spot-necked otter of Africa. Unlike the true Sea otter of the northern Pacific, this small otter's bones and teeth are not modified to cope with an essentially marine existence. Darwin, during the voyage of the *Beagle* (1831–36), reported that the natives of Tierra del Fuego ate it and used its warm fur for making hats.

The most widespread Old World representative of the genus is the European or Eurasian river otter, which ranges from Scotland to Kamchatka and south to Java. The Sumatran otter, last of the *Lutra* species, has a hairy nose like the Giant otter of Brazil, and is a spot-necked species. It lives in the high mountain streams of Southeast Asia.

The Spot-necked otter, one of the most proficient swimmers of all freshwater otters, inhabits streams and lakes of Africa south of the Sahara.

The Indian smooth-coated otter is more heavily built and larger than the Eurasian otter. It probably evolved earlier than the present-day *Lutra*. Like the Giant otter, it has short, dense fur, a flattened tail and thickly webbed paws which are nonetheless remarkably agile in manipulating and retrieving small objects. The shortened face and domed skull house broad molars, indicating a largely crustacean diet for this marsh-dwelling species; in Sumatra it even leads a coastal existence, earning it the confusing local name of "sea otter." Although sometimes included in the genus *Lutra*, it has quite distinct skeletal and behavioral characteristics.

The genus *Aonyx* contains two species, both of which are hand-oriented. The Oriental short-clawed otter is the smallest of all otters, rarely more than 90cm (35in) in overall length. Its forefeet are only partially webbed and have stubby agile fingers tipped with tiny, vestigial claws that grow like upright pegs on the top of bulbous fingertips. Aptly called "Finger-otter" in German, these diminutive otters use their sensitive forepaws constantly to search for prey by touch alone. The Cape or African clawless otter lives south of the Sahara. Its forepaws are not webbed, but have strong clawless fingers which have a truly monkey-like dexterity. Even the thumb shows freedom of movement and can be opposed when picking up or holding down objects. The hindfeet have a small web and the middle toes have claws used for grooming. The fingers are used to probe mud and crevices for crabs and frogs or, in coastal water, octopus. The broad cheek teeth are perfectly adapted to grinding the tough carapace of crustacea, such as rock crabs.

The Giant otter of Brazil, which can measure over 1.8m (5.9ft) overall and weigh up to 30kg (66lb), is among the rarest otters. Its total numbers are unknown, but the population has undoubtedly declined or disappeared over much of its former range. Almost 20,000 skins were exported from Brazil alone in the 1960s. Although the trade declined significantly when bans came into effect in the early 1970s, poaching is still widespread. Prior to overexploitation by pelt hunters, made easy by their quarry's daytime activity and inquisitive habits, the Giant otter was found in most rivers and creeks of the Amazon basin. Its annual life cycle is closely linked to the rise and fall of the water level during the rainy season from April to September. Like other otters, it is an opportunistic feeder, preferring the slower fish that lie camouflaged on the stream or lake bed. These fish move into flooded forests to spawn during the rainy season and the otters follow them until the waters recede again into the creeks a few months later.

The Sea otter of the north Pacific is in many ways unlike other members of the subfamily. Not so slender, and with a relatively short tail, the Sea otter may weigh even more than the Giant otter, and is thus the largest member of the weasel family. It is exclusively marine and rarely comes ashore. Its large, rounded molars are perfectly adapted to crushing sea urchins, abalones and mussels, which it wrestles off rocks with its forepaws. The Sea otter is one of the few tool-using mammals (see p127). Hunted close to extinction for its pelt, the species was protected by an early international agreement in 1911. Total numbers are today probably about 105,000, as a result of the ban and of efforts to reestablish Sea otters in their former range in the 1950s–1970s. Of these, 100,000 or more live from Prince William Sound to the Kurile Islands, and some 2,000 live off California.

Although the Eurasian otter, Smooth-coated otter and Clawless otters have the same distribution in Asia, they are adapted to different diets and habitats, so probably never compete directly with each other. The Eurasian otter prefers quiet streams and lakes away from human disturbance; the Smooth-coated otter can be found in marshes and coastal mangrove swamps; and the *Aonyx* species inhabit shallow estuaries or rice paddies, seldom venturing into deep water.

It seems likely, although the fossil evidence is inadequate to prove it, that *Pteronura* populated South America and *Lutrogale* Asia just before the adaptable and successful *Lutra* otters came along, and that both genera are remnant populations which may well eventually die out.

The social behavior of otters ranges from solitary to family living. *Lutra* species, such as the Eurasian otter, are basically solitary. Although a male and female may pair for several months during the breeding season, there is no strong pair bond between them and the male is dominant during their temporary associations. The Giant, Smooth-coated and Oriental short-clawed otters all live in extended family groups, with strong bonds between breeding pairs—the female is known to be the dominant partner in the first two. The Cape clawless otter is intermediate, in that its members live in pairs; in both *Aonyx* species the male helps raise the young. The Sea otter presents a further social variation: after mating the sexes separate into coastal resting areas that average 44ha (108 acres) in males and 80ha (200 acres) in areas occupied by females with their young; these areas are distinct but may be next to areas of about 30ha (74 acres) patrolled by single males.

Much has been said about the "playfulness" of otters, but this may apply mainly to captive otters with "time on their hands," rather than their wild counterparts. However, wild otters will tunnel through a snow drift or sometimes slide down a mudbank; juveniles may rough-and-tumble ashore or chase each other in water. Play serves to reinforce social bonds, so important to social otters, but also helps young otters perfect their hunting and fighting techniques. Otters "playfully" swimming on a log or rolling in a pile of leaves may in fact be rubbing themselves dry or trying to place a scent mark.

◄ **Manual dexterity** is a striking feature of some otter species. (**1**) The Oriental short-clawed otter (*Aonyx cinerea*) is hand-oriented and will always reach out with its forelimbs for food. (**2**) The Spot-necked otter (*Hydrictis maculicollis*) is mouth-oriented, reaching out with its neck and body for food. (**3**) An Indian smooth-coated otter (*Lutrogale perspicillata*) uses its heavily webbed, but highly dextrous, forepaws to hold a shell to its mouth.

The presence or absence of webbing and claws, as well as manual dexterity, distinguish many otter species. Shown here are forepaws of (**a**) Oriental short-clawed otter, (**b**) Cape clawless otter (*Aonyx capensis*), (**c**) Giant otter (*Pteroneura brasiliensis*), (**d**) Indian smooth-coated otter, (**e**) Spot-necked otter, and (**f**) North American river otter (*Lutra canadensis*).

(**4**) Head of North American river otter. The shape and size of the hairy patch on the nose pad distinguish the different *Lutra* species: (**i**) North American river otter, (**ii**) Eurasian river otter (*l. lutra*), (**iii**) Southern river otter (*L. provocax*), (**iv**) Marine otter (*L. felina*), (**v**) Hairy-nosed otter (*L. sumatrana*), (**vi–viii**) 3 subspecies of the Neotropical river otter: *Lutra longicaudis enudris*, *L. l. platensis* and *L. l. annectens*.

A Tool-using Carnivore

Sea otters are dextrous and particularly versatile in their manipulative skills, even for otters. Most food items are collected by picking them off the bottom or from kelp stalks, but when digging for clams, the otter kicks with its hind flippers to stay close to the bottom while digging rapidly with its forepaws in a circular motion and rooting with its head. It will remain submerged for 30–60 seconds and return to the same hole on three or more successive dives, to enlarge the hole laterally with each dive and retrieve clams as they are encountered.

The Sea otter is the only mammal apart from primates reported to use a tool while foraging. To dislodge abalone they grasp a stone between the mitten-like forepaws and bang it against the edge of the abalone shell. It may require three or more dives to dislodge an abalone; the same stone may be used through 20 or more dives.

Food items are almost always brought to the surface for consumption, from depths of up to 40m (130ft). The Sea otter may then place a stone on its chest and use it as an anvil on which to open mussels, clams, and other shell-encased prey. The stone is carried to the surface in a flap of skin in the armpit and the food item in the forepaws. The stones are usually flat and about 18cm (7in) in diameter. When pounding, the arms are raised to about 90 degrees to the body and the mollusc

Otters are very vocal, with a large repertoire of calls. Different vocalizations readily distinguish *Lutra* from *Lutrogale* and both of these from *Aonyx*. *Lutra* species can be recognized by their unique staccato chuckle (New World) or a twitter (Old World), both given in a context of close proximity between adults or between mother and cubs. The contact call in *Lutra* is a one-syllable chirp, a sound which can carry quite far, whereas in the five other genera the sound is more of a bark with a nasal, guttural quality and the close-contact sound is a humming purr, interspersed with a falling "coo."

Differences in vocalization are to be found mainly in these contact, summons and greeting calls, but similarities, especially in threat and alarm calls, remain. The growl and the inquiring "hah," with minor variations, are common to all the species that have been studied. It is interesting to note that the widely dispersed "giant" otters, that is, *Aonyx* (Asia and Africa), the Sea otter (North Pacific) and Giant otter (South America), share more similarities in vocal repertoire with one another than with species with which they overlap, such as the Eurasian, Indian smooth-coated and Oriental short-clawed otters.

brought down forcefully, so that the hard shell strikes the stone. An uninterrupted series of 2–22 or more blows at about two per second seems enough to crack the shell. It is then bitten and the contents extracted with the lower incisors, which project forward. The otter may roll over in the water between bites to jettison debris and to keep the fur clean. In sandy or muddy areas, where stones are not available, the otter will use one clam or mussel as the tool and bang it against another.

Wild Alaskan Sea otters, unlike captive individuals and members of the Californian population, rarely use anvils, probably because they feed on prey that they can crush in their teeth, such as crab, snails and fish. Sea otters also prey on sea urchins; it is the dye in the urchin's shell that causes the purple color of some Sea otter skeletons.   TRL

Scent marking is a common feature of otter behavior. Only the exclusively marine Sea otter lacks the paired scent glands at the base of the tail which give otters their heavy, musky smell. Scent marking delineates territorial boundaries and communicates information concerning identity, sex, sexual state, receptivity and time elapsed between scenting visits. Otters usually leave single spraints (feces) or urine marks, but the social species also use communal latrines, where the urine and feces are thoroughly mixed and trampled into the substrate by stomping with the hind paws and sometimes (Giant otter) kneading with the forepaws. A pair or a group may clear and scent mark a site together during a bout of feverish activity which leaves an area denuded of vegetation, smelling of scent, feces and urine. The strong, dank odor can be detected near any site which has been visited within the previous several weeks. For a few days the smell is overpowering, but by a week later it is pleasant.

Urine may be dribbled during vegetation marking, when the otter pulls down armfuls of leaves and rubs its body over them. Otters trampling the vegetation cover their fur with the scent they are themselves spreading and later, while resting, they rub themselves against the ground and each other until there is a composite scent characteristic of a pair or even a group.

Recent observations of Brazilian Giant otters show that, when ashore, they use specific scent-marking sites along banks which they clear of all vegetation to a semicircular shape roughly 8m long and 7m wide (26ft by 23ft). On one creek 50 such sites were monitored and at least 23 of them were in areas of perennial vegetation, so that the otters had carefully to keep them clear of grass and fallen twigs. Such sites and their communal latrines are both visual and scent marks, which are further prominently enhanced by trampling the surrounding vegetation and topsoil. One way of marking complements the other—to advertise and to inform the Giant otter that passes by.

That otters are adaptable is evident from their distribution prior to man's emergence. It is tempting to wonder how they will evolve in the next million years—will the Cape clawless otter become more raccoon-like; will the Sea otter resemble a seal more than it does today; will the Brazilian and Smooth-coated otters succumb to the *Lutra* invasion? However, we do not yet even know if otters will survive the 20th century with its pollutants, fur trappers and rampant habitat destruction.   ND

Abbreviations: HBL = head-body length; TL = tail length; wt = weight.
[V] Vulnerable.   [I] Threatened, status indeterminate.

North American river otter
Lutra canadensis
North American river otter or Canadian otter.

Canada, USA including Alaska. HBL 66–107cm; TL 32–46cm. Coat: very dark, dusky brown above, almost black to reddish-black or occasionally grayish-brown; lighter, silvery or grayish on belly; throat and cheeks silvery to yellowish-gray. Feet well-webbed, claws strong. Breeding season March–April; gestation 10–12 months with delayed implantation; litter 1–5 (2–3).

European river otter
Lutra lutra
European or Eurasian river otter.

Most of Eurasia S of tundra line, N Africa. HBL 57–70cm; TL 35–40cm. Coat: brownish-gray to dusky brown (lighter in Asian races); throat buff to cream. Feet well-webbed, claws strong; tail thick at the base. Breeding nonseasonal; gestation 61–65 days; litter 2–5 (2–3).

Marine otter [V]
Lutra felina
Marine otter, chingungo.

Coast and coastal islands of Chile and Peru; exterminated in Argentina. HBL 57–59cm; TL 30–36cm. Coat: dark brown above, with underside a lighter fawn color. Feet well-webbed, claws strong. Breeding season: no data, may be December–January; gestation 60–70 days; litters average 2.

Southern river otter [I]
Lutra provocax

Argentina, Chile. HBL 57–70cm; TL 35–46cm. Coat: dark to very dark, burnt umber above; underside a lighter cinnamon color. Claws strongly webbed. Breeding: ?

Neotropical river otter
Lutra longicaudis

C and S America from Mexico to Argentina. HBL 50–79cm; TL 38–57cm. Coat: cinnamon-brown to grayish-brown on back, sometimes with one or more lighter (buff or cream) spots or patches. Claws strong, webbing present. Breeding season varies with locality; gestation ?; litter 1–4 (average 2–3). Taxonomy in the process of revision; here considered to include *L. annectens, L. platensis, L. incarum, L. enudris, L. insularis, L. repanda, L. latidens.*

Hairy-nosed otter
Lutra sumatrana

Sumatra, Java, Borneo, Thailand, Vietnam, Malaysia. HBL 50–82cm; TL 35–50cm. Coat: very dark brown above, underside very slightly paler; throat sometimes white. Feet well-webbed; claws strong. Breeding: ?

Spot-necked otter
Hydrictis maculicollis

Africa S of Sahara; absent only from desert areas, such as Namibia. HBL 58–69cm; TL 33–45cm. Coat: very dark or raw umber above; underside slightly lighter; throat and/or groin usually with irregular patches and spots of cream-white (buff-yellow in juveniles). Webbing to near tips of toes; claws strong. Breeding season variable; gestation ?; litter 1–4.

Indian smooth-coated otter
Lutrogale perspicillata

Discontinuous: Iraq (Tigris river); lower Indus, India, SE Asia, Burma, SW China, Malay Peninsula, Sumatra, Borneo. HBL 66–79cm; TL 41–51cm. Coat: raw umber to smoky gray-brown throat and cheeks very light gray or almost white. Feet quite large; webbing well-developed and thick; claws strong. Tail tapered, but with slight flattening at sides. Breeding season October or December; gestation 63–65 days; litter 1–4 (2).

Oriental short-clawed otter
Aonyx cinerea
Oriental or Asian short-clawed or small-clawed or clawless otter.

India, Sri Lanka, SE Asia, Indonesia, Borneo, Palawan Islands, S China. HBL 41–64cm; TL 25–35cm. Coat: burnt umber to dusky brown; throat noticeably lighter, whitish to grayish. Feet narrow, webbed only to about last joint of toes; claws blunt, peg-like, rudimentary. Breeding nonseasonal; gestation 60–64 days; litter 1–6 (2–3).

Cape clawless otter
Aonyx capensis

Africa S of 15° N, from Senegal to Ethiopia S to the Cape; absent only from desert regions of Namibia. HBL 73–95cm; TL 41–67cm. Coat: dark brown above, sometimes frosted with white or grizzled hair tips; cheeks and neck white. Forefeet virtually unwebbed, looking like pinkish hands; hindfeet similar, but with some webbing; no claws on fingers, inner and outer toes; 3 middle toes have short, peg-like claws. Breeding: ?

Giant otter [V]
Pteronura brasiliensis
Giant otter, Brazilian otter.

In all countries of S America except possibly Chile, Argentina and Uruguay. HBL 96–123cm; TL 45–65cm. Coat: very dark burnt umber, groin never spotted; chin, throat and chest usually marked with cream-colored patches, blotches or spots; muzzle, lips and chin often whitish or spotted white. Claws and webbing very well developed—webs reach to tips of toes and fingers; feet very large, fleshy; tail lance-shaped, widest at middle point. Breeding non-seasonal; gestation 65–70 days; litter 1–5 (2).

Sea otter
Enhydra lutris

Kurile, Aleutian Islands and Gulf of Alaska, California coast; introduced into parts of former range along Pacific coast of N America and USSR. HBL 55–130cm; TL 13–33cm. Adults dark brown above with head straw-colored; juveniles uniform dark brown; cubs fawn-colored at birth, tail somewhat flattened, short and not markedly tapered; muzzle with thick whiskers. Forefeet small with no obvious toes; hindfeet very large, flipper-like. Breeding season variable, but may be only 4–5 months, gestation about 9 months with delay in implantation; litter 1, rarely 2.

▲ **North American river otters.** Otters range from solitary to highly sociable in their behavior. North American river otters are basically solitary. Like other *Lutra* species, they only pair up for a short while during the breeding season.

◄ **The Giant otter of the Amazon** and other South American waterways has a massive, seal-like head, and a wide flattened wedge of a tail. Its build, unlike that of most otters, does not fit it to terrestrial as well as aquatic life. Giant otters favor shallow creeks, where they prey on characins and small catfish, usually eaten headfirst, firmly clasped between the forepaws, with the elbows resting on the creek bottom.

BADGERS

Subfamilies: Melinae and Mellivorinae
Nine species in 7 genera.
Family: Mustelidae.
Distribution: widespread in Africa, Eurasia, N America.

Habitat: chiefly woodlands and forests, also urban parks, gardens; some species in mountains, steppe or savanna.

Size: 50cm (20in) and 2kg (4.4lb) in Ferret badgers to nearly 1m (39in) and 12kg (26lb) in the large species

Gestation: 3½–12 months, including period of delayed implantation.

Longevity: to 25 years in captivity (not known in wild).

▼ **Badgers of Southeast Asia.** The tail-less Malayan stink badger or teledu ABOVE and the long-tailed Oriental ferret badger BELOW overlap in Borneo and Java. The ferret badgers are the smallest species and the only tree climbers.

B ADGERS are a widespread group of mostly carnivorous, medium-sized, stocky mustelids. All species except the Honey badger are classified in the subfamily Melinae (true badgers), characterized by powerful jaws and carnassial teeth adapted for crushing, and molars that are broad, flat and multicusped. The Honey badger (subfamily Mellivorinae) is similar in behavior but is only distantly related; its teeth are not well developed for crushing, and there are only four molars in all.

Badgers have powerfully built, wedge-shaped bodies, with a small head and a short thick neck. In all but ferret badgers, the tail is short. The snout is elongate and used for foraging and, particularly in the Hog badger, is very truncated and mobile. Many species dig elaborate burrow systems, making use of the relatively long, nonretractile claws on the forefeet. In the teledu of Southeast Asia the toes of the forefeet are even united as far as the roots of the claws. Badgers walk on their toes (digitigrade) with a characteristic rolling gait.

Most badgers are nocturnal, although the Eurasian badger and the American badger are active in daylight in quiet areas, and the Honey badger will move by day. In consequence eyesight is relatively poor, the eyes small and inconspicuous, but the sense of smell is well developed. The ears are small,

and, relatively, largest in ferret badgers.

Badgers have a tough skin, bearing long, coarse guard hairs, often dull in color but sometimes with a striking facial pattern. Like all mustelids, badgers have well-developed anal glands. The Honey badger's anal glands secrete a vile-smelling liquid to deter its enemies, whereas ferret badgers, the teledu and the Palawan stink badger will squirt the contents of their anal glands into the face of an attacker.

Most badgers eat a variety of small vertebrates, invertebrates, fruit and roots. The American species, the most carnivorous of all badgers, digs out chipmunks, ground squirrels, mice and rabbits, it will eat carrion and invertebrates and also caches food. Individual American badgers may form hunting associations with individual coyotes, but this relationship is poorly understood. In another hunting partnership, the Honey guide bird's characteristic call leads the Honey badger to a bees' nest; the badger breaks open the nest, and both then feed on the contents.

In many areas the main food of the Eurasian badger is the earthworm, picked up from the surface of the ground, where it is most frequently found during spring and autumn nights. During wet weather, when earthworms are available in very large numbers, the badger will forage on a small

▲ **White facial stripe** and reddish-gray upperparts identify this American badger at the entrance to its burrow. The two northern badgers are sometimes active in daylight hours.

▼ **Familiar black-and-white face markings** of brock the Eurasian badger. Winter inactivity and delayed egg implantation help northern badger populations postpone births until food is more plentiful.

patch of pasture, 10–20sq m (100–200sq ft), slowly quartering the ground (badgers have more difficulty in locating and grabbing earthworms in longer grass, which they consequently avoid). Earthworms are detected when they are immediately below the badger's snout; the badger graps its prey with its incisors—75 percent of earthworms are pulled out entire, the rest have their tails broken off. On favorable nights a Eurasian badger can catch several hundred earthworms in a few hours. In dry weather, when earthworms are less available, badgersfollow a more meandering path rather than staying in a few small areas to forage; then badgers also eat fruit, cereals, roots such as pignut, and small mammals.

Male American badgers become sexually mature as yearlings, but 30 percent of females have been found to breed in their first year, when only 4–5 months old. In the Eurasian badger, both sexes become sexually mature when about one year old, although they may not breed until later. In both species there is a delay between fertilization and implantation of the egg. In northwest Europe, the Eurasian badger may mate between February and October, with most matings in February–May. Implantation of the fertilized egg is delayed 3–9 months, and 1–5 (usually 2 or 3) cubs are born in January–March, depending on latitude. The American badger mates in August or September, with implantation in February and birth of 1–5 cubs (usually 2) in April, or perhaps as late as June at higher altitudes. In both species delayed implantation and their reduced activity in winter may be adaptations to postpone the rearing of the young until more food becomes available. In the Honey badgers of West Asia matings occur in autumn and births after about six months in spring; in Africa matings have been reported in various months. Litter size ranges from 1 to 4.

The Eurasian badger lives in well-defined social groups or clans which usually number up to about a dozen individuals, and occasionally more. During daytime each badger group shares one large main underground burrow (sett) and several smaller outlying setts. Most setts are dug in woodland, in sloping, well-drained soils; some of the larger setts have been in continuous use for many decades or even centuries. Within the territory of each group the outlying setts are randomly distributed; the main setts of adjacent groups are evenly spaced.

Eurasian badger group territories may be as small as 15 hectares (37 acres) or, in moorland, as large as 1,500 hectares (3,700 acres). In large ranges the boundaries are not defended, and the badgers are non-territorial and roaming. On the edges of a smaller, defended territory the often conspicuous pathways are associated with a relatively large number of badger latrines (fewer where one group of badgers has no neighbors). A latrine consists of up to 50 small pits, each up to 10cm (4in) deep. An average-sized latrine might cover an area of 2–5sq m (20–55sq ft). Latrines at territorial boundaries (usually near a conspicuous landmark) are larger than those near setts or elsewhere. Latrine use reaches a peak between February and May, and to a lesser extent in October and November.

Arriving at a latrine, a Eurasian badger may squat, vigorously scratch the ground with its fore- and hindlegs, dig fresh pits with its forelegs, defecate and/or urinate. All these activities are probably accompanied by scent marking from the anal, subcaudal, digital and possibly other glands. Badgers of both sexes will also, particularly at the borders of their territory, squat in a fast action to deposit secretions from the subcaudal gland the odor of which identifies individuals. Badgers may also mark by rubbing their anal region at a height of 30–40cm (12–16in) up a tree or fencepost, while performing a handstand.

Except for sows with young cubs, badgers usually move around singly. Should a badger meet a member of its own group, one individual will press its anal region against the side or rump of the other, anointing it with secretions from its anal and/or subcaudal glands. But if two strange badgers meet, aggression follows immediately. This may involve the resident chasing and biting the intruder, coupled with growling and hair erection, which may continue for some time after the intruder has been expelled. If two animals from neighboring groups meet on the boundary path, they may simply avoid each other by walking back into their respective ranges.

True badgers (subfamily Melinae) have a long fossil record in the Tertiary (65–2 million years ago) which shows gradually increasing importance of the tubercular teeth at the back of the jaws, the shearing carnassial teeth tending to become reduced—an adaptation to an omnivorous diet. The Eurasian badger (*Meles meles*) may have originated towards the end of this period from the Pliocene genus *Melodon* found in China. The earliest *Meles* fossil in Europe is about 2 million years old (beginning of Pleistocene). The early Middle Pleistocene of Europe was inhabited by badgers similar in appearance to the modern species, and badger remains are common in Middle Pleistocene (including the Honey badger, subfamily Mellivorinae) and late Pleistocene deposits.

The Eurasian badger may be an important reservoir of bovine tuberculosis. In Southeast Asia the teledu is hunted and eaten by some natives, and the American and Eurasian badger are both still hunted for their skins, the coarse hairs being used for shaving and painters' brushes and similar items, and the skins of the Eurasian badger are said to be used in China for rugs.

Although generally shy and retiring animals, both American and Eurasian badgers are occasionally found living in urban areas in close proximity with man. The setts are dug in private gardens or on wasteland, and the diet includes garbage, handouts, fruit and vegetables. In cities badgers emerge later from their setts than elsewhere, but are often seen out in the early morning—on one occasion trotting home along the pavement in broad daylight, five meters behind a couple of joggers! With Eurasian badgers on the rural fringe depleted by snaring and digging, in some places city badgers are replenishing the rural population.   SH

▶ **Searching for its favorite food,** an African ratel or Honey badger attempts to break open a bark-covered behive. Strong claws used for digging, nauseating scent glands and muscular jaws, serve its reputation as a fearless fighter. Its thick skin, hanging like a loose coating of rubber, makes it apparently impervious to tooth, fang or sting and no adversary seems formidable enough for it. Once it has bitten, it never relaxes its grip, snarling and shaking its head, until the victim drops from exhaustion or shakes it loose. When caught young, the Honey-badger makes an interesting pet but it may become dangerous when adult, given to sudden bursts of fury, attacking friend or foe indiscriminately.

▼ **The trunk-like, mobile snout** gives the Hog badger of eastern Asia its name.

Abbreviations: HBL = head-body length; TL = tail length; wt = weight. Approximate measure equivalents: 10cm = 4in; 1kg = 2.2lb.

Honey badger
Mellivora capensis
Honey badger, ratel.

From open, dry savanna to dense forest in Africa, from Cape to Morocco in W and Ethiopia, Sudan and Somaliland in E; Arabia to Russian Turkestan, Nepal and India. Terrestrial, in burrows or among rocks. HBL 60–70cm; TL 20–30cm; wt up to 12kg. Upper parts from head to tail white (extent of mantle variable, may be absent), sometimes with gray or brown tinge; sides, underparts and limbs pure black. Young rusty brown above.

Eurasian badger
Meles meles
Eurasian or European badger.

Woodland and steppe zones. From Britain, Europe N to S Scandinavia, European Russia up to Arctic Circle, S to Palestine, E to Iran, Tibet and S China. Terrestrial; burrowing. HBL 67–81cm; TL 15–20cm; wt 12kg (male), 10kg (female). Upper parts gray-black; underparts, legs and feet black. Head and ear tips white, black facial stripe from snout through eyes to behind ears. Male has broader head, thicker neck. Tail narrow, pointed, white or pale in male, broader, grayer in female. Asiatic forms may have brown fur on back.

Hog badger
Arctonyx collaris

Forest zones from Peking in N, throughout S China and Indochina to Thailand, and Sumatra. Terrestrial; burrowing. HBL 55–70cm; TL 12–17cm; wt 7–14kg. Back yellowish, grayish or blackish; ears and tail white; feet and belly black. Dark facial stripes through eyes, bordered by white stripes merging with white of nape and throat.

Teledu
Mydaus javanensis
Malayan stink badger, teledu.

Mountain zones of Borneo, Sumatra, Java and North Natuna Islands. Terrestrial, occupying simple burrows. HBL 37–51cm; TL 5–8cm; wt 1.4–3.6kg. Coat dark brown or blackish, with white crown to head and either white stripe down back or row of white patches.

Palawan stink badger
Suillotaxus marchei
Palawan or Calamian stink badger.

Palawan and Busuanga (one of Calamian Islands) NE of Borneo. Terrestrial; burrowing. HBL 32–46cm; TL 1.5–4.5cm; wt 3kg. Coat dark brown to black above, brown below, with yellowish cap and streak down back, fading at shoulders; muzzle dirty white; anal region hairless and pale-skinned. Heavier-toothed, shorter-tailed and smaller-eared than *Mydaus javanensis*.

American badger
Taxidea taxus

From SW Canada and N central USA, S to Mexico. Terrestrial; burrowing. HBL 42–64cm in females, 52–72cm in males; TL 10–16cm; wt 3.5–12kg. Females smaller than males. Upper parts grayish to reddish, underparts buff; feet dark brown to black. Central white facial stripe from nose at least to shoulders; black patches on face and cheeks. Chin, throat and mid-ventral region whitish.

Ferret badgers
Three species in the genus *Melogale*.

Indian ferret badger (*M. personata*). India, Nepal, Burma and SE Asia; **Chinese ferret badger** (*M. moschata*), China, Taiwan, Assam, Burma and SE Asia; **Oriental ferret badger** (*M. orientalis*), Java and Borneo. All terrestrial; occasionally climb trees; burrowing. HBL 33–43cm; TL 15–23cm; wt 2kg. Upper parts pale to dark brown, with white or reddish dorsal stripe; belly paler; face with conspicuous black and white or yellowish pattern.

THE MONGOOSE FAMILY

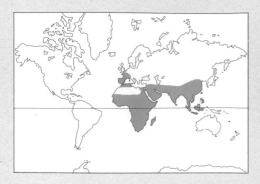

Family: Viverridae
Sixty-six species in 37 genera.
Distribution: S Italy, France and Iberian Peninsula, throughout Africa, Madagascar, Middle East to India and Sri Lanka, much of C and S China, Hainan, Taiwan, throughout SE Asia to Celebes (civets are the only native carnivores) and the Philippines. Introduced into Pacific and Indian Ocean islands, Kei Islands, W Indies, and Japan.

Habitat: from forests to woodlands, savanna, semidesert and desert.

Size: ranges from the Dwarf mongoose 43cm (16in) long overall weighing on average 320g (11.5oz) to the African civet up to 146cm (57in) long and up to 13kg (29lb) in weight.

True civets, linsangs and **genets** (subfamily Viverrinae): 9 species in 7 genera.
Palm civets (subfamily Paradoxurinae): 8 species in 6 genera.
Banded palm civets (subfamily Hemigalinae): 5 species in 4 genera.
Falanouc (subfamily Euplerinae): *Eupleres goudotii.*
Fossa (subfamily Cryptoproctinae): *Cryptoprocta ferox.*
Fanaloka (subfamily Fossinae): *Fossa fossa.*

Mongooses (subfamily Herpestinae): 27 species in 13 genera.
Madagascar mongooses (subfamily Galidiinae): 4 species in 4 genera.

THE viverrids are one of the most diverse of all carnivore families, but their natural distribution is restricted to the Old World. The family includes all species known as civets, linsangs, genets and mongooses. Several of the eight subfamilies have been at times variously raised to family status; some view the mongooses as a separate family—the Herpestidae—distinct from the other six subfamilies in the Viverridae.

Viverrids so closely resemble the ancestors of carnivores, the Miacoidea, that fossil viverrids are almost indistinguishable from these early Eocene relatives (see p22). The tooth structure and skeletal morphology has barely changed for 40 to 50 million years.

Perhaps the modern viverrids are simply a continuation of this old lineage. However, in spite of their primitive dentition, viverrids have a highly developed inner ear and so present an evolutionary mosaic of primitive and advanced features, making their systematic position uncertain. They are sometimes placed between the weasel and the cat families.

Viverrids vary considerably in form, size, gait (from digitigrade to near-plantigrade) and habits. Most civets and genets resemble spotted, long-nosed cats, with long slender bodies, pointed ears and short legs. However, the binturong (or "Bear cat") resembles a wolverine in build but has long black hair, a very long, thick, prehensile tail and a cat-like head; the African civet is rather dog-like in habits and appearance; the fossa so closely resembles a cat that some scientists once placed it in the cat family as a primitive member; the Otter civets could pass as long-nosed otters; and the falanouc resembles a mongoose with a stretched-out nose and a bushy tail like a tree squirrel. Mongooses vary less in gross form; they have long bodies, short legs and small rounded ears. Most civets have long tails equal to or exceeding their body length. Mongoose tails average half to three-quarters body length.

There is a tendency for males to be slightly larger than females, except for the binturong where females may be 20 percent larger. Females have one to three pairs of teats and males possess a baculum (stiffening bone in the penis). Vision and hearing are excellent.

Viverrids tend to be omnivorous. Most feed on small mammals, birds, reptiles, insects, eggs and fruit. Mongooses take less fruit than civets. Palm civets are almost exclusively fruit eaters.

Mongooses differ from the civet group in a variety of other morphological, behavioral and genetic characters. All mongooses have four or five toes on each foot, nonretractile claws, reduced or absent webbing between toes, and rounded ears placed on the side of the head, rarely protruding above the head's profile; some mongooses have highly developed social systems (see pp152–153); some are active in daylight, others are nocturnal and most are terrestrial. Civets have five toes on each foot, partly or totally retractile claws, webbing between toes, and pointed ears projecting above the head's profile. They tend to be solitary and are primarily nocturnal and tree-dwelling, with a few terrestrial and semiaquatic species. The coat of civets is generally spotted or striped, the ear flaps have pockets (bursae) on the lateral margins and most have a perineal (civet) gland sited near the genitals. Although true mongooses (subfamily Herpestinae) are uniformly colored, lack ear bursae and the perineal gland, Madagascar mongooses (subfamily Galidiinae) have ear bursae and some have perineal glands, and three of the four species are variously striped. In all mongooses the anal glands (containing musk) are well developed.   wcw

▲ **Carefree youth.** Two young Dwarf mongooses play with aloe berries. Dwarf mongooses are the smallest viverrids.

▶ **Long-nosed, large-eared and spot-coated,** two Common genets wide awake at night in their arboreal home. At the outer edges of the ears can be seen the pockets (bursae) characteristic of civets, linsangs and genets.

Genet 96cm

Mongoose (*Herpestes*) 97cm

Binturong 138cm

Skulls of Viverrids

Skull forms and dentition vary considerably among viverrids. The facial part of the skull is long, the canine teeth relatively small and the carnassials relatively unprominent. The normal dental formula (see p20) is I3/3, C1/1, P4/4, M2/2 = 40, but the number of molars and premolars may be reduced. Skulls of genets are cat-like (shown here is the Common genet, *Genetta genetta*), while those of civets are similar, but more heavily built. In mongooses, such as *Herpestes* species, the skull is not so long, but more robust. Skulls of Palm civets are also robust, like those of mongooses, with the binturong having a particularly domed form; the primarily vegetarian diet of this species is reflected in its flattened, straight canines, reduced premolars (with one lower pair missing) and molars, and peg-like upper incisors.

CIVETS AND GENETS

Thirty-five species in 20 genera
Family: Viverridae.

Habitat: rain forests to woodlands, brush, savanna and mountains; chiefly arboreal, but also on ground and by riverbanks.

Size: ranges from the African linsang with head-body length 33cm (13in), tail length 38cm (15in) and weight 650g (1.4lb) to the African civet with head-body length 84cm (33in), tail length 42cm (17in) and weight 13kg (29lb); while lighter, the Celebes civet and binturong may be 20 percent longer; some fossas weigh 20kg (44lb).

Coat: various textures; some monochrome species, but dark spots, bands or stripes on lighter ground, and banded tail frequent.

Gestation: 70 days in genets, 80 in African civet, 90 in Palm civets.

Longevity: to about 20 years (in captivity 15 years for Masked palm civet and 34 for genet recorded).

IN the humid night air of the West African rain forest, a loud plaintive cry is repeated like the hooting of an owl; another series of cries penetrates the dark from a kilometer away. These are African palm civets, the best known of some 32 species of a group including the civets, linsangs and genets. This diverse assemblage of mostly cat-like carnivores displays a wide range of life styles and coat markings. Primarily nocturnal foragers and ambush killers, they usually rest in a rock crevice, empty burrow or hollow tree during the day. They are solitary animals, only occasionally forming small maternal family groups.

To man, they are best known for the source of commercial civet oil (see p138). As many are inhabitants of tropical forests, a number of species are finding themselves in an increasingly smaller world—whether this be through the harvesting of lumber in Borneo or the clearing of land for cattle ranching in Madagascar. The IUCN lists as potentially threatened the Otter civet, Jerdon's palm civet and the Large-spotted civet. The status of many of the rarer species is not known. On the other hand the Common palm civet has become so plentiful and accustomed to man that it is frequently found living in and around villages and coffee plantations, and in some areas is considered a pest.

The group is divided into six subfamilies (see BELOW), and here we also discuss the largest (the Viverrinae) in two parts: the true civets and linsangs, and the genets (*Genetta*), since the latter are particularly distinct in their distribution.

The seven southern Asian and one African species of **palm civets** (subfamily Paradoxurinae) are characterized by the possession of semiretractile claws and a perineal scent gland lying within a simple fold of skin. The vocal African palm civet spends most of its time in the forest canopy, where it feeds chiefly on fruits of trees and vines, occasionally on small mammals and birds. Adult males occupy home ranges of over 100 hectares (250 acres) and regularly scent mark trees on the borders of their territory. Dominant males use many kilometers of boughs and vines to make a regular circuit once every 5–10 days through their home ranges. Subordinate males—usually smaller, immature or aged animals—occupy small areas within the range, but avoid dominant males and traverse their ranges at irregular intervals. Eventually, however, when one of these subordinates matures, the dominant male's priority to mate with a female in heat is challenged. Often fatal wounds are inflicted in the ensuing fight and the vanquished landlord, weakened by deep bites, retreats to the ground where he dies or is killed by a leopard or other predator.

One to three females live within the home range of a dominant male and he visits the home range of each for several days as he makes his rounds. For most of the year, females do not tolerate a male staying in the same tree. But in the long rainy season males and females keep track of one another's whereabouts by calling in the darkness. Mating takes place in June over several days, as the pair roost in the same tree. Three months later, 1–3 young are born in a secluded tangle of vines. They are weaned six months later and reach sexual maturity shortly after the second year. Females share their home ranges only with daughters less than two years old. Male offspring emigrate shortly after weaning.

All other species of Palm civets are confined to the forests of Asia. They are skillful climbers, aided by their sharp, curved retractile claws, usually naked soles, and partly fused third and fourth toes which strengthen the grasp of the hindfeet. The Common palm civet is one of the most widespread. Like the Masked palm civet (which, unusually, has no body markings except for the head) it probably forages on the ground for fallen fruit and for animals. The tails of both species are only moderately long and are used to brace the animal during climbing. Most other species have

SUBFAMILIES OF CIVETS AND GENETS

Palm civets
Subfamily Paradoxurinae.
Seven species in S Asia, 1 in Africa, including:
African palm civet (*Nandinia binotata*), **Common palm civet** (*Paradoxurus hermaphroditus*), **Masked palm civet** (*Paguma larvata*), **binturong** or **Bear cat** (*Arctictis binturong*), **Celebes palm civet** [R] (*Macrogalidia musschenbroekii*), and **Small-toothed palm civet** (*Arctogalidia trivirgata*).

Banded palm civets
Subfamily Hemigalinae.
Five species in rain forests of SE Asia.
Banded palm civet [*] (*Hemigalus derbyanus*), **Hose's palm civet** (*Diplogale hosei*), **Owston's banded civet** (*Chrotogale owstonii*), **Otter civet** (*Cynogale bennettii*), and **Lowe's otter civet** [*] (*C. lowei*).

True civets, linsangs and genets
Subfamily Viverrinae.
Nineteen species in Asia, Africa, Arabia, Near East and SW Europe, including:
African civet (*Civettictis civetta*), **Large Indian civet** (*Viverra zibetha*), **Large-spotted civet** [*] (*V. megaspila*), **Malay civet** (*V. tangalunga*), **Small Indian civet** (*Viverricula indica*), **Banded linsang** [*] (*Prionodon linsang*), **Spotted linsang** [*] (*P. pardicolor*), **African linsang** (*Poiana richardsoni*), **Aquatic genet** or **Congo water civet** (*Osbornictis piscivora*). **Common genet** (*G. genetta*), **Johnston's genet** (*G. johnstoni*), **Forest genet** (*G. maculata*), **Feline genet** (*G. felina*) and **Large-spotted genet** (*G. tigrina*).

Falanouc [V]
Subfamily Euplerinae.
One species in Madagascar, *Eupleres goudotii*.

Fossa [V]
Subfamily Cryptoproctinae.
One species in Madagascar, *Cryptoprocta ferox*.

Fanaloka [V]
Subfamily Fossinae.
One species in Madagascar, *Fossa fossa*.

[*] CITES listed. [R] Rare. [V] Vulnerable.

longer tails. They seem to spend more time foraging in trees. The massively muscular tail of the binturong is prehensile (uniquely among viverrids) and, along with the hind-feet, is used to grasp branches while the forelimbs pull fruiting branches to the mouth. Binturongs have also been reported to swim in rivers and catch fish. The Celebes, Giant or Brown palm civet has very flexible feet with a web of naked skin between the toes. It is an acrobatic climber and lives in steep forested ravines and ridges of central and northeastern Sulawesi. Although not seen for 30 years, a recent report (based on tracks and feces) indicates that it may be fairly common in certain limited areas.

All Palm civets eat a wide variety and a vast quantity of fruit, as well as some rodents, birds, snails and scorpions, which supplement the protein in a diet that is otherwise high in carbohydrates. In Java, the Common palm civet eats the fruits of at least 35 species of trees, palms, shrubs and creepers. Some fruits harmful to humans are eaten without ill effects. The seed of the Arenga palm, for example, has a prickly outer pulp, but it is consumed in large quantities, passing through the digestive tract undamaged. The Small-toothed palm civet has small, flat-crowned premolars which seem to be adaptations for a diet of soft fruit. Nearly all Palm civets are notorious banana thieves and the Common palm civet is also called the Toddy cat for its fondness for the fermented palm sap (toddy) which over much of southern Asia

▲ **Preferring fruit to meat,** the Small-toothed palm civet climbs about the forests of eastern Asia helped by its semiretractile claws, in search of the tree fruits which compose most of its diet.

▶ **Largest of the true civets and linsangs,** the African civet has a tail only half its body length, and does not climb trees but forages on the ground for birds, mammals, reptiles, insects and fruits.

is collected, in bamboo tubes attached to palm trunks, for subsequent human consumption.

There are five species of **banded palm civet** and **otter civet** (subfamily Hemigalinae), all confined to the rain forests of Southeast Asia. The Banded palm civet, the best known, is named for the broad, dark vertical bands on its sides. Very carnivorous, it forages at night on the ground and in trees for lizards, frogs, rats, crabs, snails, earthworms and ants, resting during the day in holes in tree trunks. One to three young are born to a litter and they begin to take solid food at the age of 10 weeks. Hose's palm civet resembles the Banded palm civet in body form, but is distinguished by skull characters and by its uniform blackish-brown color pattern. Owston's banded civet has spots as well as band markings, and seems to be a specialist on invertebrate foods; stomachs of the few specimens now in museums contained only worms.

The Otter civets are the unorthodox members of the group. They have smaller ears, a blunter muzzle, a more compact body and a short tail. There are two species—the Otter civet and Lowe's otter civet—which differ in details of coloration and teeth. Their dense hair, valve-like nostrils and thick whiskers equip Otter civets for life in water, catching fish. The toes are less webbed than in otters, which the Otter civets nevertheless resemble in habit and appearance. Otter civets are fine swimmers and they can also climb trees.

The African civet is the largest and best known of the **true civets and linsangs** (subfamily Viverrinae). It lives in all habitats from dry scrub savanna to tropical rain forest, foraging exclusively on the ground by night and resting by day in thickets or burrows. An opportunistic and omnivorous feeder, it does not disdain carrion, but mammals such as gerbils, spring hares and spiny mice are among its most frequent prey. Ground birds, such as francolins and guinea fowl, are sometimes caught; reptiles, insects and fruits complete the menu. African civets almost always defecate at dung heaps (middens or "civetries") near their route of movement. Civetries are normally less than 0.5sq m (5sq ft) in area and there is evidence that they are located at territorial boundaries serving as contact zones between neighbors. Trees and shrubs which bear fruit eaten by civets are frequently scent marked with the perineal gland, and so to a lesser extent are grass, dry logs and rocks.

Female African civets are sexually mature at one year and may produce as many as two litters a year after a gestation of about

▶ **Representative civets and linsangs.** (1) African linsang (*Poiana richardsoni*) feeding on a nestling. (2) Banded palm civet (*Hemigalus derbyanus*) eating a lizard. (3) Oriental or Malayan civet (*Viverra tangalunga*) with dorsal crest erect. (4) Common palm civet (*Paradoxurus hermaphroditus*) scenting the air. (5) Binturong (*Arctictis binturong*) foraging for fruit, while grasping a branch with its prehensile tail.

▼ **Rare glimpse** of the Celebes civet or Giant civet, which occurs only on the Indonesian island of Sulawesi (Celebes). Few zoo or even museum specimens are known but recent reports indicate that the species is still reasonably common in its very restricted range.

Civet Oil and Scent Marking

The term "civet" derives from the Arabic word *zabād* for the unctuous fluid, and its odor, obtained from the perineal glands of most viverrids, except mongooses. The gland is associated with the genitalia, but it differs in anatomy between species: in Palm civets, it is a simple long fold of skin which produces only a thin film of the scented secretions, while in the three *Viverra* species and in the African civet it is a deep muscular pouch which may accumulate several grams of civet a week. Genet scent has a subtle pleasing odor, but that of the true civets (*Viverra*) is powerful and disagreeable; the scent of the binturong is reminiscent of cooked popcorn. Civetone, which has a pleasant musky odor, is probably the most widespread component, but other compounds, such as scatole, often impart a fetid odor to the secretion.

Scent marking is important in viverrid communication, but the method differs between species. The binturong spreads its scent passively while moving about as the gland touches its limbs and vegetation. Some species scent mark by squatting and then wiping or rubbing the gland along the ground or on a prominent object. The Large Indian civet elevates its tail, turns the pouch inside out and presses it backward against upright saplings or rocks. Like most other species, genets scent mark while squatting, but they also leave scent on elevated objects by assuming a handstand posture.

The close association of the perineal gland and the genitalia suggests that the secretion may have sex-related functions. Indeed, civetone may "exalt" volatile compounds from the reproductive tract of females on heat. Perineal gland scent may also carry information indicative of sex, age and individual identity.

Civet has long played an important role in the perfume industry—it was imported from Africa by King Solomon in the 10th century BC. Once refined, it is cherished within the perfume industry because of its odor, ability to exalt other aromatic compounds and its long-lasting properties. Civet oil also has medicinal uses and has been used to reduce perspiration, as an aphrodisiac and as a cure for some skin disorders. Since the development of synthetic chemical substitutes, the collection of civet oil is not as vital as it once was to the industry. Nevertheless, several East African and Oriental countries still ship large quantities of civet oil each year and, in some instances, civets have been introduced to supply a primitive economic base for poor areas. The animals are kept in small cages, restrained by man-handling, and the scent scraped out with a special spoon.   CW

80 days. One to three young are born, probably in a secluded thicket. The mother nurses them until they are 3–5 months old. They begin to catch and eat insects before weaning and the mother summons them with a chuckling contact call when she wishes to share a rodent or bird that she has caught.

The African civet's Asian relatives probably share many features of its natural history. The similar Large Indian civet, Large-spotted civet, and Malay civet share eye-catching black and white body and back stripes, have a somewhat dog-like body plan and have a crest of long hair overlying the spine which when raised under threat gives the civet an enlarged appearance. Malay civets and Large Indian civets also have the latrine habit of the African civet.

The Small Indian civet has a narrower head and a genet-like build. It lacks a spinal crest, the body spots and tail rings are less well defined than in a genet and the coloration is drab. A skillful predator of small mammals and birds, it stalks its prey like a cat. But it is also an opportunist that feeds on insects, turtle eggs and fallen fruit. It is not a particularly good climber and often lives on cultivated land and near rural villages.

The linsangs are among the rarest, least known and most beautiful members of the group. All three species are small, quick, trimly built, secretive forest animals with darkly-marked torsos and banded tails. They depend almost entirely on small vertebrates for food. The stomachs of four Banded linsangs were found to contain remains of squirrels, Spiny rats, birds, Crested lizards and insects. In all likelihood they live alone and there is good evidence that the African linsang builds leafy nests in trees. The two Asian species, the Spotted linsang and Banded linsang, apparently sleep in nests lined with dried vegetation under tree roots or hollow logs. They lack civet glands and the second upper molar. All three linsangs, like the genets, have fully retractile claws.

The Fishing or Aquatic genet or Congo water civet is a rare and little-known inhabitant of streams and small rivers of the Central African forest block. It feeds on fish and possibly crustaceans, and local people report that it even occasionally eats cassava left to soak in streams before human consumption. It is not particularly specialized for swimming, but probably uses its naked palms to locate fish lurking under rocks and undercut river banks, grabbing them with its retractile claws and killing them with its sharp teeth.   CW

Because of their nocturnal habits and cryptic coat patterns, **genets** have been studied mainly not in the wild but in the laboratory. However, recent studies of wild genets in the Serengeti National Park, Tanzania, suggest that their effect on the ecosystem may be considerable.

There are 10 species of these medium-sized, long-bodied and short-legged carnivores, from Africa, Arabia, the Near East and southwest Europe. They all have rows of dark spots along the body, or stripes, which are denser on the upper surfaces, on a light brown or gray background. The tails are ringed and about as long as the body. They have a long face, and pointed muzzle with long whiskers, largish ears, binocular vision, fully retractile claws and five toes on all four feet. In Africa they occupy all habitats except desert, but they prefer areas of dense vegetation. In Spain, Common genets are widespread even in high mountains—one was recently found taking midwinter shelter under the bonnet of a snowplow at the Pyrenean ski resort of Astun, at an altitude of 1,700m (5,600ft).

Common genets may have been imported

▶ **The perfect killer,** a Common or European genet displays its fine, blade-like set of incisors and long canine teeth. Genets are primarily tree-dwelling carnivores, although small mammals and game birds may be hunted on the ground, and insects and fruit are also taken.

▼ **The Spotted linsang** is the smallest of the true civets and linsangs, and like most of the others is arboreal and has a tail nearly as long as its body.

to Europe as pets by the Moors in the Middle Ages, or they may be a remnant population left after the Gibraltar land bridge was broken. A size variation, with smaller specimens in the north of the range, suggests that the distribution of the Common genet is natural. However, the genets of the Balearic Islands were definitely introduced by man. The subspecies from Ibiza (*G. genetta isabellae*) is smaller than the other European forms; it closely resembles the Feline genet subspecies *G. felina senegalensis* found in Senegal.

Genets are adapted to living in trees, but they often hunt and forage on the ground. Combining speed with stealth, they approach their prey in a series of dashes interrupted by periods of immobility. Their coloration helps them avoid detection, particularly on moonlit nights. Except for Johnston's genet, which may be largely insectivorous, all species are carnivorous; insects and also fruit are a regular addition to their diet. In Africa, small mammals such as rodents make up the major part of the Common genet's diet, while in Spain lizards are also an important item. Feces analysis of Common genets in Spain shows that passerine birds comprise up to half the diet in spring and summer, fruit is important during autumn and winter, rodents (mainly wood mice) are taken all year round, and insects from spring to autumn, though they form a small part of the diet. Some genets stalk frogs at the side of rain pools. One Forest genet has been observed regularly to take bats as they leave their roosts, while in West Africa Forest genets are known to feed on the profuse nectar of the tree *Maranthes polyandra*; the flowers are bat-pollinated, so perhaps the initial attraction was to the bats rather than the nectar.

In Spain, Common genets' activity starts at or just before sunset and ends shortly after dawn. They are inactive for a period during the night, and occasionally there is no morning bout of activity. In daytime the genets only stir to move from one resting site to another. In the Serengeti, the Feline genet, unlike other small carnivores of the plain, is relatively inactive at dawn and dusk and most active around midnight. This pattern of activity may reduce competition for otherwise similar foods.

Genets breed throughout the year, but in many areas there are seasonal peaks, for example April and September for Common genets in Europe. Two to four young are born, after a gestation of about 70 days, in a vegetation-lined nest in a tree or burrow. They are blind at birth and about 13.5cm

(5in) long. Their eyes open after eight days and they venture from the nest soon after that. They are weaned after six months, although they take solid food earlier. Genets are thought to become independent after one year and are sexually mature after two years. Scent marking—by feces, urine and perineal gland secretion—plays an important role in the social life of genets, allowing animals to determine the identity, familiarity, sex and breeding status of other members of their species. Males, and to a lesser extent females, show a seasonal variation in the frequency of marking, with an increase before the breeding season. For most of the time genets live a solitary life.

In Africa, population densities of 1–2/sq km (2.5–5/sq mi) have been reported, with home ranges as small as 0.25sq km (0.1sq mi). Females appear to be more territorial than males, which wander farther. Population density is much lower in Spain. Two male Common genets have been tracked by radio over home ranges of 5sq km (2sq mi), moving quickly over quite long distances, up to 3km (1.9mi) in an hour.

Genets have been widely domesticated and make good pets. In Europe they were kept as rat catchers until they were superseded by the modern domestic cat in the Middle Ages—the cat has a directed killing bite to the nape of the neck which dispatches the prey before it is eaten, whereas genets often hold the prey with all four limbs and eat it alive. In parts of Africa, genets are considered a pest because of their attacks on poultry.   HJH

▲ **Curled up in its hollow-tree home,** a Common genet uses its long tail partly to cover its cat-like head. Before cats became popular, genets were kept as rat-catchers in medieval Europe.

▼ **Half the genet's length is tail.** The Common genet holds its tail straight out behind when it stalks prey at night, usually keeping its body close to the ground. Genets are usually seen singly, sometimes in pairs.

The rare and secretive **falanouc** inhabits wet and low-lying rain forest from east central to northwestern Madagascar. Because of its anatomical peculiarities (see p145) the falanouc is placed in its own subfamily, the Euplerinae, one of three single-species subfamilies of viverrids on Madagascar.

The specialized teeth are used to seize and hold earthworms, slugs, snails and insect larvae. Loath to bite in self-defense, the falanouc employs its sharp claws (long on the forefeet) for this purpose.

The falanouc has a solitary, territorial lifestyle, with a brief consort between mates and a longer mother–young bond that dissolves before the onset of the next breeding season. The base of the tail serves as a fat storage organ for the cold, dry months of June and July when food is in short supply. Subcutaneous fat is deposited in April and May.

The falanouc's reproductive pattern deviates from that of most carnivores: a single offspring is born in summer in a burrow or in dense vegetation. The newborn's well-developed condition suggests that mother and young are highly mobile shortly after birth. An animal born in captivity had open eyes at birth and was able to follow its mother and hide in vegetation when only two days old. It did not take solid food until nine weeks old, but weaned quickly thereafter. These traits make it easy for the young to be constantly close to the mother while she forages for widely dispersed food. Falanouc young develop locomotory and sensory skills very early, but grow and mature at a slightly slower pace than other similar-sized carnivores.

The **fossa** is the largest Madagascan carnivore and large individuals exceed in weight all other members of the civet–mongoose family. Its cat-like head (large frontal eyes, shortened jaws and rounded ears) and general appearance prompted its early classification as a felid. The fossa's resemblance to cats, however, is a result of independent (convergent) evolution. It is quite different from all other viverrids and is the only member of the subfamily Cryptoproctinae. It should not be confused with the fox-like fanaloka (*Fossa fossa*), also from Madagascar.

The fossa evolved on Madagascar to fill the niche of a medium-sized nocturnal, arboreal predator and is an ecological equivalent of the Clouded leopard of Southeast Asia.

The fossa's teeth and claws are adapted to a diet of animals that are captured with the forelimbs and killed with a well-aimed bite. Guinea fowl, lemurs and large mammalian insectivores, such as the Common tenrec, form its basic diet. It is unusual in walking upon the whole foot (plantigrade), not on the toes as in most viverrids.

The fossa lives at low population densities and requires undisturbed forests, which are disappearing fast. Fossas are seasonal breeders, mating in September and October. After a three-month gestation, they give birth to 2–4 young in a tree or ground den. The newborn are quite small—80–100g (3–3.5oz)—compared to other viverrids. Physical development is slow; the eyes do not open for 16–25 days and solid food is not taken for three months. They are weaned by four months and growth is complete at two years, although they do not reach sexual maturity for another two years. Males possess a penis-bone (baculum). Females exhibit genital mimicry of the male, although not as well developed as in the Spotted hyena (see p157).

The **fanaloka** resembles a small spotted fox in build and gait. It is nocturnal and there is also evidence that fanalokas live in pairs, unlike most other viverrids.

The fanaloka mates in August and September and gives birth to one young after a three-month gestation. The young are born in a physically advanced state. The eyes are open at birth and in a few days young are able to follow the mother. The baby is weaned in 10 weeks.

Fanalokas are not particularly good climbers. They rely on hearing and vision to find food and are reported to feed on rodents, frogs, molluscs and sand eels. The fanaloka lives exclusively in dense forests and seems to frequent ravines and valleys. The relationship of the fanaloka to other viverrids is uncertain. Its anatomy differs in many respects from the Banded palm civets with which it was once grouped and it is known only from Madagascar, far away from its presumed south Asian relatives. It is therefore now placed in a separate subfamily, the Fossinae.   cw

◀ **A Large-spotted genet.** Like all genets this southern African species is well adapted to an arboreal way of life. Excellent binocular vision enables it to judge distances accurately as it jumps from branch to branch or pounces on its prey.

▼ **Rarities of Madagascar.** Three unusual viverrids occur on Madagascar. (1) The falanouc (*Eupleres youdotii*) is mongoose-like, has an elongated snout and body, nonretractile claws, and feeds mainly on invertebrates. (2) The fanaloka, or Madagascar civet (*Fossa fossa*), is more fox-like in appearance, has retractile claws and primarily feeds on small mammals, reptiles and amphibia. (3) The fossa (*Cyrptoprocta ferox*) has a cat-like head and retractile claws used to capture its prey.

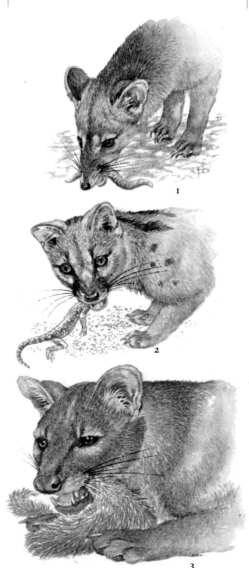

THE 35 SPECIES OF CIVETS AND GENETS

Abbreviations: HBL = head-body length; TL = tail length; wt = weight. Approximate measure equivalents: 10cm = 4in; 1kg = 2.2lb.

[*] CITES listed. [V] Vulnerable. [R] Rare.

Palm civets
Subfamily Paradoxurinae
(8 species in 6 genera)

Semiarboreal and arboreal; nocturnal. Teeth specialized for a mixed diet or a diet of fruit; carnassial teeth weakly to moderately developed; two relatively flat-crowned molars in the upper and lower jaws of all species. Perineal scent glands present in both sexes of all species, except *Arctogalidia*, in which it is lacking in the male. In *Nandinia* the gland lies in front of the penis and vulva. Claws semiretractile.

African palm civet
Nandinia binotata
African palm civet, Two-spotted palm civet.

From Guinea (including Fernando Póo Island) to S Sudan in the north, to Mozambique, E Zimbabwe and C Angola in south. Arboreal. HBL 50cm; TL 57cm; wt 3kg. Coat: a uniform olive brown with faint spots; 2 cream spots on the shoulders vary geographically in size and intensity.

Small-toothed palm civet
Arctogalidia trivirgata
Small-toothed or Three-striped palm civet.

Assam, Burma, Thailand, Malayan and Indochinese Peninsulas, China (Yunnan), Sumatra, Java, Borneo, Riau-Lingga Archipelago, Bangka, Bilitung, N Natuna Islands. Arboreal. HBL 51cm; TL 58cm; wt 2.4kg. Coat: more or less uniform, varying from silvery to buff to dark brown, sometimes grizzled on head and tail; 3 thin, dark-colored stripes on back, often from base of tail to shoulders; white streak down middle of nose; tail sometimes has vague dark bands; tip sometimes white.

Common palm civet
Paradoxurus hermaphroditus
Common palm civet, Toddy cat.

India, Sri Lanka, Nepal, Assam, Bhutan, Burma, Thailand, S China, Malaya, Indochina, Sumatra, Java, Borneo, Ceram, Kei Islands, Nusa Tenggara (Lesser Sunda Islands) as far E as Timor, Philippines. Semiarboreal. HBL 54cm; TL 46cm; wt 3.4kg. Coat: variable from buff to dark brown depending on locality; usually black stripes on back and small to medium spots on sides and base of tail; face mask of spots and forehead streak; spots variable both locally and geographically; tail tip sometimes white.

Golden palm civet
Paradoxurus zeylonensis

Sri Lanka. Arboreal. HBL 51cm; TL 46cm; wt 3kg. Coat: brown, golden-brown or rusty; spots and stripes barely visible; nap of hair forward on neck and throat; tip of tail sometimes white.

Jerdon's palm civet
Paradoxurus jerdoni

S India, Palni and Nilgiri hills, Tranvancore and Coorg. Arboreal. HBL 59cm; TL 52cm; wt 3.6kg. Coat: deep brown, or brown to black with silver or gray speckling; nap of hair as *P. zeylonensis*.

Masked palm civet
Paguma larvata

India, Nepal, Tibet, China (N to Hopei), Shansi, Taiwan, Hainan, Burma, Thailand, Malaya, Sumatra, N Borneo, S Andaman Islands; introduced to Japan. Arboreal. HBL 63cm; TL 59cm; wt 4.8kg. Coat: uniform grayish or yellowish-brown to black depending on geographic origin; face dark, but may be marked with a light frontal streak or spots under the eyes and in front of the ears; tip of tail sometimes white.

Celebes civet [R]
Macrogalidia musschenbroekii
Celebes civet, Giant civet, Brown palm civet.

NE and C Sulawesi (Celebes). Semiarboreal. HBL 88cm; TL 62cm; wt 4.2kg. Coat: uniform brown with vague darker spots on either side of midline and faint light-colored rings on the tail; hair lighter above and beneath eyes. Cheek teeth of upper jaw arranged in parallel rather than diverging rows.

Binturong
Arctictis binturong
Binturong, Bear cat.

India, Nepal, Bhutan, Burma, Thailand, Malayan and Indochinese Peninsulas, Sumatra, Java, Borneo and Palawan. Arboreal. HBL 77cm; TL 73cm; wt 7.6kg (females 20 percent larger). Coat: black with variable amount of white or yellow restricted to hair tips (yellowish or gray binturongs always have black undercoats); hair long and coarse; ears with long black tufts and white margins. Tail heavily built, especially at the base, and prehensile at the tip.

Banded palm civets
Subfamily Hemigalinae
(5 species in 4 genera)

Nocturnal. Second molar large with many cusps. Perineal scent glands present in all species, but not as large as in other subfamilies. Claws semiretractile.

Banded palm civet
Hemigalus derbyanus

Peninsular Burma, Malaya, Sumatra, Borneo, Sipora and S Pagi Islands. Semiarboreal. HBL 53cm; TL 32cm; wt 2.1kg. Coat: pale yellow to grayish-buff, with contrasting dark brown markings; face and back with longitudinal stripes; body with about 5 transverse bands extending halfway down flank; tail dark on terminal half, with about 2 dark rings on the base.

Hose's palm civet
Diplogale hosei

Borneo, Sarawak (Mt Dulit to 1,200m). Semiterrestrial. Dimensions unknown. Coat: uniform dark brown with gray eye and cheek spots; chin, throat and backs of ears white; belly white or dusky gray.

Owston's banded civet
Chrotogale owstoni
Owston's banded or Owston's palm civet.

N of Indochinese Peninsula. Terrestrial. HBL 55cm; TL 43cm; wt unknown. Coat: similar to Banded palm civet, but with only 4 transverse dark-colored dorsal bands and with black spots on neck, torso and limbs.

Otter civet [*]
Cynogale bennettii
Otter civet, Water civet.

Sumatra, Borneo, Malayan and Indochinese Peninsulas. Semiaquatic. HBL 64cm; TL 17cm; wt 4.7kg. Coat: uniform brown, soft dense hair, with faint grizzled appearance; front of throat white or buff-white. First three upper premolars unusually large with high, compressed and pointed crowns; remaining cheek teeth broad and adapted for crushing. Ears small, but designed to keep out water. Feet naked underneath.

Lowe's otter civet
Cynogale lowei

N Vietnam. Semiaquatic. Coat: dark brown above, white to dirty white below from cheek to belly; tail dark brown. Other features as *C. bennettii*.

True Civets, Linsangs and Genets
Subfamily Viverrinae
(19 species in 7 genera)

Teeth usually specialized for an omnivorous diet; shearing teeth well developed; two molars in each side of upper and lower jaws of all except for *Poiana* and *Prionodon*, which have one upper molar. Perineal gland present in all genera except *Prionodon*, presence not certain in *Poiana* and *Osbornictis*. Soles of feet normally hairy between toes and pads.

African linsang
Poiana richardsoni
African linsang or oyan.

Sierra Leone, Ivory Coast, Gabon, Cameroun, N Congo, Fernando Póo Island. Arboreal; nocturnal. HBL 33cm; TL 38cm; wt 650g. Coat: torso spotted, stripes on neck; tail white with about 12 dark rings and light-colored tip. Claws retractile.

Spotted linsang [*]
Prionodon pardicolor

Nepal, Assam, Sikkim, N Burma, Indochina. Semiarboreal; nocturnal. HBL 39cm; TL 34cm; wt 600g. Coat: light yellow with dark spots on torso and stripes on neck; tail with 8–9 dark bands alternating with thin light bands. Claws retractile.

Banded linsang [*]
Priondon linsang

W Malaysia, Tenasserim, Sumatra, Java, Borneo. Semiarboreal; nocturnal. HBL 40cm; TL 34cm; wt 700g. Coat: very light yellow with 5 large transverse dark bands on back; neck stripes broad with small elongate spots and stripes on flank; tail with 7–8 dark bands and black tip. Claws retractile.

Small Indian civet
Viverricula indica
Small Indian civet, rasse.

S China, Burma, W Malaysia, Thailand, Sumatra, Java, Bali, Hainan, Taiwan, Indochina, India, Sri Lanka, Bhutan; introduced to Madagascar, Sokotra and Comoro Islands. Terrestrial; nocturnal/crepuscular. HBL 57cm; TL 36cm; wt 3kg. Coat: light brown, gray to yellow-gray with small spots arranged in longitudinal stripes on the forequarters and larger spots on the flanks; 6–8 stripes on the back;

neck stripes not contrasting in color as in *Viverra* and *Civettictis*; 7–8 dark bands on tail and tip often light. Claws semiretractile; skin partially bare between toes and foot pads.

Malayan civet
Viverra tangalunga
Malayan or Malay civet, Oriental or Ground civet, tangalunga.

Malaya, Sumatra, Riau–Lingga Archipelago, Borneo, Sulawesi, Karlmata, Bangka, Buru, Ambon and Langkawi Islands, and Philippines. Terrestrial; nocturnal/crepuscular. HBL 66cm; TL 32cm; wt 3.7kg. Coat: dark with many close-set small black spots and bars on torso, often forming a brindled pattern; crest, which can be erected, of black hair from shoulder to midtail; black and white neck stripes that pass under throat; white tail bands, interrupted by black crest and black tip. Claws semiretractile.

Large Indian civet
Viverra zibetha

N India, Nepal, Burma, Thailand, Indochina, Malaya, S China. Terrestrial; nocturnal/crepuscular. HBL 81cm; TL 43cm; wt 8.5kg. Coat: tawny to gray with black spots, rosettes, bars and stripes on torso, neck with black and white stripes that pass under the throat; erectile spinal crest of black hair from shoulder to rump; tail with complete white bands and black tip. Claws semiretractile.

Large-spotted civet ⟦*⟧
Viverra megaspila

S Burma, Thailand, formerly the coastal district and W Ghats of S India, Indochina, Malay Peninsula to Penang. Terrestrial; nocturnal/crepuscular. HBL 76cm; TL 37cm; wt 6.6kg. Coat: grayish to tawny with small indistinct black or brown spots on the foreparts; large spots on the flanks often fusing into bars and stripes; pronounced black and white neck stripes; spinal crest of erectile black hair from shoulder to rump, bordered on either side by a longitudinal row of spots; tail with 5–7 white bands, most of which do not circle the tail completely, and black tip. Claws not retractile, soles of feet scantily haired between toes and foot pads.

African civet
Civettictis civetta

Senegal E to Somalia in N, through C and E Africa to Zululand, Transvaal, N Botswana and N Namibia in S. Terrestrial; nocturnal/crepuscular. HBL 84cm; TL 42cm; wt 13kg. Coat: grayish to tawny, torso marked with dark brown or black spots, bars and stripes (degree of striping and distinctness of spots geographically variable); spinal crest from shoulders to tail; tail with indistinct bands and black tip. Claws not retractile; soles of feet bare between toes and foot pads.

Aquatic genet
Osbornictis piscivora
Aquatic genet, Fishing genet, Congo water civet.

Kisangani and Kibale–Ituri districts of Zaire. Semiaquatic; nocturnal. HBL 47cm; TL 37cm; wt 1.4kg. Coat: uniform chestnut-brown with dull red belly; chin and throat white; tail uniform dark brown and heavily furred. Claws semiretractile.

Common genet
Genetta genetta
Common genet, Small-spotted genet, European genet.

Africa (N of Sahara), Iberian Peninsula, France, Palestine. Open or wooded country with some cover. HBL 40–50cm; TL 37–46cm; wt 1–2.3kg. Coat: grayish-white with blackish spots in rows; tail with 9–10 dark rings and white tip; prominent dark spinal crest.

Feline genet
Genetta felina

Africa S of the Sahara except for rain forest; S Arabian Peninsula. Open or wooded country with some cover. HBL 40–50cm; TL 37–47cm; wt 1–2.3kg. Coat: light gray to brownish-yellow with blackish spots in rows; tail with 9–10 black rings and white tip; prominent spinal crest of black hairs; hind legs with gray stripe.

Forest genet
Genetta maculata
(formerly *G. pardina*)

Southern part of W Africa, C Africa, S Africa (except Cape region). Dense forest. Dimensions as *G. genetta*. Coat: grayish to pale brown, more heavily spotted than Common genet; tail black with 3–4 light rings at base and tip dark or light; spinal crest short and can be erected. Relatively long-legged.

Large-spotted genet
Genetta tigrina
Large-spotted genet, Blotched genet, Tigrine genet.

Cape region of S Africa. Woodland and scrub. Dimensions as *G. genetta*. Coat: brown-gray to dirty white with large brown or dark spots; tail relatively long with 8 or 9 black rings and dark tip. Relatively short-legged.

Servaline genet
Genetta servalina
Servaline genet, Small-spotted genet.

C Africa, with restricted range in E Africa. Forest. HBL 42–53cm; TL 41–51cm; wt 1–2kg. Coat: ocherous and more evenly covered with small blackish spots than other genets; underparts darker; tail with 10–12 rings and white tip. Face relatively long.

Giant genet
Genetta victoriae
Giant or Giant forest genet.

Uganda, N Zaire. Rain forest. HBL 50–60cm; TL 45–55cm; wt 1.5–3.5kg. Coat: yellow to reddish-brown, very heavily and darkly spotted; tail bushy with 6–8 broad rings and black tip; dark spinal crest; legs dark.

Angolan genet
Genetta angolensis
Angolan genet, Mozambique genet, Hinton's genet.

N Angola, Mozambique, S Zaire, NW Zambia, S Tanzania. Forest. Dimensions as *G. genetta*. Coat: largish dark spots in 3 rows each side of erectile spinal crest; tail very bushy with 6–8 broad rings and dark tip; neck striped; hind legs dark with thin gray stripe. Relatively long-haired.

Abyssinian genet
Genetta abyssinica

Ethiopian highlands, Somalia. Mountains. HBL 40–46cm; wt 0.8–1.6kg. Coat: very light sandy-gray with black horizontal stripes and black spotting; tail with 6–7 dark rings and dark tip; back with 4–5 stripes; black spinal crest poorly developed.

Villier's genet
Genetta thierryi
Villier's genet, False genet.

W Africa. Forest and Guinea savanna. Dimensions and coat as for *G. abyssinica* but with chestnut or black spotting which is poorly defined; tail with 7–9 dark rings (first rings rufous) and dark tip.

Johnston's genet
Genetta johnstoni
Johnston's genet, Lehmann's genet.

Liberia. Ground color yellow to grayish-brown; black erectile spinal stripe; rows of large dark spots on sides; tail with 8 dark rings. Skull larger than other genets with overlapping distribution, but greatly reduced teeth suggest largely insectivorous diet.

Subfamily Euplerinae
(1 species)
Falanouc ⟦V⟧
Eupleres goudotii

East C to NW Madagascar. Rain forest. Terrestrial; solitary. HBL 48–56cm; TL 22–25cm; wt not known. Coat: light to medium brown; whitish-gray on underside. Snout elongated. First premolars and canines short, curved backward and flattened, for taking small soft-bodied prey. No anal or perineal gland.

Subfamily Cryptoproctinae
(1 species)
Fossa ⟦V⟧
Cryptoprocta ferox

Madagascar. Rain forest. Arboreal; nocturnal. HBL 70cm; TL 65cm; wt 9.5–20kg. Coat: reddish-brown to dark brown. Head cat-like with large frontal eyes, short jaws, rounded ears; tail cylindrical. Carnassial teeth well developed, upper molars reduced (formula I3/3, C1/1, P3/1, M1/1 = 32). Claws retractile. Feet webbed. Anal gland well developed, perineal gland absent. Females show genital mimicry of males.

Subfamily Fossinae
(1 species)
Fanaloka ⟦V⟧
Fossa fossa
Fanaloka, Madagascar or Malagasy civet.

Madagascar. Dense rain forest. Terrestrial; nocturnal; lives in pairs. HBL 47cm; TL 9.5cm; wt 2.2kg. Coat: brown with darker brown dots in coalescing longitudinal rows; faint dark banding on upperside of short tail. Perineal gland absent.

CW/WCW

MONGOOSES

Thirty-one species in 17 genera
Family: Viverridae.
Distribution: Africa and Madagascar, SW
Europe, Near East, Arabia to India and Sri
Lanka, S China, SE Asia to Borneo and
Philippines; introduced in W Indies, Fiji,
Hawaiian Islands.

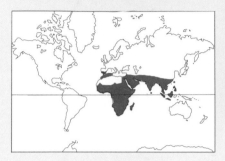

Habitat: from forests to open woodland,
savanna, semidesert and desert; chiefly
terrestrial but also semiaquatic and arboreal.

Size: ranges from the Dwarf
mongoose with head-body
length 24cm (9.5in), tail
length 19cm (7.5in) and
weight 320g (11oz) to the
White-tailed mongoose with
head-body length 58cm
(23in), tail length 44cm
(17in) and weight up to 5kg
(11lb); some Egyptian
mongooses larger in total
length.

Coat: long, coarse, usually grizzled or brindled;
a few species with bands or stripes.

Gestation: mostly about 60 days, but 42 in the
Small Indian mongoose, 105 in the Narrow-
striped mongoose.

Longevity: to about 10 years (17 recorded in
captivity).

Madagascar mongooses (subfamily Galidiinae)
Four species: **Ring-tailed mongoose** (*Galidia
elegans*), **Broad-striped mongoose** (*Galidictis
fasciata*), **Narrow-striped mongoose**
(*Mungotictis decemlineata*), and **Brown
mongoose** (*Salanoia unicolor*).

African and Asian mongooses (subfamily
Herpestinae)
Twenty-seven species in 13 genera, including:
Dwarf mongoose (*Helogale parvula*), **White-
tailed mongoose** (*Ichneumia albicauda*),
Egyptian mongoose (*Herpestes ichneumon*),
Small Indian mongoose (*H. javanicus*), **Slender
mongoose** (*H. sanguineus*), **Banded mongoose**
(*Mungos mungo*), **Ruddy mongoose** (*H. smithii*),
suricate or **Gray meerkat** (*Suricata suricatta*),
Yellow mongoose or **Red meerkat** (*Cynictis
penicillata*).

► **Almost human in pose,** Gray meerkats
(suricates) scan their surroundings in the
Kalahari desert. Like Banded mongooses,
suricates may bunch together to drive off a
potential predator. Group-living mongooses
(unlike most social carnivores) have packs
larger than a single family unit.

Aᴛ sunrise a pack of 14 Banded mongooses
leaves its termite mound den. With the
dominant female in the lead, closely followed by the dominant male, they move out
rapidly in single file and then fan out to
search for dung beetles. Contact is maintained by a continuous series of low calls;
from time to time the pitch rises to the
"moving out" call, and the group moves on.
One adult male has remained in the den to
guard the 10 three-week-old young and will
not be seen until they emerge upon the
return of the pack several hours later. Then
the lactating females briefly nurse the young
and several of the younger adults bring
them beetles. Once more the main pack goes
out in search of food, leaving two adults at
the den site to guard the young.

Like other small carnivores, most mongooses are solitary, the only stable social
unit consisting of a mother and her offspring. But some species live in pairs and
several, including the Banded mongoose,
live in groups larger than a single family
unit (see ʀɪɢʜᴛ and pp152–153). These
group-living mongooses are active during
the day, benefiting perhaps from improved
visual communication, but many solitary
species are nocturnal.

Often the most abundant carnivores in
the locations they inhabit, mongooses are
agile and active terrestrial mammals. The
face and body are long and they have small
rounded ears, short legs and long, tapering
bushy tails.

Most mongooses are brindled or grizzled
and few coats are strongly marked. No
species have spots (unlike civets and genets),
and few have shoulder stripes, and the feet
or legs, and tail or tail tip are often of a
different hue. The Banded mongoose and
the suricate have darker transverse bands
across the back. Among the four Madagascar mongooses, two species have stripes that
run along the body and one has a ringed tail.
Considerable color variation occurs, some-

▼ **Most mongooses are solitary,** like this Slender mongoose and the 10 other *Herpestes* species. Mothers and young form only stable groups. Unlike most mongooses, the Slender mongoose climbs well and will feed on bird eggs and fledglings; birds often mob and dive-bomb this species while ignoring others which pose less of a threat.

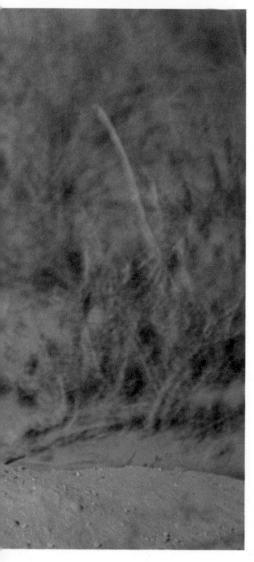

Mutual Defense in Banded Mongooses

Group-living mammals have rarely been seen to rescue one of their number from peril. However, Banded mongooses have several times been observed to come to the aid of their companions, once with dramatic success. On this occasion a Martial eagle swooped down on a foraging pack and seized an adult male, carrying it up to the fork of a tree. The pack then ran to the base of the tree and several mongooses started to climb it with the dominant male in the lead. He reached the branch where the prey struggled in the talons and lunged at the eagle, causing it to loosen its hold. The captured mongoose dropped to the ground unhurt.

Jackals have been observed to catch mongooses from small packs or catch individuals that have become temporarily separated from their pack. But a large pack of Banded mongooses has little to fear from a jackal. When a jackal approaches, the mongooses form a tightly knit bunch and begin to move toward it. Occasionally an individual will stand up to obtain a better view and the bunch gives the appearance of a large animal in constant motion. Jackals retreat from such an apparition and the mongooses may chase and attempt to nip them on the hind legs or tail. (See also p153 for Dwarf mongoose antipredator behavior.)

times even within the same species. For example, the Slender mongoose is gray or yellowish-brown throughout most of its range, but in the Kalahari desert it is red, and there is also a melanistic (black) form. Variations usually correlate with soil color, suggesting that camouflage is important to survival.

Most mongooses have a large anal sac containing at least two glandular openings. Scent marking with anal and sometimes cheek glands can communicate the sex, sexual receptivity (estrous condition), and individual and pack identity of the marker.

Ever since Kipling recounted the duel between Riki-tiki-tavi and the cobra, it has been a common assumption in the West that mongooses feed mainly on snakes, but it is unlikely that snakes are sufficiently abundant within the range of any species to predominate in its diet. Most mongooses are opportunistic and feed on small vertebrates, insects and other invertebrates, and occasionally fruits. The structure of the teeth and

feet reflect the diet. Mongooses have from 34 to 40 teeth and those which are efficient killers of small vertebrates, such as *Herpestes* species, have well-developed carnassial teeth used to shear flesh. Their feet have four or five digits each tipped by long, non-retractile claws adapted for digging. The mongoose sniffs along the surface of the ground and when it finds an insect it either snaps it up from the surface or digs it from its underground home.

Some mongooses range over large distances in search of food. On the Serengeti shortgrass plains in Tanzania, packs of Banded mongooses range over approximately 15sq km (5.8sq mi) and may travel over 9km (5.6mi) a day in the dry season. Where food resources are abundant and population density high, ranges and distances of travel are considerably smaller. Banded mongooses in Ruwenzori Park, Uganda, use ranges averaging less than 1sq km (0.4sq mi) and travel about 2km (1.2mi) a day.

In a natural population, some Dwarf mongooses have lived to at least 10 years of age. Wild Small Indian mongooses on Hawaii seldom attain the age of four years, but one Ruddy mongoose lived in captivity for over 17 years.

Most mongooses attain sexual maturity by two years of age. The earliest recorded breeding age is in the Small Indian mongoose, in which females may become pregnant at nine months. Breeding seasons vary depending on environmental conditions. In South Africa the suricate or Gray meerkat and the Yellow mongoose breed only in the warmest (and wettest) months of the year. In western Uganda where the climate is equable and food abundant, Banded mongoose packs usually produce a total of four litters spaced throughout the year, whereas in northern Tanzania, where temperature variation is slight but rainy and dry seasons are pronounced, both Banded and Dwarf mongooses breed only during the months of greatest rainfall when food is most abundant.

In the solitary Slender mongoose, adult males, whose ranges overlap, have a dominance hierarchy. The range of the dominant male includes those of several females and the male moves through these ranges checking scent cues to the females' reproductive condition. There is a brief consortship during the female's estrus. The mother raises the young alone, hiding them from predators. In the group-living Banded and Dwarf mongooses mating occurs within the pack and is regulated by a dominance hierarchy. In most species the young are born sparsely furred and blind, opening their eyes at about two weeks; young of the Narrow-striped mongoose resemble the adults in coloring and have their eyes open at birth.

Mongooses are a widespread and successful group. No species is known to be in danger of extinction, but the most vulnerable are likely to be the four Madagascar mongooses, as a result of destruction of their habitat. The Small Indian mongoose, Yellow mongoose and suricate have been persecuted by man yet are still widespread and abundant (indeed the first named is the most widespread of mongooses). The other two, southern African, species have been shot or gassed in their burrows as rabies carriers. The Small Indian mongoose has also been implicated with rabies and is considered a pest in many parts of the West Indies and Hawaiian Islands because of its attacks on chickens and native fauna. It was first introduced into the West Indies in the 1870s

and to the Hawaiian Islands in the 1880s, in an attempt to control rats in the sugarcane plantations. Although it is sometimes said that the Small Indian mongoose is responsible for causing the extinction of many native West Indian birds and reptiles, there is no proof of this. On many islands this mongoose is still an important predator on harmful rodents and its economic status should be considered separately on each island.

The Egyptian mongoose was considered sacred by the ancient Egyptians and mongoose figures have been found on the walls of tombs and temples dating back to 2800 BC. Interestingly, the well-known Welsh myth of Llewellyn and his dog (faithful pet saves child from predator, runs all bloodied to welcome his master home and is killed on presumption that he has killed the child) apparently passed through many cultures from an early Indian tale of the Brahmin, the snake and the mongoose.   JR

▶ **Representative mongoose species.**
(1) White-tailed mongoose (*Ichneumia albicauda*), largest of the mongooses. (2) Bushy-tailed mongoose (*Bdeogale crassicauda*), Kenyan subspecies, sniffing the air in typical mongoose "high-sit" posture. (3) Ring-tailed mongoose (*Galidia elegans*) in fast, active trot. (4) Dwarf mongoose (*Helogale parvula*) adult feeding beetle to juvenile. (5) Selous' mongoose (*Paracynictis selousi*) in low, sitting posture. (6) Narrow-striped mongoose (*Mungotictis decemlineata*). (7) Egyptian mongoose (*Herpestes ichneumon*) preparing to break open an egg by throwing it between its legs onto a rock. (8) Marsh mongoose (*Atilax paludinosus*) scent-marking a stone by the "anal drag" method.

▼ **In typical "tripod" posture,** a pair of Banded mongooses check for predators, before setting off on a foraging trip. While defense and care of young are social activities in some species, no mongooses hunt cooperatively, although they may forage together.

Abbreviations: HBL=head-body length; TL=tail length; wt=weight. Approximate measure equivalents: 1cm=0.4in; 1kg=2.2lb.

African and Asian Mongooses
Subfamily Herpestinae

Do not have ear bursa (pocket in flap of each ear) or perineal scent gland. Females have 2 or 3 pairs of teats.

Marsh mongoose
Atilax paludinosus
Marsh or Water mongoose.

Gambia east to Ethiopia, south to S Africa. Nocturnal; solitary; semiaquatic. HBL 50cm; TL 35cm; wt 3.5kg; Coat: dark brown to black. No webbing between toes. Bare heel pad present.

Bushy-tailed mongoose
Bdeogale crassicauda

Mozambique, Malawi, Zambia, Tanzania, Kenya. HBL 43cm; TL 24cm; wt 1.6kg. Nocturnal; solitary. Coat: dark brown to black; Kenya subspecies lighter in color. Four (not 5) toes on each foot.

Black-legged mongoose
Bdeogale nigripes

Nigeria to N Angola, C Kenya, SE Uganda. Nocturnal; solitary. HBL 60cm; TL 37cm; wt 3kg. Coat: light gray to brown with yellow to white-tipped guard hairs; fur dense and short; belly and tail white; chest and legs black. Four (not 5) toes on each foot.

Alexander's mongoose
Crossarchus alexandri
Alexander's or Congo mongoose.

Zaire, W Uganda, Mt Elgon, Kenya. Diurnal; group-living. HBL 40cm; TL 27cm; wt 1.5kg. Coat: mainly brown with black feet. Nose elongate and mobile.

Angolan mongoose
Crossarchus ansorgei

N Angola, SE Zaire. Diurnal; group-living. HBL 32cm; TL 21cm; wt about 1kg. Coat: brownish with black legs and tail tip. Nose not elongate.

Kusimanse
Crossarchus obscurus
Dark mongoose, kusimanse, or Long-nosed mongoose.

Sierra Leone to Cameroun. Diurnal; group-living. HBL 35cm; TL 21cm; wt 1kg. Coat: dark brown to black. Nose elongate and mobile.

Yellow mongoose
Cynictis penicillata
Yellow mongoose or Red meerkat.

S Africa, Namibia, S Angola, Botswana. Diurnal; lives in pairs or family groups. HBL 31cm; TL 22cm; wt 0.8kg. Coat: tan-yellow to orange, speckled with gray; chin and tail tip white. Ears large.

Pousargues' mongoose
Dologale dybowskii
Pousargues' or Dybowski's or African tropical savanna mongoose.

NE Zaire, Central African Republic, S Sudan, W Uganda. Diurnal. HBL 27.5cm; TL 20cm; wt 0.4kg. Coat: dark brown grizzled with tan; feet and legs black.

Dwarf mongoose
Helogale parvula

Ethiopia to northern S Africa, west to N Namibia, Angola and Cameroun. Diurnal; group-living. HBL 24cm; TL 19cm; wt 0.32kg. Coat: varies from grayish-tan to dark brown with fine grizzling. Bare heel pad present. (Includes *H. hirtula*.)

Short-tailed mongoose
Herpestes brachyurus

Malaysia, Sumatra, Java, Philippines. Nocturnal/crepuscular; solitary. HBL 49cm; TL 24cm; wt 1.4kg. Coat: brown to black with guard hairs banded with brown to red; legs black. (Includes *H. hosei*.)

Indian gray mongoose
Herpestes edwardsi

E and C Arabia to Nepal, India and Sri Lanka. Diurnal; solitary. HBL 43cm; TL 39cm; wt 1.5kg. Coat: gray to light brown, finely speckled with black.

Indian brown mongoose
Herpestes fuscus

S India and Sri Lanka. Solitary. HBL 38cm; TL 30cm; wt 1.6kg. Coat: blackish-brown to sandy-gray, speckled with black. Feet darker than head and body.

Egyptian mongoose
Herpestes ichneumon
Egyptian mongoose or ichneumon.

Most of Africa except for the Sahara and C and W African forest regions and SW Africa; Israel, S Spain and Portugal. Mainly diurnal; solitary. HBL 57cm; TL 50cm; wt 3.6kg. Coat: grizzled gray, with black tail tuft.

Small Indian mongoose
Herpestes javanicus
Small Indian mongoose or Javan gold-spotted mongoose.

N Arabia to S China and Malay Peninsula; Indochina; Sumatra; Java; introduced into the W Indies, Hawaiian Islands, Fiji. Diurnal; solitary. HBL 39cm; TL 26cm; wt 0.8kg. Coat: either light brownish-gray, speckled with black to dark brown (in arid regions), or red speckled with black and gray (wet tropical regions). (Includes *H. auropunctatus*.)

Long-nosed mongoose
Herpestes naso

SE Nigeria to Gabon and Zaire. Nocturnal; solitary. HBL 55cm; TL 41cm; wt 3kg. Coat: dark blackish-brown grizzled with buff; crest of hairs from nape to shoulders. Nose distinctly elongate.

▼ **Foraging as a pack,** a group of Banded mongooses search for insects on the Serengeti shortgrass plains. Packs contain up to 40 individuals.

Cape gray mongoose
Herpestes pulverulentus

S Angola, Namibia, S Africa. Crepuscular/nocturnal; solitary. HBL 34cm; TL 34cm; wt 0.75kg. Coat: brownish-gray to gray, speckled with black (black and red forms known); tail with dark brown to black tip; feet dark brown. Bare heel pad.

Slender mongoose
Herpestes sanguineus

Africa S of Sahara. Diurnal; solitary. HBL 35cm; TL 30cm; wt 0.6kg. Coat: varies from gray, yellowish or reddish-brown to red, tail tip black. Bare heel pad.

Ruddy mongoose
Herpestes smithi

India, Sri Lanka. Nocturnal; solitary. HBL 45cm; TL 40cm; wt 1.9kg. Coat: light brownish-gray to black, speckled with white and red; feet dark brown; tail tip black.

Crab-eating mongoose
Herpestes urva

S China, Nepal, Assam, Burma, Indochinese Peninsula, Taiwan, Hainan, Sumatra, Borneo, Philippines. Nocturnal; solitary. HBL 50cm; TL 32cm; wt 3.4kg. Coat: dark brown to gray; legs black; white strip from mouth to shoulder; tip of tail light-colored.

Stripe-necked mongoose
Herpestes vitticollis

S India, Sri Lanka. Diurnal and crepuscular; solitary. HBL 54cm; TL 35cm; wt 2.9kg. Coat: grizzled-gray, tipped with chestnut; legs and feet dark brown or black; tail tip black; black stripe from ear to shoulder. Bare heel pad.

White-tailed mongoose
Ichneumia albicauda

Subsaharan Africa except for the C and W African forest regions and SW Africa; S Arabia. Nocturnal; solitary. HBL 58cm; TL 44cm; wt 4kg. Coat: gray, grizzled with black and white; tail usually white but may be dark in some areas; legs and feet black.

Liberian mongoose
Liberiictis kuhni

Liberia. Diurnal; group-living. HBL 42cm; TL 20cm; wt 2.3kg. Coat: blackish-brown with dark brown stripe bordered by two light brown stripes from ear to shoulders.

Gambian mongoose
Mungos gambianus

Gambia to Nigeria. Diurnal; group-living. HBL 32cm; TL 19cm; wt 1.8kg. Coat: grizzled-gray and black; black stripe on side of neck contrasting with buffy white throat.

Banded mongoose
Mungos mungo

Africa S of Sahara excluding Congo and SW Africa. Diurnal; group-living. HBL 34cm; TL 22cm; wt 1.8kg. Coat: brownish-gray; feet dark brown to black; tail with black tip; dark brown bands across back.

Selous' mongoose
Paracynictis selousi
Selous' mongoose or Gray meerkat.

S Angola, N Namibia, N Botswana, S Zambia, Zimbabwe, northern S Africa, Mozambique. Nocturnal; solitary. HBL 45cm; TL 35cm; wt 1.7kg. Coat: brown, speckled with gray and black; tail white-tipped. Four toes on each foot.

Meller's mongoose
Rhynchogale melleri

S Zaire, Tanzania, Malawi, Zambia, C and N Mozambique. Nocturnal; solitary. HBL 47cm; TL 38cm; wt 2.6kg. Coat: reddish-brown; grizzled with tan; legs dark brown.

Suricate
Suricata suricatta
Suricate, meerkat, Gray meerkat, stokstertje.

Angola, Namibia, S Africa, S Botswana. Diurnal; group-living. HBL 29cm; TL 19cm; wt 0.9kg. Coat: tan to gray with broken dark brown bands across back and sides; head and throat grayish-white; eye rings and ears black; tail tip black.

Madagascar Mongooses
Subfamily Galidiinae

Ear bursa present; perineal scent gland present in *Galidia* and *Galidictis*. Females have one pair of teats.

Ring-tailed mongoose
Galidia elegans

Madagascar. Diurnal; live in pairs. HBL 37cm; TL 27cm; wt 0.9kg. Coat: light tan to dark red-brown; 5–7 dark bands on tail. Bare heel pad.

Broad-striped mongoose
Galidictis fasciata
Broad-striped mongoose or Madagascar banded mongoose.

Madagascar. Nocturnal; live in pairs. HBL 35.5cm; TL 29cm; wt ? Coat: grayish-brown with broad dark longitudinal stripes from nape to slightly beyond base of tail.

Narrow-striped mongoose
Mungotictis decemlineata

W Madagascar. Diurnal; live in pairs. HBL 34cm; TL 27cm; wt 0.8kg. Coat: brownish-gray with speckling on back and sides; 10–12 narrow reddish-brown to dark brown longitudinal stripes on back and sides. Bare heel pad.

Brown mongoose
Salanoia unicolor

E Madagascar. Diurnal; live in pairs. HBL 24cm; TL 16cm; wt 0.8kg. Coat: reddish-brown, speckled with black and tan.

JR/WCW

Pack Life of the Dwarf Mongoose

Anti-predator behavior and care of young in a small carnivore

The young female Dwarf mongoose dashed back and forth between the two adult males, grooming them and being groomed in turn. In human terms, she seemed ecstatic.

"Bonnie" had been observed from birth. Seven weeks after the death of her mother, Bonnie's pack had been joined by two older females from an adjacent one. Bonnie—then 19 months old—had left (or perhaps been evicted) the same day. For the following month she lived alone, gradually moving out of her natal range. Now she had just found a pack whose dominant breeding female had died in the previous month.

A few minutes later the rest of the pack returned. Bonnie was chased by a juvenile female (the only female in the pack), and again that night she slept alone. But four days later she was a fully integrated member and she was subsequently observed mating with the alpha (dominant) male. Now, as the new alpha female, her reproductive potential was high.

Dwarf mongooses, the smallest viverrids, are also one of the few social species in the family. Each Dwarf mongoose pack contains one dominant breeding pair and this status, once achieved, is often maintained for many years. One alpha female who lost a hindleg to a predator, maintained her position, in spite of this handicap, and bred until she disappeared from the pack three years later.

In addition to the dominant breeding pair (usually the oldest male and female in the group) a Dwarf mongoose pack typically contains young animals born in the pack, and immigrants. Packs of over 20 occur, but the average pack size at the start of the birth season is about eight. Because mongooses are basically monogamous it is usually essential for a mongoose to attain alpha status in order to raise offspring successfully. Some mongooses remain in their natal packs and eventually accede to alpha status when older individuals of the same sex die. The wait may be a long one.

Females are more likely than males to remain in the pack in which they were born. But most mongooses eventually emigrate. They may meet other emigrants of the opposite sex to form a new pack on unoccupied territory or they may join an already existing pack. If they are lucky, as in the case of Bonnie, they can find a pack with no older mongooses of their sex and are thus able to breed at an early age. Many join packs with one or two older residents of their sex and frequently have to contend with some aggression from these. Emigrants move to packs with fewer older mongooses of the same sex, thereby increasing their repro-

ductive potential. Male takeovers, involving the forced expulsion of resident males, have been recorded. In one instance six males joined an adjacent pack, driving out the two resident adult males and mating with the females. The following year all but the dominant male emigrated again (in groups of three and two) and took over two further packs.

In most group-living mammals, females remain in their natal groups while males emigrate. Dwarf mongooses are unusual in that *both* sexes commonly transfer between groups. Intergroup transfer helps prevent inbreeding and also can result in reinforcement of the pack. Members of small vulnerable packs which have lost breeding members can quickly improve their chances of survival through accepting immigrants.

◀ ▼ **Anti-predator behavior** is an important function of group life in the Dwarf mongoose. From vantage points, such as termite mounds, the vigilant mongoose either checks the sky for aerial predators LEFT or scans the surrounding terrain BELOW (1).

▶ ▲ **Care of young is shared.** In the early weeks of life the young are guarded by baby-sitters (2) who will rapidly retrieve any that wander away from the den TOP RIGHT. Mutual grooming BOTTOM RIGHT is frequent between members of a pack, particularly between individuals of the opposite sex, and wrestling and chasing play (3) are common among young animals. (4) Scent marking with the anal glands: from such scent marks other mongooses can identify the individual, its sex and pack membership.

for survival from numerous aerial and ground predators. Dwarf mongooses spend a large proportion of their time scanning from vantage points such as termite mounds—the alpha male is particularly active in this role. On detection of a predator, a loud series of alarm calls warns all pack members, who scatter to shelter.

Increased efficiency in care of young is also an important benefit of group living. Young Dwarf mongooses are cared for co-operatively. For the first few weeks, when confined to a breeding den, they are usually guarded by one or more babysitters of either sex while the rest of the pack forages. Changeovers occur frequently throughout the day, allowing all individuals some time to feed. Helpers collect beetles and other insects and carry them to the young, and they groom and play with the young. If any wander away, the babysitters soon retrieve them. Potential predators, such as Slender mongooses, are chased from the den site. The mother spends less time at the den than other pack members, allowing her maximum foraging time.

According to the theory on kin selection, it should (all else being equal) be close relatives that give the greatest amount of aid to the young mongooses. Yet in Dwarf mongooses unrelated immigrants are frequently good helpers and may contribute more than older siblings. Why do they do this? They may receive long-term pay-offs, such as benefiting eventually from the antipredator responses of young they help to rear. Also, immigrants are likely eventually to breed in the packs they have joined, and the young they have helped to raise may later aid them by babysitting and feeding the immigrants' own young.   JR

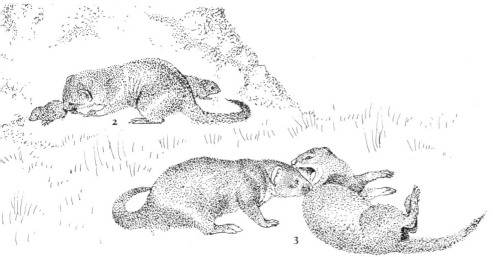

It appears that the group-living mongooses have followed a different evolutionary route to sociality from the large social carnivores such as lions, hyenas, African wild dogs and wolves. These species hunt cooperatively, which has probably been the most important selective pressure promoting their group life. In contrast, the group-living mongooses all feed primarily on invertebrates and find their food individually. For them predation has probably been the chief selective pressure favoring group living.

Antipredator behavior (as in the Banded mongoose, see p147) is an important benefit of group life. A group of animals is more likely to spot a predator than a single individual. The small Dwarf mongoose must rely on early warning and fleeing to cover

THE HYENA FAMILY

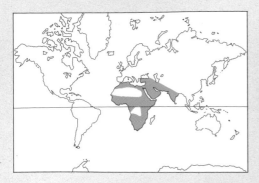

Family: Hyaenidae
Four species in 3 genera.
Distribution: Africa except Sahara and Congo basin, Turkey and Middle East to Arabia, SW USSR and India.

Habitat: chiefly dry, open grasslands and brush.

Size: the Spotted hyena can attain 80kg (176lb) and is one of the largest carnivores. The smallest member of the family is the aardwolf (see below).

Spotted hyena *Crocuta crocuta*
Brown hyena *Hyaena brunnea*
Striped hyena *Hyaena hyaena*
Ardwolf *Proteles cristatus*

Aardwolf   135cm

THE true hyenas (subfamily Hyaeninae) have thickset muzzles with large ears and eyes, powerful jaws and big cheek teeth to deal with a carnivorous diet. They walk on four-toed feet with five asymmetrical pads and nonretractile claws. The tail is long and bushy (less so in the Spotted hyena). The aardwolf is mainly insectivorous. It has retained five toes on its front feet, and its unusual dentition has led some authorities to place it in a separate family (Protelidae). Anatomy, chromosomes and blood proteins, however, clearly indicate a close relationship to hyenas.

Despite the resemblance to canids, on the basis of comparative anatomy the nearest relatives are the Viverridae (civets etc, see pp134–135), and they probably evolved from a civet-like creature similar to *Ictitherium* before the early Miocene era (26 million years ago). The earliest fossil hyenids are from Europe and Asia; one, with advanced bone-crushing teeth, dates from the late Miocene era (10 million years ago).

Abbreviations: HBL = head-body length; TL = tail length; HT = height; WT = weight. Approximate measure equivalents: 1cm = 0.4in; 1kg = 2.2lb.
⬚ CITES listed.   ⬚ Vulnerable.

Spotted hyena

Crocuta crocuta
Striped or Laughing hyena.

Africa S of Sahara, except southern S Africa (exterminated) and Congo basin. Prefers grassland and flat open terrain. HBL 120–140cm; HT 70–90cm; TL 25–30cm; WT 50–80kg. Coat: short, dirty yellow to reddish, with irregular dark brown oval spots; short, reversed, erectile mane; tail with brush of long black hairs. Gestation: 110 days. Longevity: up to 25 years (to 40 in captivity).

Brown hyena ⬚

Hyaena brunnea
Brown hyena or Beach wolf or Strand wolf.

S Africa, particularly in W; now absent from extreme S. Prefers drier, often rocky areas with desert or thick brush. HBL 110–130cm; HT 65–85cm; TL 20–25cm; WT 35–50kg. Coat: dark brown; white collar behind ears, well-developed dorsal crest extending to mantle of long (25cm) hairs on back and sides; underside lighter; dark horizontal stripes on legs; face hair short, near-black. Gestation: about 84 days. Longevity: up to 13 years in captivity.

Striped hyena ⬚

Hyaena hyaena

E and N Africa (not Sahara or West south of 10°N) through Mid East to Arabia, India, SW USSR. Habitat similar to Brown hyena. HBL 100–120cm; HT 65–80cm; WT 25–35cm; WT 30–40kg. Coat: medium to long (13–25cm), gray to yellowish gray with numerous black stripes on body and legs; woolly winter underfur present in colder areas; muzzle, throat underside, neck and two cheek stripes black; mane usually black-tipped; tail long, of uniform color. Gestation: about 84 days. Longevity: up to 24 years in captivity.

Aardwolf

Proteles cristatus.

Southern Africa north to S Angola and S Zambia; E Africa from C Tanzania to NE Sudan. Open country and grassland; also savanna, scrub and rocky areas. Head to tail-tip 85–105cm; HT 40–50cm; WT 8–12kg. Coat: buff, yellowish-white or rufous; erectile mane and black dorsal stripe to black tail tip; three vertical black stripes on body, 1–2 diagonal stripes across fore- and hindquarters; irregular horizontal stripes on legs, darker towards feet; throat and underparts paler to gray-white; sometimes black spots or stripes on neck; woolly underfur with longer, coarser guard hairs. Gestation: 59–61 days. Longevity: to 13 years in captivity.

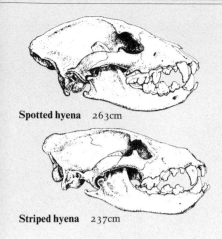

Spotted hyena   263cm

Striped hyena   237cm

Skulls of Hyenids

The skulls of hyenids are robust and long. All members of the family have a complete dental formula (see p20) of I3/3, C1/1, P4/3, M1/1 = 34 (among carnivores only members of the cat family have fewer teeth). However, in the insectivorous aardwolf the cheek teeth are reduced to small, peg-like structures spaced widely apart and often lost in adults, leaving as few as 24 teeth.

The more massive skulls of hyenas have relatively short jaws which give a powerful grip. Hyena skulls suggest two distinct trends of adaptation. That of the Spotted hyena is highly specialized for crushing large bones and cutting through thick hides, which other large carnivores are unable to consume and digest. The bone-crushing premolars are relatively large and the carnassial teeth are used almost solely for slicing or shearing.

In Brown and Striped hyenas the corresponding premolars are smaller and the carnassials do the job of crushing and chopping as well as shearing. These differences relate to the smaller species' dependence on a greater range of food items, including insects, wild fruit and eggs as well as carrion and prey.

◄ **A massive head,** jaws with large bone-crushing teeth, and powerful forequarters are hallmarks of the Spotted hyena, largest member of the hyena family. Here a pack consumes a carcass.

▼ **Feeding behavior of the four species of the hyena family.** (1) Aardwolf upwind of termites, listening for sound of termites eating. (2) Striped hyena scavenging from a carcass. (3) Spotted hyena pack cooperatively hunting down a zebra. (4) Brown hyena juveniles playing at the den while an adult approaches with its kill, a Bat-eared fox.

The radiation of hyenas was linked to an increase in open habitats where their dog-like characteristics would have evolved. Probably the hyenas and the North American "hyena-dogs" evolved their special dentition as an adaptation to the availability of the tougher portions of their kills left uneaten by the great saber-toothed cats. As the saber-tooths declined during the early Pleistocene (2 million years ago) so did the hyena-dogs and hyenas, including the massive Cave hyenas (*Crocuta crocuta spelaea*) almost twice the size of those which exist today.

The evolutionary lines leading to *Crocuta* and *Hyaena* appear, from the fossil record, to have been separate since the Miocene era. The ancestor of the aardwolf may have diverged even earlier.

Hyenas are master scavengers, able to consume and digest items that would otherwise remain untouched by mammals. Their digestive system is fully equal to their unusual tastes; the organic matter of bone is digested completely and indigestible items (horns, hooves, bone pieces, ligaments and hair) are regurgitated in pellets, often matted together with grass. This specialized means of eliminating waste is probably the reason why hyenas do not regurgitate food

for their young like many other carnivores.

The ability of Spotted hyenas to hunt is as impressive as their scavenging—a single hyena can catch an adult wildebeest weighing up to 170kg (380lb) after chasing it for 5 km (3mi) at speeds of up to 60km/h (37mph). Other individuals may join the chase and in the Ngorongoro Crater in East Africa more than 50 members of the same clan (group) may eventually feed together. Zebra hunting, on the other hand, involves parties of 10–15 hyenas. Following a hunt, Spotted hyenas feed voraciously—a group of 38 hyenas has been seen to dismember a zebra in 15 minutes, leaving few scraps. When competition is less intense, feeding is more leisurely

The three species of hyena possess the well-developed forequarters and sloping backline, anal pouch and dorsal mane that are common to all hyenids. The biggest, the Spotted hyena, exceeds in size all other carnivores except the four largest bears and three largest felids. There is no overlap in the distribution of the Brown hyena and the Striped hyena, but members of both species come into contact with Spotted hyenas.

Male and female hyenas look alike, but

How Hyenas Communicate

Hyenas are often called "solitary," a label which obscures the fact that their social systems are among the most complex known for mammals. Spotted hyenas employ elaborate meeting ceremonies and efficient long-range communication by scent and sound. Brown and Striped hyenas lack loud calls but their meeting rituals and uses of scent are no less complex. (In the aardwolf, only the scent-marking approaches that of the other members of the family in complexity: see p159.)

Scent marking. One of the most distinctive features of all hyenids is the anal pouch. This remarkable organ lies between the rectum and the base of the tail and can be turned inside out. It is particularly large in the Brown hyena, which secretes two distinct pastes from different glands lining the pouch. As the animal moves forward over a grass stalk (1) with its pouch extruded, a white secretion is deposited first, followed by a black one a few centimeters above it (2). Chemical analysis of the pastes reveals consistent differences between individuals, while pastes deposited at different times by one animal are extremely similar. Scent marks are placed throughout the territory (averaging 2.3 marks per kilometer) but the rate of pasting nearly doubles in the vicinity of borders. Striped and Spotted hyenas deposit a single creamy paste, usually on a grass stalk at about hyena nose height.

In Spotted hyenas, which have the least developed anal pouches, aggression is evident during bouts of communal scent marking at border latrines, where pasting is accompanied by defecation and vigorous pawing of the ground with the front feet, which carry glands between the toes.

Submission and aggression signals. All three species turn the anal pouch inside out during encounters with other animals. In Brown and Striped hyenas, this occurs when meeting other members of the species, whereas in the Spotted hyenas, anal gland protrusion is strongly linked with signs of aggression, for example, when approaching lions or rival hyenas.

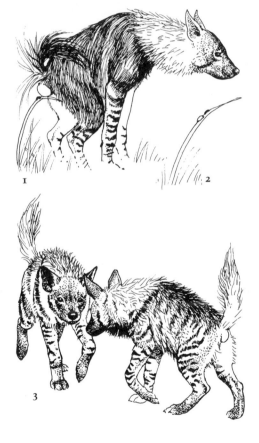

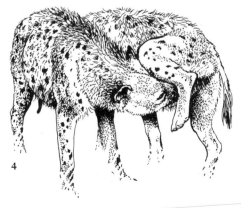

The link between anal glands and aggression in Spotted hyenas is of special interest because, unlike other hyenas, the anal region is not presented for inspection during meeting ceremonies. It seems that the selective advantage of reducing tension while re-establishing social bonds between partners after separation has resulted in two types of display. Meeting ceremonies in Brown and Striped hyenas involve varying degrees of erection of the dorsal crest (3), sniffing of the head and body, protrusion and inspection of the anal pouch and rather lengthy bouts of ritual fighting in which areas of the neck or throat of a subordinate are bitten and held or shaken. In Spotted hyenas, on the other hand, greeting includes mutual sniffing and licking of the genital area and erect penis or clitoris as the animals stand head to tail with one hind leg lifted (4). This display is very different from the state of the sex organs at mating; it is conspicuous in cubs, and the Spotted hyena which initiates contact is almost invariably lower in the dominance hierarchy. Clearly the function is one of appeasement.

Whoop calls. Even when moving alone. Spotted hyenas maintain some direct contact with their fellows. They respond to sounds which are only audible to humans with the aid of an amplifier and headphones. Calls audible to the unaided human ear include whoops, fast whoops, yells and a kind of demented cackle that gives this species its alternative name of Laughing hyena. Whoop calls, in particular, are well suited to long range communication as they carry over several kilometers; each call is repeated a number of times, which helps the listener to locate the caller, and each hyena has a distinctive voice. Woodland Spotted hyenas of the Timbavati Game Reserve in the Transvaal, South Africa, will frequently either answer tape-recordings of their companions or casually approach the loudspeaker. If, however, recordings of strange hyenas are played, the residents will often arrive in groups at the run, calling excitedly, with their manes raised, tails curled high and anal glands protruding. Infant hyenas will answer the pre-recorded whoops of their mothers, but not those of other clan hyenas.   SKB

▲ Caching food in mud. Spotted hyenas frequently bury excess food in muddy pools; they have a good memory for such caches, to which they will return when hungry.

◄ Brown hyenas TOP are mainly solitary scavengers and they search for suitable food mostly at night. This one is removing the last morsels of flesh from a buffalo skull.

▲ A frustrated Spotted hyena attempts to break open an ostrich egg by biting it. He has already tried stamping and rolling on it. He may fail to open it, although hyenas are often known to eat eggs.

the female Spotted hyena, which is socially dominant, is heavier than the male (4–12 percent). Her sexual organs mimic those of the male so exactly that it is often difficult to be certain of an animal's sex. Male Brown and Striped hyenas are 7–12 percent heavier than females, and the sexual organs are conventional.

Spotted hyenas will eat almost anything, but in the wild 90 percent or more of their food comes from mammals heavier than 20kg (44lb), which they mostly kill for themselves. The frequency of hunting depends on the availability of carrion; Spotted hyenas will loot the kills of other carnivores, including lions. Group feeding is often noisy, but rarely involves serious fighting. Instead, each hyena gorges up to 15kg (33lb) of flesh extremely rapidly. Pieces of a carcass may be carried away to be consumed at leisure or, occasionally, stored underwater.

Brown and Striped hyenas are mainly scavengers, but a significant proportion of their diet consists of insects, small vertebrates, eggs and also fruits and vegetables, an important source of water. Lone animals follow a zigzag course with the head lowered, but frequently turn and sniff into the wind. Small prey are chased and grabbed, but hunting is often unsuccessful. Apart from scents, sounds of other predators and their dying prey also attract hyenas, who may either wait patiently to scavenge,

or drive off the true owner. When Brown or Striped hyenas discover a large source of food they usually first remove portions to the safety of temporary caches among bushes, in long grass or down holes. One Brown hyena watched in the Kalahari removed all 26 eggs from an ostrich nest in one night and returned later to feed on the hidden eggs.

Striped and Brown hyenas spend more time searching for food that is widely scattered and in small clumps than do Spotted hyenas, and their social system is adapted accordingly. At one extreme, extended family groups of 4–14 Brown hyenas in the Kalahari may share territories of 230–540sq km (90–200sq mi) and be active for over 10 of the 24 hours each day, during which time they may travel an average 30km (20mi) or more. By contrast, clans of Spotted hyenas in the Ngorongoro Crater may number 30–80, occupy territories of 10–40sq km (26–105sq mi), and be active for just 4 hours of the day, traveling only some 10km (6mi). Marked variation occurs within the species: the less numerous Spotted hyenas of the Transvaal Lowveld woodlands usually move alone (60 percent of sightings) or in pairs (27 percent).

Hyenas show interesting differences in the care of young. In Spotted hyenas this is the sole responsibility of the mother, but clan females usually raise their offspring in a communal den where narrow interconnecting tunnels allow the infants to escape predators, which may include males of their own species. Up to three infants, usually twins, are born; they are relatively well developed at birth, with a coat of uniform brown. At first the young are called to the surface by the mother to suckle. Movements away from the den develop very slowly and suckling may continue for up to 18 months, but at no stage is food carried back to the den for the benefit of the offspring. Quite the reverse is true in both *Hyaena* species. Female Brown hyenas will suckle infants which are not their own, while in both species adults and subadults of both sexes carry food to related offspring. Rather surprisingly, in Brown hyenas this helping usually excludes the father, as mating seems to be only by nomadic males who wander through separate territories of each extended family. The mating system of Striped hyenas is unknown, but both species generally produce 2–4 blind and helpless young, similar in color to the adults. They are suckled for up to 12 months. Female Striped hyenas have six teats. Brown and Spotted hyenas four.

It seems that the success of Spotted hyenas is ensured through individual and cooperative hunting and sharing of food between adults. Cooperation also extends to communal marking and defense of the territory, in which both sexes play a similar role, whether or not they are related. Competition within the clan can, however, be intense. The system of communication shows adaptations which reduce aggression and coordinate group activities (see p156). Such competition probably provided the selection pressure whereby females evolved their large size and dominant position, which in turn relates also to levels of testosterone in the blood that are indistinguishable from those of the male. Thus female Spotted hyenas are able to feed a small number of offspring alone and protect them from the more serious consequences of interference by other hyenas, particularly unrelated males. Although Brown and Striped hyenas are known to share a large carcass, group members rarely eat together, so direct competition for food is avoided. Indirect competition is offset by the fact that the residents of a territory are nearly always related, and this may explain also why they cooperate in raising young. Through communal rearing of a larger number of infants and the efficient use of small food items, Brown and Striped hyenas are better able to exploit their harsher environments than is the Spotted species. On the other hand they are less well equipped to deal with large prey and their numbers may be kept down by direct competition with Spotted hyenas where their ranges overlap.   SKB

The **aardwolf** is a delicate, shy, nocturnal animal seldom seen in the wild. Its highly specialized diet consists primarily of a few species of Snouted harvester termites (*Trinervitermes* spp). The aardwolf appears to locate its prey mainly by sound, but the strong-smelling defense secretions of the soldier termites probably provide an additional stimulus. The termites are licked up by rapid movements of the long tongue. Because of the sticky saliva that covers the tongue, large amounts of soil may be ingested with the food.

The behavior of aardwolves—including their time of greatest activity, foraging method and social system—is influenced by their dependence on termites. For most of the year aardwolves' periods of activity are similar to those of the Snouted harvesters, which are poorly pigmented and cannot tolerate direct sunlight, so emerge during the late afternoon and at night. The termites

forage in dense columns and an aardwolf can lick up a great number at a time. Certain seasonal events, such as the onset of the rains in East Africa and the cold temperatures of midwinter in southern Africa, appear to limit the termites' own foraging activity. Then aardwolves often find an alternative food in the larger harvester termite *Hodotermes mossambicus*, which is heavily pigmented and may be found by day in large, locally distributed foraging parties. These termites are not the preferred food source throughout the year because they are mainly active in winter and foraging individuals are spaced much further apart than in *Trinervitermes*. Insects other than termites or ants, and very occasionally small mammals, nestling birds and carrion may be eaten but constitute a very minor part of the diet.

Aardwolves are solitary foragers. This is because *Trinervitermes* forage in small dense patches 25–100cm (1–3ft) across scattered over a wide area. One adult pair of aardwolves usually occupies an area of 1–2sq km (0.4–0.8sq mi) with their most recent offspring. An intruding aardwolf may be chased away up to 400m, and serious fights take place if the intruder is caught. Most fights take place during the mating season, when they occur once or twice a week. Fights are accompanied by hoarse barks or a type of roar with the mane and tail hairs fully erected.

When food is short, the territorial system may be relaxed, allowing several individuals from up to three different territories to forage simultaneously in the same area (usually on *Hodotermes*) without any serious conflict. However, even within a family, interaction

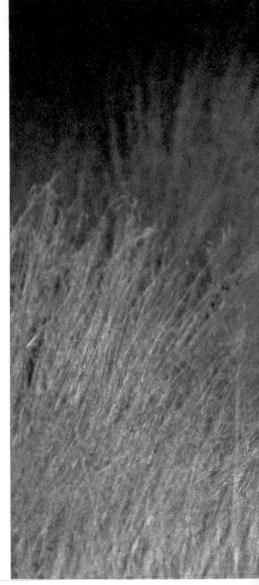

between individuals is abrupt, and there are no elaborate greeting procedures such as exist among hyenas.

Apart from aggressive encounters, the territorial system appears to be maintained also by a system of marking. Both sexes possess well-developed anal glands which can be extruded to leave a small black smear about 5mm (0.2in) long on grass stalks, usually close to a termite mound. Aardwolves mark throughout the night as they move across their territories feeding. When deep within their territories, they mark about once every 20 minutes only, pasting over old marks or around dens and middens, where they may mark up to five times during one visit. The frequency of marking goes up dramatically when they are feeding or simply patrolling the territory boundary, with marking occurring about

once every 50 metres. In this way an individual may deposit 120 marks in two hours. This high frequency of marking is most pronounced during the mating season.

An aardwolf family group may have over 10 dens and as many middens scattered throughout its territory. Defecations at middens are usually preceded by the aardwolf digging a small hole and concluded by it scratching sand back over the feces.

The dens may be old aardvark or porcupine dens, or crevices in rocks but often they are holes of a typical size, which the aardwolves may have dug themselves (aardwolf is Afrikaans for "earth wolf") or have enlarged from springhare holes. Aardwolves often visit old dens, but use only one or two at a time and change dens after a month to six weeks. During cold weather they usually go down the den and sleep a few hours after sundown. In summer they rest outside the den entrance at night and go underground during the day.

Although the aardwolf has a strict territorial system, many males are inclined to wander through adjacent territories, particularly during breeding, when resident as well as neighboring males may mate with females. The cubs, usually 2–4, are born in spring or summer. They are born with their eyes open but are helpless and spend about 6–8 weeks in the den before emerging. During the first few months while the cubs are still in the den, the male may spend up to six hours a night looking after the den while the female is away foraging. At about three months the cubs start foraging for termites, accompanied by at least one parent; by the time they are four months old they may spend much of the night foraging alone. They generally sleep in the same den as their mother, while the male may sleep there or in another den. At the start of the next breeding season the cubs often wander far beyond their parents' territory and by the time the next generation of cubs start foraging away from the dens, most of the subadults have emigrated from the area. Despite this annual movement of aardwolves, recolonization of suitable areas is severely limited by man's persecution. Aardwolves have been shot in the mistaken belief that they prey upon livestock, while in some areas they may also be killed for their meat, which is considered a delicacy, or for their pelts. An aardwolf may consume up to 200,000 termites in one night, and since Harvester termites can be serious pests on livestock farms (particularly during drought), the species deserves protection in those areas where it is threatened.

PRKR/SKB

◄ **Pack power.** A large pack of Spotted hyenas is quite capable of intimidating much larger carnivores. Here at least ten hyenas are driving away three lionesses from a kill.

▼ **Licking the platter clean,** an aardwolf feeds direct from a mound of the snouted harvester termite *Trinervitermes trinervoides*, the chief food of aardwolves in South Africa. The aardwolf's long, mobile tongue is covered with sticky saliva and large papillae to help in licking up the termites.

SEA MAMMALS

WHALES AND DOLPHINS

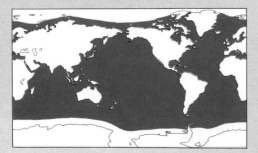

ORDER: CETACEA ⊡
Nine families: 38 genera: 76 species.

Toothed whales

Suborder: Odontoceti

River dolphins
Family: Platanistidae
Five species in 4 genera.
Includes **La Plata dolphin** (*Pontoporia blainvillei*).

Dolphins
Family: Delphinidae
Thirty-two species in 17 genera.
Includes **Bridled dolphin** (*Stenella attenuata*), **Common dolphin** (*Delphinus delphis*), **Killer whale** (*Orcinus orca*), **Pilot whale** (*Globicephala melaena*), **Risso's dolphin** (*Grampus griseus*), **White beaked dolphin** (*Lagenorhynchus albirostris*).

Porpoises
Family: Phocoenidae
Six species in 3 genera.
Includes **Common porpoise** (*Phocoena phocoena*).

White whales
Family: Monodontidae
Two species in 2 genera.
Includes **Narwhal** (*Monodon monoceros*).

Sperm whales
Family: Physeteridae
Three species in 2 genera.
Includes **Sperm whale** (*Physeter macrocephalus*).

Beaked whales
Family: Ziphiidae
Eighteen species in 5 genera.
Includes **Northern bottlenose whale** (*Hyperoodon ampullatus*).

To many people, thoughts of whales conjure up a picture of a large mysterious creature living in the gray-green depths of the ocean; fish-like with fins, and scarcely if ever to be seen in one's lifetime. Until 1758, when the great Swedish biologist Linnaeus recognized them as mammals, whales were regarded as fish, and their lifestyles were scarcely known. Only in the last half century has our knowledge of these most specialized of mammals become at all substantial—not a moment too soon as many species are in danger of extinction.

Though superficially resembling some of the large sharks, whales are clearly distinguished by a number of mammalian features—they are warm-blooded, they breathe air with lungs, and they give birth to living young that are suckled on milk secreted by the mammary glands of the mother. Unlike most land mammals, however, they do not have a coat of hair for warmth. External hair or fur would impede their progress through the water, reducing the advantage gained by the streamlining of the body. Of the marine mammal orders Cetacea, Pinnipedia (seals, p238), and Sirenia (sea cows and manatees, p292), it is the whales and dolphins which are most specialized for life in the water; seals must return to land to breed and both seals and sirenians may bask on reefs.

Although in terms of body size, whales dominate the order Cetacea, one half of the order comprises the generally much smaller dolphins and porpoises. Most of the great whales belong to the suborder Mysticeti (see pp214–237), which instead of teeth, have a system of horny "plates" called baleen, used to filter or strain planktonic organisms and larger invertebrates, as well as schools of small fishes, from the sea. However, the vast

▶ **Tail power.** The tail flukes, powered by huge muscles in the back, are the great whales' sole source of propulsion. The Humpback whale, like other great whales, sometimes produces a loud report by crashing the tail down on the surface (lob-tailing). This may be a signal to other Humpbacks.

◀ **Bursting from the surface,** a Killer whale breaches upside-down. One function of this action may be to communicate with others in the herd; it may also be used to stun or panic fish shoals.

▼ **Leaping dolphin.** Dolphins are perfectly streamlined for rapid swimming. When swimming fast, as in this Pacific white-sided dolphin, they leap to breathe, which is actually more efficient than dragging along at the surface, where resistance is greatest.

majority of cetaceans (66 out of 76 species) belong to the suborder Odontoceti (see pp 176–213). These are the toothed whales, which include the dolphins and porpoises. They feed mainly on fish and squid, which they pursue and capture with their arrays of teeth.

Body Shape and Locomotion

The largest animal ever to have lived on this planet is the Blue whale, and though its populations have been severely reduced by man's overhunting (see pp224–226), it still survives today. It reaches a length of 24–27m (80–90ft) and weighs 130–150 tonnes, equivalent to the weight of 33 individuals of the largest terrestrial mammal, the elephant. Such an enormous body could only be supported in an aquatic medium, for on land it would require limbs so large that mobility would be greatly restricted.

Despite their size and weight, whales and dolphins are very mobile, having evolved a streamlined torpedo-shaped body for ease of movement through water. The head is elongated compared to other mammals, and passes imperceptibly into the trunk, with no obvious neck or shoulders. All the rorquals, the river dolphins, and the white whales have neck vertebrae which are separate, allowing flexibility of the neck; the remainder of the species have between two and seven fused together. Further streamlining is achieved by reducing protruding parts that would impede the even flow of water over the body. The hindlimbs have been lost, although there are still traces of their bony skeleton within the body. There are no external ears—simply two minute openings on the side of the head which lead directly to the organs of hearing. The male's penis is completely hidden within muscular folds, and the teats of the female are housed within slits on either side of the genital area. The only protuberances are a pair of horizontal fins or flippers, a boneless tail fluke and, in many species, an upright but boneless dorsal fin of tissue which is firm, fibrous and fatty.

In most of the toothed whales the jaws are extended as a beak-like snout behind which the forehead rises in a rounded curve or "melon." Unlike the baleen whales (or any other mammal) they possess a single nostril, the two nasal passages, which are separate at the base of the skull, joining close below the surface to form a single opening—the blowhole; in extreme cases, one blowhole is functionally suppressed, leaving the other as the sole breathing tube. The blowhole is typically a slit in the form of a crescent,

THE CETACEAN BODY PLAN

▼ **Skeletons** of baleen TOP and toothed whales BOTTOM. The skeleton of whales, although recognizably derived from the basic mammalian plan, is greatly modified. The skeleton does not have to carry the weight of the animal but instead acts as an anchor for the muscles, which may account for 40 percent of the whale's weight. The bones of whales are light and spongy with a thin outer shell. The hindlimbs have been lost completely, except for a vestigial unattached pelvic bone present in baleen whales and some male toothed whales, which acts as an anchor for the penis muscles. The most extreme modification is that of the skull, which is greatly extended in both baleen and toothed whales. The loss of teeth in baleen whales and associated changes have produced a skull with a grotesque form, unlike that of any other animal.

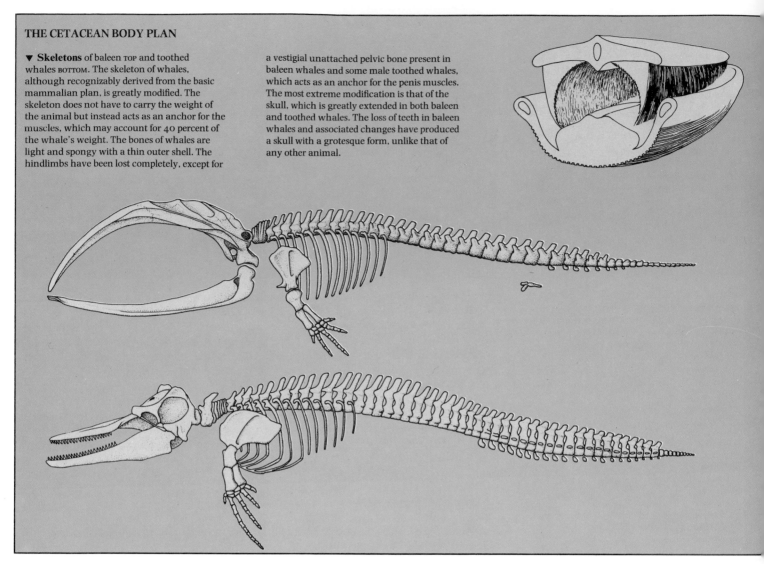

protected by a fatty and fibrous pad or plug which is opened by muscular effort and closed by the pressure of water upon it. The skull bones of the nasal region are usually asymmetrical in their size, shape and position, although porpoises and the La Plata dolphin have symmetrical skulls.

The baleen or whalebone whales differ from toothed whales in a number of ways. Besides being generally much larger, the main difference is in the baleen apparatus which takes the place of teeth in the mouth, and which grows as a series of horny plates from the sides of the upper jaw in the position of the upper teeth in other animals. Baleen whales feed by straining large quantities of water containing plankton and larger organisms through these plates (see pp214 and 223). The paired nostrils remain separate, so that the blowhole is a double hole forming two parallel slits, close together when shut. Other important differences are single-headed ribs and a breast-bone (sternum) composed of a single bone articulating with the first pair of ribs only. Despite variation between species in the size and shape of the skull, all baleen whales have a symmetrical skull.

Like all mammals, cetaceans are warm-blooded, using part of the energy available to them to maintain a stable body-core temperature. How do they maintain a stable muscle-core temperature of 36°–37°C (97°–99°F), without an insulating coat of hair, in the relatively cool environment of the sea, with temperatures usually less than 25°C (77°F)? Insulation is provided by a layer of fat, called blubber—which may be up to 50cm (20in) thick in the Bowhead whale—lying immediately beneath the skin. Larger species have a distinct advantage over smaller forms because of their much more favorable surface-to-volume ratio, and this may be why the smaller dolphins do not occur at very high latitudes. Fat is laid down not only as blubber: the liver is also import-

▶ **Blue whale bones** laid out on King George Island, Antarctica. The skeleton of the largest mammal is much reduced and simplified compared to land mammals. Most of the great bulk is flesh and blubber.

◄ **Baleen apparatus.** Instead of teeth, baleen whales have two rows of fringed plates hanging from the upper roof of the mouth. They evolved from the curved transverse ridges of the palate found in many land mammals. Despite the commercial name applied to them, "whalebone," they are not made of bone, but toughened skin.

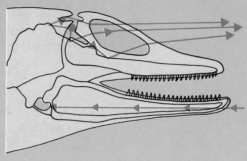

▲ **Acoustic focusing.** Toothed whales have a highly developed capacity for locating objects by means of sound (echolocation). It is thought that the melon, a waxy lens-shaped body in the forehead focuses sounds produced in the nasal passages. Returning sound waves are channeled through oil-filled sinuses in the lower jaw to the inner ear. It is thought that the extreme sensitivity of this system is assisted by the isolation of the inner ear from the skull by means of a bubbly foam. Sound is thus very precisely channeled without the interference of extraneous resonances.

▲ **The genitals** of whales are internal, only a genital slit being visible. In males, the penis lies coiled on the floor of the abdominal cavity, held there by a retractor muscle. The penis is very mobile and is often used as a sensory organ, particularly during courtship. The penis and testes are shown in blue.

ant for fat deposition and in some species there are significant quantities of fat in the form of oil (as much as 50 percent of the body total) laid down in the skeletal bones of the animal.

Whales drive themselves through the water primarily by the upward stroke of their powerful tail (unlike fishes which propel themselves by a sideways movement of the tail). This movement is powered by a great muscle mass which occupies the upper region of the animal. Most cetaceans have a well-defined dorsal fin which is assumed to stabilize the animal, although it may also help in temperature regulation. The fore-limbs have a skeletal structure similar to that of the human arm, but they have been modified to form paddle-like flippers which are used for steering. Whereas the rigid hull of a ship creates turbulence when it passes through the water, a cetacean minimizes this by its flexible body; its blubber is not tightly fixed to the underlying muscular tissues, and there is a very well-developed system of dermal ridges beneath the skin. From the smooth, outer, cellular layer of the skin epidermis comes a secretion of tiny droplets of a high polymer of ethylene oxide; these droplets assist the shedding of epidermal cells into the water and may help to maintain a laminar flow, reducing turbulence and drag by dissipating the energy of the impeding vortices.

Cetaceans spend nearly all their lives underwater, sometimes at considerable depths. Because they are mammals they breathe air direct, instead of extracting oxygen dissolved in water as fishes do. They must therefore return to the surface at regular intervals to take air, and when they dive they must hold their breath.

When a man dives for longer than he can hold his breath, he takes with him a cylinder of compressed air. This is necessary because the air pressure within his lungs must equal or slightly exceed the pressure of the water around him, otherwise his chest would be crushed. Under compression, the nitrogen of the air dissolves in the fluids and tissues of his body to their full capacity, and when he ascends the dissolved nitrogen comes out of solution in the form of bubbles of the gas. These may appear in any part of the body; in the joints they cause the painful condition called "the bends." In contrast, when a cetacean dives it takes only the amount of air that will fill its relatively small lungs; only a proportion of the air is nitrogen, so that the amount which could dissolve in the body fluids and tissues from one filling of the lungs is rather small. But even this small

amount does not enter the blood and tissues, because as the cetacean dives its lungs compress and drive the air in them into the windpipe and its branches, and into the extensive nasal passages, the thickened membrane linings of which prevent gas exchange to the tissues. In cetaceans the chest is comparatively flexible and the diaphragm set very obliquely, so that the pressure of the abdominal viscera pushing against it on one side makes the lungs on the other side collapse.

As a cetacean returns to the surface, the lungs gradually expand again, its blowhole opens wide and the foul air accumulated during the dive is expelled explosively. This produces a cloud of spray—the spout—and this process, known as "blowing" occurs in all whales, although the spout is less visible in smaller species. It is produced by water from around the blowhole being forced into the air. As soon as the animal has exhaled, it takes in fresh air, the air sacs of the lungs return to their expanded condition for maximum gas exchange, and then it dives again.

Cetaceans remain underwater for quite long periods—perhaps more than an hour in the case of the Sperm whale (see p206). Muscles need to continue functioning and they require oxygen, so how is this achieved on a single breath of air? The muscles of cetaceans contain an unusually large amount of a substance called myoglobin which combines with oxygen to form an oxygen store that allows cetaceans to function without fresh oxygen for longer than land mammals.

There is little light deep underwater, so cetaceans rely mainly on senses other than sight to inform them about their surroundings and to help them locate food. They have a very highly developed sense of hearing, and communicate with each other by making a variety of sounds. The toothed whales, which pursue agile fish and squid, locate their prey by using sonar. They emit intense, short pulses of sound in the ultrasonic range (from 0.25–220kHz). These clicks, and other sounds, bounce off objects in their path producing echoes from which the whale is able to build up a sound picture of its surroundings. The arrangement of bones in the skull may have evolved to function like a parabolic reflector to focus the sounds.

The baleen whales have not yet been shown to use echolocation and may instead rely on sight to locate the dense swarms of plankton on which they feed. Some of them communicate with other individuals by the emission of low-frequency sounds (from 20Hz to 30kHz) which may be audible over tens to hundreds of miles across the deep ocean channels.

Evolution

The origins of present-day cetaceans are poorly known. Mammals which are recognizable as cetaceans first appear as fossils in rock strata from the early Middle Eocene (about 50 million years ago). These were elongated aquatic animals, up to 21m (70ft) long, with reduced hindlimbs and long snouts, looking rather like a snake or eel. They have been classified within a separate suborder called Archaeoceti (including the

▲ **The Gray whale's spout.** Each whale makes a distinctive pattern as it blows. That of the Gray is vertical and some division of the spout is noticeable, caused by its emission from twin blowholes.

▼ **Evolution of the whale skull,** showing the modification of the bone structure and teeth. (**1**) *Protocetus*, a land-based creodont with carnivore-like teeth. (**2**) *Prosqualodon*, an intermediate form. (**3**) The Bottle-nosed dolphin, a modern toothed whale, showing the uniform teeth. (**4**) A rorqual, showing the most extreme modification of the bone structure, loss of all the teeth and their replacement by baleen (not shown).

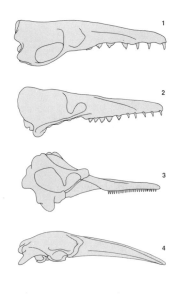

zeuglodonts, so named after the generic name *Zeuglodon* for one of these forms); they flourished during the Eocene epoch but most were extinct before the end of the Oligocene (26 million years ago), and none survived beyond the Miocene (7 million years ago). However, even by the late Middle and early Upper Eocene (40–45 million years ago), these had become so specialized, with sharp incisors and canines for grasping wriggling, slow-moving fish prey, and complex grinding teeth for breaking hard-bodied mollusks and crustaceans, that they could not have been the ancestors of modern cetaceans.

Looking further back in time, members of the terrestrial suborder Mesonychia may have given rise to the zeuglodonts (and thence to all other cetaceans) at the end of the Cretaceous and then colonized the sea during the Paleocene (60 million years ago). These are thought to share with the suborder Arctocyonia (the likely ancestors of present-day ungulates and their relatives) ancestry from the Condylarthra (otherwise known as creodonts). The Mesonychidae resemble the zeuglodonts in a number of skull and dental characters and although the similarities are not all clear-cut, at present they appear to be the most likely ancestors of the Cetacea.

Most of the early zeuglodont remains come from the Mediterranean-Arabian Gulf region, which during the Paleocene formed a narrow semi-enclosed arm of the western part of the ancient Tethys Sea. It is probably here that populations of terrestrial creodonts started to colonize marshes and shallow coastal fringes during the late Paleocene (58 million years ago), exploiting niches vacated at the end of the Cretaceous (65 million years ago) by the vanishing plesiosaurs, ichthyiosaurs and other reptiles. As population pressure on resources intensified during the Eocene, we can speculate that strong selection would have favored adaptations for the capture of fast-moving fish rather than the freshwater and estuarine mollusks and sluggish fish which previously formed their main diet. This was the age of mammals, with massive adaptive radiation into many species; such rapid evolution may help to explain the sparse fossil record for this period, with forms quite quickly developing relatively specialized cetacean characters. During the Eocene, the warm waters of the western Tethys Sea were dominated by the zeuglodonts, but as the climate started to deteriorate and the Tethys Sea enlarged during the Oligocene (38 million years ago), they probably declined in density and abundance, and by the Miocene

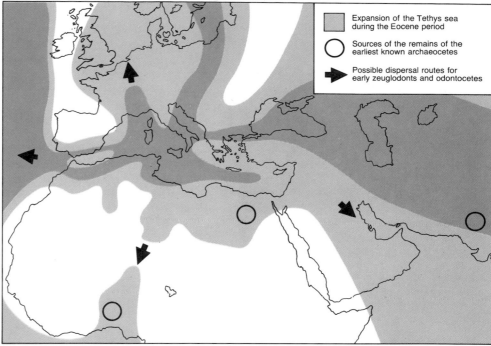

(26 million years ago) were being entirely replaced by odontocetes and mysticetes. The progressively more aquatic mode of life resulted in a backward and upward shift of the external nostrils, and the development of ways to seal them against water. The long mobile neck, functional hindlimbs and, eventually, most of the pelvic girdle were all lost, together with any coat remaining from a terrestrial creodont ancestory, and horizontal tail flukes developed as a means of propulsion by an up-and-down stroke action. The body became more torpedo-shaped to provide greater streamlining and a dorsal fin developed, particularly in the smaller species for hydrodynamic control and temperature regulation.

Most modifications of the zeuglodont skull towards an odontocete (toothed whale) form involved telescoping of the front of the skull, which probably paralleled the development of acoustic scanning as a means of locating cues in the dim underwater environment, and aided the capture of agile prey. At the same time, various specialized organs, notably the "melon," spermaceti organ and nasal diverticula developed. Their exact functions are unknown but are probably involved with both the production and reception of sounds, and with diving; later, sexual selection may have favored greater development of some of these in males of species in which inter-male competition for mates is important.

The dentition of zeuglodonts was differentiated into incisors, canines and grinding teeth, which were probably well adapted for

▲ **The Tethys Sea,** the probable center of whale evolution. The dark blue shows the original extent of the Tethys Sea, the pale blue the extent of the expansion. The black line indicates the present-day landmass.

▼ **The evolution of whales.**

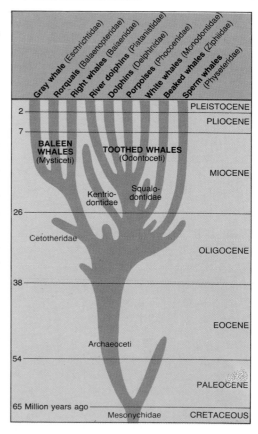

dealing with mollusks and crustaceans, but not for fast-swimming fish. These teeth either became modified during the Eocene, forming the long rows of sharp uniform teeth typical of present-day toothed whales, or later, in the late Oligocene-early Miocene (about 25–30 million years ago), gave rise to the baleen plates: the remarkable feeding structures, present in all mysticetes, which evolved from the curved transverse ridges of the palate in the roof of the mouth. Most present-day forms of baleen whales still have teeth during the early stages of fetal development, a further indication of their common ancestry with the toothed whales, which is also supported by the anatomical and chromosomal evidence.

The earliest true toothed whales were the squalodonts, a group of short-beaked whales (with triangular shark-like teeth), somewhat resembling the modern globicephalids (False killer, Killer and Pilot whales). These were possibly most abundant in the late Oligocene to early Miocene (about 25–30 million years ago), dispersed throughout the Southern Hemisphere, but by the middle Miocene (about 15 million years ago), they were being superseded by representatives of families with living relat-

ives. In particular, the Ziphiidae (beaked whales) can be traced back to a squalodont ancestor, and so can other groups including the Physeteridae (sperm whales) and, in fresh and brackish waters, the Platanistidae (river dolphins), with the Delphinidae (true dolphins) arising a little later in the Pliocene. The relationships of the latter three families are still uncertain, but the sperm whales, which have a much more marked asymmetry of the skull than any other odontocetes, and quite distinct chromosome structure, almost certainly diverged very early in the history of the line.

While the toothed-whale skull was becoming modified to contain acoustic apparatus, the baleen whale skull became modified to a different lifestyle. The upper margin of the "forehead" of the skull underwent considerable forward extension, probably mainly to combat the stresses on the skull and jaws imposed by the wide opening and closing of the mouth, at irregular intervals, as the animal moves forward to take in gulps of seawater from which its mainly planktonic food is sieved.

Food and Feeding
Many small toothed whales appear to have

▲ **Krill strainer.** A Minke whale displaying its short, cream-colored baleen plates, with which it filters its crustacean food, krill, from mouthfuls of water.

▼ **Food of giants.** Individual Antarctic krill grow to a maximum of 7.5cm (3in) but exist in staggering numbers, perhaps 500–750 million tonnes. It is the principal food of the large baleen whales, particularly the Blue whale, but also the Fin, Sei and Minke whales.

generalist diets, opportunistically taking a range of shoaling open-sea fishes, but the extent to which diets overlap between species within a region is not known. Amongst the baleen whales, the thickness and number of baleen plates is related to the size and species of prey taken. Thus the Gray whale (see p221), a highly selective sea-bottom feeder, has a shorter stiffer baleen and fewer throat grooves (usually two or three) than the rorquals (with 14–100), and is thereby adapted for "scouring" the sea bottom. In the rorquals (see p223) the baleen is longer and wider. In the largest species, the Blue whale, the plates may reach a width of nearly 0.75m (2.5ft); in the other rorquals they are correspondingly narrower, and this dictates the diet of each. In the Right and Bowhead whales the baleen is extremely long and fine, and these whales feed on the smallest planktonic invertebrates of any of the baleen whales.

Whereas baleen whales and some toothed whales, such as the Sperm whale, Northern bottlenose whale and Harbor porpoise, tend to feed independently of other members of the same species, a number of small toothed whales, for example Dusky and Common dolphins, appear to herd fish shoals co-operatively by a combination of breaching and fast surface-rushing in groups (see pp 194–195). Communication between individuals presumably is carried out by vocalization (high-pitched squeaks, squeals or grunts) and perhaps also by particular types of breaching. These latter activities often seem to be quite complex, but until we can follow marked individuals (preferably also below water) we cannot be sure of the extent of co-operation between individuals.

Ecology and Natural History

The different evolutionary courses which the baleen and toothed whales have taken have strongly influenced their respective ecologies. Generally speaking, the ocean areas with the highest primary productivity (quantities of plankton), and hence fish and squid dependent upon this, are close to the poles, whereas at tropical latitudes productivity is relatively low (though rich upwellings of nutrients do occur patchily). Polar regions show great seasonal variations, and during the summer the rapid increase in temperature, sunlight and daylength and the relatively stable climatic conditions (particularly with respect to wind) allow phytoplankton—and hence zooplankton and higher organisms such as fish and squid—to build up to very high densities. During the 120-day period of summer

feeding, the great baleen whales probably eat about 3–4 percent of their body weight daily. For an average adult Blue whale this would amount to about 2–2.5 tonnes of food every 24 hours, and correspondingly less for the smaller rorquals. Present-day whale populations in the Southern Ocean (including all species of baleen whales) consume about 40 million tonnes of krill each year. Before these whale populations were exploited by man, this figure may have been as high as 200 million tonnes. Thus during part of the year (about four months in the Southern Ocean but often more than six months in the North Pacific and North Atlantic where productivity is lower), the great whales migrate to high latitudes to feed, and here they may put on as much as 50–70 percent of their body weight as blubber. During the rest of the year, feeding rates may be reduced to about a tenth of the summer value (0.4 percent of body weight daily) and this negative net energy intake results in much of the blubber store being used by the time the whales return to the feeding grounds.

Why should the great baleen whales use up the food they have stored in their blubber to migrate to regions nearer the Equator where there is little food? This is not an easy question to answer. Many smaller cetacean species spend all the year at high latitudes and appear to be perfectly capable of rearing their young in this relatively cool environment, despite being less well insulated, so why should the larger whales travel to these warm waters to breed? It is understandable why they do not breed at high latitudes in winter since the low productivity of food and low water temperatures at this time would almost certainly impose too severe an

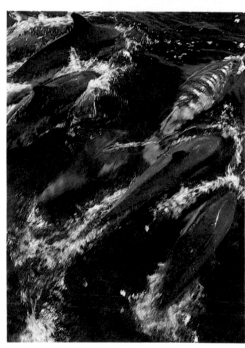

▲ **A short time to live.** TOP Trapped on an ice floe, this Weddell seal will eventually be tipped into the water and eaten by the attacking Killer whales. Killer whales are opportunist feeders.

▲ **Collaborative feeders.** ABOVE Dolphins, like these Common dolphins, cooperate in rounding up shoals of fish, presumably because it is more effective than individual hunting.

energetic strain to rear their young. On the other hand, in summer primary productivity is very high and water temperatures also much more favorable, so it is difficult to see why they do not breed there, alongside their smaller counterparts. Two plausible answers come to mind.

Firstly, it may be that the growth rates required for the young to attain anything like the large size of their parents, together with the energy intake required by the mother to sustain both herself and her calf, would require a longer period of high productivity than is available in a polar summer. It should also be noted that plankton has a short season of abundance whereas fish and squid are available the year round, and the great whales which undergo extensive migrations are all primarily plankton-feeders. Secondly, the answer may be purely historical. The earliest fossil remains of baleen whales, from about 30 million years ago, occur in low latitudes of the North Atlantic. With the juxtaposition of continental land masses by tectonic plate movement and changes in sea temperature, during the Cenozoic era, they radiated and dispersed towards the poles. As with some long-distance migrant bird species, the present-day movements of the great whales may be a vestige of earlier times, in this case when high productivity was in more equatorial regions.

Whereas baleen whales feed primarily upon zooplankton, the toothed whales feed on either fish or squid. All three prey groups have comparable energy values, weight for weight, and although this takes no account of differences in protein, fat or carbohydrate contents, daily feeding rates are comparable across groups. Body size appears to be the factor which determines whether or not they move out of high latitudes in winter; smaller species have relatively higher feeding rates, irrespective of diet (8–10 percent of body weight daily for the smallest species compared with 3–5 percent for the largest), but total daily intake for a smaller individual is obviously proportionately lower. For a 50kg (110lb) porpoise consuming about 9 percent of its body weight per day, this requires the daily capture of 8–10 fish of herring size.

The smaller cetaceans may be found at most latitudes, and though ranging over large areas (for example, the home range of the Bridled dolphin in the North Pacific appears to be 320–480km (200–300mi) in diameter), they do not tend to make strong north-south migrations.

Although the differences in migratory habits cannot be entirely attributed to diet, other features of cetaceans do appear to depend heavily upon their diets. Plankton- and fish-feeding species all have gestation periods of between 10–13 months whatever their size, whereas squid-feeders have longer gestation periods, of the order of 16 months. This may reflect the relative food values (protein, fat and carbohydrate amounts rather than simply energy values) of the different prey, squid perhaps being a poorer quality food, or it may relate to the relative seasonal availabilities of those prey. Amongst large whales, lactation periods are relatively longer in the squid-feeding Sperm whale (about two years) whereas in plankton-feeding baleen whales it is usually around 5–7 months. Amongst smaller cetaceans, the pattern is less clear but

► **Tearing itself from the sea,** a Humpback breaches in a cauldron of spray. They do this on the breeding grounds and, as here, in Glacier Bay, Alaska, on the feeding grounds. As with other whales, breaching appears to serve two functions: stunning or panicking fish shoals and communicating information to other herd members.

▼ **The antarctic world of the Humpback.** Barren though it looks, the Southern Ocean in summer swarms with vast quantities of krill, on which the whales feed.

associated with oceanographic features such as upwellings (where food concentrations tend to occur), or undersea topographic features such as continental shelf slopes (which may serve as cues for navigation between areas). Breeding areas for most cetacean species (particularly small toothed whales) are very poorly known, but are better known for some of the large whales.

Gray whales and Right whales seem to require shallow coastal bays in warm waters for calving, whereas balaenopterids such as Blue, Fin and Sei whales possibly breed in deeper waters further offshore. The former group thus has more localized calving areas than the latter

The lengths of the gestation and lactation periods do of course dictate the frequency at which a female may bear young. Cetaceans usually give birth to a single young. In the large plankton-feeding whales an individual female may bear its young every alternate year (in Right whales, perhaps every 3 years); in squid-feeding species this is every 2–5 years; and in the smaller species feeding on fish, a female may reproduce every year. In the Killer whale, with its mixed diet, females reproduce at intervals of 3–8 years. With these relatively low reproductive rates, together with delayed maturation (4–8 years in plankton-feeders; 4–10 years in fish-feeders; and 8–26 years in squid-feeders), it is not surprising that most species are long-lived (14–50 years in the smaller species, but 50–100 years in the large baleen whales, the Sperm whale, and the Killer whale). Natural mortality rates seem to decrease in different whale species as their size increases with (where it has been studied) little apparent difference between juvenile and adult rates. Current estimates are 9–10 percent per annum for Minke whales; 7.5 percent for Sperm whales; and 4 percent for Fin whales. The long maturation in squid-feeders probably results from the need for a long period to learn efficient capture of the relatively difficult and agile squid prey.

During the period of mating, most cetacean species congregate in particular areas. These may be the same warm-water areas as those in which calving occurs during the winter months, as with a number of the larger baleen whales, or they may be on feeding grounds at high latitudes during the summer, as with many small toothed whales. Mating is usually seasonal, but in a number of gregarious dolphin species sexual activity has been observed during most months of the year.

similar: squid-feeding species have lactation periods varying from 12–20 months, whereas in fish-feeding species they are generally around 10–12 months.

The breeding systems of whales can also be grouped according to diet. Thus in the plankton-feeders the males tend to mate with a single female (although some species, such as the Right and Bowhead whales seem to be promiscuous) and the whales appear to spend most of their time either singly or in pairs, although small groups of usually less than 10 individuals may be seen at feeding concentrations or during apparent long-distance movements. There is evidence to suggest that squid-feeders are polygynous, with a male keeping a harem of females and young animals, other groups being made up of bachelor males or all female herds. Lone bachelor males and other individuals which have not been accepted into a herd may travel alone. This system is exemplified by the Sperm whale (see pp204–209) but also seems to occur in other species such as the Risso's dolphin. The killer whale (see pp190–191), which has a mixed diet of squid, fish, marine birds and mammals, also has a polygynous breeding system. Most fish-feeders, on the other hand, have a rather fluid breeding system, with mixed groups or family units (which may simply be mother-calf pairs) that aggregate on the feeding or mating grounds, and also during long-distance movements. Individuals come and go so that the group is not stable although it may have a constant core. In a number of species studied, it appears that there is no stable pair bond and males are promiscuous.

Cetaceans are not randomly distributed over any region but instead appear to be

Whales and Man

Man has interacted with whales for almost as long as we have archaeological evidence of his activities. Whale carvings have been found in Norse settlements dating from 4,000 years ago and Alaskan Eskimo middens, 3,500 years old, contain the remains of whales which clearly have been used for food. It is quite possible, of course, that at this time whales were not being actively hunted but were taken only when stranded upon the coast. However, with the likely seasonal abundance of whales in the polar regions as the oceans warmed after the Pleistocene, it would be surprising if these early hunters had not actively exploited them.

At about the same time (3,200 years ago) the Ancient Greeks had incorporated dolphins into their culture in a non-consumptive way, for they appear on frescoes in the Minoan temple of Knossos in Crete, and many Greek myths refer to altruistic behavior by dolphins. Arion, the lyric poet and musician, when returning to Corinth from Italy with riches bestowed upon him at a music competition, was set upon by the crew of the boat in which he traveled. The legend goes that he asked if he might play one last tune and, on being granted this, a school of dolphins was attracted to the music and approached the boat. On sighting them near the boat, Arion leapt overboard, was rescued by the dolphins and carried to safety on the back of one of them. The Greek philosopher Aristotle (384–322BC) was the first to study whales and dolphins in detail, and although some of his information is incorrect and often contradictory, many of his detailed descriptions of their anatomy and physiology are accurate and clearly indicate that he had dissected specimens.

The earliest record of whaling in Europe comes from the Norsemen of Scandinavia between 800 and 1,000AD. Slightly later, in the 12th century, the Basques were hunting whales quite extensively in the Bay of Biscay. Early fisheries for whales probably concentrated upon the Right and Bowhead whales (see pp230–237) since they are slow-moving and they float after death (due to their high oil content), so that they could be pursued by men with hand harpoons first from promontories and later from small open boats. It is possible that a Gray whale population existed in the North Atlantic and was hunted to extinction in earlier times.

From the Bay of Biscay, whaling gradually spread northwards up the European coast and across to Greenland, where

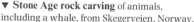
▲ **The grace of dolphins** endeared them to the great Mediterranean and Aegean civilizations. This mural from the Palace of Knossos, Crete, was executed about 1600BC.

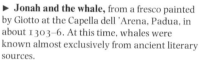
▶ **Jonah and the whale,** from a fresco painted by Giotto at the Capella dell 'Arena, Padua, in about 1303–6. At this time, whales were known almost exclusively from ancient literary sources.

▼ **Stone Age rock carving** of animals, including a whale, from Skegerveien, Norway.

Basque ships were recorded in the 16th century. Whaling was no longer a local subsistence activity and by the next century the Dutch and then the British started whaling in arctic waters, particularly around Jan Mayen Island and Spitsbergen. During the 17th century, whaling was also starting from eastern North America, mainly catching Right whales and Humpbacks as they migrated along the coast. All through this period, the whalers used small sailing ships and struck their prey with hand harpoons from rowing boats. The whales were then towed ashore to land or ice floes, or cut up and processed in the sea alongside the boat. In contrast, whaling in Japan, which developed around 1600, used nets and fleets of small boats.

As vessels improved, whalers started to pursue other species, notably the deep-sea Sperm whale. In the 18th and 19th centuries, the whalers of New England (USA), Britain and Holland moved first southwards in the Atlantic and then round Cape Horn westwards into the Pacific and round the Cape of South Africa eastwards into the Indian Ocean. In the first half of the 19th century, Hawaii became a major whaling base and others started in South Africa and the Seychelles. By this time, the arctic whalers had penetrated far into the icy waters of Greenland, the Davis Strait, and Spitsbergen, where they took Bowhead and Right whales and, later, Humpbacks. Over-hunting caused the collapse of whaling in the North Atlantic by the late 1700s and in the North Pacific during the mid-1800s. British arctic whaling ceased in 1912.

Sperm whaling flourished until about 1850 but then declined rapidly during the next decade. Whaling for Right whales also started up in the higher latitudes of the Pacific, off New Zealand, Australia and the Kerguelen Islands during the first half of the 19th century, and from 1840 onwards for Bowheads in the Bering, Chukchi and Beaufort seas. However, populations of both species had declined markedly by the end of the century.

In 1868, a Norwegian, Svend Foyn, developed an explosive harpoon gun and, at about the same time, steam-driven vessels replaced the sailing ships. Both these innovations had a significant impact on the remaining great whales, allowing ships to pursue even the fast-moving rorquals.

By the end of the 19th century, whalers concentrated on the waters off Newfoundland, the west coast of Africa and in the Pacific. Then, in 1905, the whalers discovered the rich antarctic feeding grounds of Blue, Fin and Sei whales and the Southern Ocean rapidly became the center of whaling in the world, with South Georgia its major base. All this time, whaling had been land-based, but in 1925 the first modern factory ship started operations in the Antarctic. This had a slipway and winches on the deck which allowed whales to be hauled on board, and hence allowed whaling to operate away from shore stations. A rapid expansion of the whaling industry occurred

▲ **Lancing a Sperm whale.** A painting of a typical scene from the days when large whales were hunted from small boats with hand harpoons.

▼ **Whales in the early 19th century.** Engravings of baleen whales from Lacépède's *Histoire Naturelle des Cetacés* (1804).

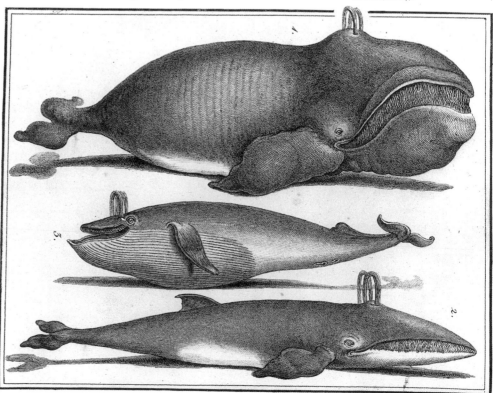

When the whale comes aboue water ẙ ſhallop rowes towards him and being within reach of him the harpoiner darts his harpingiron at him out of both his hands and being faſt they lance him to death

The whale is cut up as hee lyes floting croſſe the ſtearne of a ſhipp the blubber is cut from the fleſh by peeces 7 or 4 foote long and being raſed is rowed on ſhore ẙtowards the coppers

They place 2 or 3 coppers on a roe and ẙ chopping boat on the one ſide and the cooling boate on the other ſide to recuiue ẙ oyle of ẙ coppers, the chopt blubber being boyled is taken out of the coppers and put in wiker baſkets or barowes throug ẙ the oyle is dreaned and rúnes into ẙ cooler ẙ is ẙ fall ẙ water out of ẙ it is ẙ conuaied by trougkes into buts of hogsheads

▲ **Whaling in the 17th century,** as depicted in this woodcut of the Spitsbergen whale fishery. According to this account, the whales were cut up in the water.

▶ **Whalebone drying** in the yard at the Pacific Steamship Company, San Francisco, in the 1880s.

in this region, with 46,000 whales taken in the 1937–8 season, until, yet again, populations of successive target species declined to commercial extinction. The largest and hence most valuable of the rorquals, the Blue whale, dominated the catches in the 1930s but had declined to very few by the middle 1950s, and was eventually totally protected in 1965. As these populations declined, attention turned to the next largest rorqual, and so on (see pp226–227).

Following the population collapse of Sperm whales by 1860, whaling continued with a world catch of only about 5,000 annually until 1948. Since then, catches have increased quite rapidly, with about 20,000 a year being taken (mainly in the North Pacific and the Southern Hemisphere) in recent years, although this has now been reduced to a small quota of males only in the North Pacific.

Until the middle of this century, the whaling industry was dominated by Norway and the United Kingdom, with Holland and the United States also taking substantial shares. Since World War II, however, these nations have abandoned deep-sea whaling, and the industry has become dominated by Japan and the Soviet Union, although many nations practice coastal whaling.

Originally, the most important product of modern deep-sea whaling was oil, that of baleen whales used in margarines and other foodstuffs, and that of Sperm whales used in specialized lubricants. Since about 1950, meal for animal foodstuffs, and chemical products became increasingly important, although whale meat (from baleen whales) became highly valued for human consumption by the Japanese. The Soviet Union, the other major whaling nation, on the other hand, uses very little whale meat and instead concentrates upon Sperm whales for oil. Recent figures (late 1970s) indicate that whale catches in the Antarctic yielded 29 percent meat, 20 percent oil and 7 percent meal and solubles.

In the last 15 years, whales have become political animals, as public attention and sympathy have increasingly turned towards their plight. People watching whales in the coastal lagoons of California and dolphins at close quarters as captive animals in dolphinaria throughout the developed world were impressed by their friendliness and ability to learn complicated tricks. But most of the great whales were continuing to decline, as one section of the human population overexploited them. The International Whaling Commission, set up in 1946 to regulate whaling activities, was generally ineffective because the advice of its scientific committee was often overruled by short-term commercial considerations. In 1972, the US Marine Mammal Act prohibited the taking and importing of marine mammals and their products except under certain conditions, such as by some Indians, Eskimos and Aleuts for subsistence or native handicrafts and clothing. In the same year, the United Nations Conference on the Human Environment called for a 10-year moratorium on whaling. The latter was not accepted by the International Whaling Commission, but continued publicity and pressure, particularly on moral grounds, from environmental bodies (such as World Wildlife Fund, Friends of the Earth, and Greenpeace), and concern expressed by many scientists over the difficulties in estimating population sizes and maximum sustainable yields, finally had an effect. In 1982 a ban on all commercial whaling was agreed upon for the first time in the history of man, to take effect from 1986.

But the story of man's often unhappy relationship with whales does not end here. Even if we terminate commercial whaling forever or acquire sufficient knowledge to manage whale populations in a sustained manner, they continue to face threats from man, and these are likely to increase. Modification of the marine environment is occurring in many parts of the world as human populations increase and become more industrialized, making greater demands upon the sea either by removing organisms for food, or by releasing toxic waste products

into it. Acoustic disturbance comes from sonic testing (for example during oil exploration), military depth charge practice and particularly from motor boat traffic. These probably impose threats to whales in a number of areas of the world, notably the North Sea and English Channel, the Gulfs of California and St. Lawrence, the Caribbean, Hawaii, and tropical Australia. A number of species, such as the Humpback, the Right and Bowhead whales, the Californian Gray whale population, and small toothed whales, such as the Harbor porpoise and the beluga, are particularly vulnerable. Toxic chemical pollution (particularly from heavy metals, oil and persistent chemicals) from urban, industrial and agricultural effluents may also have serious harmful effects in enclosed seas such as the Baltic, Mediterranean and North Seas, and coastal species such as the Harbor porpoise are vulnerable and presently showing declines. Actual removal of suitable habitat by the building of coastal hotel resorts, breakwaters which change local current patterns and encourage silting, and dams which regulate water flow in rivers, all impose threats. Species most vulnerable are usually those that are rare and localized in distribution, such as the Gulf of California porpoise and the Ganges and Indus river dolphins (see pp178–179). Incidental catches in fishing nets of large numbers of dolphins have recently caused heavy mortality (see pp193 and 198).

Finally, one factor which for whales and dolphins may represent the greatest threat is the increasing need for man to exploit the sea for food. The depletion of the great whales in the early part of this century had repercussions on the populations remaining and on related species (see pp226–227). This was thought to be the result of relaxation of pressures on the food supply through lower competition. It was not only whales that were affected, but also the Crabeater seal (see pp280–281) and various seabird species, all of which showed signs of population increase. The converse now looks as if it might occur as man is beginning to harvest a variety of food organisms (for example krill in the Southern Ocean, capelin, sand eels and sprats in the North Atlantic), which form important links in the marine food chain for cetaceans, seals and seabirds alike. These potential problems are unlikely to evoke the same passions as overexploitation by the whaling nations, but nevertheless will have to be addressed if these magnificent creatures are to continue to grace our oceans.   PGHE

▼ ▲ **Whaling in the 1980s** – the Faeroes whales hunt. ABOVE Small-scale whaling for Pilot whales is still carried on, with much ritual and folklore, in the Faeroe Islands. BELOW Lining up the catch of Pilot whales at Torshavn in the Faeroe Islands.

TOOTHED WHALES

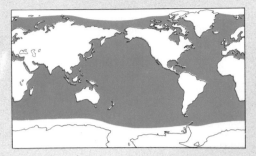

Suborder: Odontoceti
Sixty-six species in 33 genera and six families.
Distribution: all oceans.

Habitat: deep sea, coastal shallows and some
river estuaries.

Size: head-to-tail length from 1.2m (4ft) in
Heaviside's dolphin to 20.7m (68ft) in the
Sperm whale; weight from 40kg (88lb) in
Heaviside's dolphin to 70 tonnes in the Sperm
whale.

River dolphins (family Platanistidae)
Five species in 4 genera including **Ganges
dolphin** (*Platanista gangetica*), **Indus dolphin**
(*Platanista minor*).

Dolphins (family Delphinidae)
Thirty-two species in 17 genera, including
Common dolphin (*Delphinus delphis*), **Killer
whale** (*Orcinus orca*), **Melon-headed whale**
(*Peponocephala electra*), **Risso's dolphin**
(*Grampus griseus*).

Porpoises (family Phocoenidae)
Six species in 3 genera, including **Finless
porpoise** (*Neophocaena phocaenoides*).

White whales (family Monodontidae)
Two species in 2 genera: **Narwhal** (*Monodon
monoceros*), **Beluga** (*Delphinapterus leucas*).

Sperm whales (family Physeteridae)
Three species in 2 genera: **Sperm whale**
(*Physeter macrocephalus*), **Pygmy sperm whale**
(*Kogia breviceps*), **Dwarf sperm whale** (*Kogia
simus*).

Beaked whales (family Ziphiidae)
Eighteen species in 5 genera, including:
Northern bottlenose whale (*Hyperoodon
ampullatus*).

N EARLY 90 percent of the cetacean species belong to the suborder Odontoceti—the toothed whales. Most of these are comparatively small dolphins and porpoises, usually less than 4.5m (15ft) in length, but some, such as the beaked whales, pilot whales and Killer whale, may reach a length of 9m (30ft), and one, the Sperm whale, reaches 18m (60ft) or more. In most of the toothed whales the jaws are prolonged as a beak-like snout behind which the forehead rises in a rounded curve or "melon." As their name suggests, toothed whales always bear teeth, however rudimentary, in the upper or lower jaws, or both, at some stage of their lives. The teeth look alike and always have a single root, so that they are simple or slightly recurved pegs set in single sockets. One set of teeth lasts a lifetime (monophyodont dentition).

The family Platanistidae (river dolphins) is regarded as the most primitive of living cetaceans. The freshwater habit of most members of this family is probably secondary, since platanistid fossils from the Miocene and Pliocene have been found in marine deposits. All the platanistids have a long beak and rather broad short flippers, probably used for obtaining tactile cues from the environment, the eyes are very small and two species (the Indus and Ganges dolphins) are virtually blind. These animals often lie in very turbid water where sight would be of little value, and they have developed instead a relatively sophisticated capacity for echolocation.

Another evolutionary side-arm appears to be the family Ziphiidae (the beaked whales), so named because of the distinct beak which extends from the skull. In all except one species, the teeth are very re-duced in number and entirely absent from the upper jaw. On each side of the lower jaw of adult males there are only one or two teeth; these are comparatively large, sometimes projecting from the mouth as small tusks. In young males and in females their teeth do not usually emerge from the gums so that these appear as entirely toothless. Another unusual feature is the chromosome number, 42 instead of 44, which is shared by only the almost certainly distantly related sperm whales. Most of the species are extremely elusive, and many are known only from stranded specimens.

The family Physeteridae probably diverged from the main odontocete line as long ago as the Oligocene. They comprise only three living species: the cosmopolitan Sperm whale, the Pygmy sperm whale of the warmer waters of the Atlantic, Indian and Pacific Oceans, and the little-known Dwarf sperm whale of tropical waters. The first of these is the largest of the toothed whales, with the males twice as large as the females. It is characterized by a huge barrel-shaped head containing spermaceti oil, a rounded dorsal hump two-thirds of the way along the back instead of a dorsal fin, and a very narrow underslung lower jaw which lacks functional teeth. The other two species are built similarly but are much smaller, with a less pronounced head and a distinct dorsal fin.

The last three families (Monodontidae, Phocoenidae, Delphinidae) which make up the Odontoceti are all rather closely related and probably diverged sometime in the middle Miocene. The two species of Monodontidae, the narwhal and beluga, are confined to the northern oceans, particularly the Arctic. They are relatively small

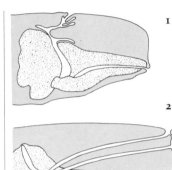

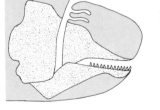

▲ **The nostrils of toothed whales** in general show a migration backwards and towards the top of the skull compared to land mammals. The Narwhal (1) and Pygmy Sperm whale (3) are typical. The Sperm whale (2) is unusual, in that its development of the huge spermaceti organ made this pattern unworkable and two new passages were formed, through the spermaceti organ to the front of the nose.

▶ **A Killer bares its teeth.** The Killer whale has fewer teeth than most toothed whales but they are large and strong for seizing large fish, squid and other marine vertebrates. The Killer does not chew its food but swallows it whole or tears off large chunks.

Skulls of Toothed Whales

In the evolution of toothed whales from terrestrial carnivores a telescoping of the skull has taken place, resulting in a long narrow "beak" and a movement of the posterior maxillary bone to the supra-occipital region (top of the skull). These changes were associated with the development of echolocating abilities and the modification of the teeth for catching fish. The teeth of the toothed whales' ancestors were differentiated into incisors, canines and molars, as in modern carnivores, but the ideal dentition for fish eaters is a long row of even, conical teeth, and this is in fact roughly the pattern in all toothed whales. The Bottle-nosed dolphin is a classic fish-eater, with numerous small sharp teeth. The number of teeth is greatly reduced (10–14 on each side of both jaws) in the Killer whale, which will feed on mammals as well as fish. The beaked whales feed on squid and have become virtually toothless. Those of genus *Mesoplodon*, like Gervais's beaked whale, have a single tooth in the lower jaw.

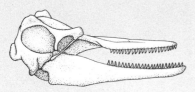

Bottle-nosed dolphin   60cm

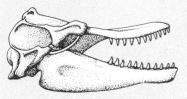

Killer whale   120cm

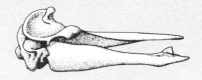

Gervais's beaked whale   120cm

whales and neither has a dorsal fin. The narwhal is unique in having a tooth modified to form a unicorn's tusk which projects from the snout.

The family Phocoenidae (the porpoises) appears to have radiated and dispersed from the tropics into temperate waters of both hemispheres, probably during the Miocene-Pliocene (about 7 million years ago). One of the six species, the Finless porpoise, may be nearest to the ancestors of this family, with a warm water Indo-Pacific distribution that includes estuaries and rivers. All are small species with a rounded snout, no beak, and a relatively small number of spade-shaped teeth (unlike the conical teeth of most other toothed whales).

The largest odontocete family is the Delphinidae (the dolphins), most of which have functional teeth in both jaws, a melon with a distinct beak, and a dorsal fin, and many have striking black and white countershading pigmentation. The largest of these is the Killer whale, in which the male is twice as large as the female; it also differs from other delphinids in having a large rounded flipper, lacking any beak, and preying upon other marine mammals. Some, for example the genus *Lagenorhynchus*, form species-pairs with an antitropical distribution (ie they are found in both hemispheres away from the tropics); others, for example the genus *Tursiops*, have virtually identical Northern and Southern Hemisphere populations, but with a smaller form in the tropics than at higher latitudes; some, for example the Common dolphin, Killer whale and Risso's dolphin, have a cosmopolitan distribution; still others, such as the Melon-headed whale have a restricted pantropical distribution.   PGHE

RIVER DOLPHINS

Family: Platanistidae
Five species in four genera.
Distribution: SE Asia, S America.

Ganges dolphin
Platanista gangetica
Ganges dolphin or Ganges susu.
Distribution: India, Nepal, Bangladesh.
Habitat: Ganges-Brahmaputra-Meghna river
system. Length 210–260cm (83–102in);
weight 80–90kg (175–200lb). Skin: light
grayish-brown, paler beneath. Gestation: 10
months. Longevity: over 28 years.

Indus dolphin [E]
Platanista minor
Indus dolphin or Indus susu.
Distribution: Pakistan. Habitat: Indus river.
Size, coat, diet, gestation and longevity
(probably): as Ganges dolphin.

Whitefin dolphin [I]
Lipotes vexillifer
Whitefin dolphin or pei'chi.
Distribution: China. Habitat: Yangtze and
lower Fuchunjian Rivers. Length 230–250cm
(90–98in); weight 135–230kg (300–510lb).
Skin: bluish-gray, white underneath.
Gestation: probably 10–12 months.

Amazon dolphin
Inia geoffrensis
Amazon dolphin or boutu.
Distribution: South America. Habitat: Amazon
and Orinoco river systems. Length 208–228cm
(82–228in) (Orinoco), 224–247cm (96–108in)
(Amazon); weight 85–130kg (190–285lb).
Skin: dark bluish-gray above, pink beneath;
darker in Orinoco. Gestation: probably 10–12
months.

La Plata dolphin
Pontoporia blainvillei
La Plata dolphin or franciscana.
Distribution: coast of eastern S America from
Ubatuba to Valdes Peninsula (not in La Plata
river). Length 155–175cm (61–69in): weight
32–52kg (71–115lb). Skin: light, warm brown,
paler beneath. Gestation: 11 months.
Longevity: more than 16 years.

[E] Endangered. [I] Indeterminate.

D OLPHINS with eyes so poor that they are only capable of distinguishing night and day, yet are able to detect a copper wire 1mm (0.03in) in diameter—such are the river dolphins, which rely on their extremely sensitive echolocation apparatus to find their food. Their vision has been all but lost in the course of evolution because in the muddy estuaries that they inhabit visibility may be only a few centimeters.

The river dolphins are the most primitive dolphins, retaining certain features of Miocene cetaceans of about 10 million years ago. They have a long slender beak bearing numerous pointed teeth, and the neck is flexible because the seven neck vertebrae are not fused. The forehead melon is pronounced, the dorsal fin undeveloped, and the flippers broad and visibly fingered. The eye and visual nerve have degenerated in the descending order: Indus and Ganges dolphins, Amazon dolphin, Whitefin dolphin, La Plata dolphin. In the Indus and Ganges dolphins the lens has been lost altogether, which means that no image can be formed and only light or dark and the direction of light can be registered.

The brains of river dolphins are small: only the Amazon dolphin at 650g (23oz) and 1.3 percent of body-weight, has a brain of comparable size to other dolphins. The small brain size relates to their early weaning and short learning period, and also to their solitary life, lacking in social behavior comparable to modern dolphins.

Because of their poor eyesight, river dolphins use echolocation to find their food, which comprises mostly fish, shrimps and,

▼ **The five species of river dolphins.** Despite their widely separated habitats, the river dolphins are very similar in appearance, differing mainly in skin color, length of beak and number of teeth. (1) Amazon dolphin (*Inia geoffrensis*). (2) La Plata dolphin (*Pontoporia blainvillei*). (3) Ganges dolphin (*Platanista gangetica*). (4) Indus dolphin (*Platanista minor*). (5) Whitefin dolphin (*Lipotes vexillifer*).

in the coastal La Plata dolphin, squid and octopus. They emit directed ultrasonic pulses or clicks, at distinctive frequencies for each species, which rebound from any object, allowing the dolphin to judge its distance by the time the pulse takes to return. The nasal air sacs and air sinuses lining the well-developed crest on the upper jawbone direct the pulse to the target. The sensory bristles along the beak also help in locating food on the river bottom. The coastal species, the La Plata dolphin, is thought to find its prey by means of the light they emit (bioluminescence) or by sound.

The teeth are conical and thickened at the base near the back. The Ganges and Indus and the Amazon dolphins have four stomach compartments, including an esophageal compartment for food storage, as in most cetaceans. The La Plata and Whitefin dolphins seem to have lost the esophageal compartment.

Information on growth and reproduction is still fragmentary. The La Plata dolphin matures at 2–3 years and females breed every two years. When growth stops at four years, females are larger than males by about 20cm (8in). This is in contrast to the Indus and Ganges dolphins, in which sexual maturity occurs somewhere around 10 years and growth lasts for more than 20 years. Although females are about 40cm (16in) longer than males, this is entirely accounted for by a greatly extended beak, and the weight difference is small. In both species, calves are weaned before 8–9

months and start their solitary life. The period of growth of the Amazon dolphin is as long as that of the Ganges, but the males are larger and heavier than the females.

Among human factors adversely affecting river dolphins, the most destructive is dam construction. In the Indus River system, the construction of dams for power and irrigation started in the early 1900s, and divided the habitat up into 10 segments, thus inhibiting movement of dolphins and fish. In winter, no water flows to the sea and many upper sections are almost dry. This and hunting for dolphin oil, used in medicine, left a significant number of dolphins only between Guddu and Sukkur barrages, and made the Indus dolphin one of the most vulnerable of all the cetaceans, with a population of about 600.

Although the Ganges dolphin is not vulnerable at present, it too is now threatened by dam construction. In the Yangtze River, the low population of Whitefin dolphins seems to be declining, and here too work is now in progress on dams and drainage systems. Fishing gear often causes accidental death or injury. The South American river dolphins are in a more favorable situation, but here too development is threatening.

Besides these human threats, river dolphins will increasingly come into competition with more adaptive and possibly more intelligent dolphins.   TK

DOLPHINS

Family: Delphinidae
Thirty-two species in 17 genera.
Distribution: all oceans.

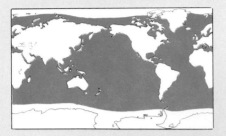

Habitat: generally coastal shallows but some open-sea.

Size: head-to-tail length from 1.2m (3.5ft) in Heaviside's dolphin to 7m (23ft) in the Killer whale; weight from 40kg (88lb) in Heaviside's dolphin to 4.5 tonnes in the Killer whale.

Gestation: 10–12 months (16 months in pilot whales and Risso's dolphin).

Longevity: up to 50–100 years (Killer whale).

Species include: **Bottle-nosed dolphin** (*Tursiops truncatus*), **Bridled dolphin** (*Stenella attenuata*), **Common dolphin** (*Delphinus delphis*), **False killer whale** (*Pseudorca crassidens*), **Guiana dolphin** (*Sotalia guianensis*), **Humpbacked dolphin** (*Sousa teuszii*), **Killer whale** (*Orcinus orca*), **Melon-headed whale** (*Peponocephala electra*), **Risso's dolphin** (*Grampus griseus*), **Spinner dolphin** (*Stenella longirostris*), **Tucuxi** (*Sotalia fluviatilis*).

THE sight of dolphins eagerly performing complicated tricks in oceanaria has probably done more than anything else to put them in a rather special position in the eyes of mankind. It has been argued that their intelligence and developed social organization are equaled only by the primates, perhaps only by man, while their general friendliness and lack of agression are compared favorably with man.

The family Delphinidae is a relatively modern group, having evolved during the late Miocene (about 10 million years ago). They are the most abundant and varied of all cetaceans.

Most dolphins are small to medium-sized animals with a well-developed beak and a central sickle-shaped dorsal fin curving backwards. They have a single crescent-shaped blowhole, with the concave side facing forwards on top of the head, and they have functional well-separated teeth in both jaws (between 10 and 224 but most between 100 and 200). Most delphinids have a forehead melon although this is indistinct in some species, for example the Guiana dolphin and tucuxi, absent in *Cephalorhynchus* species, pronounced and rounded to form an indistinct beak in Risso's dolphin and the two species of pilot whales, and tapered to form a blunt snout in Killer and False killer whales. Killer whales also have rounded paddle-shaped flippers, whereas the pilot whales and False killer have narrow, elongated flippers. The aforementioned species are not closely related to each other but several genera, particularly *Delphinus*, *Stenella*, *Sousa* and *Sotalia*, contain species which are indistinct from each other.

The extensive variation in color patterns

▲ **Dolphin dapples.** The beautiful patterns on many dolphins may help to conceal them from their prey or their predators. The light patterns near the surface blend with the dolphin's coloration to break up the outline of the dolphin. These are Common dolphins.

▶ **Apparently doing press-ups,** this Indo-Pacific humpbacked dolphin shows why this species rarely strands. It is quite at home in shallow water and can even traverse mudbanks between waters.

◀ **The exuberance of Dusky dolphins** finds expression in graceful leaps. These may not always be functional and at times may simply be for the fun of it.

◀ **Riding the surf,** a Risso's dolphin plows through a wave. This species moves around in herds of stable composition, often one or more males, some females and their young.

between species has been variously categorized. One classification recognizes three types: uniform (plain or evenly marked), patched (with clearly demarcated pigmented areas) and countershaded (black and white). The more conspicuous patched patterns are considered useful for visual recognition by individuals while the others are for concealment from their prey, the uniform ones being related to feeding at depths where light is dim, and the counter-shaded ones to feeding near the surface. The color patterns of some may also be camouflage from predators: the saddle pattern may afford protection from being seen by predators (or prey) through its counter-

lighting effect; the spotted pattern blends directly with a background of sun-dappled water; criss-crossed patterns have both counter-shading and disruptive elements.

The morphological and anatomical differences between dolphins relate partly to differences in diet. Those species with more rounded foreheads, blunt beaks, and often reduced dentition, feed primarily upon squid, or, in the case of the Killer whale, the diet also includes marine mammals and birds. The development of the cranial region may be an adaptation for receiving and focusing acoustic signals to obtain an accurate picture of the location of their agile, fast-moving prey. The other members of the family feed primarily upon fish: all appear to be opportunist feeders, probably catching whatever species of fish they encounter within particular size ranges. Some, for example Bottle-nosed and Humpbacked dolphins, are primarily inshore species, although they may feed upon both bottom-dwelling and open-sea fish. Others, such as members of the genera *Stenella* and *Delphinus* are more pelagic, ie they feed further out to sea, but take shoaling fish both close to the surface (such as anchovy,

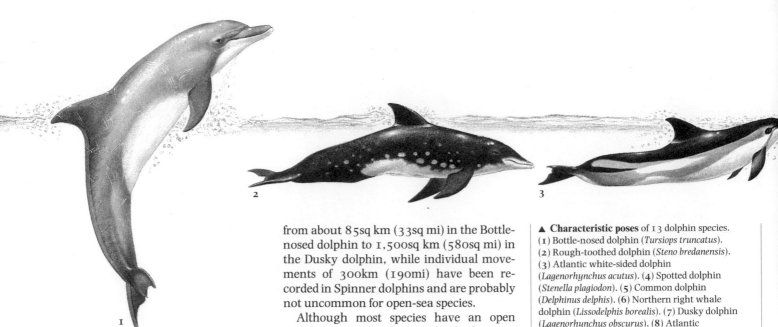

herring and capelin) and at great depths (such as lantern fish).

Most dolphins at least occasionally feed upon squid, and even shrimps. This generalist diet makes it very difficult to determine the extent of competition among dolphin species. In the tropical eastern Pacific, however, Bridled dolphins feed largely on open-sea fish near the surface, whereas the related Spinner dolphin feeds at deeper levels; both may also feed at different times of the day.

The more pelagic dolphin species tend to travel in herds of up to 1,000 or more, whose members may cooperate in the capture of shoaling fish (see pp194–195). Inshore species usually form smaller herds of 2–12 individuals. While foraging, dolphin schools often spread out to form a band, varying from about 20m (66ft) to several kilometers wide, and usually comprising small groups of 5–25 but which together may total in the hundreds. They often follow undersea escarpments. At upwellings where plankton fronts develop and shoaling fish concentrate, these groups often coalesce and frenzied feeding activity may follow.

Radio-tracking studies have shown that dolphins may have home ranges varying from about 85sq km (33sq mi) in the Bottle-nosed dolphin to 1,500sq km (580sq mi) in the Dusky dolphin, while individual movements of 300km (190mi) have been recorded in Spinner dolphins and are probably not uncommon for open-sea species.

Although most species have an open social structure, where individuals enter and leave the herd over periods of time, some, such as the Killer whale and Risso's dolphin, appear to have more stable group membership. These latter tend to be polygynous, with an adult male holding a harem of adult females and young, although there are also all-male herds of young animals. The herds of most other dolphins seem to comprise family groups of male, female and calf or mother-calf pairs, which may aggregate to form larger herds, or herds that are segregated by sex and age. Their mating system is not clear but generally appears to be promiscuous. Polygyny may also occur, but whatever the mating system, the male-female and male-calf bonds are relatively weak.

Until recently, virtually all information about dolphins was derived from dead animals that had come ashore on coasts. Most of these have died at sea and have simply been washed ashore, but some strand while alive, and such incidents are most conspicuous when groups of animals strand together, which is most prevalent among Pilot whales (see Box) and False killers. The problem with interpreting

▲ **Characteristic poses** of 13 dolphin species. (1) Bottle-nosed dolphin (*Tursiops truncatus*). (2) Rough-toothed dolphin (*Steno bredanensis*). (3) Atlantic white-sided dolphin (*Lagenorhynchus acutus*). (4) Spotted dolphin (*Stenella plagiodon*). (5) Common dolphin (*Delphinus delphis*). (6) Northern right whale dolphin (*Lissodelphis borealis*). (7) Dusky dolphin (*Lagenorhynchus obscurus*). (8) Atlantic humpbacked dolphin (*Sousa teuszii*). (9) Melon-headed whale (*Peponocephala electra*). (10) Commerson's dolphin (*Cephalorhynchus commersoni*). (11) False killer whale (*Pseudorca crassidens*). (12) Killer whale (*Orcinus orca*). (13) Risso's dolphin (*Grampus griseus*).

fluctuations in the numbers of strandings in a particular region is that the same result may be observed by a change in the population size in that area with constant mortality, or a change in mortality with constant population size.

The Melon-headed whale, for example, was scarcely ever recorded until the 1960s, since when there have been a number of mass strandings. It seems rather unlikely that these species have been overlooked previously and one must conclude that their populations have actually increased. In certain cases, increases in the number of strandings appear to be related to increases in the abundance of particular food fishes which probably attracted dolphins into the area. For example, the recent increase in numbers of Pilot whales stranding in southwest England, mainly in fall-winter (an average of less than one per year between 1913–1947; two per year between 1948–1962; more than five per year between 1963–1978) is mirrored by an increase in sightings of live animals, at the same time as large concentrations of mackerel occur in these waters. However, a number of these are drowning in fishing nets in this region, so mortality may also have increased.

The presence and direction of onshore winds and currents, together with the configuration of the coastline, may all influence where a dolphin that has died may come ashore, and if the species generally spends its time far from the coast, individuals may sink after death and so not be recovered. However, the cause of strandings of live animals is unknown. Theories seeking to explain spectacular mass strandings include: infection of the inner ear by nematode parasites which upset balance or echolocation abilities, the effects of upsetting sounds such as underwater explosions or magnetic disturbances, or disorientation having followed prey into unfamiliar or shallow waters. Obviously, disease and old age are unlikely to lead to an entire herd coming ashore, so the explanation may be that most members are following a leader, which will usually be an older experienced animal. So far as we know, mass-stranding species tend to form fairly stable herds; they are also pelagic, so they are less likely to be familiar with shallow coastal areas, and more likely to become disorientated.

Sexual behavior in dolphins occurs throughout the year although there is usually a peak in calving during the summer months, even in lower latitudes. The single calf remains with the mother for several months, with lactation lasting up to 1.5–2 years. This suggests that many species breed at minimum intervals of 2–3 years. The age of sexual maturity probably ranges between 5 years (Common dolphin) and 16 years (male Killer whale), with most species breeding at about 8–10 years old. Many species undergo seasonal migrations in search of food; these are usually offshore-inshore movements but may be latitudinal. If discrete breeding areas exist, they have rarely been identified, although it is probable that they are in deeper offshore waters where

The Mystery of Mass Strandings

Strandings of whole herds of Pilot whales are better known than for any other cetacean, probably because of the animals' abundance. Some 95 percent of beach deaths occur in mass strandings, the remainder being of sick and heavily parasitized individuals that drift ashore alone. The mass strandings are of live animals which are not obviously diseased or emaciated, and in this sense resemble strandings of animals driven ashore by fishermen. The composition of a stranded herd is also the same as in a driven herd, indicating that in both types of case all animals of a herd strand together. No one has as yet clearly detected a leader or leading group though it is possible that one or more of the older animals might have this role. If the animals are towed out to sea, all, or many, of them will usually come ashore again at a new site, and die. Mass-strandings occur on all types of coastline and the particular site seems to have no significance. At Newfoundland, stranded herds come from among the massed animals attracted close inshore in late summer by their food supply, immature squid, which themselves make a summer migration up from the continental slope and become exceedingly numerous inshore. The local Pilot whales appear, therefore, to be dependent at this season on a high density of their food resources. This may be the key to their propensity to mass-strand, although the physiological mechanisms involved are not known.   DES

there is less turbulence from coastal currents.

Dolphins are gregarious, with some species forming herds of a thousand or more, but these generally occur during long-distance movements or when concentrated at food sources. In most cases, membership of the herd is fluid; that is to say, individuals may enter or leave the group over a period of weeks or months, only a minority remaining within it for a longer time. There is no indication of the stable, well-developed social organization typical of primates.

Dolphins, like other toothed whales, rely greatly upon sound for communication. Their sounds range from trains of clicks of 0.25kHz into the ultrasonic range around 80–220kHz, which appear to be used for echolocation of, and possibly stunning, food, and a pure tone or modulated whistles. Although different whistles have been categorized and associated with particular behaviors, there is no evidence of a language with syntax. The extent to which dolphins cooperate with one another to herd fish is controversial, but even if we accept that

high degree of folding of the cerebral cortex (comparable with primates), considered to be indications of high intelligence, it is likely that these are a consequence of the processing of acoustic information requiring greater "storage space" than visual information. The density of neurones, another feature commonly regarded as suggesting high intelligence, is not particularly high. The often cited lack of aggression amongst dolphins has probably been exaggerated. Several species develop dominance hierarchies in captivity, in which aggression is manifested by directing the head at the threatened animal, displaying with open mouth or clapping of the jaw. Fights have also been observed in the wild when scratches and scrapes have been inflicted by one individual running its teeth over the back of another.

Dolphins may congregate in numbers of up to 2,000 at feeding areas, which often coincide with human fisheries, resulting in a conflict of interests. Gill-nets, laid to catch salmon or capelin, also catch and drown dolphins. Inshore species of porpoises such as Dall's and Harbor porpoises are most at risk, but in the eastern Pacific the purse-seine tuna fishery has caused the death of an estimated 113,000 individuals annually, mainly Spinner and Bridled dolphins, but also Common dolphins, during the late 1960s and early 1970s (see p193). The application of lines of floats at the surface, and similar methods to make the nets more conspicuous to dolphins, reduced the incidental kills to 17,000 by 1980. Similar large incidental catches have occurred in recent years along the Japanese coast, affecting Common and Spinner dolphins, and porpoises such as Dall's porpoise (see p198).

A less obvious threat to dolphins comes from inshore pollution by toxic chemicals, and acoustic disturbance from boats. These may explain apparent recent declines in the Bottle-nosed dolphin in the North Sea and English Channel, although direct evidence of a causal link is generally lacking. The same factors may threaten the Common and Bottle-nosed dolphins in the western Mediterranean and off southern California. The hunting of dolphins is not widespread but in certain areas such as the Black Sea very large numbers (Turkish catches of 176,000 per year reported during the early 1970s) of mainly Common dolphins have been taken. Finally, direct competition for particular fish species may be an important potential threat as man turns increasingly to the marine environment for food.

PGHE

some of the more gregarious species do do this, such behavior is also found among primates, carnivores and birds.

Dolphins can perform quite complex tasks and are fine mimics, capable of memorizing long routines, particularly where learning by ear is involved. In some tests they rank with elephants. Although they are sometimes spontaneously innovative, as are other mammals, there is no proof that they have prior knowledge of the consequences of an action. Although dolphins have the large brain size (relative to body size) and

▲ **Performing dolphins** at San Diego, USA. Such displays of agility, grace and charm have given dolphins a special place in the human imagination, and have probably helped to fuel the outrage felt by many at their continued slaughter at the hands of man.

◀ **Peaceful coexistence.** Two Bottle-nosed dolphins, one primate and a carnivore obviously enjoying each other's company.

◀ **Mass stranding.** Pilot whales appear to strand in large numbers more often than any other whale. TOP Pilot whales at sea. BOTTOM Pilot whales stranded on a beach at Sable Island, Nova Scotia in 1976. Over 130 whales stranded on this occasion. (See Box).

THE 32 SPECIES OF DOLPHINS

Abbreviations: HTL = head-to-tail straight-line length. wt = weight

Killer whale
Orcinus orca.
Killer whale or orca.

All oceans. Male HTL 6.7–7.0m; wt 4,000–4,500kg. Female HTL 6.0–6.5m; wt 2,500–3,000kg. Skin: black on back and sides, white belly extending as a lobe up the flanks, and a white oval patch above and behind the eye; regional variation in exact position and extent of white patches; indistinct gray saddle over back behind dorsal fin. Rounded paddle-shaped flippers and centrally placed dorsal fin, sickle-shaped in female and immatures, but very tall and erect in male. Broad rounded head and stout torpedo-shaped body.

False killer whale
Pseudorca crassidens

All oceans; mainly tropical and warm temperate. Male HTL 5.5m; wt about 2,000kg. Female HTL 5.0m; wt about 1,200kg. Skin: all black except for a blaze of gray on belly between the flippers, which have a broad hump on front margin near middle of flipper. Tall, sickle-shaped dorsal fin just behind midpoint of back, sometimes with pointed tip. Slender, tapered head, underslung jaw, and long, slender body.

Pygmy killer whale
Feresa attenuata

Probably all tropical and subtropical seas. Male HTL 2.3–2.4m; wt about 170kg. Female HTL 2.1–2.3m; wt about 150kg. Skin: dark gray or black on back, often lighter on flanks, extending highest at front of dorsal fin; small but conspicuous zone of white on underside (from anus to tail stock) and around lips, and chin may be entirely white. Flippers slightly rounded at tip. Sickle-shaped, centrally-placed dorsal fin. Rounded head with underslung jaw, and slender body.

◀ **The sinuous ripples** of its wake accentuate the apparent menace of the Killer whale in the foreground. In reality, Killer whales pose little threat to man, unlike the similar (and quite unrelated) sharks. These Killers are in Johnstone Strait, a narrow passage along the north coast of Vancouver Island. Killer whales are found in all oceans.

Melon-headed whale
Peponocephala electra
Melon-headed whale or Many-toothed blackfish.

Probably all tropical seas. HTL 2.2m; wt 160kg. Skin: black on back and flanks; slightly lighter on belly; areas around anus, genitals, and the lips pale gray or white. Pointed flippers. Sickle-shaped centrally placed dorsal fin. Rounded head (though slightly more pointed snout than Pygmy killer whale) with slightly underslung jaw, and slender body with slim tail stock.

Long-finned pilot whale
Globicephala melaena
Long-finned pilot whale or Pothead whale.

G. m. melaena temperate waters of N Atlantic; *G. m. edwardi* all waters of all seas in S Hemisphere. Male HTL 6.2m; wt about 3,500kg. Female HTL 5.1m; wt about 1,800kg. Skin: black on back and flanks with anchor-shaped patch of grayish-white on chin and gray area on belly, both variable in extent and intensity (lighter in younger animals). Some have gray dorsal fin. Long sickle-shaped flippers, and fairly low dorsal fin, slightly forward of midpoint, with long base, sickle-shaped (in adult females and immatures) to flag-shaped (in adult males). Square bulbous head, particularly in old males, with slightly protruding upper lip and robust body.

Short-finned pilot whale
Globicephala macrorhynchus

All tropical and subtropical waters but with possible separate form in N Pacific. Male HTL 4.75–5.5m; wt about 2,500kg. Female HTL 3.6–4.25m; wt about 1,300kg. Skin: black on back, flanks and most of belly, with anchor-shaped patch of gray on chin, and gray area of varying extent and intensity on belly (lighter in younger animals). Long sickle-shaped flippers (but shorter than Long-finned pilot whale), and fairly low dorsal fin, slightly forward of midpoint, with long base, sickle-shaped to flag-shaped. Square bulbous head particularly in old males (slightly more robust than in Long-finned pilot whale, with slightly protruding upper lip and robust body.

CONTINUED ▶

Pacific white-sided dolphin
Lagenorhynchus obliquidens

Temperate waters of N Pacific. HTL 2.1m; wt about 90kg. Male slightly larger than female. Skin: dark gray or black on back, white belly, large pale gray oval area on otherwise black flanks in front of fin above flipper and extending forward to eye which is encircled with dark gray or black; narrow pale gray stripe above eye running along length of body and curving down to anal area where it broadens out; pale gray blaze also sometimes present on posterior part of centrally placed sickle-shaped dorsal fin. Rounded snout with very short black beak and torpedo-shaped body.

Hour-glass dolphin
Lagenorhynchus cruciger

Probably circumpolar in cooler waters of Southern Ocean. HTL 1.6m; wt 100kg. Skin: black on back, white belly, two large white areas on otherwise black flanks forward of dorsal fin to black beak and backward to tail stock, connected by narrow white band; area of white variable in extent. Centrally placed sickle-shaped dorsal fin, usually strongly concave on leading edge. Rounded snout with very short black beak and torpedo-shaped body.

Peale's dolphin
Lagenorhynchus australis
Peale's or Black chinned dolphin.

Cold waters of Argentina, Chile and Falkland Islands. HTL 2m; wt 115kg. Skin: dark gray-black on back, white belly; light gray area on flanks from behind eye to anus, and above this, a narrow white band behind the dorsal fin extending backwards, enlarging to tail stock; thin black line running from leading edge of black flipper to eye. Centrally placed sickle-shaped fin. Rounded snout with short black beak and torpedo-shaped body.

Dusky dolphin
Lagenorhynchus obscurus

Circumpolar in temperate waters of S Hemisphere. HTL 1.8m; wt 115kg. Skin: dark gray-black on back, white belly; large gray area (varying in intensity) on lower flanks, extending from base of beak or eye backwards and running to anus; light gray or white areas on upper flanks extending backwards from below dorsal fin as two blazes which generally meet above anal region and end at tail stock. Centrally placed sickle-shaped dorsal fin, slightly more erect and less curved than rest of genus, commonly with pale gray on posterior part of fin. Rounded snout with very short black beak and torpedo-shaped body.

Atlantic white-sided dolphin
Lagenorhynchus acutus

Temperate and subpolar waters of N Atlantic. Male HTL 2.55m; wt 215kg; Female HTL 2.25m; wt 165kg. Skin: black on back, white belly, gray flanks but with long white oval blaze from below dorsal fin to area above anus; directly above but originating slightly behind the front edge of white blaze is an elongated yellow band extending back to tail stock. Centrally placed sickle-shaped dorsal fin, relatively tall, pointed at tip. Rounded snout with short black beak, stout torpedo-shaped body with very thick tail stock narrowing close to tail flukes.

White-beaked dolphin
Lagenorhynchus albirostris

Temperate and subpolar waters of N Atlantic. Male HTL 2.75m; wt about 200kg. Female HTL 2.65m; wt about 180kg. Skin: dark gray or black over most of back, but pale gray-white area over dorsal surface behind fin (less distinct in young individuals); commonly dark gray-white blaze from near dorsal surface, behind eye, across flanks and downward to anal area; white belly. Centrally placed, tall (particularly in adult males), sickle-shaped dorsal fin. Rounded snout with short beak, often light gray or white. Very stout torpedo-shaped body, with very thick tail stock.

Fraser's dolphin
Lagenodelphis hosei

Warm waters of all oceans. HTL 2.3m; wt 90kg. Skin: medium-dark gray on back and flanks, white or pinkish-white belly; two parallel stripes on flanks: upper, cream-white, beginning above and in front of eye, moving back and narrowing to tail stock, lower more distinct, dark gray-black from eye to anus; sometimes also a black band from mouth to flipper; white throat and chin but tip of lower jaw usually black. Small slender slightly sickle-shaped dorsal fin, pointed at tip, centrally placed. Very short rounded snout with short beak. Fairly robust torpedo-shaped body with marked keels above and below tail stock.

Hector's dolphin
Cephalorhynchus hectori

Coastal waters of New Zealand. HTL 1.4m; wt 40kg. Skin: pale to dark gray around anus. Rounded black flipper and centrally placed low rounded dorsal fin. Short rounded snout with no melon and a short beak. Small stout torpedo-shaped body, narrowing at tail stock.

White-bellied dolphin
Cephalorhynchus eutropia
White-bellied or Black dolphin.

Coastal waters of Chile. HTL 1.2m; wt 45kg. Skin: black on back, flanks and part of belly but with three areas of white, variable in extent, on throat, behind flippers and around anal area; pale gray or white thin margin to lips of both jaws; sometimes pale gray area around blowhole. Low triangular dorsal fin, centrally placed with longer leading edge and blunt apex. Short rounded snout with no melon and very short beak. Small stout torpedo-shaped body with keels above and below tail stock.

Commerson's dolphin
Cephalorhynchus commersoni
Commerson's or Piebald dolphin.

Cool waters of southern S America and Falkland Islands, possibly across Southern Ocean to Kerguelen Island. HTL 1.35m; wt 50kg. Skin: dark gray on back but with large white-pale gray cape across front half, extending down across belly, leaving only small black area around anus; white area also on throat and chin so that dark gray frontal region confined to forehead, snout and broad band across neck region to flippers. Rounded black flippers and centrally placed low rounded dorsal fin. Short rounded snout with no melon and very short beak. Small stout torpedo-shaped body.

Heaviside's dolphin
Cephalorhynchus heavisidii

Coastal waters of southern Africa. HTL 1.2m; wt 40kg. Skin: black on back and flanks, white belly, extending upwards as three lobes, two on either side of the flipper, and one from anal region up along flanks to tail stock. Small oval-shaped black flippers and centrally placed low triangular dorsal fin. Short rounded snout with no melon and no distinct beak. Small fairly stout torpedo-shaped body.

Northern right whale dolphin
Lissodelphis borealis

Offshore waters of temperate N Pacific. HTL 2.1m; wt 70kg. Skin: black on back and flanks, extending down around navel; white belly, in some individuals extending up flanks around flipper so that only the tips are black; otherwise, flippers all black. Juveniles light gray to brown on back and flanks. Dorsal fin absent. Rounded snout with distinct beak and white band across bottom of lower jaw. Small, very slender torpedo-shaped body with marked keel above tail stock.

Southern right whale dolphin
Lissodelphis peronii

Offshore, waters of Southern Ocean, possibly circumpolar. HTL 1.8m; wt 60kg. Skin: black on back and flanks, white belly extending upwards to lower flanks behind flippers and forward across forehead in front of eyes so that entire back is white; flippers all white. Dorsal fin absent. Rounded snout with distinct beak. Small, very slender torpedo-shaped body, with underside of tail fluke white.

Risso's dolphin
Grampus griseus
Risso's dolphin or grampus.

All tropical and temperate seas. Male HTL 4.0m; wt about 400kg. Female HTL 3.5m; wt about 350kg. Skin dark to light gray on back and flanks, palest in older individuals, particularly leading edge of dorsal fin, so that head may be pure white; many scars on flanks of adults; white belly enlarging to oval patch on chest and chin. Long pointed black flippers, tall centrally placed sickle-shaped dorsal fin (taller, more erect in adult males). Blunt snout, rounded with slight melon. No beak. Stout torpedo-shaped body narrowing behind dorsal fin to quite narrow tail stock.

Bottle-nosed dolphin
Tursiops truncatus

Coastal waters of most tropical, subtropical and temperate regions. Three forms recognized: a large race, *T. t. truncatus* in Atlantic, and two smaller races, *T. t. gilli* in temperate N Pacific and *T. t. aduncus* in Indo-Pacific and Red Sea. HTL 3.4 (small)–3.9m (large race); wt about 150–200kg. Usually dark-gray on back, lighter gray on flanks (variable in extent), grading to white or pink on belly. *T. t. gilli* often more brown than gray on back, and has distinct pink area around anus. *T. t. aduncus* sometimes darker than *T. t. truncatus*. Some spotting may be present on belly. Centrally placed, tall, slender, sickle-shaped dorsal fin. Robust head with distinct short beak, often with white patch on tip of lower jaw. Stout torpedo-shaped body with moderately keeled tail stock.

Rough-toothed dolphin

Steno bredanensis

Offshore waters of all tropical, subtropical and warm temperate seas. Male HTL 2.4m wt about 140kg. Female HTL 2.2m; wt about 120kg. Skin: coloration variable, often dark gray to dark purplish-gray on back and flanks, and white throat and belly; pinkish-white blotches on flanks round to belly; frequently scarred with numerous white streaks. Centrally placed sickle-shaped dorsal fin. Long, slender beak not clearly demarcated from forehead, with white or pinkish-white along both sides, including one or both lips and tip of snout. Slender torpedo-shaped body, keels above and below tail stock.

Common dolphin

Delphinus delphis
Common or Saddleback dolphin.

Usually offshore waters of all tropical, subtropical and warm temperate seas, including Mediterranean and Black Seas. Possibly separate form *D. d. bairdii*, in N Pacific. Male HTL about 2.2m; wt about 85kg. Female HTL about 2.1m; wt about 75kg. Skin: coloration variable; black or brownish black on back and upper flanks; chest and belly cream-white to white; on flanks, hourglass pattern of tan or yellowish tan forward becoming paler gray behind dorsal fin where it may reach dorsal surface; black stripe from flipper to middle of lower jaw, and from eye to base of beak; one or two gray lines running longitudinally on lower flanks in *D. d. bairdii*; flippers black to light gray or white (atlantic population). Slender sickle-shaped to erect dorsal fin, centrally placed. Long, slender beak and distinct forehead and slender torpedo-shaped body.

Striped dolphin

Stenella coeruleoalba
Striped, Euphrosyne, or Blue-white dolphin.

All tropical, subtropical and warm temperate seas, including Mediterranean. HTL 2.4m; wt 100kg. Skin: dark gray to brown or bluish gray on back, lighter gray flanks, and white belly; two distinct black bands on flanks, one from near eye down side of body to anal area (with short secondary stripe originating with this band, turning downwards towards flippers) and second from eye to flippers; most have additional black or dark gray fingers extending from behind dorsal fin forward and about halfway to eye; black flippers. Slender sickle-shaped centrally placed dorsal fin. Slender, long beak (but shorter than Common dolphin) and distinct forehead. Slender torpedo-shaped body.

Spinner dolphin

Stenella longirostris

Probably in all tropical oceans. Possibly a number of different races. HTL 1.8m; wt 75kg. Skin: dark gray, brown or black on back; lighter gray, tan or yellowish tan flanks, and white belly (purplish or yellow in some populations); distinct black to light gray stripe from flipper to eye. Slender erect to sickle-shaped centrally placed dorsal fin, often lighter gray near middle of fin; relatively large black to light gray flippers. Medium to long, slender beak and distinct forehead. Slender to relatively stout torpedo-shaped body which may have marked keels above and below tail stock.

Bridled dolphin

Stenella attenuata
Bridled or Spotted dolphin.

Deep waters of tropical Pacific and Atlantic, probably elsewhere. Some authorities recognize *S. frontalis* as separate species in western N Atlantic, *S. a. graffmani* as separate race (larger, more spotted) in coastal waters of tropical E Pacific. HTL 2.1m; wt 100kg. Skin: coloration and markings variable with age and geographically; dark gray to black on back and upper flanks, lighter gray on lower flanks and belly (sometimes pinkish on throat); white spots on upper flanks, dark spots on lower flanks and belly absent at birth but enlarging with age; may give rise to uniform dark gray belly; distinct dark gray-black area (or cape) on head to dorsal fin with black circle around eye, extending to junction of beak and melon, and broad black stripe from origin of flipper to corner of mouth (which tends to fade as spotting increases); these give banded appearance to light gray sides of head. Slender sickle-shaped centrally placed dorsal fin; medium-dark gray flippers. Long slender beak, both upper and lower lips white or pinkish, and distinct forehead. Slender to relatively stout torpedo-shaped body with marked keel below tail stock (sometimes also one above tail stock).

Spotted dolphin

Stenella plagiodon

Tropical Atlantic, possibly other waters. May be a race of Bridled dolphin. HTL 2.1m; wt 110kg. Skin: coloration and markings variable with age; dark gray on back and upper flanks, lighter gray on lower flanks and belly, white spots on upper flanks, dark spots on lower flanks and belly absent at birth but enlarging with age; dark gray area (cape) on head to dorsal fin distinctly separated (though less distinct than Bridled dolphin) from light gray flanks; bridling of face and dark line from flipper to mouth both absent; pronounced pale blaze on flanks, slanting up on to back behind dorsal fin; medium gray flippers. Sickle-shaped centrally placed dorsal fin. Long slender beak with upper and lower lips usually pale gray or white, and distinct forehead. Stout torpedo-shaped body.

Tucuxi

Sotalia fluviatilis

Amazon river system. HTL 1.4m; wt 36kg. Skin: coloration variable geographically and with age; medium to dark gray on back and upper flanks with brownish tinge, lighter gray sometimes with patches of yellow-ocher on lower flanks and belly; two pale gray areas sometimes extend diagonally upwards on flanks. Small triangular centrally placed dorsal fin. Relatively large spoon-shaped flipper. Pronounced beak (medium to dark gray above, light gray-white below), and rounded forehead. Individuals become lighter with age, sometimes cream-white. Small stout torpedo-shaped body.

Guiana dolphin

Sotalia guianensis

Coastal waters and river systems of S America. HTL about 1.5m; wt about 40kg. Skin: generally darker, but otherwise very similar to tucuxi. Blue-gray to dark brown on back and upper flanks, lighter gray on lower flanks, white on belly; sometimes a brownish band extending from anal area diagonally upward to flanks to leading edge of dorsal fin. Small but prominent triangular centrally placed dorsal fin. Relatively large, spatulate flippers. Small, stout torpedo-shaped body.

Atlantic humpbacked dolphin

Sousa teuszii

Coastal waters and river systems of W Africa. Possibly a form of Indo-Pacific humpbacked dolphin which it closely resembles (differs in having fewer teeth and more vertebrae). HTL about 2.15m; wt about 100kg. Shape and coloration variable. Skin: dark gray-white on back and upper flanks, lightening on lower flanks to white belly; young uniform pale cream. Small but prominent triangular centrally placed dorsal fin, sickle-shaped in young, becoming more rounded later. Rounded flippers. Long slender beak with slight melon on forehead. Stout torpedo-shaped body, with distinct dorsal hump in middle of back (on which is dorsal fin) and similar marked keels above and below tail stock.

Indo-Pacific humpbacked dolphin

Sousa chinensis

Coastal warm waters of E Africa to Indonesia and S China. Some authorities recognize *S. c. plumbea* (darker), *S. c. lentiginosa* (speckled) and *S. c. chinensis* (white) as separate races. HTL 2.0m; wt about 85kg. Shape and coloration variable. Skin: dark gray-white on back and upper flanks, usually lightening on lower flanks to white belly; adults may develop spots or speckles of yellow, pink, gray or brown; young uniform pale cream. Small but prominent triangular centrally placed dorsal fin, sickle-shaped in young, becoming more rounded later. Rounded flippers. Both dorsal fin and flippers may be tipped white. Long slender beak (with white patch on tip in some individuals) with slight melon on forehead. Stout torpedo-shaped body, with distinct dorsal hump in middle of back (on which is dorsal fin) and similar marked keels above and below tail stock.

Irrawaddy dolphin*

Orcaella brevirostris

Coastal waters from Bay of Bengal to northern coast of Australia. HTL about 2m; wt about 100kg. Skin: blue-gray on back and flanks, lighter gray on belly. Stout torpedo-shaped body and tailstock; robust rounded head with distinct melon but no beak; small sickle-shaped dorsal fin with rounded tip, slightly behind center of back.

*This species is considered by some authorities to be a member of the family Monodontidae.

Cooperative Killers

Hunting strategy of the Killer whale

As they approached the rocky point around which the tide flowed rapidly toward them, the pod of 20 Killer whales was spread in line abreast about 50m (160ft) apart. The whales were swimming slowly near the surface, occasionally rising to breathe and slap the surface with their long, oval flippers and large tail flukes. Underwater, the slaps sounded like muffled gunshots against a background of squeals and ratchet-like clicking sounds. Then came a long, wavy whistling sound, punctuated by a honk like that from a squeeze bulb horn at an Indian bazaar, and the whales converged methodically toward their prey—a school of several thousand Pacific pink salmon they were herding between the rock and the roaring current. For several minutes the whales had the fish loosely but effectively trapped, as one by one they picked out and swallowed several 3kg (6.6lb) salmon from the periphery of the school. Then the whales seemed to lose interest in the hunt and instead rolled lazily in the water and casually "spy-hopped" to look around at the boatfuls of salmon anglers floating near the point. With another underwater whistle and a honk, all the whales simultaneously submerged, to reappear five minutes later in a close-knit group beyond the point, upcurrent and far away from the fishermen. They remained in a close group, swimming slowly and silently for two hours toward the next rocky point, where the cooperative hunt was repeated.

Killer whales, or orcas, are the largest and fastest members of the dolphin family. The males, which may approach 10m (33ft) in length, are at once recognizable by the upright triangular fin, up to 2m (6.6ft) tall—the largest of any whale. Females are slightly smaller and the fin is curved back as in a shark. The striking black and white coloration includes a white spot above the eye, a finger-like white patch extending up onto the flank, and a grey "saddle" behind the fin, against the upperside.

The key to the foraging success of these predators is cooperation and exquisite co-ordination between individuals. All adults and the older juveniles are active participants in the hunt, while younger whales playfully mimic their actions. The coordination is apparently learned and enhanced by the tight social cohesion of Killer whales. Pod members remain together for life, and such ties may persist from one generation to the next, as has been found for some terrestrial predators. The sex and age composition of the group remains fairly stable, with one adult male to three or four adult females and several subadults of both sexes. The pod size

is typically 4–40 whales, larger groups gradually splitting into two or more smaller groups as the population grows. Some pods may inhabit ranges extending for 320–480km (200–300mi). Population control may be accomplished by separating off very small pods of 2–6 whales which are usually doomed to die out within a generation. Partitioning of the food resources may also occur, with the larger productive pods preying upon the most abundant "preferred" prey species, and the smaller pods relegated to foraging on other prey. Both splitting of large pods and partitioning of resources seem to be accomplished without overt aggressive action by these extremely powerful and intelligent creatures.

Sexual maturity is attained at 8–10 years (but may be 16 years in males) and the natural lifespan is estimated to be 50–100 years. An adult female can bear a single calf once every three years, but one calf every eight years is the average. Gestation lasts for 15 months and nursing lasts approximately one year, though a weaned calf may closely accompany its mother for several years. Female calves, at least, remain in the pod of birth.

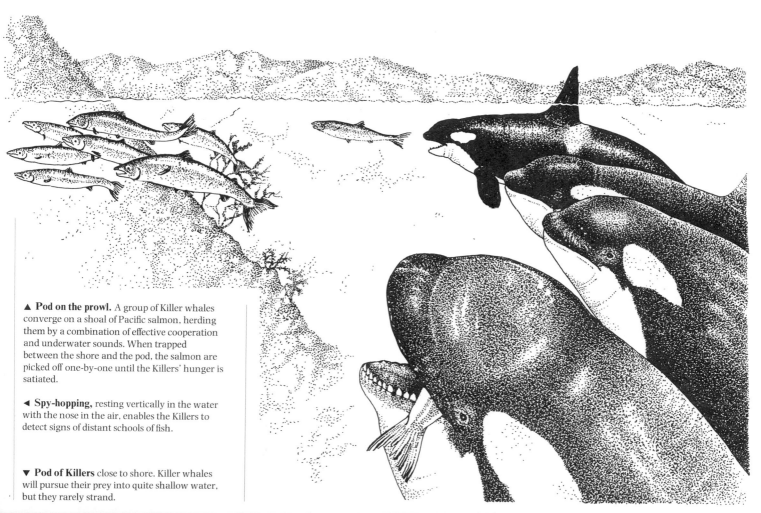

▲ **Pod on the prowl.** A group of Killer whales converge on a shoal of Pacific salmon, herding them by a combination of effective cooperation and underwater sounds. When trapped between the shore and the pod, the salmon are picked off one-by-one until the Killers' hunger is satiated.

◄ **Spy-hopping,** resting vertically in the water with the nose in the air, enables the Killers to detect signs of distant schools of fish.

▼ **Pod of Killers** close to shore. Killer whales will pursue their prey into quite shallow water, but they rarely strand.

Killer whales are distributed worldwide but are most abundant in food-rich areas at high latitudes. On average, they must eat about 2.5–5 percent of their body weight per day, so they require steady and abundant resources of prey species. They are very flexible predators, eating anything from small fish and invertebrates to the largest whales. Fish and squid form the bulk of their diet, but the Killer whale is the only cetacean that preys on warm-blooded flesh. Dolphins and porpoises are taken with some regularity, and seals, sea lions and seabirds are also eaten. Despite an (undeserved) reputation as a wanton killer, the species actually forbears from attacking another warm-blooded species, man, in the water.

Some Killer whale pods may travel many hundreds of miles to keep up with the movements of prey species, while others maintain relatively restricted ranges where food is abundant all year. Being at the very top of the food chain, Killer whales are not numerous, but the appearance of several large pods of these mobile predators in an area where prey is locally or seasonally abundant can give the false impression that their population is quite large.   KB

Sleek Spinners

School life of the Spinner dolphin

The slender dolphins leap high out of the water, twisting and spinning rapidly around their longitudinal axes. The movement at once identifies these as Spinner dolphins, inhabitants of oceans throughout the tropics and subtropics.

Spinner dolphins of Hawaii spend most of their lives close to shore. During the day, they rest and socialize in tight groups of usually 10–100 animals within protected bays and along shallow coastlines. At night, they move into deep water a kilometer or more offshore, and they dive deeply (100m or more) to feed on fish and squid. At that time, the group spreads out, and 100 animals may cover an area of several square kilometers.

These groups are ephemeral. During the night, many individual dolphins change their companions so that when they head shoreward at dawn, group membership is reshuffled. However, this daily reshuffling of group composition is not random. Small subgroups of 4–8 animals stay together and change group affiliations together for

periods of up to four months and possibly longer. Some dolphins may have close ties which last throughout their lives. It is not known if the members of these more stable subgroups are related or not. Some dolphin mothers and their calves stay together for many years, but the same mothers may also have long-term affiliations with one or more possibly unrelated adult males and females.

In Hawaii, Spinner dolphins shelter in numerous bays, and may range as far as 50km (30mi) along the coast from one day to the next. Each subgroup does however have a preferred "home area" beyond which the dolphins travel with a frequency that declines with distance; they rarely range further than 100km (62mi). There are at least two benefits in seeking out shallow water during the day. The water is usually calmer than in the open ocean, which makes resting and socializing easier, and deepwater sharks which prey on dolphins are not as numerous and are more easily detected in the shallows.

Spinners, like most species of dolphin, are

▲ **Sparring Spinners.** The Spinner dolphin is one of the most acrobatic of all dolphins. These three spinners are playing a sparring game during the evening period of social interaction.

▼ **In mid-turn,** a Spinner dolphin leaps from the water. Spinners are inventive acrobats, but spinning along their axis as they leap is their most characteristic feat.

large-brained social mammals, and they probably recognize many of the individuals with which they associate on a daily basis. They may even recognize individuals which are far from their home area and have therefore only rarely been met. When Spinners meet after a long separation, much social behavior, including vocalizations which may be part of a greeting ceremony, takes place.

Unlike the Hawaiian population, other Spinner dolphins roam throughout the tropical Pacific. These deepwater dolphins do not have the protection of nearby islands. Instead, they associate with a related species, the Bridled dolphin, and the two appear to take turns resting and feeding. While Spinner dolphins feed mostly at night, Bridled dolphins feed mostly during the day. Each species helps the other by guarding against the danger of surprise attack by large, deepwater sharks.

Deepwater Spinners may cover several thousand kilometers over a few months. It is not known whether the social affinities of deepwater spinners are as transient as those of their Hawaiian relatives. Perhaps the open-ocean school which travels together and may number 5-10 thousand animals has its coastal equivalent in the population of many of the interchanging groups of the Hawaiian coastal region.

Deepwater Spinner dolphins and Bridled dolphins commonly associate with Yellowfin tuna in the tropical Pacific. It is thought that these large fish follow the dolphins because they benefit from the excellent echolocation abilities which dolphins use to help find and identify prey. Since the tuna often swim below the dolphins, movements by the tuna, such as their breaking schooling ranks in the face of an attack by sharks, may be easily detected by the dolphins. In this way, the two dolphin and the tuna fish species each derive mutual benefit from the others.

Because dolphins surface to breathe, they can be seen by the human seafarer more easily than the tuna. Tuna fishermen take advantage of this to set their nets around dolphin–tuna schools. Unfortunately, many dolphins used to become entangled in these nets cast for the tuna and drown. In 1974 about half a million Spinner and Bridled dolphins were killed in tuna nets in the tropical east Pacific.

Tuna fishermen have recently adopted special nets and fishing procedures which greatly reduce this threat to dolphins. A panel of finer mesh—the Medina panel—is employed in that part of the net furthest

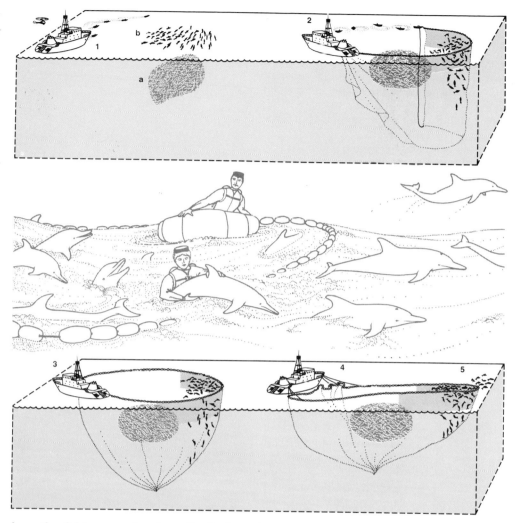

from the fishing vessels where the fleeing dolphins used to get entangled in the large mesh and drown as the net was tightened (pursed). The dolphins can thus escape over the net rim, while the tuna usually dive and are retained in the net. All US tuna fishing boats also have divers stationed in the net to monitor the movement of dolphins and to advise the boat crew when to purse and when to back down.

One further aspect of dolphin behavior has already been recognized, to the benefit of the dolphins' survival. Dolphins caught in tuna nets often lie placidly, as if feigning death (although their rigid state may in fact be due to extreme shock). Such dolphins were previously thought to be drowned and were hauled up onto the deck of the processing vessel, where they did indeed die. Now, the divers who monitor the nets manually help such unmoving animals over the net rim, and make certain that pursing does not proceed until all have been released. The divers may also release any dolphins which do still get entangled in the mesh.

BW/RSW

▲ **Saving the Spinners.** To avoid the accidental loss of Spinner dolphins caught in tuna nets, special techniques have been developed. (1) A shoal of tuna (a) accompanied by dolphins (b), is located by helicopter; the fishing boat approaches and launches inflatables to head off and contain the fish. (2) A purse seine net is pulled around the fish, while the inflatables create disturbances to stop the tuna escaping. (3) The bottom of the net is pulled in beneath the fish. (4) The net is pulled in towards the ship with the fine-mesh Medina panel furthest away from it. Some dolphins may be able to escape over the floats unaided, but they are sometimes assisted by hand from the inflatables or by divers (5).

A Dolphin's Day

Moods of the Dusky dolphin

The sleek, streamlined dolphins were leaping around the Zodiak rubber inflatable at Golfo San José, off the coast of southern Argentina. When the divers entered the cool water, a group of 15 dolphins cavorted under and above them, again and again approaching the humans to within an arm's length, and showing no fear of these strangers to their world.

These were Dusky dolphins, whose playful behavior indicated that they had recently been feeding and socializing, for Dusky dolphins have different "moods," and will not interact with humans when they are hungry or tired.

The behavior of Dusky dolphins varies according to both season and time of day. Off South America, Dusky dolphins feed on Southern anchovy during summer afternoons. Night-time is spent in small schools of 6–15 animals not more than about 1km (0.6mi) off shore. They move slowly, apparently at rest. When danger approaches, in the form of large sharks or Killer whales (see pp190–191), they retreat close inshore, seeking to evade their enemies by hiding in the tubulence of the surf-line.

In the morning, the dolphins begin to move into deeper water 2–10km (1–6mi) from shore, line abreast, each animal 10m (33ft) or more from the next, so that 15 dolphins may cover a swath of sea 150m (500ft) or more wide. They use echolocation to find food, and because they are spread out, they can sweep a large area of sea. When a group locates a school of anchovy, individuals dive down to the school and physically herd it to the surface by swimming around and under the fish in an ever-tightening formation.

The marine birds that gather above the anchovy to feed, and the leaping of the dolphins around the periphery of the fish school indicate what is going on to human observers as far away as 10km (6mi). Other small groups of dolphins, equally distant, will also see such feeding, and move rapidly toward it.

The newly arrived dolphin groups are immediately incorporated into the activity, and the more dolphins present, the more efficiently they are able to corral and herd prey to the surface. Thus, a group of 5–10 dolphins cannot effectively herd prey, and most such feeding activities die out after an average of five minutes. These small groups will seek to feed further. When dolphin groups aggregate, feeding lasts longer. A group of 50 dolphins has been observed to feed on average for 27 minutes, and 300 dolphins (the total in an area of about 500

◄ **A working leap.** A Dusky dolphin leaping around the edge of a shoal of anchovy. The noise the dolphin makes as it re-enters the water may help to keep the fish contained and the leaps may alert other dolphins to the presence of food. Dolphin sounds travel only about 1–3km (0.6–1.9mi) underwater and while leaping they can spot the tell-tale signs of food, especially circling birds, over considerable distances.

▲ **A playful leap.** After feeding, Dusky dolphins leap acrobatically with spins and somersaults. Such "play" may have a social function.

◄ **The feeding trap.** A dolphin herding anchovy, and using the water's surface as a "wall"—the anchovy thus have one less direction of escape than they would have in deeper water. The dolphins also project loud sounds at the fish, which may cause them to bunch even more tightly and to become disorientated.

sqmi) feed for 2–3 hours. By mid-afternoon, the 300 dolphins which were earlier scattered in 20 to 30 small groups may be feeding in one area. There is much social interaction in such a large group, and considerable sexual activity, particularly toward the end of feeding, with members of both the same and other subgroups.

By this time, the dolphins have rested at night and early morning, have fed—they have taken care of two important biological functions, and can now interact socially and "play." This is perhaps the most important time for these highly social animals. In order for dolphins to function effectively while avoiding predators, hunting for food, and cooperatively herding prey, they must know each other well and must communicate efficiently at all times. Socializing helps to bring this about. Toward the end of feeding, they swim together in small, ever-changing subgroups, with individuals touching or caressing each other with their flippers, swimming belly to belly, and poking their noses at each others sides or bellies. At this time, the dolphins will readily approach a boat, ride on its bow wave if it is moving, and swim with divers in the water.

In the evening, the large school splits into many small groups once again, and the animals settle down near shore to rest, the "mood" changing abruptly to quiescence

once again. Although there is some interchange of individuals between small groups from day to day, many of the same dolphins travel together on subsequent days. Some Dusky dolphins have been observed to stay together for at least two years.

On some days, Dusky dolphins will not find schools of anchovy. They remain in their small foraging parties all day and will not socialize much or associate with boats or divers. Although Dusky dolphins often appear to be carefree and happy in nature, this is probably an impression based on their behavior after successful hunting. Like all wild animals, they have to work for a living, and when food is scarce they are more interested in locating prey than in "play."

In winter, anchovy are not present, so Dusky dolphins feed in small groups mainly at night on squid and bottom-dwelling fish. Such prey does not occur in large shoals, so the feeding dolphins do not form large groups. They rest during the day, and stay quite close to shore at all times, thus avoiding the threat from deepwater sharks. There is little of the "play" or sexual activity of the summer months. Thus, their entire repertoire of group movement patterns and "moods," on both a daily and a seasonal basis, appears governed by food availability, and by the ever-present threat of possible predation.   BW

PORPOISES

Family: Phocoenidae
Six species in 3 genera.
Distribution: N temperate zone; W Indo-Pacific;
temperate and subantarctic waters of S
America; Auckland Islands.

Size: head-to-tail length from 120–150cm
(48–59in) in the Gulf of California porpoise to
170–225cm (68–89in) in
Dall's porpoise; weight
from 30–55kg (66–121lb)
in the Gulf of California
porpoise to 135–160kg
(275–353lb) in Dall's porpoise.

▲ ▼ **Elusive porpoises.** ABOVE Dall's porpoise,
seen here apparently plowing a furrow in the
sea, is one of the least shy of the porpoises.
BELOW Porpoises are retiring at sea but
frequently strand, like this Harbor porpoise in
Northumberland, England.

Harbor porpoises often provide people on the coasts of northern Europe and North America with their first sight of live cetaceans—usually a glimpse of small, elusive, rolling dark objects some hundreds of feet from a ferry or a vantage point on shore. Sometimes Harbor porpoises will pass close to a small fishing dinghy, giving a few characteristic snorting "blows" before disappearing. They are also one of the commonest species to strand, which they usually do singly on the sloping shelves of sandy beaches or on mudflats. Yet less is known about these coastal animals than many other cetaceans—a matter of concern especially as numbers of the "Common" porpoise may be declining rapidly, for example off Holland and Denmark, and in Puget Sound on the west coast of North America.

The only species that is readily attracted to moving vessels is Dall's porpoise. They are fast and boisterous swimmers, generating fans of spray visible for hundreds of meters. The Harbor and Finless porpoises are less obtrusive, although the former may make horizontal leaps partly clear of the surface when chasing prey.

In anatomy, true porpoises are a rather uniform group. They lack the "beak" characteristic of most of the dolphins, and all six species are pigmented with various combinations of black, gray or white. They are small, rarely exceeding 190cm (6.2ft) in length at maturity and, with the exception of the Finless porpoise, have small, low triangular fins. The teeth, 60 to 120 in number, are typically laterally compressed and flattened into a spade shape at the tip, in contrast to the pointed teeth of dolphins. The Finless porpoise is the only porpoise to have a bulging "melon" rather like that of the Pilot whale; although lacking the fin, it has a series of small tubercles (found on the leading edge of the fin in other species) along the dorsal ridge. Dall's porpoise is the largest species; as well as having the most striking color patterns it has a prominent dorsal "keel" on the tail stock, and the tip of the lower jaw protrudes slightly beyond that of the upper jaw. The premaxillary bones of porpoise skulls have rather prominent "bosses" just in front of the blowholes, and 3–7 neck vertebrae are fused in adults. In contrast to the 60–70 vertebrae in the other two genera, 95–100 are present in *Phocoenoides*.

Some striking adaptations occur in this family, and some peculiar distributions as well. On the basis of skull characters, limited fusion of neck vertebrae, and general morphology, the Gulf and Burmeister porpoises appear to be the most "typical," even though the rather flattened head and fin spines of the latter are unique. In the Harbor porpoise 6 of the 7 neck vertebrae are fused, and the Spectacled porpoise has somewhat sleeker proportions than the other *Phocoena* species. But despite these and other anatomical modifications both probably derive from a basic *sinus-spinipinnis* stock.

The Finless porpoise appears to be closely related to the *Phocoena* species. Except for the lack of a dorsal fin and the squat foreshortened head with relatively large cranial capacity, *Neophocoena* is a typical member of the family in basic anatomical respects. The differences seem to be adaptations to its turbid river and estuarine habitat where it probably "grubs" for its food on the bottom. It has been suggested that Dall's porpoise should be accorded separate family status. However, the skull and teeth of *Phocoenoides* are those of a porpoise and all the differences appear to be adaptations. The large number of relatively small vertebrae, which probably improves the flexion of the vertical swimming stroke, the complete fusion of all 7 neck vertebrae, the sharply tapered head, and perhaps the tail-stock keel, all appear to be adaptations that contribute to the species' swimming ability. These features have parallels among the deep-sea dolphins. The increased number of ribs, the proportionately large muscle mass and the large thoracic cavity, are probably adaptations that enhance the diving capabilities of this oceanic species which, alone among porpoises, exploits prey at some depth (over 100m; 330ft).

The porpoises probably emerged as a distinct group in the middle of the Miocene

▲ **Porpoise rescue.** A Harbor porpoise trapped in a herring weir at New Brunswick, Canada, being retrieved by means of a small seine net and manual capture. Once restrained, the animals are usually quite docile if handled slowly, gently and firmly.

most tropical Asian coasts and estuaries. *Phocoena*, in the east, first colonized coastal shelves of the Neotropical region, then with further isolation differentiated into parallel Northern Hemisphere (Harbor porpoise) and Southern Hemisphere (Spectacled porpoise) forms. *Phocoenoides* colonized temperate waters of the North Pacific and exploited the food resources along open-ocean current boundaries.

The fossil record more or less supports this picture: porpoise-like fossils have been found in Miocene strata of southern California, but in Europe and the Southern Hemisphere phocoenid fossils occur only in the Pliocene (7–2 million years ago). The isolation of the Black Sea and Sea of Azov population of *P. p. relicta* probably results from warming of the Mediterranean following penetration from the Atlantic through the Mediterranean when the latter was cooler than it is today.

Porpoises feed on relatively small schools of mobile prey items 10–30cm (4–12in) in length. When prey density is low they forage far apart, but they can gather rapidly when large concentrations of prey are located.

Acoustic emissions have been studied extensively only in the Harbor porpoise, although all porpoises probably have a wide repertoire of sounds. Relatively low frequency "click-series" may be used to scan the immediate general environment, high frequencies to echolocate specific objects, including mobile prey. There is little doubt that much hunting is also by sight, and passive listening for fish noise. Fish and squid are swallowed whole or bitten into pieces (not chewed) if large and digested in 3–6 hours.

period (about 15 million years ago) in the northern part of the Pacific Basin. There is some evidence that shallow water habitats there were more extensive than today. Subsequent changes in that region appear to have isolated three main lines represented by the existing genera. *Neophocoena*, in the west, gradually extended its range along

---

Abbreviations: HTL = head-to-tail length. Wt = weight.
[v] Vulnerable.

Harbor porpoise
Phocoena phocoena
Harbor or Common porpoise.

Coastal waters of temperate N Pacific and N Atlantic, Bering Sea, Baltic Sea; Black Sea and Sea of Azov (*P. p. relicta*). HTL 150–190cm; wt 54–65kg. Skin: dark gray, paler gray patch on flanks, white beneath. Gray line from flipper to jaw angle. Dorsal fin low, with concave trailing edge. Gestation: 11 months. Longevity: 12–13 years.

Gulf of California porpoise [v]
Phocoena sinus
Gulf of California porpoise, *cochito* ("little pig").

Gulf of California. HTL 120–150cm; wt 30–55kg. Skin: darker than

Harbor porpoise, otherwise similar. Dorsal fin with concave trailing edge, but higher than in Harbour porpoise.

Burmeister's porpoise [v]
Phocoena spinipinnis
Coastal waters of America from Peru to Uruguay; possibly also Falkland Is. HTL about 140–180cm; wt 40–70kg. Skin: blackish gray above and on flanks, lighter patches below. Fin low with convex trailing edge, tubercle at base of front of fin characteristically spinose. Gestation and longevity unknown.

Spectacled porpoise
Phocoena dioptrica
Coastal waters of southeastern America, Falkland Is, S Georgia, Auckland Is. HTL 155–204cm; wt 60–84kg. Skin: black above, white below, with eyes and lips rimmed with black; gray stripe from jaw angle to flippers, which are often white. Low, straight-edged dorsal fin. Gestation and longevity not known.

Dall's porpoise
Phocoenoides dalli
Dall's or True's porpoise.

Coastal and deep waters of boreal North Pacific and Bering Sea; S Japan to S California. Length 170–225cm; wt 135–160kg. Skin: black with variable white patch on belly and

flank, and further white areas on fin and flukes. Dorsal fin often largely white, with hooked tip, characteristically higher than in *Phocoena*. Gestation 11.4 months. Longevity: 16–17+ years.

Finless porpoise
Neophocoena phocoenoides
Finless or Black or Black finless porpoise.

Indo-Pacific from Iran to New Guinea and Japan, usually along coasts and in estuaries. HTL 140–165cm; wt 30–45kg. Skin: gray, with lips and chin lighter except for dark "chinstrap." No dorsal fin, but dorsal ridge of back bears row of short spinose tubercles. Gestation: 11 months. Longevity: about 23 years.

Incidental Catches of Porpoises

Because most porpoises prefer to prey on open-sea fish, they are vulnerable to "incidental" capture by certain types of fishing gear set for those fish. In addition to the thousands of porpoises hunted down by gun or harpoon, several thousand Dall's porpoises drown each year after becoming entangled in Japanese gill nets (usually caught by their pectoral flippers). Harbor porpoises are caught in salmon gill nets from New England to Greenland, and in herring weirs in the Maritime Provinces of Canada; Burmeister's porpoises are taken in nets off southern Chile and elsewhere, while the population of the Gulf of California porpoise appears to have been seriously reduced since the late 1940s by gill net fisheries for the commercially important "totoava" and other fish. Some Finless porpoises are trapped in all the areas they frequent off Japan and China.

The porpoises appear to be trapped or entangled while they are pursuing fish—they are simply too intent on their prey to appreciate the danger. They are also caught, especially at night, where they do not anticipate obstruction. Modern synthetic monofilament netting does not reflect porpoises echolocating clicks; there is in any case no reason to assume that porpoise echolocate continuously. Gill net captures are almost invariably fatal, but porpoises caught in Canadian herring weirs or Danish pound nets can be seined out and released alive if the fishermen are so inclined.

At present we do not know if Dall's, Harbor, Burmeister's, and Finless porpoise populations are being reduced by these catches. The herring weir captures in New Brunswick and Nova Scotia do not seem to be serious, but the Gulf of California porpoise may have been reduced to near extinction during the 1970s. Despite current research into the problems of gill net entanglements, no convincing solution is in sight. Acoustic warning devices, which emit continuous pinging sounds, may help, but may not be effective when porpoises are in hot pursuit of prey near the nets, or when they have become habituated to the noise. Considering the number of nets involved, they are also likely to be prohibitively expensive to use, unless the fishermen receive government subsidies.

▲ **The six species of porpoises.** (1) Gulf of California porpoise (*Phocoena sinus*).
(2) Burmeister's porpoise (*Phocoena spinipinnis*).
(3) Finless porpoise (*Neophocoena phocoenoides*).
(4) Dall's porpoise (*Phocoenoides dalli*).
(5) Spectacled porpoise (*Phocoena dioptrica*).
(6) Harbor porpoise (*Phocoena phocoena*).

All species have a varied diet. Finless porpoises take crustaceans such as prawns as the main prey; Dall's porpoises take oceanic fish such as hake and several species of squid; Harbor porpoises eat mostly clupeid fish (eg herring and sardines), scombroids (eg mackerel) and small gadoids (eg cod and whiting). Gulf of California porpoises eat croakers and grunts, and the diet of the two South American species is not known, but probably comprises pelagic fish such as mullet or anchovies, and squid. An adult Harbor porpoise requires 3–5kg (6.6–11lb) of food per day, Dall's porpoise perhaps 10–12kg (22–26lb). When foraging (often above underwater scarps and mounts, or along boundaries between currents) porpoises execute series of short breathing rolls, separated by dives of 1–4 minutes, in contrast to their traveling behavior, when dives last only 15–30 seconds, between rather regularly spaced surfacings.

North Sea and western North Atlantic Harbor porpoises are sexually mature at 5–6 years and 4–5 years respectively, Dall's porpoises at about 7 years. Little is known about the sex life of porpoises, but Harbor porpoises at least seem not to form lasting pairs. There is evidence for a male sexual cycle in some species, based on seasonal changes in testis size and activity. However, since the pairing season is relatively short (1–2 months), and the animals are relatively small, these changes may be a function of energy conservation. For females, the interval between births is about 2 years in Finless, 3 years in Dall's, and 1–3 years in Harbor porpoises. Lactation probably continues for 6–8 months in Harbor and Finless porpoises but may be as long as two years in the larger, pelagic Dall's porpoise. Mothers with calves are usually segregated from other animals, or form schools of two or more mother-calf pairs. The largest such school seen by the author contained six pairs. The presence of a young animal with a mother-calf combination early in the summer is quite common and may indicate that the weaned calf stays with the mother for some months after it has begun to feed independently; fish remains have been found in the stomachs of Harbor porpoises of 104–111cm (3–4ft) in length, apparently less than one year old. Young Finless porpoises may "ride" their mothers' backs attaching themselves to the ridge of tubercles which are peculiar to adults of this species.

The life spans of porpoises are a matter of some controversy. At least 16–17 years for Dall's porpoise and 23 years for Finless porpoises have been suggested, but most direct estimates for Harbor porpoises indicate an upper limit of 12–13 years.

In contrast to deep-sea dolphins, porpoises are not particularly gregarious. The basic social unit consists of only 2–4 animals in Harbor and Dall's porpoises, and observation suggests that the composition of most groups (with the exception of mother-calf pairs) is rather fluid. One school of Harbor porpoises caught in a herring weir in New Brunswick in late August 1982 consisted of a mother and calf and two immature males. Over 50 percent of Finless porpoises recently observed off Japan were solitary. The small size of the average porpoise school is probably geared to the quantity of prey likely to be encountered while foraging. Larger schools in all three of the most-studied species seem to result from chance meetings or temporary feeding aggregations. During feeding, the small basic groups may split up and individuals dive hundreds of feet apart, but later come together again prior to moving off to a new area. Some sexual segregation occurs: all-male schools of immature Harbor porpoise have been encountered off western Nova Scotia, but since whole schools are trapped only on rare occasions, little is known about sex ratios in small schools.   DEG

WHITE WHALES

Family: Monodontidae
Two species in 2 genera.*
Distribution: North temperate and circumpolar.

Beluga
Delphinapterus leucas
Beluga, belukha or White whale.
Distribution: N USSR, N America, Greenland.
Habitat: mainly coastal; estuaries and pack ice.
Size: head-to-tail length 300–500cm (10–16ft), weight 500–1,500kg (1,100–3,300lb).
Skin: adults white; young slate-gray to reddish-brown, changing to medium gray at two years and white on maturity.
Diet: schooling fish, crustacea, worms, mollusks.
Gestation: 14–15 months. Longevity: 30–40 years.

Narwhal
Monodon monoceros
Distribution: N USSR, N America, Greenland.
Habitat: coastal and pack ice.
Size: head-to-tail length 400–500cm (13–16.5ft); male tusk length 150–300cm (5–10ft); weight 800–1,600kg (1,760–3,520lb).
Coat: mottled gray-green, cream and black, whitening with age, beginning with the belly; young dark gray.
Diet: shrimps, arctic cod, flounder, cephalopods.
Gestation: 14–15 months.
Longevity: 30–40 years.

* A third species, the Irrawaddy dolphin (*Orcaella brevirostris*), is considered by some authorities to belong to the Monodontidae, but is here considered as a member of the Delphinidae, see p189.

THE white whales—the beluga and the narwhal—are the nonconformists among toothed whales. A large herd of brilliant white beluga makes an impressive enough sight, but a "procession" of narwhal moving along the coast is truly awesome. The body coloration alone is highly unusual: small patches of gray-green, cream and black pigmentation painted on, as it were, by short strokes of a stiff brush. What is more astonishing however is to see the legendary unicorn tusks thrust above the water as the male breaks the surface. Not only does his large spiral tusk—up to 3m (10ft) long and three-fifths of body length—seem out of place on such a relatively small whale but it is oddly offcenter: protruding from the left upper lip and at an awkward angle to the left and pointing downwards. To crown these oddities, the tails of older males appear to be put on backwards! Such is the narwhal, *Monodon monoceros* (one tooth, one horn).

Despite their superficial dissimilarity, the body forms of the beluga and narwhal are similar, although the narwhal is slightly larger. The beluga is notable for its well-defined neck: unusually for whales, it can turn its head sideways to a near right-angle. The beluga has no true back fin, hence its scientific name, *Delphinapterus* = "dolphin-without-a-wing," but there is a ridge along the back, from mid-body to the tail, more darkly pigmented than the body and generally scarred from encounters with ice. In both species, males are about 50cm (20in) longer than females and their flippers increasingly turn upwards at the tips with age. The flippers of beluga are capable of a wide range of movements, and appear to serve an important function in close-quarters maneuvering, including very slow,

reverse swimming. In ageing male narwhals, the shape of the tail changes to one in which the tips migrate forwards, giving a concave leading edge, when viewed from above or below.

The narwhal has only two teeth, and both are non-functional. In the female these are about 20cm (8in) long; in the male, the left tooth continues to grow to form the tusk. About 1–3 percent of males produce twin tusks and a similar proportion of females

have single tusks; twin-tusked females have been reported but have only rarely been verified. The purpose of the tusk has inspired many theories but it appears to be simply an exaggerated male characteristic which may play a role in establishing dominance in social life and breeding.

Beluga are capable of a wide range of bodily and facial expressions, including an impressive mouth gape displaying 32–40 peg-like teeth which abut one another. There is considerable wear of the surfaces, sometimes to the extent that they appear to be ineffective for grasping prey. This and the fact that they do not fully emerge until well into the second or third year suggest that feeding may not be their prime function: they may serve an equal or greater role in visual threat displays and jawclap noise-making.

▲ **Beluga and calf.** Suckling may last up to two years, during which time the mother and calf are almost inseparable. Newborn beluga are brown and the skin lightens through gray, as in this one-year-old, to white.

▼ **The narwhal,** with its remarkable tusk resulting from spiral growth of the left tooth. The spiral runs counter-clockwise and in old animals the whole tusk may spiral.

The beluga is a highly vocal animal, some of the sounds being easily heard in the air. The sound-spectrum ranges from moos, chirps, whistles and clangs, while the underwater din from a herd is reminiscent of a barnyard and long ago earned them the name "sea canary." In addition to its vocal and echolocation skills the beluga obviously also uses vision for both communication and predation. The versatility of its expressions suggests the likelihood of subtle social communication.

Both beluga and narwhal are diverse feeders: the beluga on a variety of schooling fish, crustacea, worms and sometimes mollusks, and the narwhal on shrimps, Arctic cod, flounder and cephalopods. Beluga are capable of herding schools of fish by working closely together as a group of five or more, forcing the exhausted fish into shallow water or towards a sloping beach. They are equally adept at pursuing single prey on the bottom. The highly flexible neck permits a wide sweep of the bottom and they can produce both suction and a jet of water to dislodge prey. Small stones, bits of seaweed and mud from the stomachs of calves attest to the skills that must be learned by the young. Much of the food gathered during the feeding season is stored as fat or blubber 10–20cm (4–8in) thick, providing insulation as well as an off-season energy supply. The narwhal, with no functional teeth at all, also seems to have a capacity for suction. The tusks appear to play no part in feeding, because the male and the tuskless female have similar diets.

The beluga and the narwhal are similar in their growth and reproduction, although more is known about the beluga. Females become sexually mature after five years, males after eight years. In both sexes the age of sexual maturity may depend to some degree on the population density. Dominant males appear to mate with many females. Soon after mating, the beluga migrate through the pack ice, often for 300km (185mi) or more to shallow, invariably warmer, often muddy estuaries, arriving in June or July and staying till August or September. Here the young from the previous year's mating are born. Single calves are the norm, with twinning an extremely rare event. Those that are about to calve within the estuary tend to move away from the main herd but may be accompanied by a non-pregnant or immature female. Whether this companion attends to assist the mother or is simply curious, is open to question. It is possible that it may simply be an older calf attempting to maintain maternal ties.

Births have been observed to take place in isolated bays or near shore. Initially, mother and newborn remain separate from the nearby herd and may join up with several other mother–calf pairs. There is a strong bond established and physical contact is maintained even while swimming— swimming so close together that the calf functions almost as an appendage to the mother's side or back. Nursing is accomplished underwater, beginning several hours after birth and at hourly intervals thereafter. Lactation may last two years, at which time the mother is again in early pregnancy. The complete reproductive cycle of gestation and lactation takes three years.

Narwhal move from the offshore pack ice into fjords during mid-summer but, unlike the beluga, do not consistently frequent shallow estuaries during the calving period.

Beluga appear to remain in herds for their entire life, the degree of dispersion depend-

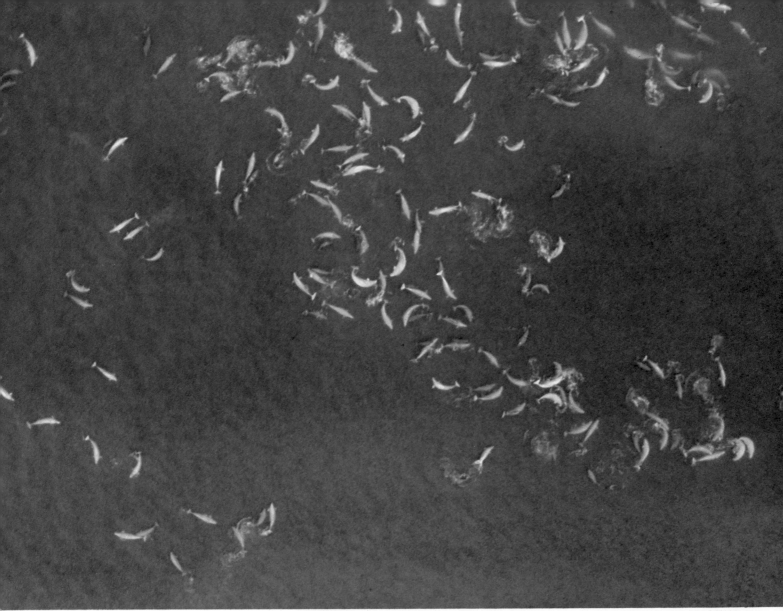

ing on the season: being closely aggregated on the breeding ground or spread out over a larger feeding area. Within the herd there is obvious segregation by age and sex. Groups or pods of adult males can be seen as well as nursery groups of mothers with newborn and older calves. Whether the groups of adult males represent the dominant, breeding animals or are nonbreeders excluded by some dominant bull within the herd has yet to be determined.

Present-day herd sizes may range from hundreds to several thousand, but these numbers may be not so much an indication of the carrying capacity of that region as of the historic and present-day exploitation pressure. While various summering populations may share a common wintering or feeding ground further offshore and away from solid ice, they appear to return to their site of origin for calving. Thus there is no apparent exchange between populations.

Although not as readily observed as beluga, the narwhal herd composition is similar: groups of females with calves;

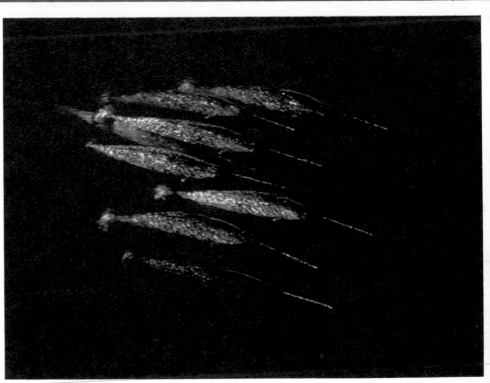

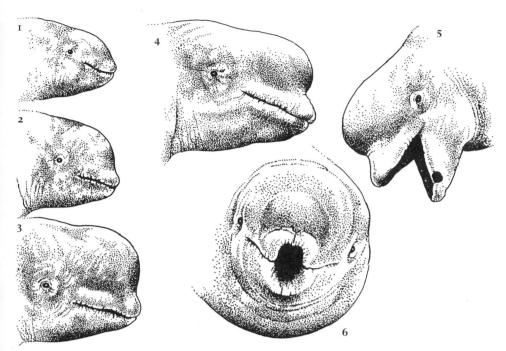

▲ **Smiling beluga**—development of facial features and expressions. Adult beluga have a very pronounced forehead melon, but this is show to develop: in newborn beluga (1) it is almost absent; in yearlings (2) the melon is quite large but the beak undeveloped; maturity (3) is reached at 5–8 years. The beluga's mouth and neck are highly flexible, and they communicate with each other a great deal by sound and facial expression. In repose (4) the beluga seems to our eyes to be smiling. Beluga are versatile feeders and the pursed mouth (6) is believed to be used in bottom feeding. Besides clicks and bell-like tone, beluga produce loud reports by clapping their jaws together (5).

▶ **Seemingly carved from chalk,** a beluga breaches to breathe, revealing its open blowhole.

◀ **Beluga swarm.** TOP From June to September beluga congregate in hundreds and thousands in traditional estuaries such as the Mackenzie Delta on the Beaufort Sea, Nelson and Churchill rivers in Hudson Bay, and Clearwater Fjord on the coast of Baffin Island, where they give birth.

◀ **Iridescent narwhal** make a dramatic sight, swimming in a dark blue sea between two ice floes.

groups of large males of similar body size, color and tusk length roaming through the herd. Narwhal tend to be more widely dispersed in the fjords, unlike the beluga's tight aggregation in smaller estuaries. Narwhal are not as vocal as beluga, which may, in part, be compensated or displaced by the added feature of tusk display. While the beluga often bite the flukes and flippers of others in rather mild social combat, narwhals perform a "joust" with their tusks and, based upon the body scars observed, some injuries are inflicted. It is not unusual to find both narwhal and beluga in the same fjord and, while they may often be in close proximity, they do not appear to conflict.

The predictable migratory behavior of beluga, dictated by the strict seasonality of higher latitudes and their gregarious nature while summering in estuaries, has made this species particularly vulnerable to exploitation. In the 18th and 19th centuries American and European whalers would force mass strandings of hundreds of beluga in order to "top up" their cargo of whale oil rendered from their primary quarry, the

Bowhead. Aboriginal peoples, being superb animal behaviorists and hunters, were technically capable of taking a large toll of the stocks during the calving season and, no doubt, there were instances of their harvests exceeding immediate needs. By the early 20th century, some stocks, having experienced excessive commercial whaling, continued to be exploited by native hunters both for domestic consumption of oil, meat and edible skin and also for trade in hides and oil.

While some populations have been greatly reduced as a result of past hunting practices they are being monitored by fisheries management scientists, and native hunters are being encouraged to become involved in the process. The beluga's affinity for shallow, coastal areas poses other modern-day problems: those of habitat alteration through the construction of hydroelectric dams and offshore petroleum exploration and extraction via pipelines. It is possible that, as with many wild stocks, beluga will adjust to increased marine activity associated with shipping and petroleum-related activities, provided there is little harassment. In the case of hydroelectric development, there could be significant alteration of habitat either through regulated river flow and/or water temperature.

With the exception of a few complaints of beluga consuming salmon migrating up rivers, their presence has no adverse impact on man and in fact their nearshore migrations make whale-watching the basis of small tourist industries in a few areas.

The narwhal's tendency to avoid estuaries and to overwinter further offshore than the beluga reduces several potential threats from industrial development. Environmental studies coincident with the increased pace of mining and petroleum exploration in the Arctic have resulted in a clearer picture of narwhal distribution and population size. While they were originally thought to number some 12,000, the present estimate ranges from 25,000–30,000. The narwhal is not an endangered species but, as in all wild stocks, hunting pressure is not evenly distributed. If there is little exchange with larger populations, isolated populations will be slow to rebuild. This, however, may be more critical with the multi-stock beluga than with the narwhal. The narwhal's tusk is highly valued by collectors and museums, which provides an added incentive for native hunters. Catches are monitored and quotas are imposed, incorporating estimates for those which sink and are lost when killed.   **PB**

SPERM WHALES

Family: Physeteridae
Three species in 2 genera.
Distribution: worldwide in temperate waters to latitudes of about 40°; bull Sperm whales to polar regions.

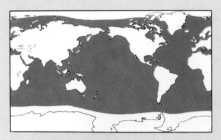

Sperm whale

Physeter macrocephalus
Sperm whale, cachalot, Spermacet whale.
Size: head-to-tail length up to 20.7m (68ft); in recent years 18.5m (60ft); males considerably larger than females, up to 12m (39ft); weight: males 45–70 tonnes; females 15–20 tonnes.

Skin: dark gray with white marks and circular scars (from Giant Squid) especially on head.

Gestation: 14–15 months, possibly 16 in some areas.

Longevity: up to 70 years.

Pygmy sperm whale

Kogia breviceps
Pygmy, Short-headed, Small or Lesser sperm whale, Lesser cachalot.
Distribution: populations may be discontinuous. Size: head-to-tail length up to 3.4m (11ft); weight: about 500kg (1,100lb).

Skin: dark gray, shading to gray-white on underside; lighter "bracket" marks on side of head.

Gestation: about 9, possibly 11 months.

Longevity: may be 17 or more years.

Dwarf sperm whale

Kogia simus
Dwarf or Owen's pygmy sperm whale, Rat porpoise.
Size: head-to-tail length up to 2.7m (9ft); weight: about 350kg (770lb).

Skin: dark gray, shading to gray-white on underside.

Gestation: probably as *K. breviceps*.

Longevity: unknown.

CELEBRATED as the great white whale Moby Dick in Herman Melville's novel of that name, the Sperm whale is the largest of the toothed whales. At sea it is unmistakable for its spout, which issues at a 45° angle from the tip of a great, blunt head. When it sounds, lifting its great tail flukes clear of the water, the Sperm whale may dive deeper than any other cetacean.

Today a few white Sperm whales exist, but the giant bulls once reported by whalers are no longer found. The head occupies about one-third of the body length in the Sperm whale. In the smaller species the head is large but more conical and much shorter in relation to the whole. The wax organ in the uppper part of the head probably functions as both an acoustic lens for focusing sound by refraction through the near-concentric layers of the wax—used in echolocation (sonar)—and as a regulator of buoyancy in deep diving (see boxed feature).

Only in the Sperm whale is the blowhole placed at the tip of the head but in all species it is displaced to the lefthand side, and the nasal bones are markedly asymmetrical. The lower jaw is small in relation to the upper jaw, which in the fully grown Sperm whale can project about 1.5m (5ft) beyond it. The whales are born without teeth and teeth often erupt only at sexual maturity and even then may only appear in the lower jaw and in the male. In the Sperm whale there are usually 20–25 similar teeth on each side of the lower jaw, although not necessarily paired. In males these teeth may grow up to 25cm (10in) in length, although 15cm (6in) is a more usual size; both number and size of teeth are less in females. In the upper jaw, up to 10, frequently highly curved teeth up to 10cm (4in) long may erupt on each side. In the two *Kogia* species also, the teeth in the upper jaw, if they are present, do not usually erupt. The number per side in the lower jaw may be 16 in the Dwarf and 11 in the Pygmy sperm whale.

In all sperm whales the body is compact and robust. The flippers are paddle-shaped, and the body tapers abruptly at the tail stock. The brain of the Sperm whale is almost spherical and may be between 5.5 and 9.5kg (25–43lb) in weight, irrespective of body size or sex. Like some other (mostly baleen) whales, occasionally a Sperm whale is found to have vestigial hindlimbs attached to small pelvic bones. Fossil records indicate that the family became distinct from other toothed whales at a relatively early date, in the Miocene (26 to 7 million years ago), the genus *Kogia* becoming recognizable at a later date, in the Pliocene (7 to 2 million years ago).

Blubber and muscle each form about 33 percent of body weight in the Sperm whale, and about 22 and 33 percent respectively in the Pygmy sperm whale. Compared with the size of the animal, the eye of the Sperm whale is smaller than in other whales, and it is not typically mammalian, the anterior chamber of the eye being almost non-existent, reduced to a narrow slit between the pupil and the cornea. The eyeball is fixed in its socket and as it cannot swivel there is a "blind" area both forward and aft.

Sperm whales have "taste" receptors (chemoreceptors) in the mouth which can

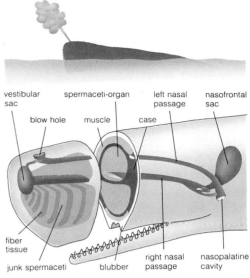

vestibular sac
blow hole
spermaceti-organ
muscle
left nasal passage
case
nasofrontal sac
fiber tissue
junk spermaceti
blubber
right nasal passage
nasopalatine cavity

▲ **The corrugated skin** of a Sperm whale calf catches the sun's glint as it breaks the surface. These corrugations give mature whales a shriveled appearance, but in this calf the effect is curiously slug-like. The lop-sided blowhole is clearly visible on the left.

▶ **Head of the Sperm whale.** TOP The unique oblique blow, to the left of the animal's direction and at a forward angle of 45°. BELOW A cross section shows the huge volume of spermaceti wax which the whale can cool or warm to alter its buoyancy by the passage of water through the nasal passages.

probably detect minute changes in the salinity and chemical components of the water.

Sperm whales show an interesting differential distribution: females and juveniles are usually restricted to equatorial and subtropical waters while males range from the Equator to polar regions. It is possible that the males' use of more distant food resources thus relieves pressure on the food resources of the females and young, who need female protection and have insufficient blubber to meet the polar waters.

There are probably at least two stocks (east and west) of Sperm whale in the North Pacific and possibly a third in western

coastal areas. The wide range of the North Atlantic stock was demonstrated when a hand-harpooned individual broke loose and escaped off the Azores in August 1980, and was caught again off Iceland a year later, a distance of 2,560mi (1,600nmi). Another individual marked off Nova Scotia in 1966 was captured seven years later off Spain. In the Southern Hemisphere there may be 7–9 different stocks. It is thought that Northern and Southern Hemisphere stocks do not mingle, even though there may be some movements across the Equator. There may be some migration towards higher latitudes in the summer months; regular seasonal migration by males to the polar waters is less certain.

Pygmy and Dwarf sperm whales are generally restricted to warmer latitudes. They strand fairly frequently off the USA, South Africa, Australia, New Zealand, India and Japan. The Pygmy sperm whale appears to prefer more oceanic waters, whilst the Dwarf sperm whale inhabits waters of the continental shelf. Little is known of migratory habits, and even this appears contradictory for different areas. Off Japan there is a seasonal occurrence, whereas off South Africa animals have been observed all year round.

Sperm whales almost certainly use echolocation (sonar) to find their prey as they dive into total darkness to at least 1,200m (3,950ft) for up to an hour (see boxed feature). Indeed, totally blind Sperm whales have been captured in perfect health and with food in their stomach. Sperm whales are often found along current lines and in areas of oceanic upwelling, where prey are usually abundant. Squid form about 80 percent of the Sperm whale diet,

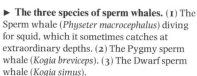

▶ **The three species of sperm whales.** (**1**) The Sperm whale (*Physeter macrocephalus*) diving for squid, which it sometimes catches at extraordinary depths. (**2**) The Pygmy sperm whale (*Kogia breviceps*). (**3**) The Dwarf sperm whale (*Kogia simus*).

◀ **The marguerite formation** in which members of a pod will encircle an injured Sperm whale while it remains alive. Such supportive bahavior used to be disastrous for the whales, allowing them to be picked off one-by-one by the whalers.

Champion Divers

Sperm whales may be considered to be the champion divers among all aquatic mammals. They have been accurately recorded by sonar as diving to 1,200m (3,936ft) and carcasses of Sperm whales have been recovered entangled in cables from 1,140m (3,740ft), where they had probably been feeding on the bottom-dwelling squid that form the bulk of their diet. One of two bulls observed diving for one to nearly two hours each dive, was found on capture to have in its stomach two specimens of *Scymodon*, a small bottom-living shark. The depth of water in the area was about 3,200 m (10,500ft), suggesting an amazing diving ability. The fact that Sperm whales dive right to the seabed for food is borne out by the discovery of all manner of strange objects in their stomachs, from stones to tin cans, suggesting that they literally shovel up the bottom mud.

Bulls are the deepest and longest divers, and females may dive to 1,000m (3,280ft), for more than one hour. Juveniles and calves dive for only half this time to about 700m (2,300ft). Females often accompany young whales and this may be what limits their diving range rather than an inability to dive deeper. However, the gregariousness and caring behavior within the nursery school means that young calves may temporarily be adopted by other females, thus enabling the mother to dive deeper for food than she might otherwise be able to do.

If diving as a group, Sperm whales appear to remain close and do almost everything together throughout a dive. They are able to recover quickly from a long deep dive and dive again after only 2–5 minutes. After several long dives, they reach their physiological limit and need to recover by lolling on the surface for many minutes.

The descent and ascent rates are astonishing. The fastest recorded averaged 170m (550ft) per min in descent and 140m (450ft) per min in ascent. The adaptations that enable the Sperm whale to perform these prodigious feats are largely similar to those of other cetaceans (see p165) but more efficient. For example, the muscle in Sperm whale can absorb up to 50 percent of the total oxygen store—at least double the proportion in land mammals, and significantly more than in baleen whales and seals.

A unique feature of the Sperm whale is the vast spermaceti organ, which fills most of the upper part of the head, and is thought to be an aid to buoyancy control. The theory is that the nasal passages and sinuses which permeate the organ can control the cooling and warming rate of the wax, which has a consistent melting point of 29°C (84.2°F). As the whale dives from warm surface waters to the colder depths, the flow of water into the head passages is controlled to quickly cool the head wax from the whale's normal body temperature of 33.5°C (92.3°F). As a result, the wax solidifies, shrinking as it does so, increasing the density of the head, and thus assisting the descent. On ascending, the blood flow to the capillaries in the head can be increased, so warming the wax slightly and increasing buoyancy, to provide lift to the exhausted whale. This is the Sperm whale's trump card for survival, ensuring that it will always rise with the minimum of effort after a dive.

the remainder being octopus, fish and crustaceans, mostly shrimp and crabs. The smaller species have a similar diet, but the type of prey suggests that the Pygmy sperm whale feeds in oceanic waters to at least 100m (330ft), while the Dwarf sperm whale frequents waters of the continental shelf at depths less than 100m. How the Sperm whale captures its prey is not known. One suggestion is that its white teeth attract the squid on which it feeds. Another is that the whale transmits a beam of very high-frequency sound which creates a short-term field of high pressure capable of temporarily stunning the prey. Most food items recovered from the stomach are complete—even Giant squid of 12m (39ft) or longer; worn, broken teeth do not affect feeding ability, nor do broken or badly deformed lower jaws. However, the Sperm whale clearly does not always capture its meal easily—the heads of many whales are covered in disk-shaped scars and wounds made by the suckers of squid which have fiercely resisted capture. Sperm whales may consume up to 200kg (440lb) at a time (a Giant squid found in one individual weighed this much), although the first stomach (there are three) is large enough to hold more. Probably the Sperm whale fills its stomach up to four times a day, and consumes about 3–4 percent of its body weight each day. Sperm whales appear to have a high gut parasite load—presumably transmitted via the food. They frequently have vast quantities of roundworms (nematodes) in the stomach with no detrimental effect, and tapeworms are found both in the worm stage in the intestine and in the larval cyst form in the blubber.

The peak breeding and calving season in the two hemispheres are some six months out of phase; southern stocks conceive in December and they give birth in

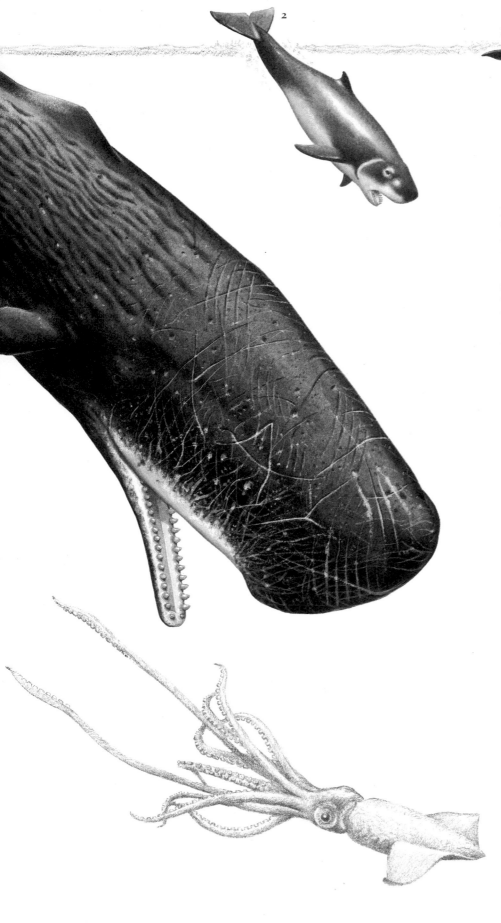

February–March, some 14–15 months later. These activities all occur in warm temperate waters, at times when the bulls seek the nursery schools, as decribed below.

Suckling calves remain in nursery schools, and continue to suckle, for at least two years. They may even suckle after weaning for several more years, suggesting a social rather than a feeding function. At weaning the calf is 6.7m (22ft) long and weighs about 2,800kg (6,175lb). The female matures sexually at 7–12 years (determined as in all Sperm whales from dentinal growth layers in the teeth) when she is about 8.5m (28ft) long. Unlike the female, the male matures in uneven stages with a growth spurt towards sexual maturity. Puberty in males is prolonged—from 9–11 up to maturity at 18–19 years, when they are some 12m (39ft) in length. The males may then move to polar waters, and be successful in obtaining harem bull status, serving several females, but they are not socially mature until about 26 years old and some 13.7m (45ft) long.

Newly mature females are only about half as fertile as the older ones—perhaps because they are still growing. The demands of pregnancy and lactation may require the female to consume 30 percent more food, even 60 percent in the newly mature female. The mother must supply her calf daily with about 20kg (44lb) of milk, containing about one-third fat.

Unlike Sperm whales, female Pygmy and Dwarf sperm whales frequently conceive while they are still nursing. At sexual maturity female Pygmy sperm whales are some 2.7m (9ft) long, males 2.7–3.0m (9–10ft). Both sexes of the Dwarf sperm whale are 2.1–2.2m (7ft) in length at maturity.

The Sperm whale forms several different types of school according to season, age, sex and place. In polar waters only large adult males (bulls) are found and they are usually solitary. In warmer waters, five types of school have been observed: bull school, bachelor school (young adult males), juv-

enile school, nursery school (adult females, calves and juveniles of both sexes), and harem school (a nursery school temporarily joined by one bull for the breeding season). The size of schools varies from one to over 100, averaging 20 in coastal and 3–7 in oceanic waters. Some schools, notably of the nursery type, tend to keep their integrity. In one instance, a female marked with a tag was found to be still in the same company of other tagged females 10 years later.

A harem school served by one bull may contain 10–40 females, but usually numbers about 14 females. The bull may have to fight established males to gain control of a harem; in such competition the male uses his more prominent teeth, as well as butting with the head. Females may help to drive out old bulls.

The Dwarf sperm whale probably occurs in groups of less than 10 animals. Adult females and their calves probably form groups, as may juveniles, and sexually adult males and females may occur together.

▲ **The power of the Sperm whale** is dramatically apparent as this pod forges ahead in formation. The dorsal hump, slightly suggestive of a submarine, is prominent here, and the individual on the right is demonstrating its oblique blow.

◄ ▼ **Sperm whaling.** LEFT In the 19th century, the Sperm whale was a prime target for whalers, and it was hunted so ruthlessly in the 1850s that the population collapsed in 1860. BELOW Modern Sperm whaling at Nova Scotia. This whale being flensed, ie stripped of its skin and blubber, demonstrates the narrow bottom jaw and conical teeth.

The Sperm whale is often said to be protective, and not only the female towards her calf. In one instance, after the shooting of the largest in a school of 20–30 whales, the others formed a tight circle around the injured whale with heads towards the centre and tails outstretched—the so-called "marguerite flower" formation.

Interaction between whales ranges from play, such as tossing timber baulks, leaping and lob-tailing, to fighting, in which wounds and injuries such as broken jaws may result.

Sperm whales produce "clicks" under water in the 5–32kHz range, each click comprising up to nine short pulses. These clicks are heard when groups meet. Individual whales have unique clicking patterns called "codas," which they repeat 2–60 times at intervals of seconds or minutes. Other sounds produced by the Sperm whale resemble low roars and "rusty-hinge" creaks.

One mystifying aspect of the family's behavior, common to many cetaceans, is mass stranding (see p184), when an entire school of dozens of Sperm whales may beach.

In the 18th and, particularly, the 19th centuries, the main target of New England whalers was the Sperm whale, taken for sperm oil. Today a small commercial whaling operation in the Azores uses the methods the islanders were taught by New Englanders before the advent of steam—the whales are harpooned by hand from canoes driven by oars and sail.

Whaling is still active for Sperm whales (the two *Kogia* species are taken only incidentally) in the Antarctic, North Pacific and Atlantic coasts. Most of this is based on factory vessels served by whaling ships. Modern whaling began with the use of faster steam-driven whaling ships and continued with the invention about 1868 of the explosive harpoon gun by Svend Foyn.

Any whale species taken in fishing operations must be considered to be under threat. In the Southern Hemisphere alone, the estimated original stock of 170,000 males and 160,000 females is now reduced to about 71,000 and 125,000 respectively. However, extinction now seems extremely unlikely for all three species. Certain Sperm whale stocks are already afforded protection and all Sperm whaling is scheduled to cease before the end of 1985 (a decision made by the International Whaling Commission in July 1982) although this ruling may not prevent individual nations from continuing to whale in coastal territorial waters.

There is considerable concern over depletion of the male population. Because of the "harem" social structure, most males have been considered by some people to be "surplus." This view is now being challenged because of the falling pregnancy rate in some areas.

In addition to exploitation in the modern whaling industry of the flesh (for human consumption) and blubber (for oil), the Sperm whale yields two products which are unique and have long been valued. The spermaceti oil obtained from the head, and the body oils provide a high grade lubricating oil that is used in many industries, including, today, space research. The other well-known Sperm whale derivative is the "ambergris" used as a fixative in the perfume and cosmetic industries. Ambergris is found in the intestine and is thought to be a form of excrement. A huge lump of this material from a 15m (49ft) male taken in the Antarctic was found to weigh 421kg (926lb)!

CL

BEAKED WHALES

Family: Ziphiidae
Eighteen species in 5 genera.
Distribution: all oceans.

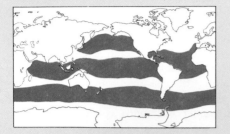

Habitat: deep sea beyond the continental shelf.

Size: head-to-tail length 4–12.8m (13–42ft);
weight 1–10 tonnes.
Diet: mainly squid and some deep-sea fishes.

Genus *Tasmacetus*
One species: **Shepherd's beaked whale** or
Tasman whale or (*T. shepherdi*). Circumpolar.

Genus *Ziphius*
One species: **Cuvier's beaked whale** or
Goosebeaked whale (*Z. cavirostris*). All oceans
except high latitudes.

Genus *Hyperoodon*
Two species: the bottlenose whales. **Northern
bottlenose whale** (*H. ampullatus*). N Atlantic.
Southern bottlenose whale (*H. planifrons*) or
Flower's or Flat-headed or Antarctic bottlenose
whale; Pacific beaked whale. Temperate waters
in Southern Hemisphere.

Genus *Berardius*
Two species: the fourtooth whales. **Arnoux's
beaked whale** (*B. arnuxi*) or Southern fourtooth
whale. Southern Ocean south of 30°S. **Baird's
beaked whale** (*B. bairdii*) or Northern giant
bottlenose or Northern fourtooth whale.
N Pacific from about 30°N to S Bering Sea.

Genus *Mesoplodon*
Twelve species: a group of beaked whales with
a single pair of teeth in the middle of the jaw.
Cool temperate waters in the Northern and
Southern Hemispheres. Species include
Blainville's beaked whale (*M. densirostris*),
Gervais' beaked whale (*M. europaeus*), **Gray's
beaked whale** (*M. grayi*).

▶ **Barrelheads.** The massive forehead of the
Northern bottlenose whale led Norwegian
whalers to call them "barrelheads" or "gray
heads." Bottlenose whaling ceased in 1972 and
the Northern bottlenose whale was declared a
provisional protected species in 1977.

THE 18 species of beaked whales tend to be
elusive creatures, and indeed one
species, Longman's beaked whale, has never
been seen in the flesh—two skulls, one
found in 1822 and the other in 1955, are
the sole evidence for its existence. Similarly,
Shepherd's beaked whale is known from
only 10 specimens and may never have
been seen alive. Not all, though, are quite as
shy as this: about 50,000 Northern bottlenose whales were caught by whalers between 1882 and 1920 and the Baird's
beaked whale has been taken off Japan.

The beaked whales are amongst the most
primitive of whales, along with the river
dolphins. The beak (strictly, elongated upper
and lower jaws) that gives them their name
varies from long and pointed in Shepherd's
beaked whale to short and stubby in the
whales of genus *Mesoplodon*. The scientific
name Ziphiidae derives from the Greek
xiphos = sword; hence Ziphiidae: "the
sword-nosed whales." They have become
specialized feeders, generally on squid, and
in some genera—*Hyperoodon*, *Ziphius* and
Mesoplodon— only one pair of teeth develops
fully, in the lower jaw. In the genus
Berardius there are two pairs of teeth in the
lower jaw and in Shepherd's beaked whale
there are many teeth in both jaws.

In all the beaked whales except
Shepherd's beaked whale and those of genus
Berardius the teeth of females never erupt
from the gums. It is possible to determine the
species, sex and maturity of a beaked whale
skull from the teeth: their number and place
in the jaw determine the species; teeth with
filled or virtually filled pulp cavities provide a
criterion of maturity; teeth exhibiting
natural wear as a sign of having erupted in
life signify male; teeth exhibiting no such
wear but with pulp cavities completely or
virtually filled out signify adult female.

The beaked whales are medium-sized
whales, some of them smaller than 6m
(20ft) long (*Mesoplodon*), others up to and
exceeding 12m (40ft) (*Berardius*). Under the
throat, there are two characteristic grooves
which make a V shape, but they do not
meet. There is no notch in the tail fluke.
Sexual dimorphism becomes very marked
by adolescence: sometimes the male is bigger, as in the Northern bottlenose whale,
and sometimes the female, as in Baird's
beaked whale. The forehead of old males
often has a pronounced bulge, which in
some species, such as the Northern bottlenose whale, becomes white. At sea, it is
difficult to distinguish between immature
specimens and females of almost all beaked
whales because the foreheads are similar in
shape. All beaked whales except the Northern bottlenose whale are liable to have a
pattern of scars on their backs, inflicted by
the teeth of other members of the same
species. These scars are usually more pronounced in older males—the result of fights.
Most species of beaked whales live in the

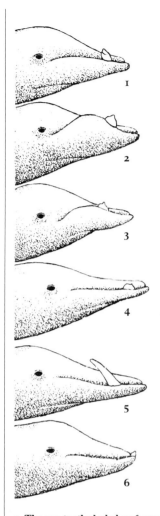

▲ **The one-toothed whales** of genus *Mesoplodon*. Beaked whales feed on squid, which do not require many sharp teeth either to catch or to eat them. Nevertheless the 12 species of *Mesoplodon* have a single tooth, whose position in the jaw is characteristic for each species. (**1**) Arch beaked whale (*M. carlhubbsi*). (**2**) Blainville's beaked whale (*M. densirostris*). (**3**) Ginkgo-toothed beaked whale (*M. ginkgodens*). (**4**) Gray's beaked whale (*M. grayi*). (**5**) Strap-toothed whale (*M. layardii*). (**6**) True's beaked whale (*M. mirus*).

deep-sea areas outside the continental shelf. They all appear to eat squid and sometimes deep-sea fishes.

Most beaked whales are hard to identify at sea. They are usually encountered singly or in groups of two or three, but some of them may be seen in schools of 25–40 animals. They are deep divers and some of them possibly dive deeper than any other cetaceans. A diving time of up to 2 hours is recorded for the Northern bottlenose whale.

Records of the distribution of beaked whales are often based upon reports of stranded animals. Such records also involve dead animals which have been washed ashore, although the death of the animal may have occured far from the stranding area. This is demonstrated by the Northern bottlenose whale, which is recorded in the Baltic and the White Sea, even though its main area of distribution is outside the continental slope. The reason that presumably healthy animals become stranded is not fully understood (see p184). Mass strandings seldom or never occur in beaked whales. It is still not known how deep-sea species of whales navigate across thousands of miles in the open sea, but it is possible that they orientate themselves by water currents and the contours of the sea bottom.

The ancestors of the "modern" beaked whales are found in fossils from the Miocene (about 20 million years ago). They were once classified with the sperm whales in a superfamily because of the many similarities between the two families. Later research has shown that the chromosomes of beaked and sperm whales are quite different, which indicates that these two groups of animals diverged early and independently.

The Northern bottlenose whale is one of the few species for which there is any knowledge of its migratory and social behavior. This species is widely distributed in the North Atlantic, occurring as far north as the edge of the ice in the summer. In the winter it occurs as far south as the Cape Verde Islands, off West Africa, in the east, and off New York in the west. Local concentrations of bottlenose whales off Spitsbergen, the coast of Norway, around Iceland and Jan Mayen Island and off Labrador may represent separate stocks. Herds of bottlenose whales are seen as early as March in the waters off the Faroes. A great number occurs between Jan Mayen Island and Iceland at the end of April, in May and early June. At the same time they are found off Spitsbergen and Bear Island. The southern migration starts at the beginning of July.

Bottlenose whales recorded on the coast of Europe are animals which have stranded mainly in the late summer and fall. Many of these whales seem to have been caught by the shallow water in the North Sea on their southern migrations. Only one bottlenose whale has been reported caught at sea in the period 1938–1972 in the shallow waters of the North Sea. In spite of intensive whaling for small whales in the Barents Sea, not a single bottlenose whale has ever been reported caught in this shelf area. These findings conflict with several reports that this species is distributed as far east in the Barents Sea as Novaya Zemlya. Reports of bottlenose whales caught by Norwegian whalers show that the greatest number has been caught at depths of more than 1,000m (3,300ft). Geographical segregation of males and females may occur; fully grown males are generally found closer to the ice than females and younger males.

In the North Atlantic, bottlenose whales usually occur in herds of 2–4 animals, but groups of up to 20 animals have been seen. Groups including two or three whales are usually animals of the same sex and age. Groups of four animals are often dominated by older males. Mother and calf usually appear alone, but sometimes two females with their calves form a group. A group of animals will usually stay with an injured companion until it is dead. If a calf approaches a ship, the mother will swim between the ship and the calf.

Male Northern bottlenose whales become sexually mature at a body length of 7.3–7.6m (23–25ft) at the age of 7–9 years; females attain sexual maturity at 6.7–7.0m (22–23ft), at an age between 8 and 14 years, with an average of about 9 years. Mating and birth occur mainly in April. The calf is about 300cm (120in) long at birth, and weaning takes place when the calf is about one year old. They give birth every second year.

Growth curves of Northern bottlenose whales based upon age determined from growth layers in the teeth (the teeth erupt when the animal is 15–17 years old) show that males continue their growth till they are about 20 years old; Females stop growing at about 15 years of age.

Obscurity has largely saved the beaked whales from exploitation, but although there has been little pressure from whaling, their future is uncertain. Like other primitive, highly specialized species such as the river dolphins, they would seem to be incapable of exploiting changes in the ecosystem and hence may well succumb to competition from more adaptable species.   IC

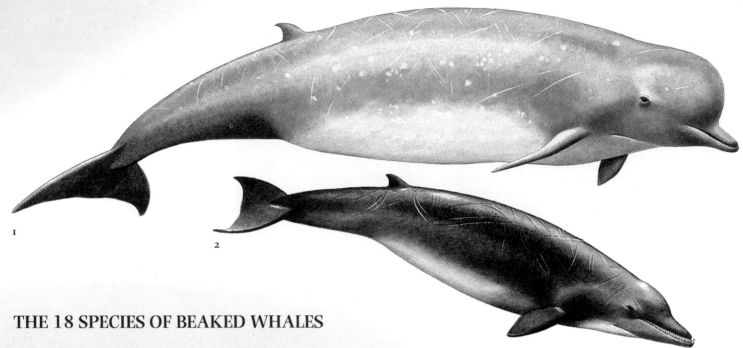

1

2

THE 18 SPECIES OF BEAKED WHALES

Abbreviations: HTL = head-to-tail straight-line length. wt = weight (estimated from a weight-
length key for the Northern bottlenose whale).
[v] Vulnerable.

Genus *Tasmacetus*

Beak long and slender; two large
conical teeth at tip of lower jaw, with
26–27 conical teeth on lower jaw and
19–21 similar teeth on upper jaw.

Shepherd's beaked whale
Tasmacetus shepherdi
Shepherd's beaked whale or Tasman whale.

Circumpolar (known only from 10
specimens recorded in S Hemisphere,
including New Zealand, Argentina,
Chile and Tierra del Fuego). Female
HTL 6.6m; wt about 5.6 tonnes. Skin:
dark gray-brown above, flanks
lighter, belly almost white.

Genus *Ziphius*

Head slightly concave; beak less
developed than in bottlenose whales,
distinctly goose-like.

Cuvier's beaked whale
Ziphius cavirostris
Cuvier's beaked whale or Goosebeaked whale.

All oceans except high latitudes.
Strandings from Atlantic Ocean north
to Cape Cod in west, North Sea in
east; Mediterranean and south to
Cape of Good Hope; Pacific Ocean
north to Bering Sea and Alaska, south
to Tierra del Fuego. Male HTL 6.7m;
wt about 5.6 tonnes; female HTL 7m;
HTL at birth 2.1m. Male sexual
maturity at 5.4m, female at 6.1m.
Skin: very variable; mustard to dark
umber in Pacific, gray or smoke blue
in Atlantic; white patches on belly
caused by parasites.

Genus *Hyperoodon*

Forehead bulbous, becoming more
pronounced with age, particularly in
males. Older males with a single pair
of pear-shaped teeth that erupt at the
top of the lower jaw.

Northern bottlenose whale [v]
Hyperoodon ampullatus
Widely distributed in N Atlantic, to
edge of the ice in summer; in winter,
south to Cape Verde Islands in the
east and off New York in the west.
Male HTL 9m; wt about 10 tonnes;
female HTL 7–8.5m; HTL at birth
about 3m. Male sexual maturity at
7.3–7.6m. Skin: very variable;
greenish-sienna above, smoke gray
beneath, lightening to cream all over
with age; calves uniform umber
brown. Gestation: 12 months.
Longevity 37 years.

Southern bottlenose whale
Hyperoodon planifrons
Southern or Flower's or Flat-headed or
Antarctic bottlenose whale; Pacific beaked
whale.
Temperate waters in the Southern
Hemisphere. Strandings in Argentina,
off Falkland Islands, Brazil, Chile,
Australia, New Zealand, South Africa.
Male HTL 7m; wt about 6.2 tonnes;
female HTL 7.5m; wt about 7.9
tonnes. Skin: deep metallic gray,
lightening to bluish on the flanks and
paler beneath (these are colors of dead
animals; in life they may be more
brown than blue).

Genus *Berardius*

The largest of the beaked whales.
Unlike other Ziphiidae, 2 pairs of
strongly compressed functional teeth
near tip of lower jaw, 75mm in front
and 50mm behind, erupt in both
sexes. Weals and other wounds on the
body of males, particularly older ones.

Arnoux's beaked whale
Berardius arnuxi
Arnoux's or New Zealand beaked whale.

Throughout Southern Ocean south of
30°S. Strandings reported from S
Australia, New Zealand, S Africa,
Argentina, Falkland Islands, S
Georgia, S Shetlands, Antarctic
Peninsula. HTL about 9–9.8m; wt
about 9.8–10.6 tonnes; HTL at birth
3.5m. Skin: blue-gray with
sometimes a brownish tint; flippers,
flukes and back darker; old males
dirty white from head to dorsal fin.
Gestation: probably 10 months.

Baird's beaked whale
Berardius bairdii
Baird's beaked or Northern giant bottlenose or
Northern fourtooth whale.

Widely distributed in N Pacific from
about 30°N to S Bering Sea (from
Pribilof Islands and Alaska to S
California in NE Pacific, and from
Kamchatka and Sea of Okhotsk to Sea
of Japan in W Pacific. Offshore waters
deeper than 1,000m. Male HTL
11.8m; wt about 13.5 tonnes; female
HTL 12.8m; wt about 15 tonnes; HTL
at birth 4.4m. Male sexual maturity
at 9.4m, female at 10m. Skin: bluish
dark gray, often with brown tinge;
underside lighter with white blotches
on throat, between flippers, around
navel and anus; female lighter.
Gestation: 17 months.

Genus *Mesoplodon*

A single pair of teeth in the lower jaw
(the name *Mesoplodon* means "armed
with a tooth in the middle of the jaw"
and is derived from the position of the
teeth in *M. bidens*, the first species of
the genus to be described). Position,
shape and size of the teeth, which
erupt only in older males, are used to
separate the species. Skin: dark gray
to black. Deep divers.

Strap-toothed whale
Mesoplodon layardii

Circumpolar in relatively cool water in
the Southern Hemisphere south of
30°S. Strandings in New Zealand,
S Australia, Falkland Islands,
Uruguay, Tierra del Fuego. HTL about
5m; wt about 3.4 tonnes; HTL at birth
about 2.2m.

Gray's beaked whale
Mesoplodon grayi
Gray's beaked or Scamperdown whale.

Circumpolar in all cool temperate
waters of Southern Hemisphere.
Strandings in S Africa, S Australia,
New Zealand, Patagonia, Argentina
south of 30°S. HTL 6.0m; wt 4.8
tonnes.

Hector's beaked whale
Mesoplodon hectori

Circumpolar in all temperate waters
of the Southern Hemisphere.
Strandings in Tasmania, New
Zealand, Tierra del Fuego, Falkland
Islands, S Africa. HTL 3.7m; wt about
2 tonnes. Known mainly from skulls.

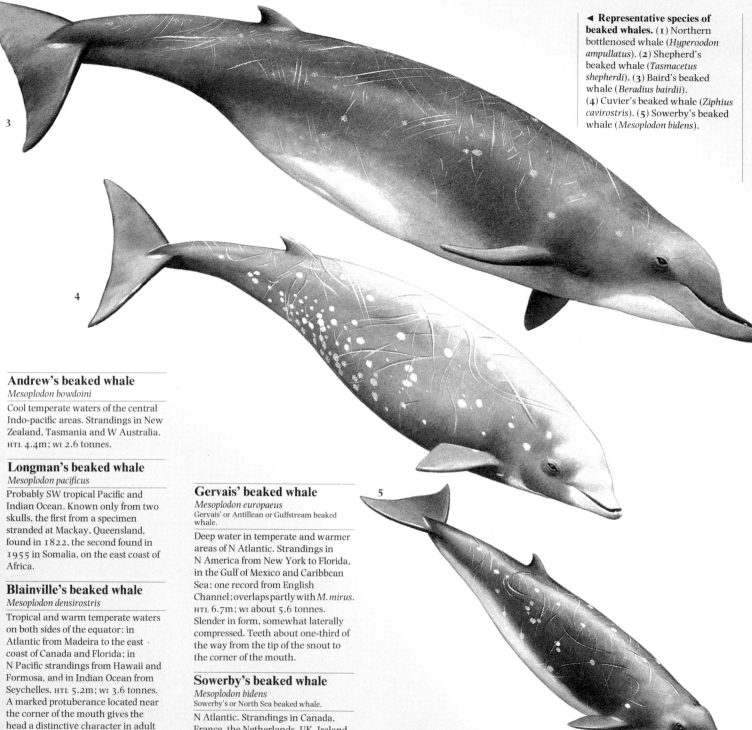

3

4

5

◄ **Representative species of beaked whales.** (1) Northern bottlenosed whale (*Hyperoodon ampullatus*). (2) Shepherd's beaked whale (*Tasmacetus shepherdi*). (3) Baird's beaked whale (*Beradius bairdii*). (4) Cuvier's beaked whale (*Ziphius cavirostris*). (5) Sowerby's beaked whale (*Mesoplodon bidens*).

Andrew's beaked whale
Mesoplodon bowdoini

Cool temperate waters of the central Indo-pacific areas. Strandings in New Zealand, Tasmania and W Australia. HTL 4.4m; wt 2.6 tonnes.

Longman's beaked whale
Mesoplodon pacificus

Probably SW tropical Pacific and Indian Ocean. Known only from two skulls, the first from a specimen stranded at Mackay, Queensland, found in 1822, the second found in 1955 in Somalia, on the east coast of Africa.

Blainville's beaked whale
Mesoplodon densirostris

Tropical and warm temperate waters on both sides of the equator: in Atlantic from Madeira to the east · coast of Canada and Florida; in N Pacific strandings from Hawaii and Formosa, and in Indian Ocean from Seychelles. HTL 5.2m; wt 3.6 tonnes. A marked protuberance located near the corner of the mouth gives the head a distinctive character in adult males.

True's beaked whale
Mesoplodon mirus

Temperate waters in N and S Atlantic, with *M. densirostris* in the middle. Strandings on French coast, Outer Hebrides and Orkney Islands, coast of Ireland. More abundant on American side of North Atlantic; strandings here from Florida, N Carolina, New England, Canada; also strandings on the east coast of S Africa. HTL 4.9m; wt about 3.2 tonnes.

Gervais' beaked whale
Mesoplodon europaeus
Gervais' or Antillean or Gulfstream beaked whale.

Deep water in temperate and warmer areas of N Atlantic. Strandings in N America from New York to Florida, in the Gulf of Mexico and Caribbean Sea; one record from English Channel; overlaps partly with *M. mirus*. HTL 6.7m; wt about 5.6 tonnes. Slender in form, somewhat laterally compressed. Teeth about one-third of the way from the tip of the snout to the corner of the mouth.

Sowerby's beaked whale
Mesoplodon bidens
Sowerby's or North Sea beaked whale.

N Atlantic. Strandings in Canada, France, the Netherlands, UK, Ireland, Norway, Sweden. Earlier literature suggested a distribution in the North Sea because of many strandings in the area, but the only observations in open sea are outside the continental shelf at 1,000–3,000m depth. HTL about 5m; wt about 3.4 tonnes. HTL at birth about 2m.

Stejnegeri's beaked whale
Mesoplodon stejnegeri
Stejnegeri's or Bering Sea beaked whale.

N Pacific, between 40°N and 60°N, but mainly between 50°N and 60°N.

Strandings from Bering Sea to Japan in western Pacific and to Oregon in eastern Pacific. HTL 6m; wt about 4.8 tonnes. Sometimes caught by whalers from Japanese coastal stations.

Arch beaked whale
Mesoplodon carlhubbsi

Distribution in temperate waters of N Pacific from 50°N to 30°N, south of the range of Stejneger's beaked whale. Strandings in Japan, Washington and California. HTL about 5m; wt about 3.4 tonnes.

Ginko-toothed beaked whale
Mesoplodon ginkgodens
Ginkgo-toothed or Japanese beaked whale.

Warm waters of the Indo-pacific from Sri Lanka, Japan to California. HTL 5.2m; wt 3.6 tonnes.

BALEEN WHALES

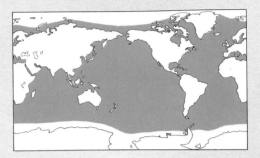

Suborder: Mysticeti
Ten species in 5 genera and 3 families.
Distribution: all major oceans.
Habitat: deep sea.

Size: head-to-tail length from 2m (6ft) in the
Pygmy right whale to 27m (90ft) in the Blue
whale; weight from 3 tonnes in the Pygmy
right whale to 150 tonnes in the Blue whale.

Gray whale (family Eschrichlidae)
One species in 1 genus: *Eschrichtius robustus*.

Rorquals (family Balaenopteridae)
Six species in 2 genera, including **Blue whale**
(*Balaenoptera musculus*), **Humpback whale**
(*Megaptera novaeangliae*).

Right whales (family Balaenidae)
Three species in 2 genera: **Right whale**
(*Balaena glacialis*), **Bowhead whale** (*Balaena
mysticetus*), **Pygmy right whale** (*Caperea
marginata*).

THE suborder Mysticeti, or baleen whales, contains rather few living species, although they make up for this by their size, the Blue whale being the largest animal ever to have lived on earth. In baleen whales teeth are present only as vestigial buds in the embryo. Instead, they have evolved a new structure, the baleen plates, which are totally unconnected to teeth. These act to strain small zooplanktonic organisms, krill, which the whales ingest in large quantities. The baleen plates are fringed with bristles and the organisms are dislodged from the baleen by the tongue.

The baleen whales are thought to have evolved in the western South Pacific, where rich zooplankton deposits in Oligocene strata, together with the occurrence of fossils of the earliest mysticete forms (early cetothere ancestors), suggest that these may have favored the evolution of baleen and a filter-feeding mode of life. From here they may have dispersed into the Pacific and Indo-Pacific regions along lines of high productivity during the late Cenozoic, although the rorquals appear to have been originally distributed in the warm temperate North Atlantic. The Gray whale is the sole member of the family Eschrichtidae, and is confined to the North Pacific (although a North Atlantic population became extinct in comparatively recent historical times). It has a rather narrow gently arched rostrum, two (rarely four) short throat grooves and no dorsal fin.

The slim, torpedo-shaped rorquals, members of the family Balaenopteridae (which also include the Humpback), have a series of throat pleats which expand as they ingest water filled with plankton, and then contract to force the water over the baleen plates. This leaves the plankton stranded on the fibrous mat that forms the frayed inner edges of the plates. The Humpback differs from other rorquals in being rather stoutly built, with fewer and much coarser throat grooves, and a pair of very long robust flippers. The head, lower jaw and flipper edge are covered with irregular knobs, and the trailing edge is indented and serrated. The rorquals, with the exception of the tropical Bryde's whale, are found throughout the world's oceans, the Bowhead has a restricted arctic distribution, the Right whale occurs only in the North Atlantic, and the Pygmy right whale is confined to the Southern Ocean.

Two of the three species of the family Balaenidae, the Right and Bowhead whales, have much larger heads, up to one-third of the total length of the body, the rostrum is long and narrow, and arched upwards, though the bones of the lower jaw are not. This leaves a space which is filled by the huge lower lips that rise from the lower jaw and enclose the long narrow baleen plates hanging from the edges of the rostrum. Neither of these species has a dorsal fin, unlike the relatively primitive Pygmy right whale, though all three species have the seven neck vertebrae fused into a single mass.

PGHE

▶ **Skimming the water** for food organisms, this Southern Right whale demonstrates its regular array of baleen plates.

▼ **Baleen types.** Although the principle of baleen functioning is similar in all such whales, there are variations. The two extremes are typified by the Right whale (1) and the rorquals such as the Sei whale (2). The Right whale has a narrow rostrum and long baleen plates. It feeds by skimming the surface, collecting food organisms which it then dislodges with the tongue. The Sei whale has a wide rostrum with short baleen plates. It gulps huge mouthfuls and raises the tongue to force the water through the baleen plates, leaving the food behind. Baleen plates from the ten species of Mysticeti (all to scale) are as follows: (**a**) Minke, (**b**) Bryde's, (**c**) Sei, (**d**) Pygmy Right, (**e**) Gray, (**f**) Humpback, (**g**) Fin, (**h**) Blue, (**i**) Right, (**j**) Bowhead.

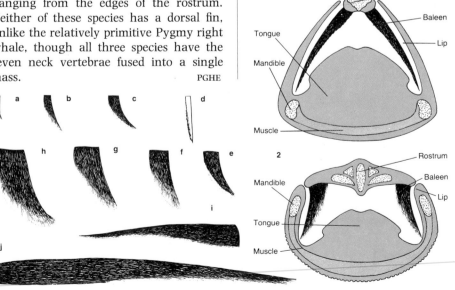

Skulls of Baleen Whales

Baleen whales show a more extreme modification of the skull than do toothed whales, so much so that it is at first hard to believe that such bones could support the head and enclose the brain of these creatures.

The principal modifications are the extension of the jaws, the upper one (rostrum) supporting the baleen plates, forward movement of the supraoccipital region (back of the skull) over the frontal, and consequent merging of the rostral and cranial bones. In the Bowhead whale the rostrum has a pronounced curve to accommodate the long baleen plates. In rorquals, like the Humpback whale, the rostrum is broader and only gently curved. The Gray whale is a bottom feeder, "plowing" the sea bed, and its jaws are shorter and thicker than the other species, the upper supporting short, stiff baleen. For the baleen characteristics of all the baleen whales, see below left.

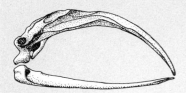

Bowhead whale   500cm

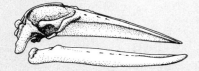

Humpback whale   350cm

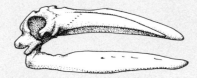

Gray whale   240cm

GRAY WHALE

Eschrichtius robustus
Gray whale, California gray whale or devilfish.
Family: Eschrichtidae.
Sole member of genus.
Distribution: two stocks, one from Baja California along Pacific coast to Bering and Chukchi seas; Korean stock from S Korea to Okhotsk Sea. Usually in coastal waters less than 100m (330ft) deep.

Size: head-to-tail length (male) 11.9–14.3m (39–47ft); weight 16 tonnes; head-to-tail length (female) 12.8–15.2m (42–50ft); weight (pregnant) 31–34 tonnes.

Skin: mottled gray, usually covered with patches of barnacles and whale lice. no dorsal fin, but low ridge on rear half of back. Two throat grooves. White baleen. Spout paired, short and bushy.

Diet: bottom-dwelling amphipods, polychaete worms and other invertebrates.

Gestation: 13 months.

Longevity: sexually mature at 8, physically mature at 40 years; maximum recorded 77 years.

Gray whales are the most coastal of the baleen whales and are often found within a kilometer of shore. This preference for coastal waters, and the accessibility of the breeding lagoons in Mexico make them one of the best-known cetaceans. Gray whales migrate each fall and spring along the western coast of North America on their yearly passage between summer feeding grounds in the Arctic and winter calving areas in the protected lagoons of Baja California. Thousands of people watch the "grays" swimming past the shores of California each year. Their migration is the longest known of any mammal; some individual Gray whales may swim as far as 20,400km (12,500mi) yearly from the Arctic ice-pack to the subtropics and back.

The Gray whale averages about 12m (40ft) in length but can reach 15m (50ft). The skin is a mottled dark to light gray and is one of the most heavily parasitized among cetaceans. Both barnacles and whale lice (cyamids) live on it in great abundance, barnacles particularly on top of the relatively short, bowed head, around the blowhole and on the anterior part of the back, adding greatly to the mottled appearance; one barnacle and three whale lice species have been found only on the Gray whale. Several albino individuals have been sighted. Gray whales lack a dorsal fin but do have a dorsal ridge of 8–9 humps along the last third of the back. The baleen is yellowish-white and is much heavier and shorter than in other baleen whales, never exceeding 38cm (15in) in length. Under the throat are two longitudinal grooves about 40cm (16in) apart and 2m (6.6ft) long. These grooves may stretch open and allow the mouth to expand during feeding, thus taking in more food.

While migrating Gray whales swim at about 4.5 knots (8km/h), they can attain speeds of 11 knots (20km/h) under stress. Migrating Grays swim steadily, surfacing every 3–4 minutes to blow 3–5 times. The spout is short and puffy and is forked as it issues from both blowholes. The tail flukes often come out of the water on the last blow in the series as the whale dives.

The Gray whale's sound repertoire includes grunts, pulses, clicks, moans and knocks. In the lagoons of Baja California calves emit a low resonant pulse which attracts their mothers. But in Gray whales sounds do not appear to have the complexity or social significance of those produced by other cetaceans.

At present there are only two stocks of Gray whales, the Californian and the separate Korean or western Pacific stock. Gray whales once inhabited the North Atlantic but disappeared in the early 1700s, probably due to whaling.

The Californian Gray whale calves during the winter in lagoons, such as Laguna Ojo de Liebre and Laguna San Ignacio, on the desert peninsula of Baja California, Mexico. They summer in the northern Bering Sea near Saint Lawrence Island and north through the Bering Straits into the Chukchi Sea, almost to the edge of the Arctic pack ice. The Korean Gray whale summers in the Okhotsk Sea off the coast of Siberia and migrates south each fall to calve among the

▲ **Gray whale blowing.** Gray whales swimming just below the surface appear very pale, almost white. The vertical spout, emerging from twin blowholes, may or may not appear divided.

▶ **Barnacle clusters** create a world of tiny bejewelled grottoes on the Gray whale's skin. Most of the great whales have barnacles, but the Gray is particularly well decorated. INSET Around the barnacles live whale lice, pale spidery creatures about 2.5cm (1in) long.

◀ **Gray whale mother and calf.** Young gray whales are smooth and sleek compared to their encrusted elders.

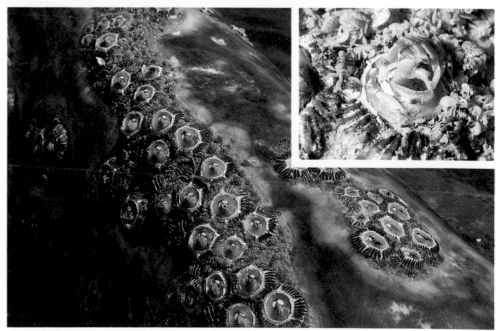

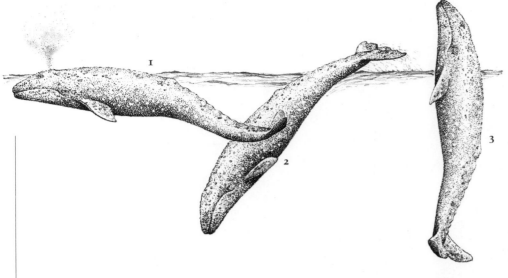

Gray whales are adapted to migration, and many aspects of their life history and ecology reflect this yearly movement from the Arctic to the Tropics. The Californian Gray spends from June to October in arctic waters feeding heavily on bottom-dwelling invertebrates.

At the start of the arctic winter their feeding grounds begin to freeze over. The whales then migrate to the protected lagoons, where the females calve. The calves are born within a period of 5–6 weeks, with a peak occurring about 10 January. At birth the calves have coats of blubber too thin for them to withstand cold arctic water, but they thrive in the warm lagoons. For the first few hours after birth the breathing and swimming of the calf are uncoordinated and labored, and the mother sometimes has to help the calf to breathe by holding it to the surface with her back or tail flukes. The calves are nursed for about seven months, beginning in the confined shallow lagoons, where they gain motor coordination and perhaps establish the mother-young bond necessary to keep together on the migration north into the summering grounds where they are weaned. By the time the calves have arrived in the Arctic, they have built up thick insulating blubber coats from the milk of the nursing females. In the lagoons

▲ **Characteristic attitudes** of the Gray whale. (1) Blowing. (2) Diving. (3) Spy-hopping.

▼ **Two years in the life of the Gray.** The gestation period of Gray whales is just over a year, 13 months in fact, which leads to a 2-year breeding cycle. Not all whales migrate the full distance but the extremes of the range represent a 20,400km (12,675mi) round trip.

inlets and islands of the south Korean coast. Much research has been done on the California Grays and most of the facts presented here refer to that stock.

Gray whales reach puberty at about 8 years of age (range 5–11 years), when the mean length is 11.1m (36ft) for males and 11.7m for females, and they attain full physical maturity at about 40. Like the other baleen whales, females of the species are larger than males, probably to satisfy the greater physical demands of bearing and nursing young. Females give birth on alternate years, after a gestation period of 13 months, to a single calf about 4.9m (16ft) long.

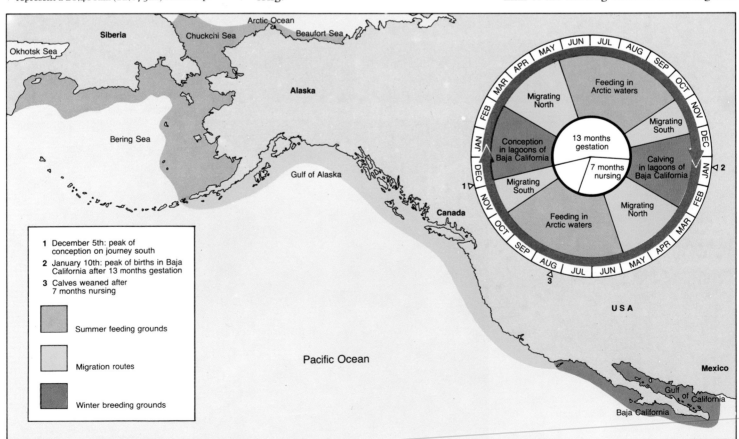

1 December 5th: peak of conception on journey south

2 January 10th: peak of births in Baja California after 13 months gestation

3 Calves weaned after 7 months nursing

Summer feeding grounds

Migration routes

Winter breeding grounds

▲ **Gray whales mating** in a warm lagoon of Baja California, Mexico. Occasionally, triads have been reported, in which an additional animal supports the mating pair.

▼ **A young Gray,** in San Ignacio Lagoon, Baja California, showing its large blowhole, and already considerable collection of barnacles.

▷ **Like a giant tusk** OVERLEAF, the head of a Gray whale protrudes from the water as it surveys its surroundings. This maneuver, spy-hopping, although seen in many whales, is very prominent in the Gray whale.

and off southern California, the calves stay close to and almost touching their mothers; but when they reach the Bering Sea in late May and June the calves are good swimmers and may be seen breaching energetically away from their mothers.

Since the migration route follows the coast closely, the whales may navigate simply by staying in shallow water and keeping the land on their right or left side, depending on whether they are migrating north or south. At points of land along the migration route Gray whales are often seen "spy-hopping." To spy-hop a whale thrusts its head straight up out of the water and then slowly sinks back down along its horizontal axis. This contrasts with the breach, where a whale leaps half way or more out of the water and then falls back on its side, creating a large splash. It is possible that Gray whales spy-hop to view the adjacent shore and thus orient their migration.

Mating and other sexual behavior have been observed at all times of year throughout the range, but most conceptions occur within a three-week period during the southward migration, with a peak about

5th December. Sexual behavior may involve as many as five or more individuals rolling and milling together. Unfortunately, little is known about the sexual behavior of Gray whales, although some authors have speculated that the extra animals are necessary to hold the mating pair together. If so this would be an extreme example of cooperation.

The migration off California occurs in a sequence according to reproductive status, sex and age-group. Heading south, the migration is led by females in the late stages of pregnancy. Next come the recently impregnated females who have weaned their calves the previous summer. Then come immature females and adult males and finally the immature males. The migration north is led by the newly pregnant females, perhaps hurrying to spend the maximum length of time feeding in the Arctic to nurture the developing fetus inside them. The adult males and non-breeding females follow, then immature whales of both sexes, and finally, meandering slowly north, come the females with their newborn calves.

Observers have noticed changes in the sizes of groups as the migration progresses past a certain point. In the early part of the southward migration single whales predominate, presumably mostly females carrying near-term fetuses, and almost no whales are in groups of more than six. These leading whales swim steadily, seldom deviating from the migratory path, which suggest that they are hurrying south to give birth to the calves. During the remainder of the migration, groups of two predominate, but there are as many as 11 in one group in the middle of the procession. These later whales seem to have a tendency to loiter more *en route*, particularly toward the end of the migration.

In the calving grounds the males and subadults are concentrated in the areas around the lagoon mouths where much rolling, milling and sexual play can be seen, while the mothers and calves seem to use the shallower portions deep inside the lagoons. In the Arctic 100 or more Gray whales may gather to feed in roughly the same area.

Some individuals do not make the entire migration north. Gray whales can be found in most of the migration areas during summer months. Off British Columbia some individuals stay in the same area for three months or more, apparently to feed. These residents seem to include both sexes and all age groups, including females with calves. Many of the same individuals return for

several summers to the same area. This is perhaps an alternative feeding strategy to making the full migration, but it is one that only a few whales can afford, since feeding areas south of the northern Bering Sea are probably rare and can only support a fraction of the population.

The only known non-human predator on the Gray whale is the Killer whale. Several attacks have been observed, most often on cows with calves and presumably in an attempt to get the relatively defenseless calf. Killer whales seem to attack particularly the lips, tongue and flukes of the grays, the areas that may most readily be grasped. Adult Grays accompanying calves will place themselves protectively between the attackers and the calves. When under attack, Grays swim toward shallow water and kelp beds near shore, areas which Killer whales seem hesitant to enter. Gray whales respond to underwater playback of recordings of Killer whale sounds by swimming rapidly away or by taking refuge in thick kelp beds.

The Korean Gray whale is currently endangered and may be on the edge of extinction. Heavy whaling pressures in the first third of this century and sporadic whaling since are undoubtedly responsible for this decline. Eskimo, Aleut and Indian whaling tribes took Gray whales from the California stock for thousands of years in the northern part of its range. In the 1850s Yankee whalers began killing Gray whales both in the calving lagoons and along the migration route. The whaling pressures were intense and by 1874 one whaling captain, Charles Scammon, was predicting that the Californian Gray would soon be extinct. Whaling virtually ceased by 1900, with the California stock reduced to a mere remnant of its population before commercial whaling, estimated at about 30,000. In 1913 whaling resumed, and it continued sporadically until 1946, when the International Whaling Commission was formed, which prohibited a commercial take of Gray whales. The Soviet Union, however, was permitted an aboriginal take of Gray whales for the Eskimo people living on the Chukotsky peninsula. At present the Soviet Union has an annual quota of 179 Gray whales. With the decline in whaling, the California stock began to show signs of recovery. The present population is estimated at 15,000–17,000 and is still growing.   ABT

Deep Harvest

Gray whales are adapted to exploiting the tremendous seasonal abundance of food that results as the arctic pack ice retreats in spring, exposing the sea to the polar summer's 24-hour daylight and thus triggering an enormous bloom of microorganisms in the water from the surface down to the sea floor. While present in the Arctic from June to October, Gray whales store enough fat to sustain them virtually without feeding through the rest of the year, as they migrate to calve in warm waters while their summer feeding grounds are covered with ice. By the time they return to their feeding grounds they may have lost up to one-third of their body weight.

The whales feed in shallow waters 5–100m (15–330ft) deep on amphipods and isopods (both orders of crustaceans), polychaete worms and mollusks that live on the ocean floor or a few centimeters into the bottom sediment. The gammarid amphipod *Ampelisca macrocephala* is probably the most commonly taken species. To feed, Gray whales dive to the sea floor, turn on their side (usually the right), and swim forward along the bottom forcing their heads through the top layer of sediment, sucking or scooping up invertebrate prey, mud and gravel and trailing a large mud plume behind. The whales then surface, straining sediments through the baleen to leave food items inside the mouth which are then swallowed; they take a few breaths, and

dive again. As Gray whales feed they leave a shallow scrape. Some scientists have speculated that they may thus effectively plow the sea floor, possibly increasing its productivity in subsequent years.

Although Gray whales feed primarily during the months spent in arctic waters, they will feed, if the opportunity arises, in other parts of their range. Grays have been found surface feeding on both small fish and shrimp-like kelp mysids (*Acanthomysis sculpta*) off the coast of California while migrating.

Several species of sea bird associate with feeding Gray whales, such as Horned puffins, Glaucous gulls and Arctic terns. These birds apparently feed on crustaceans which escape through the baleen during the straining process while the whales are surfacing. The discovery of this association answered the perplexing question of how large numbers of bottom-dwelling invertebrates, from beyond the birds' diving depth, got into their digestive tracts.

RORQUALS

Family: Balaenopteridae
Six species in two genera.
Distribution: all major oceans.

Size: head-to-tail length from
11m (36ft) in the Minke whale to
27m (90ft) in the Blue whale; weight
from 10 tonnes in the Minke whale to
150 tonnes in the Blue whale.

▶ **The slim, wedge-shaped nose** of a Sei whale
in the Pacific Ocean off Japan. Rorquals are
streamlined in the water. When landed, their
sheer bulk quickly distorts the body shape.

▼ **The bulging throat** of a rorqual is shown
here by a Humpback whale gulping a mouthful
of food at the surface. In all rorquals, the throat
grooves allow a massive expansion of the
mouth cavity. The Humpback whale is a
generalist feeder, taking both crustaceans and
schooling fish.

THE rorquals include the largest animal
that has ever lived—the giant Blue
whale weighing up to 150 tonnes—and one
of the most tuneful and acrobatic—the
Humpback whale, which not only produces
eerie and wide-ranging sounds (see pp228–
229) but also performs considerable acro-
batics, leaping from the water for no apparent reason. Many travel great distances
across the world's oceans on regular annual
migrations, from the Tropics to the polar
regions. The larger species have been
hunted intensively during the last 100
years, and their numbers have been seriously reduced.

The rorquals are all streamlined in appearance, and have a series of folds or
grooves which extend from the chin backwards under the belly; these do not reach
the umbilicus in Sei whales as they do in the
other species. Underwater photographs
show that the body form is sleek and pointed
towards the snout, and not baggy-throated
as previously thought from dead animals
seen floating at the surface or pulled out of
the water. During feeding, however, the
throat grooves allow the throat to expand
considerably.

In all species the female grows to a slightly
larger size than the male, while animals in
the Southern Hemisphere are a little bigger
than those in the Northern Hemisphere. The
head occupies up to a quarter of the body
length and, except in the Humpback whale,
has a distinct central ridge running forward
from the blowhole to the snout. There is an
additional ridge on either side on the Bryde's
whale. The head is relatively broad and U-
shaped in the Blue whale, markedly triangular in the Fin whale, even narrower in the
Minke and intermediate in shape in the Sei
and Bryde's whales. The Humpback has a
broad and rounded head bearing a series of
fleshy knobs or tubercules, which also occur
on the lower jaw. The lower jaw is bowed
and protrudes beyond the end of the snout in
all species.

The flippers are lancet-like and narrow in
all but the Humpback whale, where they are
much more robust and almost a third of the
body length, up to 5m (17ft) in length and
scalloped on at least the leading edge. The
dorsal fin is set far back on the body; it is
extremely small in the Blue whale, and set
on a fleshy pad of tissue in the Humpback
whale. It is larger and forms a shallow angle
with the back in the Fin whale, but is more
upright with a distinctly backward pointing
tip in the Sei and Minke whales. The tail
flukes are broad, with a conspicuous indentation in the middle. They are remarkably

wide in their spread in the Humpback whale
compared with the other rorquals. The blow
as the whale exhales consists of a single
spout from the double blowhole on the top of
the head, the height and relative bushiness
varying between the different species.

All rorquals have essentially similar patterns of distribution and migration throughout the world, with the exception of the
Bryde's whale. This occurs only in temperate and warm waters, generally near shore
in the Atlantic, Pacific and Indian Oceans.
Blue, Fin, Sei, Minke and Humpback whales
are found in all the major oceans. They
spend the summer months in the polar
feeding grounds and the winter months in
the more temperate breeding grounds. The
Humpback whales swim close to coasts
during their migrations, unlike the other
rorquals.

Blue whales start to migrate in the Southern Hemisphere ahead of the Fin and
Humpback whales, with Sei whales rather
later. Within each species there is also a
segregation by age and sexual class. In
general, the older animals and pregnant
females migrate in advance of the other
classes, with the sexually immature whales
at the rear of the stream. There are also
differences in the degree of penetration of the
whales into the higher latitudes. Blue
whales and Minke whales occur right up to
the ice-edge. Fin whales do not seem to go
quite so far and Sei whales are much more
subantarctic in their distribution. In all
species the bigger, older animals tend to go
further towards the pole than the younger
whales. This succession is not so clearly
apparent in the Northern Hemisphere, perhaps because the pattern of land masses and
water currents is more complicated there
compared to the more open southern
Hemisphere waters.

The various species of rorquals are
thought to be divided into a number of
stocks throughout the world's oceans.
These units approximate to separate breeding groups, but there is a degree of interchange evident from the recovery of marked
whales which indicates that within each
hemisphere at least the stocks recognized
are not totally independent genetically. The
stocks are spread widely across the oceans in
all species except the Humpbacks, which
breed in coastal waters and are also more
concentrated on the feeding grounds.

The life cycles of the Blue, Fin, Sei, Minke
and Humpback whales are very closely
related to the pattern of seasonal migrations
outlined above. Although conceptions and
births may occur at almost any time of the

year, most of this activity is confined to relatively short peak periods of 3–4 months. The whales mate in the warm waters of low latitudes in both hemispheres during the winter months and then migrate to the respective polar feeding grounds where they spend 3–4 months feeding on the rich planktonic organisms which constitute their diet. After this period of intensive feeding they migrate back to the temperate zone once again and 11–12 months after mating the females give birth to a single calf in the same waters. The newborn calves accompany their mothers on the spring migration towards the polar seas once again, living on their mother's milk. Six to seven months after birth they are weaned in the high latitude feeding grounds and can follow the normal cycle of migrations independently. Humpbacks appear to suckle their calves for 12 months before weaning occurs outside the polar seas, which is also the case in Minke whales. These latter have a gestation period close to 10 months, suggesting that they may experience a shorter interval between pregnancies than the two years expected in the other species. The mating and calving seasons for Minke whales are not clearly defined, nor in the Bryde's whale, for which little is known about the breeding cycle.

The sex ratio at birth and throughout the greater part of life is approximately equal in all species, but because of the differential segregation of the sexes and sexual classes at various times in the seasonal migration, the numbers of males and females present in an

Rorqual Feeding Habits

Rorquals are filter-feeders, that is they strain their food out of the water by means of the baleen plates growing down from either side of the roof of the mouth. The whale opens its mouth widely, engulfing the food organisms in a large quantity of water. The water is then sieved through the spaces between the baleen plates as the mouth closes and the previously expanded throat region tightens up and the tongue is raised. The food material is held back on the bristles lining the inner edges of the baleen plates before being swallowed.

Sei whales can also feed by skimming through patches of water containing the food organisms with the mouth half open. The head is normally raised a little above the surface, so that the water and food are sieved continuously through the baleen plates. When enough food has been collected the mouth is closed and the food swallowed.

The bristles fringing the baleen plates vary in texture between the species, as do the

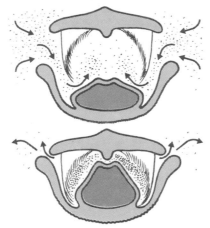

shapes and sizes of the plates, thus determining which food organisms can be retained. The Blue whale has rather coarse baleen bristles, and feeds almost exclusively on shrimp-like food—especially krill in the Antarctic. This organism is the basic food for all the baleen whales in the Antarctic, but a

wider range of food appears in other areas, and especially in the Northern Hemisphere.

Fin whales, with their medium texture baleen bristles, eat mainly krill and copepods, with fish third in importance, although there is considerable variation by area and season. Sei whales have much finer baleen fringes and they are primarily copepod feeders, but krill and other crustaceans are also consumed. Minke and Humpback whales feed mainly on fish in the Northern Hemisphere and krill in the south, while Bryde's whales are more exclusively fish eaters, with only a little crustacea in the diet.

The fish taken by these whales are generally schooling species, and include herring, cod, mackerel, capelin, and sardines. The Humpback and Minke whales have characteristic breaching behavior which may serve to scare and concentrate the prey fish as the whale circles them before shooting up vertically with the mouth open to engulf the food. Humpback whales may also "herd" their prey by releasing a circle of bubbles which whirl to the surface around them.

Abbreviations: HTL = head to tail length. wt = weight.
E Endangered. V Vulnerable.

Blue whale E

Balaenoptera musculus

Polar to tropical seas.
HTL 27m; wt 150 tonnes.
Skin: mottled bluish-grey; flippers
pale beneath. Baleen plates:
270–395, blue-black. Throat
grooves: 55–88. Longevity: 80 years.
Subspecies: 2. **Blue whale**
(*B.m. musculus*). **Pygmy blue whale**
(*B.m. brevicauda*). S India Ocean,
S Pacific. HTL 24m; wt 70 tonnes.
Skin: silvery-gray; baleen plates:
280–350, black; throat grooves:
76–94; longevity: 65 years.

Fin whale V

Balaenoptera physalus

Polar to tropical seas.
HTL 25m; wt 80 tonnes.
Skin: gray above, white below,
asymmetrical on jaw; flipper and
flukes white below. Baleen plates:
260–470, blue-gray with whitish
fringes, but left front white. Throat
grooves: 56–100.

Sei whale

Balaenoptera borealis

Polar to tropical seas. HTL 18m; wt 30
tonnes. Skin: dark steely-gray, white
grooves on belly. Baleen plates:
320–400, gray-black with pale
fringes. Throat grooves: 32–62.

Bryde's whale

Balaenoptera edeni

Tropical and subtropical seas. HTL
13m; wt 26 tonnes. Skin: dark gray.
Baleen plates: 250–370, gray with
dark fringes. Throat grooves: 47–70.

Minke whale

Balaenoptera acutorostrata

Polar to tropical seas. HTL 11m; wt 10
tonnes. Skin: dark gray above, belly
and flippers white below; white or
pale band on flippers, especially in
N hemisphere; pale streaks behind
head. Baleen plates: 230–350,
yellowish-white, some black. Throat
grooves: 50–70. Longevity: 45 years.

Humpback whale E

Megaptera novaeangliae

Polar to tropical seas. HTL 16m; wt 65
tonnes. Skin: black above, grooves
white; flukes with variable white
pattern below. Baleen plates:
270–400, dark gray. Throat grooves:
14–24. Longevity: 95 years.

4

area at a particular time may show an imbalance. The breeding group in these animals tends to be a male and female pair, although the duration of the pair-bond is not known.

It is characteristic of whales, as of many other animals, that they reach sexual maturity at a given body size, which is most conveniently measured in terms of length. Because it appears that there has been an increase in the growth rates of at least the Blue, Fin, Sei, and Minke whales in the Southern Hemisphere since the major reduction in the population numbers of the Blue and Fin whales, all these species are now reaching the critical sizes at which they become sexually mature earlier than before.

For Fin whales born before 1930 the mean age at maturity was a little over 10 years. From the mid-1930s onwards this mean age declined and is now about 6 years. Sei whales up to 1935 had a mean age at maturity of just over 11 years. This age fell to a little under 10 years by 1945 and now has decreased to 7 years in some areas. Even greater reductions are indicated in southern Minke whales, in which the age at sexual maturity has decreased from around 14 years in 1944 to 6 years now.

The future of the rorquals depends on the success of the protection they have received in recent years and, in the Southern Hemisphere, on the conservation of their food-base, krill. There is evidence of increasing numbers in some species, but because of their very slow birth-rate, it will be many decades before there is full recovery, if ever.

RG

▲ **Species of rorquals.** (**1**) Humpback whale (*Megaptera novaeangliae*). (**2**) Minke whale (*Balaenoptera acutorostrata*). (**3**) Bryde's whale (*Balaenoptera edeni*). (**4**) Fin whale (*Balaenoptera physalus*). (**5**) Blue whale (*Balaenoptera musculus*). The Sei whale, not shown here, is similar to Bryde's whale, but they can be distinguished by the top of the head, which has three ridges in Bryde's whale (**a**), only one in the Sei (**b**).

a

b

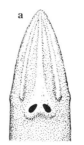
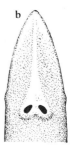

In the Wake of the Giant

The ecological consequences of overexploitation of the Blue whale

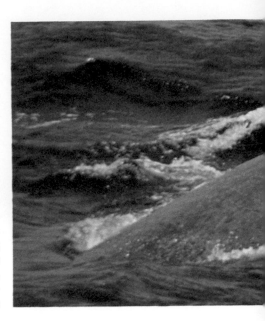

The sheer size of the Blue whale made it peculiarly vulnerable to exploitation. The oil from its body was used in edible foodstuffs, and it very soon became the prime target for whalers, once they had developed adequate technology to chase, kill and hold on to such a massive carcass, which sinks when dead. This development came in the 1860s, and Norwegian and other European whalers soon caught so many Blue and other large whales in the North Atlantic and adjacent waters that they were forced to find new areas in which to operate.

Rorquals are equally at home in northern and southern polar waters but it was not until 1906 that the whales of the Southern Ocean were discovered. European whalers were quick to exploit these vast whale resources of the Antarctic. The coastal Humpbacks were quickly reduced by shore-based whaling from subantarctic islands and tropical coasts before the oceanic Blue whales became the prime targets. This fishery accelerated in the mid-1920s, with the development of free-ranging floating factory ships on which the whales, killed by a fleet of fast catcher boats, could be processed. The island of South Georgia became the center of the whaling industry.

Over 29,000 Blue whales were killed in the single summer season of 1930/31, and the stocks could not sustain so great a slaughter. The record of the Blue whale fishery in the Antarctic is a tragic illustration of the depletion of a major resource by gross over-catching. The whaling nations continued to reduce the Blue whale stocks despite the warnings of scientists, until they were reduced to about one-thirtieth of their original abundance. The

▲ **The churning power** of the Blue whale at sea, a sight that, earlier this century, almost disappeared from the earth forever.

◀ **Last of the giants.** A Blue whale waiting to be cut up at a whaling station on South Georgia in 1926, during the peak period of Blue whale exploitation.

▼ **Diminishing catch.** Fin whales at Grytviken, South Georgia, in 1961. As the catch of Blue whales dwindled, attention turned to the smaller rorquals, until they too were depleted.

Antarctic industry was maintained by diverting its attention to the smaller Fin whales, and Blue whales were not given total protection from hunting in the Southern Hemisphere until 1965. By this time the original population of some 200,000 Blue whales had been reduced to about 6,000, with about the same number of Pygmy blue whales, a form which has been described as a separate subspecies, paler in color, rather shorter in the tail region and with relatively shorter baleen plates than the ordinary Blue whale. The Pygmy blue whale was first recognized in the southern part of the Indian Ocean, but has also been identified in the waters off Chile.

In the Antarctic, all rorquals tend to have the same food, krill, as the mainstay of their diet. It is not surprising, therefore, that the reduced abundance of the large Blue, Fin and Humpback whales in particular has had some effects on the smaller Sei and Minke whales, and also on the reproductive potential of the larger whales themselves. Now, some 50–55 per cent of mature non-lactating female Blue whales are pregnant. This is an approximate doubling of the rate before the 1930s and reflects a halving of the average interval between successive births. The same change has occurred in Fin and Sei whales, while in Minke whales up to 90 percent of the females sampled in the Antarctic fishery are pregnant (this very high figure may be the result of sampling bias if the catching operations happen to fall on this component of the segregated populations). Proper management of the natural renewable resources represented by the great whales should be based on a harvesting policy which ensures that only the surplus after making good natural deaths is cropped. Because many of the rorquals have been so heavily depleted in the past, the International Whaling Commission has protected them from capture in recent years. This should allow the most rapid rebuilding of the stocks. Those stocks which are still numerous, such as the Minke (more than 425,000) and Bryde's whales (90,000), can at present only be captured in numbers which will not reduce their abundance and there is the prospect that all commercial whaling will end in 1986.

If Blue whales are reproducing more frequently and from an earlier age than in former years, it might be expected that their numbers will start to increase. Unfortunately, the research devoted to monitoring their abundance is insufficient to provide very firm evidence. However, there are some signs from sightings by survey vessels in parts of the Southern Hemisphere that the Blue whales there are slowly increasing, as well as in the North Atlantic, while the stocks in the North Pacific appear to be at least stable rather than declining.

It seems unlikely that total protection will lead simply to a recovery of rorqual populations to their pre-1906 levels. The release of vast quantities of krill that was once consumed by the whales has lead to large increases in the populations of other krill-eating species, especially the Crabeater seal (see pp280–281), the Antarctic fur seal (see pp260–261), penguins and other seabirds. The effects of protection of the whales on this complex food-chain, based on krill, will be watched with great interest. RG

Water Voices

The songs of the Humpback whale

Snores, groans, whos, yups, chirps, ees and oos ... These are some of the "words" man has inadequately used to describe the unique songs of the Humpback whale. Although complex, these songs are repeated according to identifiable patterns, and some can be detected by hydrophones at a range of more than 100 nautical miles (185km).

Like so many discoveries, the songs of Humpbacked whales became known to science almost by chance: attention was first drawn to the songs because they interfered with naval acoustic surveys. The songs' existence has probably been common knowledge to sailors for centuries, since the sounds are transmitted through the hulls of ships. However, the fact that the noises stem from whales has only recently been confirmed by means of directional arrays of underwater hydrophones and simultaneous surface observation. Live skin sampling of the singing subject, and subsequent sexing of the skin chromatin, has so far indicated that it is solitary males in their coastal winter breeding and calving grounds of the warm subtropics who sing, perhaps seeking mates for the first time.

The sounds usually range in frequency between 40Hz and 5kHz, and the song itself is a true song, consisting of an ordered sequence of themes comprising motifs and phrases, like that of birds. It can last from 6 to 35 minutes, and forms part of a "song session" which can continue throughout the day and night with only brief pauses of a minute or so, for breathing, between successive songs. In a session, each song is well defined, following a set sequence, with a beginning and ending, which is usually indicated by the so-called "surface ratchet" noise, followed by blowing. If there is a temporary interruption in singing, the whale recommences where it broke off, and the sequence remains intact.

The song consists of six basic themes which are composed, in descending order of complexity, of so-called phrases, motifs, and approximately 20 syllables, which are often described onomatopeically. Throughout all the themes are interspersed individual "chirps," "cries" and other sundry notes and syllables. The motifs and phrases may be repeated any number of times (a phenomenon known as redundancy) and while the basic song is continually repeated in sessions, the individual phrases can vary in length considerably, which explains the great variability in overall song duration.

While songs of individual animals have their own characteristics, within one season all whales in one region sing what is rec-ognizably the same song. There are at least three regionally distinct dialects in (a) the North Pacific (Hawaii and Pacific Mexico), (b) the North Atlantic (West Indies and Cape Verde Islands) and (c) Tonga in the Southern Hemisphere. The song slowly changes over several seasons: the content of phrases within themes changes slightly throughout each season, new motifs are included or old ones dropped; exceptionally, an entire theme may disappear from an individual's repertoire from one season to the next.

Individual whales appear to have voice characteristics that confer a personal signature on their songs, and the differences between individuals remain recognizable even when within-song variations occur. This may enable females to identify particular mates at any time and any place.

The versatility and acoustic range of vocalizations within the song may increase the efficiency of transmission of information in a noisy environment, and also avoid monotony. The song's repetition of phrases probably reinforces communication and can be detected at least 17 nautical miles (31km) away. The low frequency notes of snores and moans are of high amplitude (60 db.u bar^{-1}) and the detection range of such sounds is over 100 nautical miles (185km).

▶ **Humpback themes.** The basic unit of the songs is the syllable, rendered onomatopoeically as "yups," "cries," "chirps" etc. These are the equivalent of the notes in our music and are shown here as their sonogram patterns. Motiffs, recurring groupings of these syllables, are combined into phrases, which make up the themes. There are six basic themes.

▼ ▶ **The underwater world of the Humpback** is eerily beautiful, both in the songs they sing and their movement. The extremely long flippers have a white leading edge which gleams against the dark blue of the water.

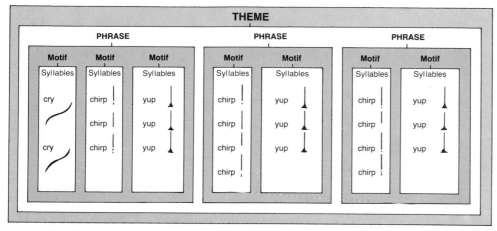

While most singing is in relatively shallow coastal water, calls (if made) in the range 20–100Hz in colder, deeper water could be detectable at even greater distances. The changing frequencies could also be used to determine range and bearing, so that whales could home in on each other.

It is clear from its continuous nature and ordered sequence that the song potentially contains much information, but its precise function is not known. Most evidence at present indicates that the prime function of the song is sexual.

Humpback whales migrate to the warm (24–28°C) subtropical (latitude 10–22°C) waters for the winter breeding season. On the breeding grounds, the strongest bond is that between cows and their calves. The female, whether with a calf or not, forms the nucleus of any group formation that develops while on these grounds. All the whales appear to return to the same sites from year to year. The males arrive on the grounds and commence singing. They favor shallow coastal areas of depth 20–40m (65–130ft) with smooth bottom contours which probably help sound propagation. Females appear to attract the attentions of the males to a different extent throughout the season, perhaps reflecting whether or not they are receptive or already pregnant. Some believe that the female may experience several receptive cycles while on the grounds if conception fails initially, so optimizing her chances of conceiving.

The female initially attracts a single male escort who for that day or for a few hours acts as her "principal" escort. Soon, other male "hangers-on" jostle for position close to the female. The males all struggle to oust each other by tail-thrashing, lunging and creating bubble-streams. The group size around the female may range from one to six or so males. The principal escort may change daily or even more frequently throughout the season, so that fidelity to one mate does not seem likely, at least in the pre-mating stage.

When the whales join an animal at the center of the group (the "nuclear" animal) they are frequently singing. They then stop until they leave, when they usually resume singing. The nuclear animal never sings, and this, together with the facts that this animal often has a calf, and that the singing escorts are solitary before joining strongly suggest that the nuclear whale is female and that the newcomers are males. One role of the singing is thus likely to be sexual, and probably advertises availability.

CL

RIGHT WHALES

Family: Balaenidae
Three species in 2 genera.
Distribution: arctic and temperate waters. One
species in the north only, one in the south only,
one in both hemispheres.

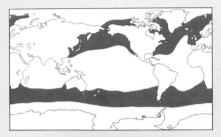

Right whale [E]
Balaena glacialis
Distribution: temperate waters of both
hemispheres; recorded as far south as Florida
and as far north as Southern Brazil respectively.
Size: length 5–18m (16–60ft), average adult
about 15m (45ft); weight about 50–56 tonnes.
Skin: black, with white patches on the chin and
belly, sometimes extensive. Head and jaws
characteristically bearing several large
irregular skin callosities infested with parasites.
Baleen gray or grayish-yellow, up to 2.5m (8ft)
in length.
Gestation: about 10–11 months.
Longevity: not known but probably greater
than 30 years.

Subspecies: 3. *B. g. glacialis*; N Atlantic.
B. g. japonica; N Pacific. *B. g. australis*; Southern
Ocean.

Bowhead whale [E]
Balaena mysticetus
Distribution: Arctic Basin, with winter
migration into Bering and Labrador Seas.
Size: Length 3.5–20m (11–66ft), average adult
about 17m (51ft); average adult weight
probably 60–80 tonnes.
Skin: body black, except for white or ochreous
chin patch; no callosities. Baleen narrow, dark
gray to blackish, up to 4m (13ft) in length.
Gestation: 10–11 months.
Longevity: not known, but probably greater
than 30 years.

Pygmy right whale
Caperea marginata
Distribution: circumpolar in southern
temperate and subantarctic waters. Not a true
Antarctic species.
Size: length 2–6.5m (6–21ft), average adult
about 5m (15ft); weight about 3–3.5 tonnes.
Skin: body gray, darker above and lighter
below, with some variable pale streaks on the
back and shoulders, and dark streaks from eye
to flipper. Baleen plates relatively long for its
size, whitish with dark outer borders.
Gestation: probably 10–11 months.
Longevity: not known.

[E] Endangered.

THE Right whale might well wish it had
been christened differently. It was so
called because it was the "right" whale to
hunt—it swam slowly, floated when killed
and had a high yield of baleen and oil. In
consequence, it is unlikely that any other
whale—the Blue whale included—was
hunted to such precariously low levels as
were the Right whale and its close relative,
the Bowhead. Even today, after decades of
protection from industrial whaling, the entire Bowhead population still numbers only
about 3,000, and the scattered breeding
herds of Right whales perhaps barely 4,000
animals.

Despite the definitive-sounding name,
there is in fact not one right whale but
three—Right whale, Bowhead whale and
Pygmy right whale which share certain
characters that distinguish them from the
rorquals. These include an arched rostrum,
giving a deeply curved jawline in profile, in
contrast to the nearly straight line of the
rorqual mouth; long slender baleen plates
instead of relatively short ones as in the
rorquals; and only two throat grooves in the
Pygmy right whale and none in the large
species, compared to many in all rorquals.
There are also a number of marked differences in cranial features, not visible in the
living or stranded specimen: in particular,
the upper jawbone is narrow in right whales
and broad in rorquals. In all three species
the head is large in proportion to the rest of
the body; the two large species are exceptionally bulky in comparison to the
rorquals.

A unique feature of the Right whale is the
group of protrusions or callosities on the
head in front of the blowhole. These outgrowths are infested with colonies of barnacles, parasitic worms and whale lice. The
largest patch, on the snout, was called the
"bonnet" by old-time whalers, and is a
feature by which the species is easily recognized at sea. The function of the callosities
is unknown but they are useful in enabling
cetologists to identify individuals. In the
Bowhead whale the curved jawbone is at its
most pronounced and the head may be up to
40 percent of the total body length. The
Pygmy right whale is a small, slim species,
more like a rorqual in build than either of its
large relatives; unlike the other two species,
it has a small triangular dorsal fin.

Nothing is known of vocalizations in the
Pygmy right whale, and little of those of the
Bowhead, but the Right whale has an
extensive repertoire. One of these, best described as a loud lowing or bellowing, is

▲ **Basking Right whales** off Península Valdés, South America. The callosities give them a strangely crocodile-like apearance.

◀ ▼ **The Right whale's bonnet** LEFT and other callosities BELOW. Unlike the Gray and Humpback whales, which have parasites scattered randomly over their bodies, the Right whale has concentrated outgrowths, one of which, the bonnet, is always present on the top of the head. The pattern of callosities is individually unique and so facilitates recognition of individuals by scientists.

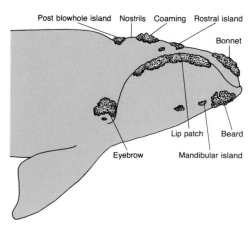

Post blowhole island   Nostrils   Coaming   Rostral island
Bonnet
Lip patch   Beard
Eyebrow   Mandibular island

made when the animal's head (or at least the nostrils) is above the water. On a quiet day it can be heard for several hundred meters. Low frequency sounds have been recorded underwater during travel, courtship and play. Vocal activity is said to be greatest at night. Right whales do not seem to produce repeated sequences like the "songs" of Humpback whales (see pp 228–229), but make many single and grouped sounds in the 50–500 Hz range, some lasting as much as one minute, variously described as "belches" or "moans." The latter may be the sound sometimes heard above the surface. There is also a pulsed sound with a wide frequency spread (30–2,100 Hz). Functions are not yet assigned to any of these calls, but it is known that a variable 2–4 kHz noise taped during surface feeding is made by water rattling across partially exposed baleen plates.

All the three species feed primarily on copepods, but the North Atlantic Right whale also takes the larvae of krill, and the Southern Ocean population appears to eat adult krill regularly as well. Bowhead feeding is usually associated with restricted belts of high productivity in arctic areas, such as the edge of the plume from the Mackenzie River, where nutrient enrichment and water clarity are both optimal for active photosynthesis by phytoplankton, resulting in turn in relatively high zooplankton production. Both Bowhead and Right whales generally feed by skimming with their mouths open through surface concen-

trations of zooplankton; this is in contrast to the feeding methods of most rorquals (other than Sei whales) which tend to gulp patches of highly concentrated shrimp or fish. In the Bay of Fundy, eastern Canada, Right whales feed as often below the surface as above, diving for 8–12 minutes at a time. Some of the feeding areas there are thickly scattered with fragments of floating rockweed, torn from the beaches by surf action and carried back and forth by the large tides of Fundy; surface feeding runs tend to be short and the whales stop frequently to clean debris from the baleen; they seem to be able to use the tongue to roll the weed into a bolus, and flick it from the mouth, rather like a spent wad of chewing tobacco. When prey concentrations are dense, Right whales feed side by side; under other circumstances because of their considerable food requirement, it is presumably advantageous for animals of such large size to separate to feed. Based on work on rorquals, Bowhead and Right whales probably need 1,000–2,500 kg (2,200–5,500 lb) of food per day. The Pygmy right whale might require 50–100 kg (110–220 lb); little is known of its feeding habits, except that two animals taken by the Russians had stomachs full of copepods.

The migratory habits of the Right whale are not fully known, and it is difficult to generalize from the only two areas where rather intensive studies have been made—the Bay of Fundy to Cape Cod region in the North Atlantic, and the Patagonian shelf in

the South Atlantic—since the former is a summer ground and the latter a winter ground. Combined data suggest that calves are born in the late spring–early summer and that mating leading to conception occurs during mid and late summer in the respective hemispheres. The implication, therefore, is that the mating activity observed during the southern winter is more related to social bonding than actual reproduction. The migrations are rather diffuse in comparison to those of the Bowhead, reflecting the less rigorous habitat provided by the temperate zones of the world. Southern populations generally winter off the coasts of southern America, South Africa, Australia and New Zealand, and spend the summer feeding in the Southern Ocean. The North Atlantic population is probably centered somewhere along the Cape Cod to Carolinas region in winter, and spends the summer from Cape Cod to southern Newfoundland, scattered along the edge of the productive North Atlantic Drift.

The Right whale social unit is small, 2–9 animals, and fluid in its composition. Recognizable individuals may be seen alone at some times of day, and within one or other groups later on that day, or on other days. In the Bay of Fundy, they separate, sometimes by as much as several kilometers, when they begin to feed. Breaching behavior (leaping from the surface) and lobtailing (slapping the water with the flukes) occur frequently in this species; sometimes during courtship, but they are also believed to be a method of indicating position, especially when disturbance increases sea surface noise and limits the range at which vocalizations might otherwise be heard. It is parti-

cularly common in calves, which are especially playful (see pp236–237).

Mating appears to be promiscuous. The reproductive cycle is at least two, and probably three years long, so less than half the adult females in a given area may be receptive to males each year. A female may be surrounded by 2–6 competing males. "Triads" are very common, in which one male supports the female from below while the other copulates. The female circles and dives, with the males accompanying her, in what looks like a courtship "dance" or ritual. She may refuse their advances, either by swimming away or by lying on her back with both flippers in the air, so that her

genital region is inaccessible. Males will then attempt to roll her over in the water, sometimes successfully, other times not. Many of the scars and gouges on the skin of these animals result from pushing and head-butting activity; the callosities are rough enough to inflict abrasions.

The mating activity of Right whales in the Bay of Fundy takes place not only in the summer when most activity might be expected to be directed towards feeding, but also over deep water (more than 200m; 660ft); in contrast, on the coasts of the southern continents, mating is invariably in shallow waters (5–20m; 16–66ft). Probably shallow-water southern winter mating is non-reproductive in nature. No significant shallow-water mating has been noted in the North Atlantic in modern times. Is the Bay of Fundy–Gulf of Maine population a remnant that has adapted to the loss of former shallow-water habitat now that the eastern seaboard of North America is densely settled? Or did this population escape the depredations of coastal whaling because of this offshore-mating and calf-rearing habit? These questions remain unanswered.

The annual migratory cycle of the Bowhead is best seen in the Bering Sea–Beaufort Sea population, which is by far the largest surviving stock of this species, and the best-known in the Arctic. Distributions are closely connected with seasonal changes in the position and extent of ice-free areas. The route and timing of migration in any given year are dictated by the patterns of development of open channels (leads) between the ice floes from the northern Bering Sea eastward to the Amundsen Gulf during the spring and summer months.

Bowheads winter in the Bering Sea, particularly in the vicinity of St. Lawrence and St. Matthew Islands, and it is here that the calves are born. Mating occurs during the first stage of the northeastward migration in the spring. Aerial and satellite photographs reveal that the ice in the northern Bering and southern Chukchi Seas develops series of fractures in April which first open to Cape Lisburne and then Point Barrow. The leads are relatively close to shore, so that most of the population passes Barrow on their way

▲ **The three species of right whales.** (1) Right whale (*Balaena glacialis*), showing its huge baleen and tongue, deeply arched lower jaw and callosities. (2) Bowhead whale (*Balaena mysticetus*), with an even more pronounced curve to the lower jaw than the Right whale, but no callosities. (3) Pygmy right whale (*Caperea marginata*), which has a dorsal fin and only moderate bowing of the lower jaw.

◄ **The mating chase.** ABOVE Northern Right whales mating in the Bay of Fundy, Canada. BELOW A female Southern Right whale pursued by three males in shallow water at José Gulf, off Patagonia.

into the Beaufort Sea. Beyond Barrow, however, the winds and current circulation open large offshore leads and the eastward migration shifts further from land. Whales reach Cape Bathurst and the Amundsen Gulf as early as May. The slow breakup of coastal ice east of Alaska normally prevents Bowheads utilizing the Mackenzie Delta and Yukon shore in any numbers until the second half of July.

Eskimo hunters state that there is segregation by age and sex during this migration (as in Australian Humpback whales). The migration certainly takes place in "pulses," with animals during May and June straggling in a column along the whole length of the route from Barrow to southwestern Banks Island. The return migration to the Bering Sea in late summer-early fall tends not only to be rather rapid (according to old whaling records) but also further offshore along the route, and hence less easy to observe.

Until recently the Pygmy right whale was one of the least known cetaceans, ranking with the rarer beaked whales. It is easy to confuse at sea with the Minke whale. In the 1960s however, some South African biologists noted unusual whales in False Bay, which proved to be Pygmy right whales. Prior to this, most information had come from specimens stranded in southern Australia, Tasmania and southern New Zealand. In 1967 the species was sighted again in South Africa, in Plettenberg Bay, and this time some underwater cine film was obtained.

The species resembles the Right whale in its preference for relatively shallow water at some times of year, and there is speculation that mating occurs during this inshore phase. Nevertheless, Pygmy rights have been seen during most months of the year in all the regions from which it has been reported, so it may be a species which has localized populations and limited migrations. There, however, the resemblance to its large distant cousins ends; no deep diving for long periods has been noted despite an earlier suggestion that the peculiar flattening of the underside of the ribcage might indicate that it spent long periods on the bottom. There is none of the exuberant tail-fluking or lob-tailing and breaching characteristic of the large species. It swims relatively slowly, often without the dorsal fin breaking the surface, and the whole snout usually breaks clear of the water at surfacing, behavior similar to that of Minke whales. The respiratory rhythm of undisturbed animals is regular, somewhat

less than one blow per minute, in sequence of about five ventilations, with dives of 3-4 minutes between them. Its general behavior has been characterized as "unspectacular"—another feature, coupled with its small size, that has certainly contributed to the lack of records of the species. It appears to be present in subantarctic and southern temperate zones right around the globe; areas of low human population density and relatively little land mass.

All remaining concentrations of Bowhead and Right whales are but remnants of much larger populations. The earliest Right whale hunting, by the Basques, began shortly after the Norman invasion of Britain, and the last Right and Bowhead whaling by Europeans and Americans was in the 1930s; they were finally given almost total protection, except for the arctic Eskimo hunt, in 1936. Much Right whale hunting was carried out in Southern Hemisphere bays; some of the richest hauls were made on the coasts of New Zealand, sometimes at considerable risk of attack from the war-like Maori tribes of the notorious Cloudy Bay and elsewhere. Traditionally, the whalers would attempt to take a calf first to draw the mother close inshore for an easy kill and retrieval. This tactic hardly favored replenishment of the exploited populations. The carcasses were hauled ashore, or into the shallows, and the baleen cut out. If the oil was taken, the blubber was stripped and cut into pieces to be "rendered down" in large cast iron "try pots." Some of these pots , several feet in diameter, have been preserved; one is on

▲ **The importance of the Bowhead** to Alaskan Eskimos is symbolized by this print, *One Chance*, by Bernard Katexac; 1974.

▶ **Cutting up a Bowhead.** Alaskan Eskimos are still heavily dependent on the Bowhead (see Box).

▼ **Going down.** The tail of a Southern Right whale about to disappear beneath the waves. Right whales are noted for their exuberant lob-tailing, bringing the tail crashing down onto the sea's surface.

The Alaska Bowhead Hunt

The Eskimo peoples of Alaska hunted Bowhead whales with ivory or stone-tipped harpoons and sealskin floats for thousands of years; when the whale population in the Bering Sea region still numbered 10,000 or more, the effect of this village hunt was negligible. In the 19th century, American and European whalers reduced both western and eastern Bowhead populations to a few hundreds or less in a matter of decades. This type of whaling ceased in the 1930s but the Eskimo hunt persists and may now be having a significant impact on the recovery of at least the western (Bering Sea) Bowhead population. Other factors, such as predation by Killer whales and death by crushing or suffocation under ice they cannot break, may also be implicated in the failure of the eastern population to recover to its pre-mass-exploitation levels.

The traditional hunting methods of the Eskimos have been replaced by modern rifles and grenade-tipped darting guns. This has increased the catch, but the number of animals wounded but not landed has not decreased as might have been expected—in fact, this may actually have increased. While some wounded animals obviously survive, it is probable that many more do not, so that the landed catch of Bowheads represents only part of the annual mortality caused by hunting. The Bowheads follow the inshore lead in the pack ice eastward in the spring, making them vulnerable to the Alaskan

hunters even when they are present in very low numbers.

Many world conservation groups, and the scientific committee of the International Whaling Commission, have recommended that the hunt cease. The Alaskan Eskimo vehemently insist that it is materially and culturally necessary for their own welfare, and must continue. Biologists have recently concluded that present population size and the annual production rate of western Bowhead whales can permit only the most limited catch, to prevent the population from decreasing again, if indeed it has not already done so. What little evidence there is suggests that Bowheads are slow to mature and that females do not give birth more often than once every two or three years. Preferably, there should be no catch at all, so that the population can increase at the maximum rate. It is clear that the United States government will have to make a politically unpleasant choice in the relatively near future between the "cultural survival" of the whale-hunting communities, and the physical survival of the Bowhead. They rejected the thesis that Bowhead whale products were necessary for the *material* survival of the Eskimo communities in the 1980s. The question of *cultural* necessity defies definition, but these authors suggest that substitution of a small catch of the much more numerous Californian Gray whale by the Eskimo could satisfy both nutritional and cultural needs.

display at Kaikoura on the east coast of the South Island of New Zealand.

Although, technically, right wales have worldwide protection, the Bowhead is still hunted by some Eskimo on the coast of Alaska, and there are some acute threats locally to their shallow, coastal habitats. The relatively large southwest Atlantic population shelters in the Golfo Nuevo and Golfo San José region of Patagonia, perilously close to oil rigs and other industrial activity sanctioned by Argentina.

What then is the general prospect for right whales? Some evidence has been presented that the Southern Ocean and western North Atlantic populations of the Right whale might be increasing, but in each case the figures are inconclusive. The North Pacific population appears to have stabilized at a few hundred. The Bowhead population of the western North American Arctic is in a perilous situation, yet would seem to have more prospect of survival than the remnants of the eastern Arctic and European Arctic stocks. The inshore habit of both the large species will continue to render them vulnerable to the expansion of human regions, and the consequent impact of interference and pollution. Unless the right whales are given active protection in some critical areas, it is possible that only the Pygmy right whale will survive long into the 21st century. DEG

Life in the Nursery

The playful Right whale calf

In Right whales the period of nursing is prolonged and the antics of the young calves notably boisterous and playful. Southern Right whale females bear a single calf every three years. The 5.5m (18ft) long infant is born in mid-winter after a gestation of about a year, and stays with its mother for up to 14 months. One major calving area is at Península Valdés, Argentina. The calves are born in protected bays of this peninsula and the mother/calf pairs remain there until the calves are about four months old. During this time in sheltered waters, the suckling calves are gradually acquiring skills in a wide variety of activities.

No one has witnessed the birth of a Right whale calf, but like other whales they are probably born tail first and may be pushed to the surface for their first breaths of air. The newborn calf's tail, which shows fold marks from being doubled over in the mother's womb, is quite floppy at birth, but stiffens up quickly with use, and the calf is probably able to swim on its own within a few hours of birth.

Right whale calves must dive down to the underside of their mothers to nurse. The mother can probably squirt milk forcefully from her nipples into the calf's mouth. Other species have been reported to nurse their calves while lying on their sides, but this has not been observed for Right whales.

To begin with, the newborn calf simply swims beside its mother. It breathes in a jerky, awkward fashion, throwing its head up sharply to ensure that its blowholes clear the water before it inhales. Its mother, by contrast, comes up smoothly, often barely rippling the calm waters as she surfaces to breathe. After about three weeks the calf moves away from its mother's side for the first time. At first it hurries back to her, but later it makes a game of repeatedly leaving and approaching the mother.

The calf further develops the circling behavior when it learns to breach. In breaching the whale jumps to bring three-quarters of its body clear of the water, and then lands on its back with a huge splash. Young calves first experience the sensation of breaching while swimming quickly after their mothers in large waves. The upward thrust of the head to breathe combines with the rapid forward motion to throw the body out of the waves. Later, calves breach intentionally, several times during each circle out from the mother and up to 80 times or more in an hour.

Most early activity is centered around the mother—circling, touching, lying on her back. At other times the calf plays near the mother but does not pay her much attention. Rolling upside down is one such absorbing activity. The calf has learned to do this at the age of one and a half months, controlling its stability by flattening or rounding its lung-chest cavity. At first, it can only manage a quick complete roll, but with practice it is able to remain upside down for several minutes. Other behavior that does not center around the mother includes slapping a flipper or the tail flukes onto the water. These actions produce a large splash and a sharp report.

In play the calf learns and practices many behavior patterns that are important in adult life. Courting adult Right whales often roll upside-down to bring themselves belly to belly with a sexual partner. They stroke one another with their flippers and approach each other much as the circling calf does its mother. Adult whales slap their flippers and flukes as a defensive measure against Killer whales and an agitated mother may slap its flipper when separated from its calf.

As with most animals, the movements involved in play are combined in a different manner from their use in activity. Instead of concluding its approach with a roll underneath, as an adult would approach a potential mate, the Right whale calf may approach its mother, and hug her with its flipper, but then circle away and repeat its approach several times. Instead of slapping its flipper in the direction of a Killer whale or a

▲ **A close bond.** Mother and calf Southern Right whale stay together for up to 14 months, when the calf is weaned, and the mother leaves for the feeding grounds alone.

▶ **Shallow playground.** A Southern Right whale and her calf in the warm green-blue shallows off Argentina. On the beach are basking elephant seals.

◀ **Suckling and circling.** The calf has to dive beneath its mother to suckle, between visits to the surface to breathe (1). From about three weeks old, the calf begins to elaborate this into a game of approaching and leaving the mother (2). Tentative at first, the calf becomes more and more playful when it learns to roll onto its side. Now it makes quick careening corners, banking like an airplane, the pectoral flipper rising out of the water. The calf's repeated and increasingly complex circles and figures-of-eight incorporate rolling, putting the chin up against the mother's side, and slapping the water with the flipper.

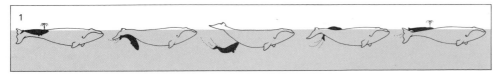

restlessness strengthens the calf's muscles for the long voyage ahead and gives the calf practice in staying beside its now more rapidly moving mother. Close contact with her is essential, not only for nourishment and protection but also because the calf gets hydrodynamic lift from the mother, much as a goose in a flock saves energy by flying beside and slightly behind another.

It is not known if the calves feed on plankton during their first southern summer on the feeding grounds, though they certainly do continue to nurse. Their mothers feed for the first time in the 4–6 months since their calves were born. Mothers save energy during the nursery period at Península Valdés by resting quietly in the shallows for about a quarter of the time spent there, but they also bear large costs at that time, supporting their calves' growth of a meter a month, and their boisterous play (calves play up to 28 per cent of the time), on milk produced during that period. The summer feeding is crucial for the mothers if they are to rebuild their depleted reserves of the fat necessary to survive the calving season.

By the time the mothers return to Península Valdés with their yearling calves, after six months in deeper waters, they are beginning to wean them. If the calf strays from its mother's side she no longer goes to retrieve it. At this stage it is the calf which ensures that they remain together. It is remarkable that a female abandons her calf a full year before she will mate again. This suggests that she needs this year to replenish her resources in preparation for her next period of pregnancy and lactation. During the year before mating, the mother, unburdened by the demands of a calf, probably feeds intensively. Female Right whales are larger than males, and this probably reflects the need of the female to store large energy reserves which help her bear the cost of gestating and suckling her young.

There is conflict between the need of the mother to prepare physiologically to bear another calf, and the benefit that the calf will derive from continuing to get nourishment and protection from its mother. This conflict is resolved when the mother leaves the Valdés area after 2–8 weeks there. The calf stays in the sheltered waters, interacting on the fringes of groups of older sub-adults engaged in boisterous play, occasionally joining up with other yearlings, or playing quietly in the vicinity of adults. In late spring the yearling migrates to the feeding grounds, perhaps in the company of other whales.

competitor for a mate, the calf slaps its flipper onto its mother's back.

Though several dozen mother-calf pairs may be seen along a few miles of coastline, each pair is largely solitary, rarely interacting with other pairs in the area, with which they form a large loose herd. Also in the area, generally somewhat removed from the mothers and calves, are groups of up to 10 adults and sub-adults, often engaged in active social and sexual behavior. Mothers and calves tend to avoid these groups, keeping closer to the shore than the other whales in the area.

In mid-November the behavior of mother and calf changes suddenly, as they prepare to leave the sheltered lagoons for summer feeding grounds in mid-ocean. The calves cease their boisterous play and the mother-calf pairs begin to move quickly back and forth along the shores of the peninsula. This

POT

SEALS AND SEA LIONS

ORDER: PINNIPEDIA
Three families: 17 genera: 33 species.

Eared seals
Family: Otariidae.
Fourteen species in 7 genera.
Includes **Antarctic fur seal** (*Arctocephalus gazella*), **California sea lion** (*Zalophus californianus*), **Northern fur seal** (*Callorhinus ursinus*), **South American sea lion** (*Otaria flavescens*).

Walrus
Family: Odobenidae
One species: **Walrus** (*Odobenus rosmarus*).

True or Hair seals
Family: Phocidae.
Nineteen species in 10 genera.
Includes **Bearded seal** (*Erignathus barbatus*), **Crabeater seal** (*Lobodon carcinophagus*), **Grey seal** (*Halichoerus grypus*), **Harbor seal** (*Phoca vitulina*), **Harp seal** (*Phoca groenlandica*), **Leopard seal** (*Hydrurga leptonyx*), **Northern elephant seal** (*Mirounga angustirostris*), **Ribbon seal** (*Phoca fasciata*), **Ross seal** (*Ommatophoca rossi*), **Southern elephant seal** (*Mirounga leonina*), **Weddell seal** (*Leptonychotes weddelli*).

Few people have difficulty in recognizing a seal. A lithe, streamlined body with all four limbs modified into flippers is sufficient to assign any member of the group correctly to the order Pinnipedia, the seals in the broad sense. The word Pinnipedia refers to this modification and is derived from two Latin words: *pinna*, a feather or wing, and *pes* (genitive, *pedis*), a foot. The pinnipeds are thus the wing-footed mammals.

The Pinnipedia include three families—the Odobenidae, which today has only a single species, the walrus; the Otariidae, the eared seals, containing 14 species, and the Phocidae, the true seals, with 18 species (or possibly 19, if the Caribbean monk seal is not in fact extinct). The similarities between the Odobenidae and the Otariidae are sufficient to justify combining them into a superfamily: the Otarioidea. They are, however, quite distinct from the Phocidae, and most biologists today believe that the two groups arose separately from the carnivore stock: the eared seals about 25 million years ago and the true seals about 15 million years ago (see pp253, 265 and 271). The degree of relationship between pinnipeds and carnivores is a matter of debate. Some authorities believe its groups to be sufficiently related to place the pinnipeds within the Carnivora. Here we keep them separate.

The similarities between eared and true seals are more striking than the differences and it is these, in fact, that make recognition of a "seal" easy. The reason for this similarity is simple—all pinnipeds had to modify the basic mammalian pattern, which is designed for life on land, into a body form adapted to life in the three dimensional environment of water. Water is very much denser and more viscous than air. This meant that body form and locomotion methods had to change. Animals lose heat to water far more rapidly than they do to air; this meant that in order to avoid damaging losses of body

heat, pinnipeds had to develop strategies of heat conservation. Finally, because the oxygen dissolved in water is not available for respiration by mammals, the pinnipeds had to develop a suite of adaptations connected with maintaining activity while ventilating the lungs relatively infrequently—the whole comprising the physiology of diving.

These problems have confronted all three mammalian groups that have become aquatic. However, while the Cetacea (whales and dolphins) and Sirenia (manatees and sea cows) have severed all links with the land, the Pinnipedia find their food in the sea but are still tied to the land (or to ice) as a place where they must bring forth their young and suckle them. These two characteristics, offshore marine feeding and terrestrial birth, have left their mark on most aspects of the lives of pinnipeds.

▲ **Underwater acrobats.** All pinnipeds are agile and graceful in the water, less so on land. These are Australian sea lions.

▶ **The characteristic features** of the families of pinnipeds. (**1**) The Harbor seal (*Phoca vitulina*), a typical true seal, showing (**1a**) the sleek hair and lack of external ear flaps. True seals are cumbersome on land (**1b**), being unable to raise themselves by their foreflippers. (**2**) The Cape fur seal (*Arctocephalus pusillus*), a typical eared seal, showing (**2a**) the scroll-like external ear flaps and thick fur; the male shown here has a particularly thick mane. On land (**2b**) eared seals support themselves on their foreflippers and bring the rear flippers beneath the body. (**3**) The walrus (*Odobenus rosmarus*), showing (**3a**) its distinctive tusks, which on land (**3b**) are often used as levers.

ORDER PINNIPEDIA

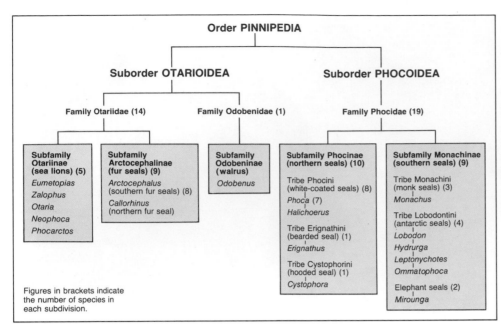

Order PINNIPEDIA

Suborder OTARIOIDEA

Family Otariidae (14)

Subfamily Otariinae (sea lions) (5)
Eumetopias
Zalophus
Otaria
Neophoca
Phocarctos

Subfamily Arctocephalinae (fur seals) (9)
Arctocephalus (southern fur seals) (8)
Callorhinus (northern fur seal)

Family Odobenidae (1)

Subfamily Odobeninae (walrus)
Odobenus

Suborder PHOCOIDEA

Family Phocidae (19)

Subfamily Phocinae (northern seals) (10)
Tribe Phocini (white-coated seals) (8)
Phoca (7)
Halichoerus
Tribe Erignathini (bearded seal) (1)
Erignathus
Tribe Cystophorini (hooded seal) (1)
Cystophora

Subfamily Monachinae (southern seals) (9)
Tribe Monachini (monk seals) (3)
Monachus
Tribe Lobodontini (antarctic seals) (4)
Lobodon
Hydrurga
Leptonychotes
Ommatophoca
Elephant seals (2)
Mirounga

Figures in brackets indicate the number of species in each subdivision.

The Pinniped Body Plan

The sleek pinniped body is spindle-shaped and the head rounded, tapering smoothly into the trunk without any abrupt constriction at the neck. External projections have been reduced to a minimum. In the eared seals (sea lions and fur seals), the external ear flaps have been reduced to small elongated scrolls. It is these that have given the group its name, from the Greek *otarion*, a little ear. In the true seals and the walrus, external ears have been dispensed with altogether. In these two groups also, the testes are internal, while in all pinnipeds the penis lies in an internal sheath so that there is no external projection. The non-scrotal, internal testes of true seals are protected from sterilizing body heat by the flow of cool blood from a network of blood vessels in the hind flippers. Similarly, the nipples of pinnipeds (two in true seals, except for the Bearded seal and the monk seals, which have four, as do eared seals) are retracted and lie flush with the surface of the body. The mammary glands form a sheet of tissue extending over the lower surface and flanks, and even when actively secreting milk do not cause any projection on the body outline. The general contours of the body are smoothed by the layer of fatty tissue or blubber that lies beneath the skin, though as we shall see later, this has a more important role to play than just streamlining.

The flippers, of course, necessarily project from the body, though even they project much less than the limbs of most mammals. The arm and leg bones are relatively short and are contained within the body, the axilla (which corresponds to the armpit of

man) and crotch occurring at the level of the wrist (forearm in eared seals) and ankle respectively. However, most of the bones of the hand and foot are greatly elongated. The digits are joined by a web of skin and connective tissue, and this combined surface provides the propulsive thrust against the water in swimming.

The method of locomotion is different in eared and true seals, with the walrus intermediate between the two. Eared seals swim by making long, simultaneous sweeps of the foreflippers, "flying" through the water like a penguin, or rowing themselves along. The foreflippers form broad blades with elongated digits, the first being much longer than the others. The hindflippers appear to play no part in sustained swimming (except perhaps as a rudder), but in confined quarters or when maneuvering slowly the webs of the hindflippers may be expanded and they appear to play some role as paddles.

True seals, on the other hand, use their hindflippers almost exclusively for swimming. The locomotory movements are alternate strokes of the flipper, the digits being spread on the inward power stroke, so as to apply the greatest area to the water, and contracted on the recovery stroke. The movements of the flippers are accompanied by lateral undulations of the hind end of the body, which swings from side to side alternately with the flipper movements. Normally, the foreflippers are held close to the sides, where they fit into depressions in the surface. However, they may be used as paddles for positioning movements during slow swimming.

The walrus, which is a slow and cum-

THE PINNIPED BODY PLAN

▼ **Skulls** of walrus, California sea lion (an eared seal) and Harbor seal (a true seal). The skulls of true and eared seals are generally similar, except for the region behind the articulation of the lower jaw.

walrus   35cm

California sea lion   30cm

Harbor seal   23cm

▼ **The teeth** of pinnipeds are more variable in number than those of most land carnivores. The teeth of the Crabeater seal (**a**) have quite elaborate cusps which leave only small gaps when the jaws are closed. This relates to its habit of feeding almost exclusively on the small crustacean, krill. In contrast, the Weddell seal (**b**), feeding on fish and bottom invertebrates, has far simpler teeth. The dental formula of both Crabeater and Weddell seals is I1/1 or 2, C1/1, P5/5, that of the South American sea lion (**c**) I3/2, C1/1, P6/5.

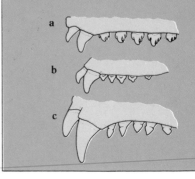

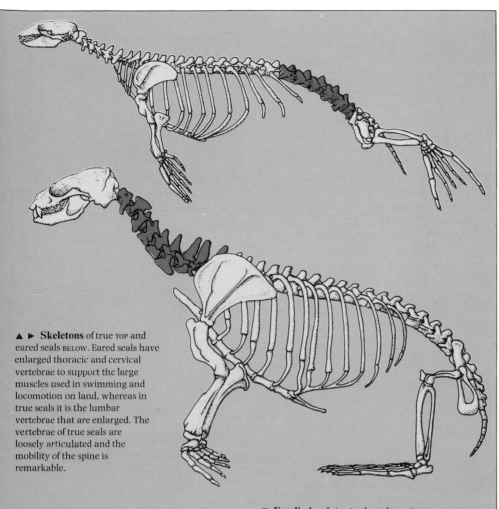

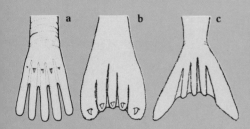

▲ ▶ **Skeletons** of true TOP and eared seals BELOW. Eared seals have enlarged thoracic and cervical vertebrae to support the large muscles used in swimming and locomotion on land, whereas in true seals it is the lumbar vertebrae that are enlarged. The vertebrae of true seals are loosely articulated and the mobility of the spine is remarkable.

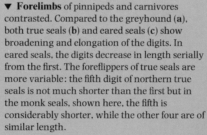

▼ **Forelimbs** of pinnipeds and carnivores contrasted. Compared to the greyhound (**a**), both true seals (**b**) and eared seals (**c**) show broadening and elongation of the digits. In eared seals, the digits decrease in length serially from the first. The foreflippers of true seals are more variable: the fifth digit of northern true seals is not much shorter than the first but in the monk seals, shown here, the fifth is considerably shorter, while the other four are of similar length.

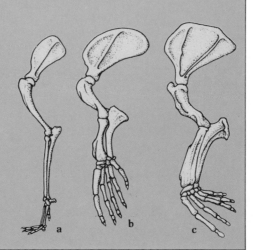

▲ **Hindflippers** of (**a**) a sea lion, (**b**) Harbor seal, (**c**) an elephant seal. In sea lions there are cartilaginous extensions to the digits and the nails are reduced to nonfunctional nodules, some distance from the edge. The Harbor seal, like all northern true seals, has large claws, but these are reduced in southern seals, like the elephant seals, which have fibrous tissue between the digits, increasing the flipper's surface.

brous swimmer, uses its foreflippers to some extent but relies mainly on the hindlimbs for its propulsive power. The flippers are similar to those of eared seals, although the foreflippers are shorter and more square.

Grooming, which is an important subsidiary function of the limbs, is generally carried out by the hindflippers in eared seals and by the foreflippers in true seals. How the Ross seal, which has practically no claws, grooms itself is a mystery.

The different swimming techniques of eared and true seals are reflected in their anatomy. The main source of power in the eared seal comes from the front end of the body, and it is here that the main muscle mass is concentrated. True seals, on the other hand, have their main muscles in the lumbar region. The muscles of the hindlimb itself are mainly concerned with orientation of the limb and spreading and contracting the digits, and play little part in applying the power.

On land, eared seals are much more agile than the other groups. When moving, the weight of the body is supported clear of the ground on the outwardly turned foreflippers and the hindflippers are flexed forwards under the body. The foreflippers are moved alternately when the animal is moving slowly, and the hindflippers advanced on the opposite side. Only the heel of the foot is placed on the ground, the digits being held up. As the speed of progression increases, first the hindflippers and then the foreflippers are moved together, the animal moving forward in a gallop. In this form of locomotion, the counterbalancing action of the neck is very important, the body being balanced over the foreflippers. It has been suggested that if the neck were only half its length, eared seals would be unable to move on land. Walruses move in a similar, though much more clumsy, manner.

On land, true seals crawl along on their bellies, "humping" along by flexing their bodies, taking the weight alternately on the chest and pelvis. Some, such as the elephant seals, or the Grey seal, use the foreflippers to take the weight of the body. Grey seals may also use the terminal digits of the foreflippers to produce a powerful grip when moving among rocks. Other true seals, such as the Weddell seal, for example, make no use of the foreflippers. Ribbon and Crabeater seals can make good progress over ice or compacted snow by alternate backward strokes of the foreflippers and vigorous flailing movements of the hindflippers and hind end of the body, almost as though they were swimming on the surface of the ice.

Heat Conservation

Because sea water is always colder, and usually very much colder, than blood temperature—approximately 37°C (99°F)—and heat is lost much more rapidly to water than to air, seals need adaptations to avoid excessive loss of heat from the body surface. One way of doing this is to reduce the area of surface. The streamlining of the seal's body, which has reduced projecting appendages, has already gone some way towards achieving this. Another important method is to take advantage of the relationship between surface and volume: for bodies of the same shape, larger ones have relatively less surface area. Seals have exploited this strategy to reduce heat loss, and seals are all large mammals in the literal sense, there being no small pinnipeds, as there are small rodents, insectivores or carnivores.

Another way to control heat loss is to insulate what surface there is. The layer of air trapped in the hair coat typical of mammals is an effective insulator in air. However, in water a hair coat is much less effective, since the air layer is expelled as the hair is wetted. Even so, by retaining a more or less stationary layer of water against the

surface of the body it will have a significant effect. One group of pinnipeds, the fur seals, has, however, developed hair as a method of effective insulation. The coat of all pinnipeds consists of a great number of units, each composed of a bundle of hairs and a pair of associated sebaceous (oil) glands. In each hair bundle, there is a long, stout, deeply rooted guard hair and a number of finer, shorter fur fibers. In true seals and sea lions only a few (1–5) of these fibers grow in each bundle, but in the fur seals they comprise a dense mat of underfur. The fine tips of the fur fibers and the secretions of the sebaceous glands make the fur water-repellent, so that the water cannot penetrate to the skin surface.

Fur is an effective insulator, but it has the disadvantage that if the seal dives the air layer in the fur is compressed, by half its thickness for each 10m (33ft) depth, reducing its efficiency accordingly. Because of this, seals have developed another mode of insulation. This is a thick layer of fatty tissue, or blubber, beneath the skin, which also provides energy during fasting and lactation. Fat is a poor conductor of heat and a blubber layer is about half as effective an

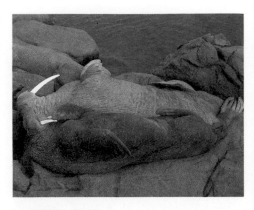

KEEPING COOL

▲ **The blushing walrus.** The skin of walruses becomes engorged with blood during hot weather, giving rise to a brick-red coloration. In contrast, old bulls, in which the natural pigmentation has faded, can appear deathly pale after immersion in cold water.

▼ **Flipper fanning.** In very warm conditions, seals fan their flippers to lose heat across their broad surfaces. These are California sea lions.

insulator as an equal thickness of fur in air. When in water, however, the blubber insulation is reduced to about a quarter of its value in air, but this is unaffected by the depth to which the seal dives. Seals commonly have in excess of 7–10cm (3–4in) of blubber, which effectively prevents heat loss from the body core. True seals have thicker blubber than eared seals.

In cold conditions, loss of heat from the flippers, which do not have an insulating covering, is minimized by reducing the flow of blood to them, only sufficient circulation being maintained to prevent freezing. Beneath the capillary bed, there are special shunts between the arterioles and venules known as arterio-venous anastomoses, or AVA's. By opening the AVA's more blood can be circulated through the superficial layers and heat can be lost when necessary.

Insulation which is effective in the water will also be effective in air, and a Weddell seal, for example, can comfortably endure an air temperature of −40°C (−40°F) on the ice. Skin surface temperatures, of course, may be much higher than the air temperature if the sun is shining. Most seals can thus easily tolerate cold climates, since almost any air temperature can be endured and water can never become much colder than about −1.8°C (28°F). Pinnipeds are indeed characteristic of the polar regions, both north and south. However, not all pinnipeds live in cold climates, and for those in temperate or tropical regions (mainly eared seals and monk seals) a major problem is likely to be disposing of excess heat when out of the water. Monk seals in Hawaii avoid dry beaches on sunny days and, at the other extreme, Harbor seals in Nova Scotia take to the water when the air is below −15°C (5°F).

Fur seals can suffer severely from heat stress after periods of activity. Heat can be lost only across the surface of the naked flippers. To do this, the AVA's are dilated, so that more blood is diverted through the superficial layer, and heat is then radiated away from the black surface of the flippers. This may be aided by spreading the flippers widely, fanning them in the air, or by urinating on them.

True seals have AVA's over the whole of the body. Blubber contains blood vessels, and a true seal can divert blood through to the skin surface and lose heat. Conversely, the system can be used to gain heat from radiation in bright sunshine, even at very low air temperatures. Walruses also have AVA's over their body surface and a herd of basking walruses may appear quite pink in

color because of the blood being diverted to the skin.

Periodically, it is necessary for any pinniped to renew its hair covering and the superficial layer of its skin. In eared seals, molt is a relatively prolonged process. The underfur fibers are molted first; in fur seals some of the molted fibers are retained in the hair canal. Guard hairs are molted shortly afterwards, but not all are lost at each molt. In true seals, molt is a much more abrupt process. In order that the necessary growth of new hair may take place, the blood supply to the skin has to be increased, which means also an increased heat loss. Because of this, most seals stay out of the water for much of the duration of the molt and some, such as elephant seals, may gather in large heaps, conserving heat by lying in contact with their neighbors.

Diving

An air-breathing mammal in an aquatic environment must, as a first necessity, be able to prevent water from entering its lungs. Pinnipeds reflexly close their nostrils on immersion. The slits of the nostrils are under muscular control, and once immersed the pressure of the water will tend to hold them closed. Similarly, the soft palate and tongue together at the back of the mouth close off the buccal cavity from the larynx and esophagus when a seal needs to open its mouth under water, for example to seize prey.

Coupled with these adaptations is, of

▲ **A map of the molt.** During the molt, the skin of elephant seals resembles a map of the oceans they inhabit! Uniquely among seals, elephant seals shed the superficial layer of the skin in large flakes and patches, along with the rather scanty hair.

▼ **Hair bundles** of true seal LEFT and a fur seal RIGHT. In true seals the primary (guard) hair is accompanied by only a few secondary hairs, but in fur seals there may be 50 such fibers to each guard hair, giving a fiber density of up to 57,000 per sq cm. This dense mat is supported by the shafts of the guard hairs, as in the pelt section BELOW.

course, the need to be able to hold the breath for extended periods. True seals have much better breath-holding capacities than eared seals, which seldom dive for more than five minutes or so. Despite this, the Cape fur seal has been shown to be able to hunt its prey below 100m (330ft), and the California sea lion has reached 73m (240ft) under natural conditions and 250m (820ft) after training. In comparison, true seals can dive for much longer periods. Elephant seals can stay submerged for at least 30 minutes and a Weddell seal has been timed in a dive lasting 73 minutes in the wild.

Breath-holding capacities can be increased by taking down more oxygen with each dive. Seals increase their rate and depth of breathing before diving, but they do not dive with full lungs, since this would create buoyancy problems. True seals exhale most of the breath before they dive. Sea lions, on the other hand, seem often to dive with at least partially inflated lungs. True seals have greater blood volume per unit body-weight than other mammals, that of the Weddell seal being about two-and-half times that of an equivalent-sized man. Additionally, the blood contains more oxygen-carrying hemoglobin, so that the oxygen capacity of the blood is about three times that of man. There are also greater concentrations of another oxygen-binding protein, myoglobin, in the muscles of seals. Myoglobin concentrations in the Weddell seal are about ten times that in man.

Even these increased oxygen stores would not be sufficient for prolonged diving unless there were associated physiological changes. When a seal dives, a complex response occurs, of which the most obvious component is a slowing of the heart-rate—the output of the heart drops to 10–20 percent of its pre-dive value and the blood flow is diverted largely to the brain. This enables the seal to use its available oxygen in the most economical manner, and the oxygen requirement of several organs, the liver and kidney for example, is significantly curtailed.

In the Weddell seal, under natural conditions, dives are usually fairly short, lasting less than 20 minutes, and metabolism is of the conventional aerobic (oxygen-using) kind, with carbon dioxide as the waste product. If dives longer than 30 minutes are undertaken the metabolism (except in the brain) becomes anaerobic (does not use oxygen) and lactic acid accumulates in the muscles as a waste product. Seals have considerable resistance to high concentrations of lactic acid and carbon dioxide in

their blood, but after such a dive there has to be a period of recovery, which leaves the animal incapable of further intense diving activity for some time. A 45-minute dive, for example, requires a surface period of 60 minutes. Consequently, long anaerobic dives are rare in nature.

Dives to great depth also involve the seals in problems relating to pressure. Weddell seals commonly dive to 300–400m (1,000–1,300ft), and have been known to reach 600m (2,000ft). At this depth, the pressure in the seal will be about 64kg per sq cm (910lb per sq in), compared to a pressure in air of 1kg per sq cm (14lb per sq in). As liquids are virtually incompressible, there will be little effect on most organs. However, where a gas space occurs this will be important. This is the case with the middle

▲ **The sleek lines** of a Galapagos sea lion underwater. Unlike true seals, which empty the lungs before diving, sea lions dive with some air in the lungs (note the bubbles here), which allows them to vocalize underwater. This ability is used by males in patrolling underwater territories. Although not such proficient divers as the true seals, sea lions have been trained to dive to 250m (820ft).

ear. The middle ear of seals is lined with a system of venous blood sinuses. When the seal dives, the increasing pressure causes the blood-filled sinuses to bulge into the ear, taking the place of the compressed air and matching the ambient pressure. By far the largest gas-space is in the respiratory system. When a seal dives it partially empties its lungs, but some air remains in the minute air sacs (alveoli) and air passages. As pressure increases, air is forced out of the lungs into the relatively non-absorptive upper airways, where there is less risk of nitrogen being absorbed and causing the condition known as "the bends" when the seal surfaces again. Despite this, repeated diving could raise nitrogen concentrations to a dangerous level, and it has been calculated that because of the depth and duration of some of their dives, the bends could be contracted from a single dive by a Weddell seal. As a last resort, collapse of the alveoli prevents high concentrations of nitrogen developing in the blood and tissues and thus avoids the bends.

Senses

Pinnipeds have well-developed senses of sight, hearing and touch, but little is known about smell in these animals. Both eared and true seals produce strong odors in the breeding season and mothers identify their pups by scent, so it is likely that this sense is reasonably acute. A sense of smell would, of course, be of no value under water.

The eyes generally are large, and in some species, such as the Ross seal, very large indeed. Because of the absence of a nasolacrimal duct, which would remove tears, there is often the appearance of tears running down the face, a feature which evokes misplaced sympathy in many people. The retina is adapted for low-light conditions. It contains only rods (hence there is no color vision) and is backed by a reflective tapetum (as in cats) which reflects light back through the sense cells a second time. Pinnipeds can see clearly in both air and water. Because the cornea has no refractive effect when immersed in water, the lens has a stronger curvature than that of terrestrial mammals. In air, the pupil constricts to a vertical slit. This combines with a cylindrically, rather than spherically curved cornea to avoid extreme accommodation for the change from water to air.

The hearing of seals is acute. Apart from the absence of the external ear flaps in the walrus and true seals and the modification associated with diving mentioned earlier, the structure of the ear is similar to that of

most other mammals. Some seals produce click vocalizations under water, probably from the larynx, and it has been suggested that these are used in echolocation. The evidence for this is good for the Harbor seal, but attempts to demonstrate this in the California sea lion have not been successful. However, many seals are unable to use vision as a means of finding their food, for example in muddy estuaries or under ice in polar winters. There are many accounts of well-nourished seals chronically blind in both eyes. It is therefore clear that some means of locating prey, other than vision, must be present.

The whiskers of seals are usually very well developed and it is possible that these are used to detect vibrations in the water. The whiskers, or vibrissae, are smooth in outline in eared seals, the walrus, the Bearded and monk seals; they have a beaded outline in the others. The mystacial vibrissae, which emerge from the side of the nostrils, are the longest: up to 48cm (19in) in length in the Antarctic fur seal. Other vibrissal groups, above the nose and on the forehead, are usually shorter. Each whisker is set in a follicle surrounded by a connective tissue capsule richly supplied with nerve fibers. Their structure suggests that the whiskers would be most useful in detecting water displacements produced by swimming fish. Removal of the whiskers impairs the ability of Harbor seals to catch fish.

Food and Feeding

When the pinnipeds first appeared, about 25 million years ago, they underwent a rapid species radiation. This was perhaps a response to the appearance of increased food

▲ **The stout whiskers** of a Galapagos sea lion, well displayed by this yawning bull. The whiskers may be used to detect disturbances of the water caused by the seal's prey.

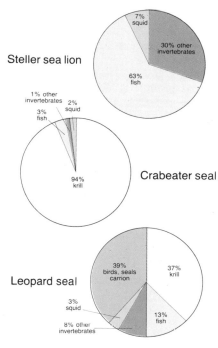

▲ **The contrasting diets** of the Steller sea lion, Crabeater seal and Leopard seal.

stocks in the sea at that time. These might have been associated with an increase in upwelling processes (caused by climatic events or movements of the earth's crust), bringing nutrients to the surface and increasing oceanic productivity. Upwelling is common along western coastlines at high latitudes, and at current divergences, and it is in such places that we find large numbers of pinnipeds today.

Pinnipeds generally are opportunistic feeders, able to feed on a variety of prey. This is well seen off the coast of British Columbia where three pinnipeds, the Harbor seal, the Steller sea lion, and the Northern fur seal occupy different niches. Seals will surface to eat large prey but the smaller prey are eaten underwater.

Not all pinnipeds are generalist feeders. Some, such as the Crabeater seal, are extreme specialists (see pp280–281). Ninety-four percent of the Crabeater's diet consists of the small shrimp-like crustacean, Antarctic krill. The Ringed seal, of the Arctic, also feeds extensively on crustacea; the Southern elephant seal and the Ross seal feed largely on squid; the walrus and the Bearded seal feed mainly on bottom-dwelling invertebrates, such as clams. Some pinnipeds feed on warm-blooded prey. Many sea lions commonly take birds and some take the young of other seals. Walruses occasionally feed on Ringed seals. The most consistent predator on other seals is the Leopard seal, which feeds extensively on young Crabeater seals, as well as taking fish, krill and birds (see pp290–291).

The jaws and teeth of pinnipeds are adapted for grasping prey, not chewing it. Most prey is swallowed whole, although pieces may be wrenched off a large item. Plankton feeders, like Crabeater or Ringed seals, have elaborately cusped teeth through which water can be strained out of the mouth before the prey is swallowed. In many seals, the cheek teeth are reduced. The Antarctic fur seal, although a krill eater, has very reduced cheek teeth. The teeth of the Bearded seal, although large, are very shallowly rooted and may fall out early in life.

The stomach is simple and aligned with the long axis of the body, which may assist in engulfing large prey. The small intestine is often very long. In the South American sea lion it may measure 18m (59ft), while in an adult male Southern elephant seal it can be as long as 202m (660ft); the small gut in man is about 7m (23ft) long. The cecum, colon and rectum in seals are relatively short.

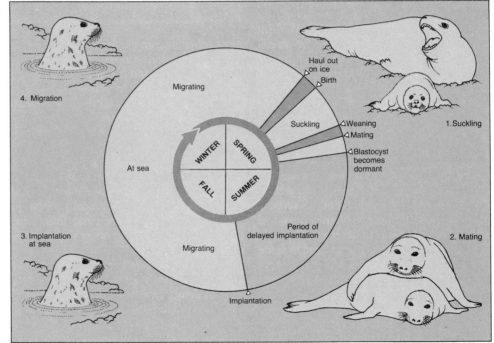

◄ **Year in the life of seals.** Seals have an annual cycle which begins with hauling out to give birth. (1) The suckling period varies from about 9–10 days in some ice-breeding true seals such as the Harp seal to up to a year in some eared seals like the Australian sea lion TOP LEFT. (2) Mating in true seals follows weaning, about 1 month after birth in the Northern elephant seal ABOVE. (3) Following fertilization, all seals have a period of 2.5–3.5 months of delayed implantation in which the embryo does not develop. After weaning, true seals return to the water and may migrate. The birth coat (lanugo) of seals differs from the adult coat. BELOW Two fat Grey seal pups bask in the sun. True seals lose their birth coat after 2–3 weeks, eared seals after 2–3 months. This Australian sea lion pup BOTTOM LEFT will soon shed his two-tone coat for an adult dark brown all over. While the seals are at sea, implantation occurs and the cycle begins again (4).

There is little information on the feeding rates of seals in the wild. Activity and water temperatures can affect these greatly. The Northern fur seal has been calculated to require 14 percent of its body-weight of food daily for maintenance alone, though seals in captivity can be maintained on a ration of as little as 6–10 percent of body-weight. Juveniles need proportionately more food than adults to allow for growth and the greater heat losses from smaller animals. Most pinnipeds are capable of undergoing prolonged fasts in connection with reproductive activities or molting. The blubber layer, which acts as a food store as well as insulation, is very important in this.

Reproductive Strategies

Pinnipeds have failed to make the complete transition from land to water. Those adaptations that fit them so supremely well for life in the sea render them clumsy and vulnerable on land, to which they must resort to reproduce. Because seals are vulnerable to terrestrial predators when ashore they have had to adopt various strategies to ensure their safety during the period of birth and the dependence of the young. These relate to the selection of secure breeding sites, the social structure of breeding assemblies, and the duration of the period of dependence of the young.

Typically, pinnipeds breed in the spring or early summer. After a period of intensive feeding, they assemble at the chosen breeding site. All the northern true seals except the Harbor and monk seals, and all the southern true seals except the Northern and Southern elephant seals breed on ice. None of the eared seals breeds on ice. Walruses are

ice breeders, but do not usually breed far off shore.

Often the males arrive on the breeding ground a few days or weeks before the females and take up territories ashore (this is always the case with the eared seals). The breeding females, carrying fetuses conceived the previous season, come ashore only shortly before giving birth. In elephant seals, for example, this period is about a week (see pp284–285), but in Harbor seals, which have their pups on sandbanks or half-tide rocks, it may be only a few minutes. Birth is a speedy process in all pinnipeds, as the pup forms a convenient torpedo-shaped package which can slip out with equal facility either head or tail first. A single young is produced at a birth. Twins are very rare and are probably never reared successfully. The newborn pup is covered with a specialized birth coat or lanugo. This is more woolly than the next coat and is often of a different color (eg black in fur seals, white in most ice-breeding true seals). This is molted after two or three weeks in true seals, or two or three months in eared seals, by which time the young pup has laid down some blubber and is better able to resist heat loss. Surprisingly, in some true seals, such as the Harbor seal, the lanugo is molted while still in its mother's womb.

Usually, a few hours elapse before the mother first feeds her pup. There is much variation in suckling patterns. Ice-breeding true seals, such as the Harp seal (see pp 286–287), suckle their pups for as little as nine or ten days; the instability of pack ice may be a factor in this. In other true seals, lactation is longer, about three weeks in Grey and elephant seals, or six weeks in Ringed seals. Many true seal mothers do not feed themselves at all while suckling their pups. At the end of lactation, the mother comes into season and is mated, weans her pup abruptly and deserts it. There is no further contact between mother and pup except casually. In eared seals, the mother-pup association lasts somewhat longer (see p256). About one week after the birth, the female comes into season and is mated by the nearest dominant bull. She then departs for a series of feeding excursions between which she returns to feed her pup. The pup may be independent after 4–6 months, but often continues to receive some milk from its mother almost till the arrival of the next pup, or beyond it.

In both eared and true seals the fertilized egg initially develops only as far as a hollow ball of cells called a blastocyst. It then lies dormant in the womb until the main period

of feeding the previous pup is completed. Usually this is four months or earlier after birth. After this, the blastocyst implants in the wall of the womb, develops a placenta and begins to develop normally. This phenomenon, known as delayed implantation, may serve to enable seals to combine birth and mating into a single period and avoid the potentially dangerous period spent ashore.

Some seals remain near their breeding grounds throughout the year, but most disperse, either locally or in some cases, such as the Northern fur seal, migrating for thousands of miles. During this period the seals are building up reserves to see them through the next breeding season. Juveniles and adolescents may follow the same pattern, or occupy different grounds from the adult seals. Unfortunately, we know very little about the life of seals at sea.

Seals and Man

Seals and man have had a close relationship since primitive man first spread into the coastal regions where seals were abundant: the northern coast of Europe, the coast of Asia from Japan northwards, and arctic North America and Greenland. Seals were ideally suited to hunter-gatherers, in part as a result of the modifications that fitted them to an aquatic life. They were sufficiently large that the pursuit and killing of a single animal provided an ample reward, yet not so large that there were major risks involved. Their furry skins made tough and waterproof garments to keep out the elements. Beneath their skin was a layer of blubber, which besides its use as food with the rest of the carcass, could be burnt in a lamp to provide light and warmth during the long nights of the arctic winter.

Stone Age hunters have left records of

◄ ▲ **Splendid isolation.** Pinnipeds in general choose remote and inaccessible localities for breeding. Many breed on isolated rocks or islets where there are no natural predators, or on mainland coasts that are inaccessible from the interior, such as these Grey seals breeding on a cliff-bounded beach on the Cardigan coast, Wales LEFT. Other seals, like this breeding pair of Crabeater seals ABOVE, resort to seasonal pack ice. Ice has many advantages for a breeding seal. It affords immediate access to deep water, a virtually limitless area for breeding, and it is much easier for a seal to move over than sand or rock.

their association with seals in the form of engravings on bones and teeth and as harpoons, sometimes embedded in seal skeletons. In the Arctic, the Eskimos developed a culture which was largely dependent on seals for its very survival. They hunted Ringed seals, Bearded seals, walrus and what other species were available, developing a complex technology of harpoon and kayak to do so. Seal carvings figure importantly in Eskimo art.

North American Indians, from British Columbia southwards, hunted seals and sea lions. At the extreme tip of South America, in Tierra del Fuego, the Canoe Indians hunted fur seals, and when the European seal hunters all but exterminated these, the Indians starved.

Subsistence sealing as practiced by primitive communities, or by crofter-fishermen in Europe up to this century, made relatively little impact on seal stocks. The concept of investing in hunting equipment and engaging crews, with the object of securing as large a catch of seals as possible to be sold on a cash basis, introduced a new dimension into seal hunting. Harp seals were the first to be hunted in this way. Their habit of aggregating in vast herds at the breeding season made them vulnerable to the sealers. Hunting began in the early part of the 18th century. The Harp seal hunt, from a reduced stock, continues today (see pp286–287). Walruses were similarly hunted, mostly by arctic whalers, and their numbers were even more severely diminished (see pp268–269).

Eared seals have suffered equally, if not more, with fur seals being hunted avidly in both hemispheres. The Northern fur seal was first hunted in the late 18th century, perhaps 2½ million being killed at the Pribilof Islands between 1786 and 1867. With the sale of Alaska by Russia to the USA, controls were placed on the sealing operations on shore. These were not, however, sufficient to prevent the drastic reduction of the stock, since sealing, which mainly took lactating females, began in 1886 and dealt the seals a severe blow. In 1911 the North Pacific Fur Seal Convention (the first international seal protection agreement) was signed, which banned open-sea sealing. Under careful management, the Pribilof stock of fur seals has recovered satisfactorily. Sealing continues today on one of the Pribilofs, St. Paul Island; the other island, St. George, is used as a research sanctuary.

In the Southern Hemisphere, fur sealing was combined with the hunting of elephant seals for their oil. Elephant seal stocks recovered in this century and formed the basis of a properly controlled and lucrative industry in South Georgia between 1910 and 1964. There is no commercial elephant sealing today. The Antarctic fur seal, almost exterminated in the 19th century, has now regained its former abundance (see pp 260–261).

Another early association between man and seals was competition between fishermen and seals. Seals damage fisheries in three main ways. To most fishermen the most conspicuous damage is that done to nets and the fish contained in them. Set nets are most affected and the damage can be serious when valuable fish, such as salmon, are being caught. A second form of damage is the toll taken by seals of the general stock

of fish in the wild. This is difficult to calculate, for not only are the numbers of seals and the amount of fish they eat often unknown, but it is also difficult to discover how the amount of fish eaten by the seals affects the catch of the fishermen. Common sense suggests that the feeding activities of seals will reduce the catch of fish, but this is difficult to demonstrate in practice. Nevertheless, seals are often killed, or "culled," to reduce their impact on fisheries. The final form of damage to fisheries by seals is that caused by the seals acting as hosts for parasites whose larval stages occur in food fishes. The best known example of this is the Cod worm, a nematode worm which lives as an adult in the stomach of seals, predominantly Grey seals, and whose larvae are found in the gut and muscles of cod and other cod-like fish. When cod are much infested with Cod worm they may be valueless. Cod worm increased with increasing Grey seal stocks around the United Kingdom up to 1970, but though the seals have continued to increase, there has been no evidence of increase in the infestation rate.

Besides deliberate attempts to kill seals, either for their products, or because of the damage they do to fisheries, human activities may prove detrimental to seals in other ways. Purse-seining (fishing with large floating nets) and trawling operations often catch and drown seals. Discarded synthetic net fragments (which have a long life in the sea) and other debris may entangle seals.

Possibly the major impact fishing operations have on seals is the alteration of the ecosystem of which seals form part. However, there is no direct evidence that any commercial fisheries have adversely affected seal stocks. Seals can mostly turn to other species if one fish stock is seriously depleted by fishing. However, as man becomes ever more efficient in cropping the fish stocks, and widens the range of species caught, seals might have few alternatives.

Increasing industrialization in the Northern Hemisphere has led to the dump-

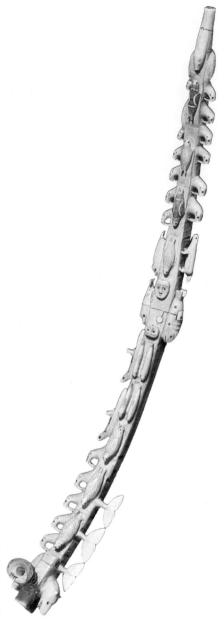

▲ **Pipe dreams.** An elaborately carved Eskimo ivory pipe probably from King Island, Alaska; 1870–1900. The pipe is carved from a walrus tusk and shows several of the species important to Eskimos: besides the walrus, there are two species of seal represented—the Ribbon seal and the Spotted seal.

◄ **Eskimo artefacts.** The importance of seals and other sea mammals to the Eskimos is reflected in the many art objects that they carve from walrus ivory and the teeth of whales in the shape of the animals.

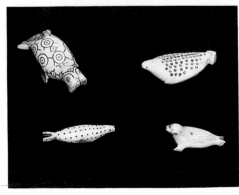

▲ **Cycle of conflict**—life history of the Cod worm, a pest that brings man into conflict with seals. The mature worm lives in the stomach of seals. The eggs, expelled from the seal in the feces, find their way, via a first larval stage in an invertebrate, to the second larval stage, which lives in the gut and muscles of cod, rendering them unfit for consumption.

▼ **Plastic torture**—an Antarctic fur seal with a plastic packing band cutting into its neck. The band is trapped by the backward pointing hairs and cuts into the hide.

ing of many biotoxic products in the ocean. Some of these are persistent and tend to accumulate in animals, like seals, at the top of the food chain. Pinnipeds accumulate organochlorine compounds, like DDT and PCB, mainly in the blubber, and heavy metals in the liver. The most convincing evidence for toxicity comes from north of the Baltic Sea where the population of Ringed seals has declined abruptly and the survivors show impaired reproduction (see pp 282–283).

Pollution by petroleum is a feature of many Northern Hemisphere coasts. Seals are often conspicuously contaminated by oil spills. However, they do not seem to suffer much from this. Unlike birds which preen, ingest oil and are poisoned, oiled seals make no attempt to clean their coats and thus rarely ingest oil. Fur seals, of course, might suffer heat loss from contaminated fur.

Habitat disturbance may affect seals. Reclaiming of productive shallow water areas, such as the Dutch polders, can deprive seals of their habitat. Recreational activities, particularly power-boating, can cause severe disturbance to seals at the breeding season. This is particularly serious for monk seals, which have a low tolerance of disturbance (see pp288–289).

Seals, like most wildlife, are adversely affected by increasing human populations and industrialization. However, there is much real concern today for the welfare of seals, and though some species, such as the monk seals, are endangered, the great majority of seal stocks would seem assured of survival.   WNB

EARED SEALS

Family: Otariidae
Fourteen species in 7 genera.
Distribution: N Pacific coasts from Japan to
Mexico; Galapagos Islands; W coast of S
America from N Peru, round Cape Horn to S
Brazil; S and SW coasts of S Africa; S coast of
Australia and South Island, New Zealand;
oceanic islands circling Antarctica.

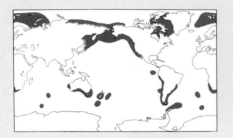

Habitat: generally coastal on offshore rocks and
islands.

Size: head-to-tail length
from 120cm (47in) in the
Galapagos fur seal to
287cm (113in) in the
Steller sea lion; weight
from 27kg (60lb) in the
Galapagos fur seal to
1,000kg (2,200lb) in the
Steller sea lion.

Gestation: 12 months, including a period of
suspended development (delayed implantation).
Longevity: up to 25 years.

Genus *Callorhinus*
One species: **Northern fur seal** or Alaskan fur
seal (*C. ursinus*). Pribilof Islands, W Bering Sea,
Sea of Okhotsk, Kuril Islands, San Miguel
Island.

Genus *Arctocephalus*
Eight species: the southern fur seals. Southern
Ocean, coasts of Australia and New Zealand,
north to Baja California. Species include:
Antarctic fur seal or Kerguelen fur seal (*A.
gazella*), **Guadalupe fur seal** (*A. townsendi*),
South American fur seal (*A. australis*)

Genus *Neophoca*
One species: **Australian sea lion** (*N. cinerea*).
Islands off W Australia.

Genus *Phocarctos*
One species: **New Zealand sea lion** (*P. hookeri*).
Islands around New Zealand.

Genus *Otaria*
One species: **South American sea lion**
(*O. avescens*). Coasts of S America.

Genus *Eumetopias*
One species: **Steller sea lion** (*E. jubatus*).
N Pacific.

Genus *Zalophus*
One species: **California sea lion**
(*Z. californianus*). W coast of N America,
Galapagos Archipelago.

O
N a sandy beach, a huge maned bull seal,
head thrown back, bellows to proclaim
his mastery, around him his harem of up to
80 females; beyond them, further groups,
all presided over by a beachmaster—these
are eared seals, all the species of which are
gregarious, social breeders.

The living eared seals comprise the fur
seals and sea lions. As a group, they are
distinguished from the true seals by their use
of the foreflippers as the principal means of
propulsion through the water. Generally,
most sea lions are larger than most fur seals,
and have blunter snouts than those of the
fur seals, which tend to be sharp. The
flippers of sea lions tend to be shorter than
those of fur seals. However, the most obvious difference is the presence of abundant
underfur in the fur seals, and sparse underfur in sea lions. Nevertheless, it is clear that
the two fur seal genera, *Callorhinus* and
Arctocephalus, are less closely related to each
other than *Arctocephalus* is to the sea lion
genera, and the division which is sometimes
made, into subfamilies Arctocephalinae and
Otariinae, is unjustified.

Because the hindlimbs have not been
greatly involved in aquatic locomotion,
eared seals have retained a useful locomotory function on land, and they are comparatively agile. Circus sea lions can be
trained to run up a ladder; more to the point,
a bull fur seal can gallop across a rocky
beach in pursuit of a rival. On broken
terrain, a fur seal can progress faster than a
man can run.

Eared seals are a more uniform group
than the true seals, both in appearance and
behavior. In all eared seals, males are substantially larger than females: up to five
times heavier in the Northern fur seal. This
disparity in size is rivaled among mammals
only by the Southern elephant seal, in
which the male may be up to four times
heavier than the female, although both are
very much heavier than the fur seals. Also,
successful breeding males maintain a harem
during the breeding season, a strategy
known as polygynous breeding, as opposed
to monogamous breeding, in which a male
mates with only one female. We shall see
that these two traits are in fact related. All
eared seals are generalist feeders, there
being no specialists as there are in true seals.
No eared seal populations have adopted a
freshwater existence, as have several true
seals such as the Ringed and Baikal seals.

The 14 living species of eared seals are
found today on the North Pacific coasts from
Japan to Mexico; on the Galapagos Islands
and on the western coast of South America,
from northern Peru, round Cape Horn to
southern Brazil; on the south and southwest
coast of southern Africa; on the southern
coast of Australia and South Island, New
Zealand; and on the oceanic island groups
circling Antarctica. These locations tend to
be cool- rather than cold-water areas
(although the Northern fur seal, Steller sea
lion and, particularly, the Antarctic fur seal
all occur in regions of near freezing water),
and eared seals are characteristic of temperate and subtemperate climates. There are no
ice-breeding eared seals. Eared seals concentrate in areas where rising currents
carry nutrients to the surface, feeding on a
variety of open-sea and sea-bottom organisms, both fish and invertebrates—whatever
food is most abundant and easy to catch.
Many take their food, such as rock lobsters

▲ **The brush off.** This pair of New Zealand sea lions exemplifies the extreme sexual disparity in form found in most eared seals, with the shaggy mane of the bull making him look even larger than he is.

◄ **Seal spray.** The thick underfur of fur seals is prevented from becoming waterlogged by the oily secretions of the sebaceous glands and by the support given by the guard hairs. Nevertheless, the fur does hold a certain amount of water, as this Cape fur seal shows, spinning a halo of spray around itself.

and octopus, from the bottom of the sea. Australian fur seals have been caught in traps and trawls at a depth of 118m (387ft), but eared seals are probably relatively shallow feeders compared with true seals. Sometimes eared seals turn to warm-blooded prey. At Macquarie Island, the New Zealand sea lion feeds largely on penguins, and some Southern fur seals, often the subadult males, also take penguins. Steller sea lions occasionally take young Northern fur seals. The Antarctic fur seal is one of the few specialist feeders. It lives largely on Antarctic krill, which is the only food found to be taken by the breeding females (see pp 260–261).

The amount of food consumed by eared seals is not easily determined. It varies from species to species, of course, and small animals need proportionately more food than large ones. Female Northern fur seals, and males under four years, need about 14 percent of their body weight of food a day, simply for maintenance purposes. Water temperature greatly affects the food requirement, since, despite their fur coats, much energy is required to compensate for heat lost to the sea. Some fur seals in the Seattle Aquarium were fed just short of satisfaction on 26–27 percent of their body weight per day and grew normally without getting unduly fat.

The ancestors of the Otariidae diverged from the dog-like carnivore stock in the North Pacific Basin in the early Miocene or late Oligocene, about 25 million years ago. These small, primitive seal-like creatures, the Enaliarctidae, had teeth like those of typical carnivores, with carnassial teeth in the upper and lower jaws. They were probably coastal dwellers. Quite early on, the enaliarctids gave rise to a group, the Desmatophocidae, which had many otariid-like characteristics. These were larger animals with uniform teeth (unlike cats and dogs) and considerable modification of the ear region, associated with diving. It seemed that the desmatophocids had become adapted to an open-sea, rather than a coastal life. *Allodesmus*, a desmatophocid that flourished in the middle and late Miocene, showed the sexual dimorphism (males larger than females), strong canines and teeth with marked growth zones associated with periodic fasting, that indicate that it had a polygnous breeding system very like that of the existing fur seals and sea lions. However, although the desmatophocids were a successful group, by the late Miocene (about 10 million years ago) they had disappeared. By that time, primitive walruses were abundant, having appeared in the early Miocene.

Meanwhile, some time in the early Miocene, the enaliarctids had given rise to the otariids—the eared seals. The earliest known otariid is *Pithanotaria*, known from several localities in California from about 11 million years ago. *Pithanotaria* was very small, somewhat smaller than the smallest living otariid, the Galapagos fur seal, and had a uniform dentition and bony processes about the eye sockets, both characteristic of modern otariids. However, its cheek teeth had multiple roots, and it did not show sexual dimorphism.

By 8 million years ago there were otariids in the North Pacific that showed an increase in body size and were clearly sexually dimorphic. Except for slight differences in some of the limb bones and the retention of double-rooted cheek teeth, these forms could easily be taken for modern sea lions. The Northern fur seal, *Callorhinus*, diverged from the main otariid stem about 6 million years ago, and soon afterwards otariids dispersed southwards to the Southern Hemisphere. There is no evidence that any otariid managed to follow the walrus ancestors through the Central American Seaway into the North Atlantic.

From 6 million years ago to about 2–3 million years ago there was little diversification in the otariid stock, which remained very similar to the existing genus *Arctocephalus*, the southern fur seals. In the past 2 million years, however, there was a sudden acceleration in the increase of size, the development of single-rooted cheek teeth and generic diversification. The existing five sea lion genera appeared from the arctocephaline stock in the last 3 million years or so.

Eared seals are all more or less social animals, tending to live in groups and to gather in aggregations, which may be very large during the breeding season. At their peak, the breeding haul-out of Northern fur seals at the Pribilof Islands represented perhaps the largest aggregation of large

mammals anywhere in the world. As already noted, male eared seals are polygynous, maintaining a harem of very many females, as do other socially-breeding pinnipeds, notably the elephant seals (see pp 284–285). The fact that similar behavior has evolved separately in the eared and true seals is believed to be related to the basic facts of life for seals, involving offshore marine feeding and birth on land.

Because seals have limited mobility on land, they seek out specially advantageous sites where the absence of terrestrial predators allows them to breed successfully. Such sites are relatively rare and space is often restricted, factors which tend to bring the females together. The males are more widely spaced because of their aggressive drive towards each other. This tendency of the females to clump and the males to space out means that some males will be excluded from a position among the females while the females will be drawn to the more successful males. Such behavior is believed to favor large size in the males, for two reasons. Firstly, males need to be powerful to defend their territories, and to have impressive features which they can use in threat displays and in courtship. Secondly, a successful male cannot relinquish his territory, by feeding in the water, until he has mated with as many females as possible; to do so requires a lengthy period of fasting, with reliance on a large store of blubber for energy (also, large animals need less energy per unit weight than do small animals). Thus the larger bulls will tend to be more successful—ie will produce more offspring, which will inherit the gross characteristics of the father.

▲ **Beach master.** A bull Subantarctic fur seal, surrounded by his harem of cows and their young still in their birth coats.

▶ **Representative sea lions and fur seals.** All species are sexually dimorphic, males being larger and generally darker in color than females. (**1–4**) Sea lions, which have broader muzzles than fur seals and lack underfur. (**1**) A male California sea lion (*Zalophus californianus*). (**2**) Female Steller sea lion (*Eumetopias jubatus*). (**3**) Female South American sea lion (*Otaria flavescens*). (**4**) Male New Zealand sea lion (*Phocarctos hookeri*). (**5–6**) Fur seals, which have thick coats that cause overheating on land. (**5**) Female South American fur seal (*Arctocephalus australis*). (**6**) Male Northern fur seal (*Callorhinus ursinus*).

▼ **Evolution** of sea lions and fur seals.

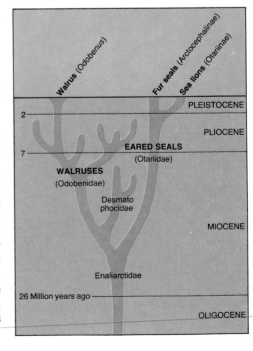

As a consequence of this course of evolution, an otariid breeding beach is a lively scene (see pp262–263). Bulls patrol their territorial boundaries, displaying frequently to neighbors. Most encounters between neighboring territorial bulls go no further than display and threat but actual fights are frequent when a newcomer attempts to establish a place on the beach. The development of a tough hide and a massive mane over the forequarters does something to lessen injuries, but even so serious wounds are common, and it is not unusual for a bull to die from his wounds. Many pups are trampled to death in these battles, but the great fecundity of the bulls is ample compensation for this. Because of the strain imposed by intense activity in territorial encounters and the long period of fasting (for example, 70 days in the case of the bull New Zealand fur seal), few males are able to occupy dominant positions on a breeding beach for more than two or three seasons.

The Antarctic fur seal shows a fairly typical annual pattern. During the winter, from May to October, the adults are at sea, and little is known of this phase of their life. In late October the breeding bulls begin to come ashore to establish territories. At this stage there is little fighting, as there is ample space on the beach. Later, as the beach fills up, boundary disputes are frequent and there is much fighting. The first cows arrive ashore 2–3 weeks later, pregnant from the previous year's mating. By the first week in December, 50 percent of the pups have been born, and 90 percent are born in a three week period. Cows come ashore about two days before giving birth. For the next six days the mother stays with her pup, suckling it at intervals, and coming into heat again eight days after the birth. During this time the bulls are very active, fighting with neighbors and endeavoring to accumulate more cows in their territories. Though they cannot actively collect cows, they do their best to prevent cows already in their territory from leaving. This interception of cows that show signs of leaving brings the bull into contact with all the females coming into heat, when they become restless. Copulation follows once a receptive cow has been detected, and very soon after being mated the cow departs to sea on a feeding excursion.

There then follows a lactation period of about 117 days, during which the cow makes periodic returns to her pup to suckle it between feeding trips. There are on average about 17 of these feeding/suckling episodes, about twice as long being spent at sea feeding as on shore suckling. While the cows are away the abandoned pups migrate to the back of the breeding beach, where they lie about in groups. A cow returning from a feeding trip comes back to the beach where she left her pup and calls for it with a characteristic pup-attraction call. The pup answers with its own call, which is recognized by the mother. She confirms recognition by smelling the pup, then leads it to a sheltered place, often on top of a clump of tussac grass, to feed it.

Eventually, weaning takes place. Surprisingly, in the Antarctic fur seal this occurs by the pup taking to the sea, so it is not present on the female's final return. Pups tend to take to the sea in groups, so weaning is more synchronized than birth. Consequently, late-born pups tend to have a shorter lactation period, and lower weaning weights,

than those born earlier. Perhaps this grouping of pups is an anti-predator strategy, since Leopard seals are known to kill young fur seals.

The abruptly terminated lactation period of the Antarctic fur seal is not typical of eared seals. The only other species that shows it, the Northern fur seal, is also migratory, abandoning its breeding places completely in the winter. Most other eared seals will continue to feed their pups till the arrival of the next, alternating suckling and feeding trips. Some, indeed, will go further and can be seen suckling a pup and a yearling, or even with a two-year-old as well. This has been recorded, for example, in northern populations of Steller sea lions. The Galapagos fur seal is another species that may suckle its pup for 2–3 years, and it has been shown that the presence of an unweaned yearling or two-year-old inhibits the birth of a younger sibling. When a pup is born in these circumstances, it almost always dies in the first month if its older sibling is a yearling, or in about 50 percent of cases if it is a two-year-old.

Many of the eared seals were hunted almost to extinction in the 19th century, but the general picture in the 20th century has been one of recovery. The Juan Fernandez fur seal, considered extinct, was rediscovered in 1965, the Guadalupe fur seal, thought to have been exterminated in 1928, was rediscovered in 1954, and the Antarctic fur seal has made the most dramatic recovery of all, from near-extinction to a healthy population of between 700,000 and 1 million today (see pp260–261).

The South American fur seal has the longest continuous record of exploitation of any fur seal, the first skins coming from Uruguay in the 16th century; the seals on Isla de Lobos are still exploited under government control. The Northern fur seal has been heavily exploited at the Pribilof Islands since 1786, but in this century the population has been well managed and the stock is in good condition today.

Some seals are still harrassed by fishermen, especially the California, South American and Steller sea lions, but, apart from unexplained declines, such as that of the South American sea lion in the Falklands (from 300,000 in the 1930s to 30,000 today), eared seals are now in a fairly healthy position. The Australian sea lion is perhaps symbolic of the improved relationship between seals and man: at Seal Bay, Kangaroo Island, the sea lions are so accustomed to human visitors that tourists can mingle with the seals on the beach. WNB

▲ **Australian sea lions** on Kangaroo island, Australia. In the foreground, a mature female (yellowish belly), immature male (gray belly and black back but no mane), and in the background pups that have already molted to resemble females. Seals are present on this colony throughout the year and have become tolerant of human visitors.

◄ **New Zealand fur seal** ABOVE at Kangaroo Island, Australia. Note the scroll-like ears typical of eared seals.

◄ **Cape or South African fur seal** hauled out on a rock. Males of this species grow to be the longest of all fur seals.

► **Galapagos sea lion,** ABOVE a subspecies of the California sea lion, leaping from an old stone jetty.

► **New Zealand sea lion** mother nuzzles its pup on return from a feeding trip. Recognition of pups is by both scent and calls. The pup in the foreground belongs to another cow.

THE 14 SPECIES OF EARED SEALS

Northern fur seal
Callorhinus ursinus
Northern or Alaskan fur seal.

Main population of about 1,300,000 animals breeds at Pribilof Islands, E Bering Sea. Some 265,000 animals breed at the Commander Islands, W Bering Sea, and 165,000 at Robben Island, Sea of Okhotsk. About 33,000 breed at the Kuril Islands in W Pacific, and a very small, but increasing group of about 2,000 breeds at San Miguel Island, off the California coast. Except for the San Miguel population, which probably remain in Californian waters all year round, the seals leave the breeding islands in October–December and migrate south. Females and juveniles migrate furthest. Male HTL 213cm; wt 180–270kg. Female HTL 142cm; wt 43–50kg. Coat: appears dark or near black when wet, but various shades when dry. Young males and females of all ages generally silvery gray above and reddish brown below, with paler chest. Adult males with heavy manes and darker body, often black or dark brown. Muzzle short, giving a characteristic profile. Female first birth about 3–4 years, male maturity 4–5 years but social maturity not till 9–15 years. Longevity: about 25 years. Births from June to early August. Mating occurs about one week after the birth of the pup. Lactation about 4 weeks. Diet: varies with season, age and area. Principal items include squid, herring, wall-eye pollack and lantern fish.

Genus *Arctocephalus* ☐*☐

The southern fur seals. The eight species of *Arctocephalus* all look rather similar. As in *Callorhinus*, there is a dense layer of underfur beneath the guard hairs. The hair line forms a sinuous curve over the metacarpals of the foreflipper—a feature distinguishing this genus from *Callorhinus*, where the hair stops at the wrist. *Arctocephalus* seals are generally a grizzled dark gray-brown above and paler beneath. Only in *A. tropicalis* is there a clear color pattern. The pups of all species are black or very dark brown, though exceptionally pups may be born with grizzled fur.

South American fur seal
Arctocephalus australis

Occurs along the coast of S America from Recife des Torres in S Brazil, through Uruguay (a major breeding colony at Isla de Lobos in the Plate estuary), around Magellanes, the islands of the W coast of Tierra del Fuego, and around the Archipelago de los Chonos as far north as Peru. About 15,000–16,000 breed on the Falkland Islands. South American population about 307,000. Male HTL 189cm; wt 159kg. Female HTL 143cm; wt 49kg. Forehead flat, muzzle moderately long. Postcanine medium sized and usually tricuspid, though in some specimens the lateral cusps are missing. Births in November–December, mating about a week after the pup is born. Lactation 6 months, or up to arrival of next pup. Female first birth at 3 years, male maturity about 7 years. Diet: a variety of cephalopods, fish (anchovies, horse mackerel etc), crustacea (rock lobster, lobster krill etc).

Juan Fernandez fur seal ☐v☐
Arctocephalus philippii

Confined to the three islands of the Juan Fernandez Archipelago, Isla Robinson Crusoe (I. Mas a Tierra). Isla Alejandro Selkirk (I. Mas Afuera), Isla Santa Clara, and Isla San Ambrosio. One of the rarest of all seals, with a population probably less than 1,000. No reliable measurements, but male HTL probably 150–200cm; wt 140kg; female HTL 140cm; wt 40kg. Forehead convex with a long muzzle and a prominent snout. Postcanine teeth large and unicuspid. Diet: said to consist of fish, cephalopods and rock lobsters.

Guadalupe fur seal ☐v☐
Arctocephalus townsendi

Breeding range now restricted to Isla Guadalupe, Baja California. Formerly found on islands off the coast of California. Population probably about 1,000. No definite measurements; similar to, but believed to be smaller than the Juan Fernandez fur seal, and with a flatter forehead.

Galapagos fur seal
Arctocephalus galapagoensis

Confined to the Galapagos Archipelago, where about 40,000 seals breed on several islands, notably Isabela and Fernandina in the west and Pinta, Marchesa, Genovesa and Wolf in the north. Breeding places rocky beaches, in contrast to sea lions in the same area, which tend to breed on sandy beaches. Male HTL 154cm; wt 64kg. Female HTL 120cm; wt 27kg. The smallest and least sexually dimorphic of the eared seals. Forehead flat in profile and the muzzle very short with an inconspicuous snout. Postcanine teeth small and unicuspid. Births August to November, with a peak in October. Mating about a week after birth. The breeding regime is much affected by the high temperatures to which the fur seals are exposed: females tend to seek out shaded places or caves in the lava rocks, while the males ensure their territories have access to the sea, so that they can cool off in the water when overheated. Duration of suckling notably extended: females are often seen suckling young larger than themselves.

Antarctic fur seal
Arctocephalus gazella
Antarctic or Kerguelen fur seal.

Islands to the south of the Antarctic Convergence, the region where the cold northward-flowing antarctic water dips sharply beneath the warmer subantarctic water. Rarely found south of 65°S; main breeding colony at NW South Georgia; much smaller groups in S Shetland Islands, S Orkney Islands, S Sandwich Islands, Bouvetøya, Heard Island and McDonald Island. Some animals may breed on Iles Kerguelen, where the species was once very abundant (hence the name). A very small population on Marion Island, in the Prince Edward group, together with *A. tropicalis*. Total population probably between 700,000 and one million. Male HTL 183cm; TL 133kg. Female HTL 129cm; TL 34kg. Coat: probably the finest and densest of any *Arctocephalus*. Both sexes and all age groups tend to be more silvery than the other members of the genus. Chest and belly of the female and young male pale cream. A small proportion (about one in 1,000) of individuals have white guard hairs and appear totally white (adult males very pale golden yellow). This color variation has not been reported for any other eared seal. Forehead convex, muzzle short and broad. Postcanine teeth often being no more than buttons of enamel. Many seals develop peculiar wear facets of unknown origin on the surfaces of the postcanine teeth close to the tongue. Female first young 3–4 years. Male maturity 6–7 years, but do not usually hold harems till later. Longevity: male about 13+, female 23. Seals spend the winter at sea, returning to the breeding places in October. Births in early December. Lactation about 17 weeks, with the pups molting towards the end of this period. Seals leave the breeding ground in April, to resume an open-sea existence till the next breeding season. Diet: mainly Antarctic krill. This appears to be the only food taken by the breeding females, but subadult males are often observed killing penguins (perhaps as a play activity), and juveniles are known to take fish.

Subantarctic fur seal
Arctocephalus tropicalis

Islands to the north of the Antarctic Convergence: Gough Island, New Amsterdam Island, St. Paul Island, Prince Edward Island and Marion Island. Stragglers reported from other islands of the Tristan group, the Crozet Archipelago, the South African coast, Macquarie Island and South Georgia. A remarkable recent record is from the Juan Fernandez Archipelago. Population: perhaps 100,000 at Gough Island and about 5,000 each at the Prince Edward Islands and at St Paul/Amsterdam Islands. Male HTL 180cm; wt 165kg. Female HTL 145cm; wt 55kg. Coat: the only fur seal to show a clear color pattern. Chest and face to behind the ears a bright nicotine yellow, or pale creamy color. A conspicuous crest on the top of the head in adult males, formed from longer guard hairs. Forehead only slightly convex, muzzle short and narrow. Postcanine teeth small and unicuspid. Births in November to December. Lactation period 7 months. Diet: fish, cephalopods and crustaceans; penguins are sometimes taken.

New Zealand fur seal
Arctocephalus forsteri

Coast of New Zealand from Three Kings Island in the north to Stewart Island in the south and on various New Zealand subantarctic islands and Macquarie Island. Also in Australia from about 117°–136°E in W and S Australia. Population between 30,000 and 50,000 around New Zealand, several thousand around Australia. Male HTL 145–250cm; wt 120–185kg. Female HTL 125–150cm; wt 40–70kg. Forehead slightly convex, muzzle moderately long and sharply pointed. Postcanine teeth small and unicuspid. Female first birth 4–6 years, males mature at same age but are not socially mature till 10–12. Births from November to January. Lactation 10–11 months, some seals being present on the breeding grounds throughout the year. Diet: (New Zealand) squid, barracouta and other surface fish, and octopus taken from the bottom; further south said to be penguins and squid.

Cape fur seal
Arctocephalus pusillus
Cape or Australian fur seal.

In South Africa, subspecies *A. p. pusillus* along the coast from Cape Cross (Namibia) southward to the Cape Peninsula and then eastward to Algoa Bay. Subspecies *A. p. doriferus* (Australian fur seal) from Seal Rocks (New South Wales) to S Tasmania, through the Bass Strait and along the Victorian coast to Lady Julia Percy Island. Population about 850,000 in South Africa and about 20,000 in Australia. Male HTL 234cm; wt 700kg. Female HTL 180cm; wt 122kg. Coat: underfur sparser than in other *Arctocephalus*, though much more abundant than in sea lions. Easily recognizable by its great size. Forehead convex, muzzle relatively long, but heavy. Postcanine teeth robust and tricuspid, with prominent anterior and posterior cusps. Teeth and skull very similar to those of the sea lion *Neophoca cinera* and in many respects *Arctocephalus pusillus* is closer to the sea lions than to the fur seals. Female first birth 3–6 years, male maturity 4–5 years, but not socially mature till 9–12 or later. Births from October to January (but most around 1 December) in South Africa, and from November to December in Australia. Lactation about 12 months or longer, with a small proportion of young being suckled a second year or even a third. Diet: mainly medium-sized open-sea schooling fish such as maasbanker, pilchard and Cape mackerel; also squid and cuttlefish. They are also capable of feeding from the bottom, taking octopus, for example. Recoveries of drowned seals in traps and trawl nets indicate that they are able to hunt at a depth of at least 120m.

Australian sea lion
Neophoca cinerea

Islands from Houtman's Abrolhos in W Australia to Kangaroo Island in S Australia, islands of the Recherche Archipelago, and in Spencer Gulf, particularly on Dangerous Reef. Population about 2,000–3,000 animals. Male HTL about 200cm; wt 300kg. Female HTL about 150cm. Coat: adult females silver gray above, creamy yellow beneath, fading to brownish; adult males dark blackish brown, with a mane of longer coarser hairs over the shoulders. A cream colored cap from the level of the eyes to the back of the head. Newborn pups are chocolate brown with a pale fawn crown. Birth season variable from October to December, mating 6–7 days after birth. Lactation often till next pup, with females suckling young up to three-quarters of their own length. Diet: cephalopods and fish are probably the main food but there are few details. They have been seen taking whiting from the nets of fishermen, eating penguins (sometimes on land), and taking crayfish.

New Zealand sea lion
Phocarctos hookeri

Subantarctic islands of New Zealand between about latitudes 48° and 53°S. Colonies on the Auckland Islands, Enderby, Dundas and Figure-of-eight Islands, the snares and Campbell Island. Stragglers occasionally seen at Macquarie Island and on the coasts of Stewart Island and the South Island of New Zealand. The population numbers between 3,000 and 4,000 animals. Male HTL 220cm; wt 400kg. Female HTL 180cm; Wt 230kg. Coat: adult males dark blackish brown all over, with well-developed manes; adult females silver gray above, pale yellow beneath. Pups dark brown with cream markings on the top of the head, extending down the nose and over the top of the head to the nape. Births on open sandy beaches, December and early January, the bulls having arrived in October and early November, and the cows from late November to December. Mating 6–7 days after giving birth. Lactation nearly a year; females sometimes seen suckling young estimated to be yearlings or older. Diet: general, including squid, octopus, small fish, crabs and mussels. Penguins occasionally taken, and regularly eaten at Macquarie Island.

South American sea lion
Otaria flavescens

Coast of South America from Recife des Torres (29°S) in Brazil (stragglers occasionally seen as far north as Rio de Janiero), around the southern tip of the continent and on the Diego Ramirez Islands (50° 30′S), up the Pacific coast to 6° 30′S in Peru. Stragglers further north than this, at least one having been recorded from the Galapagos Islands. Continental population about 240,000; about 30,000 in the Falkland Islands. Male HTL 256cm; wt 300–340kg; Female HTL 200cm; wt 144kg. Coat: very variable, but males generally dark brown to golden, with a pale mane. Females similar, though without the mane. Pups black. The most lion-like of the sea lions, the male with a blunt and broad, slightly upturned muzzle and very full mane. Births from December to February, with a peak in the middle of January. Lactation 6–12 months; rarely a cow will suckle both a newborn pup and a yearling. Diet: fish, cephalopods and crustaceans; in the Falkland Islands, squid, lobster-krill and fish are taken in that order of abundance.

Steller sea lion
Eumetopias jubatus

N Pacific from the sea of Japan, northward around the Pacific rim as far as 66°N, and down the N American coast to San Miguel Island in California. Important breeding colonies in the Kuril Islands, Kamchatka, on islands in the sea of Okhotsk, the Aleutian Islands and on the Alaskan-Canadian coastline. Some breed at San Miguel. World population estimated at 250,000. Male HTL 287cm; wt 1,000kg. Female HTL 240cm; wt 273kg. Coat: both sexes light to reddish brown. Pups dark brown to blackish. Adult males with a heavy mane, but not so conspicuous as in *Otaria*. Births from mid-May through June. Lactation 8–11 months, but occasionally a female will suckle a newborn and a yearling (rarely a two-year old as well). Female first birth 4–5 years, male maturity 5–7 but not socially mature till 7–9 years. Diet: a wide variety of fish, cephalopods (both squid and octopus), bivalve mollusks, shrimps and crabs, occasionally pups of the Northern fur seal.

California sea lion
Zalophus californianus
California sea lion, Galapagos sea lion.

West coast of N America from British Columbia southward to the tip of Baja California and in the Sea of Cortez. Breeding colonies from the southern part of the range northward to the Channel Islands off California and on the Farallon Islands near San Francisco. This form, described as the subspecies *Z. c. californianus*, probably numbers about 50,000 animals. In the Galapagos Archipelago another subspecies, *Z. c. wollebaeki*, the Galapagos sea lion, found on most islands and breeding on many of them, numbers about 40,000. A population (*Z. c. japonicus*) once occurred in Japan, but is now almost certainly extinct. Male HTL 220cm; wt 275kg. Female HTL 180cm; wt 91kg. Coat: both sexes generally a dark chestnut brown, though females sometimes lighter. Adult males sometimes have a lighter crest and muzzle. Mane not as well developed as in the Steller or South American sea lions. Births from May to June in Mexico and California. In the Galapagos, births extend over a long season from May/June to December/January. Lactation 5–12 months, but females occasionally seen suckling yearlings. Diet: poorly known. Probably an opportunistic feeder, taking what is available, whether fish or cephalopods. Both night and daytime feeding occur.

WNB

Antarctic Renaissance

The recovery of the Antarctic fur seal from near-extinction

Reduced to only a few tens of individuals by fur hunters in the 19th century, after 75 years of protection the Antarctic fur seal is now well on the way to regaining its former abundance, numbered in millions. How has this happened?

Captain Cook was the first to discover the Antarctic fur seal, when he landed at South Georgia in 1775. By that time, sealing was in full swing at the Falkland Islands, so even if Cook had not announced his discovery, it is unlikely that sealers would have overlooked this rich resource. By 1800/1 fur sealing had reached a peak at South Georgia: 17 British and American vessels visited the island in that year and took 112,000 skins.

Sealing was wasteful at every stage. The sealers landed on the breeding beaches before the main body of seals arrived and took what they could find. Then they methodically slaughtered the seals as they arrived, taking preferentially the juvenile males and the breeding females, since these yielded the finest quality skins. The large harem bulls were usually avoided—their skins were inferior and they needed more salt for curing.

By 1822 the Scottish sealer James Weddell calculated that at least 1,200,000 fur seal skins had been taken at South Georgia, and the species was nearly extinct there. Meanwhile, however, another great refuge of the species had been discovered at the South Shetland Islands in 1819. Within three years, almost a quarter of a million seals had been taken and many thousands killed and lost, and the seals had been all but exterminated there too.

The fur sealers turned to killing Southern elephant seals for their blubber, meanwhile taking any fur seals they happened to find. Other island groups were searched and their seals hunted to virtual or actual extinction. There was a brief revival of sealing at South Georgia and the South Shetland Islands, which yielded a few thousand skins, but by the turn of the century the seals seemed to have disappeared entirely. The last recorded catch was in 1907 when an American whaler took 170 skins from South Georgia.

By this time, both South Georgia and the South Shetlands were regularly visited by modern steam whalers, and shortly afterwards government restrictions were placed on the killing of seals, fur seals being totally protected. Opportunities for sighting survivors were good, but it was 1916 before a single young male was found (and illegally shot) on South Georgia. Somewhere, probably on the islets and rocks just to the

northwest of South Georgia, a tiny remnant of the stock, perhaps as few as 50 animals, had managed to survive. In 1933 a party landed at one of these, Bird Island, and found 38 seals. Three years later, at the same place, 59 were found, of which 12 were pups.

The first proper scientific investigation of the recovery, in 1956, found a thriving colony at Bird Island that had produced at least 3,500 pups. Thereafter, regular visits were made. As numbers increased, it became increasingly more difficult to obtain accurate totals of the numbers of pups born, and indirect methods had to be used to estimate abundance. Between 1958 and 1972 the South Georgia population increased at 16.8 percent annually—a rate of

growth at which the population would double every $4\frac{1}{2}$ years! There are indications that the rate has slowed since then, but it still remains much higher than the rate of recovery of other species of fur seals enjoying similar protection. The present population of Antarctic fur seals (mainly at South Georgia) is estimated at between 700,000 and 1,000,000.

Such a spectacular recovery ought to have a visible cause and a likely one is to hand, in the equally spectacular decline of the baleen whales of the Southern Ocean, which commercial whaling has reduced to about 16 percent of their original biomass (see pp 66–67). Baleen whales and Antarctic fur seals both feed on krill, and the virtual removal of baleen whales around South Georgia must have reduced competition for food between the seals and whales. Consumption of krill by baleen whales in the Antarctic has fallen from about 180 million tonnes to 33 million tonnes per year while the present population of Antarctic fur seals consumes about 1.2 million tonnes per year. Lactating fur seals, when making feeding excursions between bouts of suckling their pups (see p 96) would have benefited greatly from this reduced competition, perhaps improving the growth and survival of their pups, and their own chances of bearing pups in successive seasons.

Although the recovery has been mainly in South Georgia, fur seals are now found in increasing numbers in most of their old haunts. This is not simply a success story,

however—success brings problems too. The present density of fur seals at the northwest end of South Georgia is in fact higher than has previously been recorded. At Bird Island, raised beach features which remained intact for many thousands of years are in places being eroded, as the constant passage of fur seals destroys the fragile vegetation cover that holds their gravels together. Tussac grass, which clothes the lower slopes behind the seal beaches, is a favorite place for the seals to bask, and repeated use denudes the tussac clumps, which die off to leave naked peaty stumps. Elsewhere, the grass is trampled and flattened. This is not just unsightly: it destroys the habitat of birds dependent on the tussac areas for nesting sites. These are mainly burrowing petrels, such as prions and Blue petrels, as well as the endemic Antarctic pipit. Destruction of the tussac may not only deprive the birds of their nest sites, but can also make them more vulnerable to predation by skuas. The seals also interfere with the breeding of Wandering albatrosses.

The interaction of the whales-seals-krill system has allowed an explosive recovery of the fur seals which conservationists generally will applaud, but the future of the fur seals will not simply be a return to the past. Conditions are very different now to the pre-exploitation days. The balance of an ecosystem is not simple, and while populations may prove very resilient when pressures are removed, there is no guarantee that former situations will be restored.   WNB

ANTARCTIC FUR SEALS ON BIRD ISLAND

▲ **Spectacular backdrop.** A beach breeding ground with large, maned males, smaller females and black pups.

▶ **Cows in clover,** or rather tussac, the thick clumped grass that clothes the lower slopes and beaches of breeding colonies. Here females bask among mature clumps, but lower down the beach SEE ABOVE overcrowding by seals has flattened the clumps, leading to severe erosion.

◀ **Chilly encounter.** A cow repels the advances of a bull during a snow storm.

The Fight to Mate

Breeding strategy of California sea lions

Evenly spaced bursts of bubbles rising to the surface offshore of a California sea lion rookery indicate that, below, a male sea lion is patrolling his territory and barking underwater. These, the best-known of all sea lions, thanks to their performances in circuses and oceanaria, sometimes have territories that are mostly in the water, and males bark to warn intruders of their territorial boundaries.

The California sea lion is currently found in the eastern North Pacific from British Columbia to Baja California and in a separate population on the Galapagos Islands, near the Equator. Male sea lions are larger than females and maintain territories on the rookeries (pupping/mating sites) during the breeding season which lasts from May to August in California. Each male mates with as many females as possible. A successful adult male must defend his stretch of beach from all other males in order to maximize his mating success. Fighting occurs during the establishment of territories but is soon reduced to ritualized boundary displays. The displays include barking, head shaking, oblique stares and lunges at the opponent's flippers. These displays are most likely to occur on territorial boundary lines and can be used to plot the locations of individual territories on the rookery.

Ritualized fighting and large size are the two most important factors enabling the males to stay on their territories for long periods of time without feeding. For a male to maximize the numbers of his offspring he must remain on the rookery for as long as possible. Ritualized fighting uses less energy than does actual combat. Large size is not only an asset in combat but also confers a lower rate of energy expenditure and the ability to store abundant blubber. The blubber serves as a layer of insulation when the sea lion is in cold water and is its only source of food when it is on its territory.

Also important in the male sea lion's reproductive strategy is the timing of territory occupation. Ideally, territories should be occupied when the greatest number of receptive females are present. On average, there are 16 females for every territorial male and 2 females for every pup. In the Northern fur seal the females are receptive about five days after they have given birth. In this species, the males establish their territories before the females arrive on the rookeries in the Bering Sea. But in the California sea lion the females are not receptive until about 21 days after they have given birth. The fact that male California sea lions only hold their territories for an average of 27 days means that it is counterproductive for them to establish territories before the females arrive. In fact they do not even begin to set up territories until after the first pups are born. The number of territories on a rookery increases gradually and reaches a peak about five weeks after the peak of the pupping period.

The weather also affects the sea lions' breeding strategy. Temperatures of more than 30°C (86°F) occur during the breeding

▲ **Rookery on the rocks.** The breeding grounds or rookeries of California sea lions are often in very isolated and inhospitable locations.

▼ **Oblique aggression.** Ritualized gestures are used by territorial male California sea lions to maintain the boundaries of their territories after initial establishment. These take the place of fighting, allowing the males to save energy for mating. The individual gestures are performed in a variable order, but a typical sequence is: (1) head-shaking with barking as the males approach the boundary, followed by (2) oblique stares interspersed with lunges, and (3) more head-shaking and barking. During lunges, the males try to keep their foreflippers as far as possible from each other's mouths. The thick skin on the chest fends off potentially serious blows.

▲ **Water territories.** Where bull sea lion territories are in the water they maintain the boundaries by patrolling and barking.

season, and while this is generally favorable to the pups, which have not yet fully developed their ability to regulate their body temperature, the territorial males may suffer. All sea lions have only a limited ability to regulate body temperature on land and normally cool off by entering the water. But for a territorial male to do this is to risk losing his territory. Therefore a successful territorial male must have access to water as a part of his territory. During hot weather territories without direct access to water cannot be defended.

Sometimes territories are mostly in the water. This often occurs at the base of steep cliffs where there is a little beach but still enough room for females to come ashore and give birth. Here, the males patrol their territories, barking underwater. It is possible that a male with a large portion of his territory under water would have an energetic advantage over one with most of his territory on land. What is certain is that any advantage a male can gain in order to leave more offspring will be exploited to the full. DKO

WALRUS

Odobenus rosmarus
Sole member of genus.
Family: Odobenidae.
Distribution: Arctic seas, from E Canada and
Greenland to N Eurasia and W Alaska.

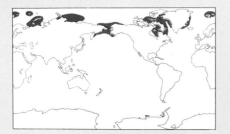

Habitat: chiefly seasonal pack ice over
continental shelf.

Size: regionally-variable; smallest in Hudson
Bay, where adult males average 2.9m (9.5ft),
adult females 2.5m (8.2ft) in length and about
795kg (1,750lb) and 565kg (1,250lb),
respectively, in weight; largest in Bering and
Chukchi Seas, where adult males average about
3.2m (10.5ft), adult females 2.7m (8.8ft) in
length and about 1,210kg (2,670lb) and
830kg (1,835lb), respectively, in weight. Tusks
of Hudson Bay animals very short, averaging
about 36cm (14in) in adult males and 23cm
(9in) in adult females;
tusks of Bering-
Chukchi walruses
nearly twice as long,
averaging about 55cm
(22in) in adult males
and 40cm (16in) in
adult females.

Color: cinnamon brown to pale tawny, darkest
on chest and abdomen; immature animals
darker than adults. Surfaces of flippers hairless,
black in young animals, becoming brownish to
grayish with age. Hair sparse on neck and
shoulders of adult males.

Diet: mainly mollusks.

Gestation: 15–16 months, including 4–5
months of suspended development (delayed
implantation).

Longevity: up to 40 years.

Subspecies: 2 or 3. **Atlantic walrus** (*O. r.
rosmarus*); Hudson and Baffin bays to Kara and
Barents seas; males to 3.5m (11.5ft) long, with
length of tusks about 12 percent of head-to-tail
length. **Pacific walrus** (*O. r. divergens*); Bering
and Chukchi seas; males to 4.2m (14ft) long,
with length of tusks about 17% of head-to-tail
length. Males with "squarer" snout than
Atlantic walrus, and jutting chin. The name
O. r. divergens was originally assigned on the
basis of the tusks being more widely spread
than those of the Atlantic walrus; this
difference has never been confirmed. Walruses
of Laptev Sea intermediate in size; sometimes
considered as Atlantic, sometimes as Pacific,
occasionally as a separate subspecies (*O. r.
lapievi*).

THE image of the walrus, stout-bodied and
bewhiskered, with long white tusks, is as
symbolic of the Arctic as are ice and snow.
And rightly so, for walruses inhabit only the
Arctic Ocean and adjacent ice-covered seas.
Few other creatures have adapted so successfully to the pack-ice regime of the far
northern seas, and for that they are revered
by the maritime Eskimos, who see in them
many human attributes as well. Highly
social and gregarious, slow to mature and
reproduce, fiercely protective and gently
caring for their young, vocally communicative with each other, and long lived, walruses
are easy subjects to interpret in a human
way.

Walruses are also cherished by the
Eskimos as a major source of food and other
materials, on which these people have de-
pended for thousands of years. Farther
south, in Europe, Asia, and North America,
however, the main interest in walruses has
been for their ivory—the great white tusks,
second in size and quality only to those of
elephants. In the quest for that ivory and for
the thick hides and oil, Europeans nearly
eliminated walruses from the Arctic more
than 100 years ago.

Early descriptions of walruses drew attention to their resemblance to swine, in part
because of the tendency to huddle together,
sometimes one on top of another, and in part
because of the sparsely haired, rotund body,
about as large in circumference as in length.
In size, coloration, and general appearance,
however, walruses actually bear little resemblance to pigs. Outwardly they are most
similar to sea lions, except for their squarish
head and long tusks. Male walruses have a
pair of highly inflatable air sacs in the throat
which are used to produce special sounds
during courtship and as an aid to floating
while resting at sea.

When on land or ice, walruses stand and
walk on all four limbs. The heels of the
hindflippers are brought in under the rump
for support, and the toes are turned forward
and outward; the palms of the forelimbs
support the trunk, and the fingers are
turned outward and back.

In water, the walrus propels itself almost
exclusively by means of the hindlimbs, the
forelimbs being used mainly as rudders. This
sculling with the hindlimbs is an adaptation
for bottom-feeding, in which a slow, meth-
odical pace is more advantageous than high
speed.

One of the principal anatomical peculiarities of the walrus is the skin, 2–4cm
(0.8–1.6in) thick, which is thrown into
creases and folds at every joint and bend of
the body. This thick skin is a protective
"armor", guarding against injury by the
tusks of other walruses. Everywhere but on
the flippers, the skin is covered by coarse
hair about 1cm (0.4in) long, which imparts
a furry to velvety texture to the body surface
of females and young males; adult males
(bulls) tend to be sparsely haired and to have
nearly bare, knobby skin on the neck and
shoulders. That knobby skin is up to 5cm
(2in) thick, for added protection, and it

▲ **Walrus haul-out.** Walruses are extremely gregarious, hauling out in vast aggregations, normally on ice, but when not available they select rocky islands as here at Round Island, Alaska.

◄ **Lord of the floe.** A male walrus on a floe in the Bering Sea in spring. At this time of the year male and female populations are entirely separate, the females having migrated north to the Chukchi Sea.

▷ **A pile of walruses** OVERLEAF. In restricted locations, walruses are quite happy to haul out onto other walruses. Note the contrast between the basking pink herd and the pale individual emerging from the sea.

forms were fish-eaters, but some had already changed their diet from fishes to mollusks and other bottom fauna. With that change in diet, they gradually changed in appearance and behavior. Probably in that connection, the change from forelimb to hindlimb propulsion took place, and the tusks began to enlarge.

Between 5 and 8 million years ago, some of these bottom-feeding walruses with tusks made their way into the North Atlantic Ocean, through what was then an open passage, known as the Central American Seaway, in what is now Costa Rica and Panama. Subsequently, they flourished in the North Atlantic, while all of those in the North Pacific died out. Within the past million years, those in the Atlantic invaded the Arctic, and some made their way back to the Pacific via the Arctic Ocean as recently as 300,000 years ago.

Walruses today feed primarily on bivalve mollusks—the clams, cockles, and mussels that abound on the continental shelves of northern seas. They also eat about 40 other kinds of invertebrate animals from the sea floor, including several species of shrimps, crabs, snails, polychaete and priapulid worms, octopus, sea cucumbers, and tunicates, as well as a few fishes; occasionally they even eat seals.

To locate their food, walruses probably rely more on touch than on any other sense, for they feed in total darkness during the winter and in murky waters or at depths where penetration of light is very poor most of the rest of the time. Their sense of touch appears to be most powerfully developed on the front of their snout, where the thin skin and about 450 coarse whiskers are highly sensitive. The upper edge of the snout is armored with tough, cornified skin and is apparently used for digging, pig-fashion, to unearth many of the small clams and other invertebrates lying at shallow depths in the bottom mud. Those buried deeper in the sediments are believed to be excavated by means of jetting water into their burrows. The ability of walruses to squirt large amounts of water under high pressure from their mouth is well known to zoo keepers. The old hypothesis that walruses dig clams with their tusks is now known to be incorrect; the tusks are primarily "social organs," like the antlers of deer and the horns of sheep. They become worn not from digging but from being dragged along in the mud and sand, while the walrus moves forward excavating its prey with the snout and oral jet.

A few females first breed at 4 years and a

imparts a distinctive appearance which clearly separates the bulls from all other animals. The folds of the skin are infested by blood-sucking lice which seem to cause some irritation, for walruses often rub and scratch their skin.

The walrus's nearest living relatives are the fur seals, with which it evolved from bear-like ancestors, the Enaliarctidae, in the North Pacific Ocean about 20 million years ago. Early walruses were similar in appearance to modern sea lions, and from about 5–10 million years ago they were the most abundant and most diverse pinnipeds in the Pacific Ocean. Some of those early few as late as 10 years of age; the average is 6 or 7 years. Males are much slower to mature, for they may not take part in breeding until they are physically as well as sexually mature. For most males, that development requires about 15 years. Full maturity is necessary for breeding because the bulls are highly competitive for mates, and only those that are large enough in body and tusk size are capable of competing successfully.

Mating takes place in January-February, probably in the water, during the coldest part of the winter. At that time, the adult females (cows) and young congregate in traditional breeding areas, forming into herds of 10–15 animals which travel and feed together. Several such herds may coalesce when they haul out onto the ice to rest, between feeding bouts. Each herd is followed by one to several bulls, which mostly remain in the water, nearby. These bulls engage incessantly in vocal displays, consisting of set sequences of repetitive "knocks" and "bells" made underwater, and shorter sequences of "clacks" and "whistles" at the surface. Like the songs of birds, these repetitive calls probably serve to attract mates and to repel potential competitors. The bell-like sound is apparently produced by using one of the inflatable sacs in the throat as a resonance chamber and is used only in sexual display. The normal sounds of walruses are barks of variable pitch.

The female gives birth to a single calf in the spring of the following year, usually in May. Because of the long pregnancy, females cannot breed more often than at two-year intervals, and the intervals become longer with age. For this reason, the walrus has the lowest rate of reproduction of any pinniped and one of the lowest among mammals in general.

The calf at birth is about 1.1m (3.6ft) long and weighs about 60–65kg (130–140lb). It has a short, soft coat of hair, pale grayish flippers, a thick white mustache, and no visible teeth. It feeds only on milk for the first 6 months, but begins to eat some solids by the end of that time.

After one year, the calf has approximately tripled in weight and has developed tusks 2.5cm (1in) long. For another year, the calf remains with its mother, dependent on her for guidance, protection and milk, while gradually developing its ability to bottom-feed and range independently. At 2 years of age, it separates from the mother, who then gives birth to another calf.

After weaning, the young walruses con-

Why do Walruses have Tusks?

In both male and female walruses, the upper canine teeth develop into great "tusks." These serve many functions, from ice-choppers to defensive weapons, but their primary role lies in the establishment of the bearer's status within walrus society. In any herd, the largest walrus with the largest tusks tends to be the dominant one. Simply by adopting postures that display the size of its tusks, the dominant animal can move unchallenged into the most comfortable or advantageous positions, displacing subordinates which have shorter tusks. If the dominant walrus encounters another with tusks of comparable size, however, their confrontation may escalate from visual displays to stabbing with the tusks. Eventually one of the combatants concedes defeat by turning away and withdrawing. Such contests occur in males and females but they are more intense between bulls in the breeding season.

The social value of the tusks extends beyond the competition for dominance. By their size and shape, the tusks convey much information about the sex and age of their bearer. For about the first year and a half after birth, young walruses have no visible tusks, since their canine teeth do not emerge through the gums until 6–8 months of age, and they are covered by the ample upper lip for another year thereafter. Hence, any small animal with no tusks is immediately recognizable by all others as young and dependent, and its larger companion is tentatively identifiable as an adult female.

At all ages, the tusks of females tend to be rounder in cross section, shorter in length, as well as more slender and more curved than those of males. In old age, the tusks of both sexes tend to be stout but shortened and blunted by fracture and abrasion. A human observer can identify the sex and approximate age of a walrus from its tusks, so other walruses are probably at least as perceptive.

Occasionally, a walrus emerging from the water onto an ice floe uses its tusks as a fifth limb, jabbing the points into the ice and heaving the body forward. Tales of this behavior led the 18th-century zoologist Brisson to give the walrus the generic name *Odobenus*, a contraction of the Greek words *odontos* and *baenos*, meaning literally "tooth-walk." The tusks are sometimes also used to break breathing holes in the ice.

tinue to associate and travel with the adult females. Gradually, over the next 2–4 years, the young males break away, forming their own small groups in winter or joining with larger herds of bulls in the summer. Seasonal segregation of sexes appears to take place to some degree in all walrus populations, but it is most clearly expressed in the Bering-Chukchi region. There, most of the bulls congregate in separate haul-out and feeding areas in the Bering Sea during the spring, while the cows and most of the immature animals migrate northward into the Chukchi Sea. They remain separated in this way throughout the summer; then as the cows come southward again in the fall, the bulls apparently meet them in the vicinity of the Bering Strait and accompany them to the wintering-breeding areas in the Bering Sea. At that time, the immature males move off separately to spend the winter in other parts of the pack ice, outside the breeding areas. By segregating in this way, Pacific walruses distribute their impact on the food supply and minimize the potential conflict between adult and adolescent males in the breeding season.

Walrus populations throughout the Arctic were severely depleted during the 18th, 19th, and 20th centuries by commercial hunters from Europe and North

▲ Slaughter on the ice. The walrus is still vital to the economies of the Eskimos, but stocks may not be sufficient to sustain exploitation.

▶ Walrus engraving on a whale's tooth. The Eskimos' reliance on sea mammals is symbolized by this representation of walrus hunting drawn on a Sperm whale's tooth.

◀ Versatile tusks. The walrus's tusks are primarily social organs, used in dominance disputes (1). Such encounters are usually ended by the less bulky or strong walrus turning away (2). Walruses sometimes use their tusks simply to prop the head up (3). The tusks also function as a fifth limb when emerging from the water onto ice (4).

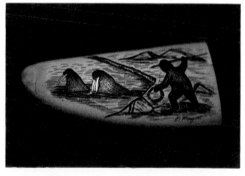

America, who sought the animals principally for their tusks, skins and oil. At that time, little was known about the biology and ecology of walruses, hence there was little scientific basis for managing the hunters by regulating their catch. The North Atlantic population is about 30,000 individuals; these stocks were the first to be depleted, were reduced to the lowest numbers and have never recovered. The Bering-Chukchi population, although depressed twice to about 50 percent of its former size, appa-

rently rebounded each time within a 15–20 year period, the latest being from about 1960 to 1980; it now numbers about 260,000. There are less than 10,000 walruses in the Laptev Sea. Currently, about 6–7 percent of the western North Atlantic population and 2–4 percent of the Bering-Chukchi walrus populations are killed annually.

For several thousand years, walruses have been the mainstay of numerous Eskimo communities from eastern Siberia and Alaska to eastern Canada and Greenland. In recent years, management of walruses as a natural resource in the USSR, Canada and Greenland has recognized aboriginal subsistence as the first consideration, after that of survival of the walruses themselves. The North Atlantic stocks are so low that they may not be able to bear continued exploitation by the Eskimos, while the high level of the North Pacific stock has opened the way for renewed consideration of potential commercial use.   FHF

TRUE SEALS

Family: Phocidae
Nineteen species in 10 genera.
Distribution: generally in polar, subpolar and temperate seas, except for the monk seals of the Mediterranean, Caribbean, and Hawaiian regions.

Habitat: land-fast ice, pack ice and offshore rocks and islands.

Size: head-to-tale length from 117cm (50in) in the Ringed seal to 490cm (193in) in the male Southern elephant seal; weight from 45kg (100lb) in the Ringed seal to 2,400kg (5,300lb) in the male Southern elephant seal.

Gestation: 10–11 months, including 2.5–3.5 months of suspended development (delayed implantation).
Longevity: up to 56 years.

Genus *Monachus*
Three species: **Caribbean monk seal** (*M. tropicalis*). **Hawaiian monk seal** (*M. schauinslandi*). **Mediterranean monk seal** (*M. monachus*).

Genus *Lobodon*
One species: **Crabeater seal** (*L. carcinophagus*).

Genus *Leptonychotes*
One species: **Weddell seal** (*L. weddelli*).

Genus *Hydrurga*
One species: **Leopard seal** (*H. leptonyx*).

Genus *Ommatophoca*
One species: **Ross seal** (*O. rossi*).

Genus *Mirounga*
Two species: **Northern elephant seal** (*M. angustirostris*). **Southern elephant seal** (*M. leonina*).

Genus *Erignathus*
One species: **Bearded seal** (*E. barbatus*).

Genus *Cystophora*
One species: **Hooded seal** (*C. cristata*).

Genus *Phoca*
Seven species: smaller northern seals. Species include: **Baikal seal** (*P. sibirica*), **Harbor seal** (*P. vitulina*), **Harp seal** (*P. groenlandica*), **Ribbon seal** (*P. fasciata*). **Ringed seal** (*P. hispida*). **Spotted seal** (*P. largha*).

Genus *Halichoerus*
One species: **Grey seal** (*H. grypus*).

A SEAL laboriously humping across the ice, unable to raise itself by means of its foreflippers, is, moments later, plunging to 600m (2,000ft) and staying underwater for over an hour—true seals are wonderfully adapted to diving, but at the expense of agility on land. Despite the extreme refinement of their physiology to equip them for diving, they are still not fully emancipated from their otter-like ancestors of some 25 million years ago. The tie to land or ice for birth and nurture of their young sets the basic pattern of their lives.

Unlike eared seals (but like otters), true seals swim by powerful sideways movements of their hindquarters. The trailing hindlimbs are bound to the pelvis so that the "crotch" is at the level of the ankles and the tail scarcely protrudes. The long, broadly webbed feet make very effective flippers but are useless on land. The forelimbs, unlike those of eared seals, are not strongly pro-

pulsive; they are buried to the base of the hand and are used for steering in the water and, sometimes, to assist in scrambling on land or ice. The northern true seals have evolved more powerful arrangements of muscle attachments along the spine, whereas antarctic species may have longer, more mobile foreflippers.

Respiration and circulation in true seals are adapted to one overwhelming purpose; that of spending long periods of time underwater. The Weddell seal is a supreme diver, with dives of 600m (2,000ft) to its credit.

Anatomically, the 18 living species of true seals fall into two subfamilies. The southern seals, or Monachinae, include the tropical Hawaiian and Mediterranean monk seals (another monk seal, the Caribbean monk seal, is thought to be extinct, see pp 288–289), the Northern and Southern elephant seals, and the Antarctic seals (Crabeater, Leopard, Ross and Weddell

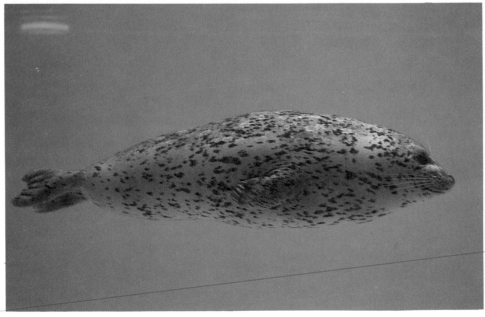

Red balloon/Black hood. The Hooded seal has two bizarre forms of nasal display. The lining of one nostril can be forced out through the opposite nostril to form a red bladder ABOVE. Alternatively, the whole of the black hood, an enlargement of the nasal cavity, can be inflated RIGHT.

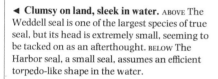

◀ **Clumsy on land, sleek in water.** ABOVE The Weddell seal is one of the largest species of true seal, but its head is extremely small, seeming to be tacked on as an afterthought. BELOW The Harbor seal, a small seal, assumes an efficient torpedo-like shape in the water.

▼ The evolution of true seals.

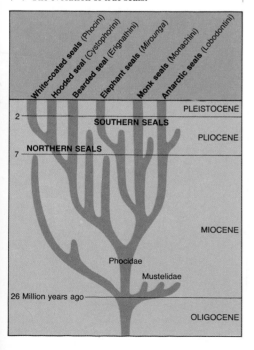

seals), as three distinct tribes. The northern seals, or Phocinae, also have three tribes: for the Bearded seal, the Hooded seal, and for the remaining, primitively ice-breeding seals: the Baikal, Caspian, Grey, Harbor, Harp, Ringed and Spotted seals.

Although now largely found in high latitudes of both Northern and Southern Hemispheres, the true seals probably originated in warm waters, where the monk seals still live. All of the northern seals except the Harbor seal breed on ice, the Harbor seal breeding as far south as Baja California (the Grey seal can breed on land or ice). Of the southern seals, the Northern and Southern elephant seals breed respectively from California to Mexico and in the temperate to subantarctic parts of the Southern Ocean. The four Antarctic seals breed on ice and occur generally south of the Antarctic Convergence at 50°–60°S.

The most obvious differences between species are in size and the relative sizes of the sexes. Some populations of Ringed seals reach weights of only about 50kg (110lb), whereas a fully grown male Southern elephant seal may be 50 times heavier. In most species, males and females are of similar size: The females of southern seals, especially the monk seals, the Leopard and Weddell seals, tend to be larger than the males, whereas the males of some northern seals—the Grey, Hooded and elephant seals—are much larger than the females; these large males also have heavy, arched skulls and nasal protuberances for aggressive displays. The size disparity is most marked in the Southern elephant seal, in which the male can be more than three times the weight of the female.

The fossil record has recently yielded many new insights into the evolution and spread of the true seals. Their origin in the North Atlantic region is certain, and their derivation from otter-like ancestors in Europe or western Asia is highly probable. The oldest, mid-to-late Miocene fossils (12–15 million years ago) of eastern USA and Europe are assignable to the modern tropical and northern seal groups.

Evidently the monk seals arose near the Mediterranean, where they still occur, and crossed to the Pacific through the Caribbean and the open (until 3.5–4 million years ago) Central American Seaway. They may have soon after crossed to Hawaii, for the isolated monk seal there is, in bone structure, more primitive than any living and many fossil seals. Ancestral elephant seals from the same Atlantic tropical seal stock, made the same crossing and invaded the Southern Hemisphere via the west coast of South America, leaving behind the more primitive northern species.

Analyses of fossils from eastern USA and Europe, along with recent finds in Argentina, Peru and South Africa, suggest that the tropical ancestors of the antarctic seals likewise entered the Southern Ocean along western South America, but also possibly along eastern South America and West Africa. Such multiple invasions may help account for the present diversity of antarctic true seals in the absence of geographical barriers in the Southern Ocean.

The Bearded seal, although a northern

seal in terms of bone structure, is linked with the tropical seals by its less-developed pelvic and ear regions, by the presence of four mammae (two in other northern seals), and by the dark lanugo. The Hooded seal, formerly classed with the elephant seals, is clearly a true northern seal, perhaps the remnant of a more primitive ice-breeding group in the North Atlantic.

The remaining northern seals evidently had a common ancestor, as they all have 32 chromosomes (34 in all other true seals), a similar bone structure and a clearly ice-adapted white lanugo. Seals of the latest Miocene, some 10 million years ago, in southern Europe, included forms allied to the modern Ringed seal and were possibly ancestors of the other northern seals. The Caspian and Baikal seals may thus be relics of a more extensive inland distribution of such seals well before the Pleistocene (about 2 million years ago).

True seals are unknown as North Pacific fossils much before the early Pleistocene (about 7 million years ago), and the ancestral Spotted and Ribbon seals, the latter closely related to the Atlantic Harp seal, must have arrived from the north after the submergence of the Bering land bridge, some 3.5 million years ago. A form like the Spotted seal (once classed as a race of the Harbor seal) is a plausible ice-breeding ancestor of the Pacific Harbor seal, which may have returned as a land-breeding form

to the Atlantic during a warm period. The Grey seal alone among this primitively ice-breeding group has no Pacific counterpart.

Although some fossil seals are possible ancestors and intermediates in the evolution of modern seals, some clearly are not. Perhaps the most unusual is a recently discovered form from Peru, *Acrophoca longirostris*, related to the antarctic seals, but curiously long-snouted, like a dolphin. Nevertheless, the true seals do not seem to have undergone the "bursts" of evolutionary diversification that occurred among the eared seals in the North Pacific.

Aquatic life restricts seals to a diet of relatively small or soft food, hence the array of premolars and molars, for cutting and crushing, which is found in terrestrial carnivores, is reduced to rows of uniform teeth, usually five. Most seals are somewhat opportunistic, with few obvious specializations for feeding.

Where several species inhabit the same area, some differentiation is apparent. In the Okhotsk and Bering seas, the Ringed seal breeds on land-fast ice or heavy pack (drift-

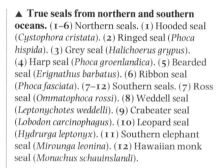

ing) ice and feeds on small fish and planktonic crustaceans, while the Spotted and Ribbon seals use somewhat lighter pack ice and feed respectively on shallow-water fishes and deep-water fishes and squids. The Bearded seal, which also inhabits this region, is unique among true seals in feeding on bottom-dwelling mollusks and shrimps; its teeth are worn down quite early in life.

Under fast ice around Antarctica, the Weddell seal eats fishes, and in the pack ice the Ross seal subsists on deep-water squids, the Leopard seal mainly on seals and penguins (see pp290–291), and the Crabeater seal (see pp288–289) lives mostly on krill, which it strains through its many-pointed teeth. Competitive interactions may be intense in confined waters like the Gulf of St. Lawrence, where Grey and Harbor seals are resident, Ringed seals rare and local, and Harp and Hooded seals present during the breeding season.

Since the discovery, in the mid-20th century, of a method of age determination from layers in their teeth, the basic patterns of growth, reproduction and survival rates

▲ **True seals from northern and southern oceans.** (1–6) Northern seals. (1) Hooded seal (*Cystophora cristata*). (2) Ringed seal (*Phoca hispida*). (3) Grey seal (*Halichoerus grypus*). (4) Harp seal (*Phoca groenlandica*). (5) Bearded seal (*Erignathus barbatus*). (6) Ribbon seal (*Phoca fasciata*). (7–12) Southern seals. (7) Ross seal (*Ommatophoca rossi*). (8) Weddell seal (*Leptonychotes weddelli*). (9) Crabeater seal (*Lobodon carcinophagus*). (10) Leopard seal (*Hydrurga leptonyx*). (11) Southern elephant seal (*Mirounga leonina*). (12) Hawaiian monk seal (*Monachus schauinslandi*).

of true seals have been extensively documented. Ages of sexual maturity vary somewhat unexpectedly, being later in small species like the Ringed and Caspian seals than in the large antarctic species or the huge elephant seals. Early maturity may be a disadvantage in species, like the Harbor and Ringed seals, that disperse in complex, near-shore environments where land (or ice) predation is a threat and where learning about surroundings is essential for safe reproduction. Although both sexes of the Grey and elephant seals (see pp284–285) are fertile when quite young, males are incapable of securing mates until they are much larger, some years later.

Although species differences remain, females of the Baikal, Ringed, Harp, Harbor and elephant seals have all been shown to mature earlier in populations reduced by exploitation. This has been attributed to increased food availability or reduced social interaction, but the mechanisms are not known. A remarkable decrease in mean age of first reproduction by female Crabeater seals, from more than 4 years in 1945 to less than 3 years in 1965, was associated with a vast "release" of its krill food base through depletion of the great whales (see pp 280–281).

Reproductive seasons may be set by female receptivity at optimal times for rearing young or fostering their independence; males are often potent long before and after. Occasional newborns occur as much as six months outside the normal season, and have been attributed to young mothers whose cycles had not been set. Most females of a species reproduce at about the same time, although populations at higher latitudes may be later. Grey seals show marked regional differences in timing and choice of breeding sites. Extreme local variability occurs among Harbor seals in western North America, where nearby populations may differ by up to four months, perhaps from "drift" in this relatively nonseasonal region.

Mean lactation periods are 1–2 weeks in pack-ice seals and up to 11–12 weeks in the Ringed and Baikal seals, which suckle their young in snow "caves" on the fast ice (see pp282–283). The difference seems related to stability and protectiveness of the nursery. Pups of Weddell seals on fast ice and of Harbor and Monk seals on land are weaned when about 5–6 weeks old, whereas those of the elephant and Grey seals (in which the males mate on land with as many females as they can) are weaned at 3–4 weeks, perhaps an evolutionary response to pre-emptive

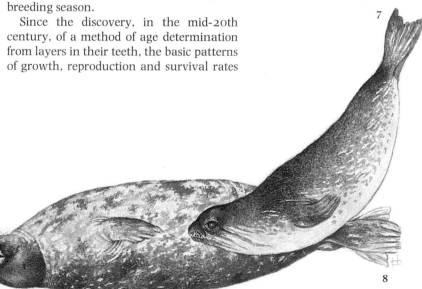

males (see pp284–285). Pups of most species increase in weight on average 2.5–3.5-fold during lactation and the Baikal seal, with a lactation of 8–10 weeks, is said to grow 5.5-fold. The blubber of females is transferred to the pup as very rich, fatty milk. For example, the fat content of Harp seal milk increases from around 23 percent at the start of lactation to more than 40 percent at the end, with a complementary decline in water content. As the female fasts while lactating, the decreasing water content may be important in maintaining her water balance. Abandoned or prematurely weaned pups may become dwarfed adults. Pups are occasionally adopted, and some male pups of Northern elephant seals may solicit an unrelated "nurse" after being weaned normally, thereby gaining unusual weight and, possibly, adult fitness.

Copulation is on land in elephant and Grey seals and normally in water among all others. In all species, mating evidently occurs soon after, and sometimes shortly before, pups are weaned, so gestations are 10–11 months. However, the period of active embryonic growth is only 6.5–8 months. This delay in implantation and growth of the embryo has the consequence that males compete for females when they are localized and restrained by maternal duties, and at the same time adjusts the rate of fetal growth to the feeding and physiological capacities of the females.

Although some true seals have been casually reported to mate with a single partner, males of all species are probably at least opportunistically promiscuous and some mate with very many females. Individual male elephant seals (see pp284–285) may control access by others to spontaneously clumped females (misleadingly called "harems"), or dominant males may be spaced among continuously distributed females. Females may incite male combat by vocalizing and by trying to escape from attempted matings; this is probably done to assess paternal fitness, giving a more dominant male opportunity to displace the original one. Some male Grey seals in Britain may patrol true territories of 260 sq km (100 sq mi) or more, excluding other males and sometimes thwarting the departure of females, whereas on a Nova Scotia beach spaces used by males are flexible and overlapping (ie not territorial), and males copulate with nearby females as these become receptive. Although such behavior varies within species, what does not vary is the fact that only a proportion of males is successful; in the Southern eleph-

▲ **Bobbing like corks,** a group of adult Grey seals swim in a bay of the Orkney Islands. Although seals spend much of the year at sea, very little is known of this aspect of their lives.

◄ **Face-to-face confrontation.** Two male Grey seals dispute a boundary at Sable Island, east of Nova Scotia. This is one of the few sites where Grey seals breed on sand.

► **Resplendent lanugo.** A dewy-eyed Grey seal pup, still in its creamy-white birth coat, awaits its mother's return. The lanugo is molted after 2–3 weeks and replaced by a coat similar to that of the adult.

ant seal, for example, the effective sex-ratio may locally exceed 100 females to 1 male.

Among species that mate in water, underwater territoriality has been suspected or confirmed in some. Male Weddell seals display in, and aggressively defend, narrow stretches of water, up to 200m (650ft) long, under females congregated with young along ice cracks. Individual male Ringed seals (see pp282–283) may use ice holes as much as 1km (0.6mi) apart, excluding other males, but not females. Male Harbor seals may patrol waters off restricted stretches of shoreline, and bite wounds suggest that they too are territorial. Although Crabeater, Grey, Hooded, and Spotted seals are said to form "families" of male and female with young, the males are merely awaiting receptivity of females for mating. The females are aggressively defended, but may be abandoned once mated, as males leave to seek other matings.

The fact that the difference in size between males and females is generally small among species that mate in water suggests that agility and speed may be more advantageous than brute size in males of such species. Exceptions are the large males of Hooded seals and Grey seals. The large size of the male Hooded seal suggests that they, like the Grey seal, may once have been land-breeders.

The social behavior of most species has been little studied outside the breeding season. Species may be basically solitary, aggregating merely because of clumped food or resting places, or may interact in truly social ways. Harbor seals in Quebec were shown to reduce their individual rates of scanning for danger when in larger groups. The navigational skills of Harp seals may be enhanced when they migrate in herds. Weaned young Crabeater seals may gather for protection from Leopard seals. Group "herding" of fishes has been mooted in Grey and Northern elephant seals.

Only the monk seals are truly endangered as species (see pp288–289). Isolated populations or subspecies of other seals are rare or declining. Female Ringed and Grey seals in the inner Baltic show pathological sterility, attributed to pollutants (see p283). There may be fewer than 200 Ringed seals remaining there, isolated in Lake Saima, Finland, although the population of 10,000 or so in Lake Ladoga, USSR, seems secure under restricted hunting. The distinctive Harbor seal of the Kuriles, with some 5,000 individuals, is protected in the USSR, but some are killed in northern Japan. Some lake populations of Harbor seals in northern

Canada have been reduced and possibly eliminated.

By contrast, most populations of seals are probably stable or increasing, some after heavy exploitation in the past. A striking example is the Northern elephant seal, which has increased from fewer than 100 in 1912 to some 50,000 today.

Although the killing of young Harp seals in eastern Canada is repugnant to many, research on, and management of, this population in recent years have been more thorough than for almost any other wild mammal, and recent evidence indicates slow increase under current quotas (see pp 286–287). The White Sea herd is managed less scientifically but probably more conservatively. The scientific basis for killing young Hooded seals in the North Atlantic is much more tenuous. Commercial hunting by Soviet sealers of several species in the Bering and Okhotsk seas was sharply curtailed after overexploitation in the 1960s. Hunting of Baikal and Caspian seals has also been recently reduced on the basis of stock assessments.

Seals are also killed for subsistence and commerce in skins by aborigines in northern regions and, on a smaller scale, by coastal peoples elsewhere. Although subjected to scientific scrutiny only in some regions, notably northern Canada, Alaska and Greenland, there is no evidence of any but localized declines in the populations.

Bounties and culls by authorities have been used to reduce populations of seals perceived as threats to fishermen. Today, apparently only Grey seals in Britain, Iceland, Norway and Canada are subject to such controversial controls, although other seals are shot without official sanction. IAM

THE 19 SPECIES OF TRUE SEALS

Mediterranean monk seal E
Monachus monachus

Main population in Aegean and E Mediterranean seas, also in SW Black Sea, C and W Mediterrancan, Adriatic Sea, and Atlantic around Madeira, the Canaries, and Spanish Sahara. Population 500–700. Male HTL about 250cm; wt about 260kg. Female HTL 270cm; wt 300kg. Coat: dark above, gray below, sometimes with large white area. Newborn with black lanugo. Female first young and male age of maturity unknown. Longevity unknown. Births May–November, peak September–October, generally now in caves and grottos in sea cliffs. Lactation 6 weeks? Males possibly polygnous, mating in water; social structure unknown, although somewhat gregarious. Diet: fishes and octopus, some quite large.

Caribbean monk seal E
Monachus tropicalis

Last reliable sighting in 1952; probably extinct. Historically in Florida Keys, Bahamas, Greater and Lesser Antilles, Yucatan, on offshore islets and atolls. HTL about 220cm; wt about 200kg? Coat: dark above and light below, the latter less extensive in females? Newborn with dark lanugo. In form, evidently closer to Mediterranean monk seal than to Hawaiian monk seal. Reproductive characteristics and longevity unknown. Births in December. Other features of life history unknown.

Hawaiian monk seal E
Monachus schauinslandi

Breeds regularly on 6 atolls of the NW Hawaiian Islands and comes ashore on 3 others, but rarely elsewhere. Population 500–1,000. Male HTL about 210cm; wt about 170kg. Female HTL about 230cm; wt about 250kg. Coat: dark above, pale below. Newborn with dark lanugo. Like *M. tropicalis*, but perhaps the most primitive of all phocids in structure of posterior *vena cava*, of ear region of skull, and in the unfused bases of the tibia and fibula. Female first young about 5 years, male maturity unknown. Longevity: 30 years. About two-thirds of adult females give birth each year in January–August, on beaches. Lactation 6 weeks. Males may harass females with pups, but mate later in water. Diet: fishes, cephalopods.

Crabeater seal
Lobodon carcinophagus

Distributed throughout antarctic pack ice, most abundantly near the broken periphery in the southern winter, in residual ice nearer the continent in summer. Has strayed as far north as Heard Island, S Africa, Uruguay, N New Zealand, S Australia. World population 15+ million? Both sexes HTL 235cm; wt about 220kg. Coat: uniform, usually pale gray, sometimes darker; immature darker and may be somewhat mottled. Often heavily scarred from fights with other Crabeaters and Leopard seals. Newborn with brownish or grayish lanugo. A rather slender, small-headed species. Cheek teeth elaborately multicuspid for straining macroplanktonic food. Female first young 2.3–4.5 years, according to year and region. Male maturity about 4.5 years. Longevity: male 30+ years, female 36 years. Births on pack ice in September–October. Lactation 4 weeks? Males form "triads" with female and pup, sequestering female until she is ready to mate on the ice. Generally non-gregarious, but young may form (protective?) groups. After breeding, continue to use ice floes to rest and as escape from Killer whales and Leopard seals. Diet: predominantly krill, also some fishes, squids.

Weddell seal
Leptonychotes weddelli

The most southerly seal, breeding in fast ice around Antarctica and on islands north to S Georgia. Has strayed as far north as Uruguay, Juan Fernandez Island, N New Zealand, S Australia, Kerguelen. World population about 1 million? Male HTL 250cm; wt 390kg. Female HTL 270cm; wt 450kg. Coat: gray, darker above, mottled with black, gray and whitish blotches. Newborn with brownish-gray lanugo. Canines and two large, protruding incisors often worn from "sawing" at ice holes. Female first young about 3 years, male maturity about 4 years, but probably breeding successfully only when older. Longevity: male 21 years, female 25 years. Births on fast ice, rarely on islands, mid-September to early November. Lactation 5–6 weeks. Adult females along ice cracks are spaced in relation to holes for access to water. Adult males vocalize, display and fight under the ice along such cracks to mate in elongated "territories," or may simply prevent access to breathing holes by other males. Adults later join immatures at edges of fast ice and rest on ice floes, rarely land. Diet: mostly fishes (some large), cephalopods, some krill, bottom invertebrates (secured by deep-diving).

Leopard seal
Hydrurga leptonyx

Found generally near the fringes on the antarctic pack ice and around subantarctic islands. May show periodic dispersal northward; has strayed as far north as Sydney, Australia, Rarotonga in the Cook Islands, S Africa, Tristan da Cunha, N Argentina. World population about 500,000? Male HTL 280cm; wt about 325kg. Female HTL 300cm; wt about 370kg. Coat: dark gray above, pale below, with light and dark spots on throat, shoulders and sides. Newborn with lanugo resembling adult pattern. Bodies elongate, heads large and jaws massive, set with saw-like cheek teeth. Female first young about 6 years, male maturity about 5 years. Longevity: male 23+ years, female 26+ years. Births in November–December on loose pack ice, occasionally on islands. Lactation 4 weeks? Males not seen with females and young on ice. Female may only reproduce in alternate years? Usually found in association with Crabeater seals and large colonies of penguins, which form prey; diet also includes fishes, some krill.

Ross seal
Ommatophoca rossi

Found sparsely and patchily throughout Southern Ocean. Has strayed to Heard Island. World population 100,000–220,000? HTL about 200cm ?; wt about 180kg ?, with little sexual difference? Coat: dark above, silvery-white below, with light and dark flecks, and with light and dark stripes from chin to chest and sometimes along sides of neck. Lanugo of newborn has pattern similar to adult coat. A thick-necked, short-muzzled, large-eyed species, with long foreflippers. Incisors and canines sharp and recurved to secure slippery prey, but cheek teeth small, often loose or missing. Female first young about 4 years, male maturity about 4 years. Longevity: male 21 years, female 19 years. Births in November on pack ice. Lactation period unknown. Males make trilling sounds with larynx. Non-gregarious, patchy distribution probably related to preference for more productive waters, not for very dense pack ice as previously supposed. Diet: mainly squids, some fishes and occasionally bottom invertebrates.

Northern elephant seal
Mirounga angustirostris

Breeds on islands from central California to central Baja California, mostly on the Channel Islands; some recently on mainland sites. After breeding and molting, disperses northward, a few as far as S Alaska. World population about 55,000. Male HTL about 420cm; wt about 2,300kg. Female HTL about 310cm; wt about 900kg. Coat: silvery when young, becoming darker above with age. Newborn with black lanugo. Males become corrugated and heavily scarred in thick-skinned neck region, and develop pendulous, inflatable enlargement of nasal cavity. Canines very large, cheek teeth peg-like, but sometimes with cusps and double roots. Female first young about 4 years, male maturity about 4.5 years, sexually competent when 9–10 years old. Longevity: male and female 14 years. Births on islands mid-December through January. Lactation 4 weeks. Females group on beaches after smaller number of large males establish dominance hierarchies by vocalizations, displays, combat. A single male may mate with up to 80 females in a season. After breeding season, largely offshore. Diet: bottom and mid-water fishes, some squids.

Southern elephant seal
Mirounga leonina

Breeds mostly on islands both sides of Antarctic Convergence, in 3 separate groups, perhaps subspecies (another group eliminated on Juan Fernandez Island): 1) S Georgia, Falkland, Gough, S Shetland islands, islands and mainland of Antarctic Peninsula, Patagonia north to Valdes Peninsula; 2) Kerguelen, Heard, Marion, and Crozet islands; 3) Macquarie and Campbell islands. Scattered births found elsewhere, north to S Africa, S Island of New Zealand, Tasmania, Tristan da Cunha. Migrates to Antarctic mainland and has strayed north to S Australia, Mauritius and Rodriguez Island, Uruguay, Peru, N New Zealand. World population about 650,000. Male HTL 490cm; wt 2,400kg (S Georgia). Female HTL 300cm; wt 680kg (S Georgia). Male HTL 425cm (Macquarie Island).

Female 265cm (Macquarie Island). Coat: silvery when young, darker with age, especially in female. Newborn with black lanugo. Adult males with thick, scarred neck shield, proboscis less developed than in Northern elephant seal. Skull generally more massive than in Northern elephant seal, and cheek teeth never (?) cuspid or double-rooted. Female first young 4.2 years at S Georgia, 5.6 years at Macquarie Island, male maturity about 4 years, sexually competent at 9+ years at S Georgia, 8+ years at Macquarie Island. Longevity: male 20 years, female 18 years. Births on shore, occasionally shore ice, late September and October. Lactation 3–3.5 weeks. Breeding behavior as in Northern elephant seal, but single males may defend "harem" of up to 50 females, or "share" much larger aggregations, in which the sex ratio may reach 300 females to each male, with some male exchanges during the season. After breeding, disperse widely, molting ashore in January–April. Diet: fishes (often large), squid.

Bearded seal
Erignathus barbatus

Circumpolar in relatively shallow arctic and subarctic waters, south to S Labrador, S Greenland, N Iceland, White Sea, Hokkaido, Alaska Peninsula. Has strayed to Tokyo Bay, Cape Cod, N Spain. World population 0.6–1 million? Atlantic subspecies E. b. barbatus weakly distinct from E. b. nauticus, found from W Canadian Arctic to central Siberia. HTL both sexes 220–230cm, wt 235–260kg in various localities; HTL 200cm, wt 190kg in Okhotsk Sea. Coat: gray above, rarely with few faint spots. Newborn lanugo dark brown, often with light spots on back and head. Four mammae (2 in other northern seals); large crinkled whiskers. Skull with deep jaw, teeth rudimentary and often missing when older. Female first young 6.5–7.2 years, various regions, male maturity 5.5 years Bering Sea. Longevity: male 25 years, female 31 years. Births on pack ice mid-March to late April. Lactation 2 weeks. Males "sing" underwater during the breeding season. Solitary individuals rest on ice floes when available, some on land in Okhotsk Sea. Diet: bottom-dwelling mollusks, crustaceans, sea cucumbers and fishes.

Hooded seal
Cystophora cristata

Breeds in Gulf of St. Lawrence; northeast of Newfoundland; in Davis Strait; northwest of Jan Mayen Island; occasionally near White Sea. Migrates to summer mainly in waters off Greenland, with large molting region in Danmark Strait. Has given birth on land in Norway, Maine, and strayed to N Alaska, Florida, S Portugal. World population 250,000–400,000? Male HTL about 250cm; wt about 400kg. Female HTL 220cm; wt 320kg. Coat: both sexes gray with large black blotches and spots and black heads. Pale lanugo shed before birth, the newborn silvery with dark back. Mature male can inflate "hood" on snout and force nasal membrane through either nostril as red "balloon." Skull heavy, with 2 lower, 4 upper incisors, large canines and peg-like cheek teeth. Female first young about 4.5 years, male maturity about 5 years but mating only when older. Longevity: male 34 years, female 35+ years. Loose aggregations of females give birth mid-March to early April on old, heavy ice floes. Lactation 10–14 days. Female and pup attended by one male, rarely more, which uses "hood" in aggressive displays and calls under water. Rests on ice, rarely land, at other seasons. Diet: deepwater fishes, eg redfish, Greenland halibut, and squid.

Harbor seal
Phoca vitulina
Harbor or Common seal.

In N Atlantic, Murmansk to outer Baltic and N France, UK south to E Anglia, S Ireland, Faroes, Spitsbergen, Iceland, SE and W Greenland, Canadian Arctic south to Cape Cod; in N Pacific region from Bristol Bay, Pribilof, Aleutian, Commander islands, south to central Baja California and Hokkaido. Has strayed to Florida and Azores. World population 300,000–400,000? Male HTL 160–170cm; wt 110–120kg. Female HTL 150–170cm; wt 80–90kg (most of range); in Kurile Islands and Hokkaido, the distinctive subspecies P. v. stejnegeri is larger and more sexually dimorphic (male HTL about 200cm, wt about 185kg; female HTL 170cm, wt 120kg). Coat: varies from pale to dark gray, and ringed; P. v. stejnegeri all (?) dark. Whitish lanugo shed before birth, occasionally soon after. Dog-like face with teeth set obliquely in jaws. Large male

P. v. stejnegeri with more arched skulls. Female first young 4.8–6.2 years, male maturity 4.8–5.9 years, in various populations. Longevity: male 26 years, female 32 years. Births on land January–September in wide range, generally late spring. Rests on islets, rocks, sandbars, sometimes ice, generally in inshore waters. A few freshwater populations in E and N Canada; wanders up rivers elsewhere. Adults relatively sedentary, young dispersing. Diet: migratory, bottom-dwelling and open-sea fishes, some invertebrates.

Spotted seal
Phoca largha

Separate populations in Bering and Chukchi Seas, Okhotsk Sea to Hokkaido, Tartar Strait, Peter the Great Bay, Po Hai and N Yellow Sea. Some geographical variation in this range. World population about 400,000? Male HTL 156cm; wt 90kg. Female HTL 150cm; wt 80kg (Bering and Okhotsk Seas); some 10cm longer and 15kg heavier near Hokkaido and in Peter the Great Bay. Coat: typically light gray, darker above, with many small, dark spots, as in light form of Harbor seal. Born with whitish lanugo. Unlike closely related Harbor seal, teeth set straight in jaws. Female first young about 5 years, male maturity about 4.5 years. Longevity: male 29 years, female 32 years. Births in mid-February to April, latest in north, on ice floes near margin of pack ice in Bering Sea, closer to shore elsewhere. Lactation 3–4 weeks. Male, female and pup in "triads" scattered widely on ice. Moves to coasts in summer, resting on land and sometimes entering rivers. Diet: migratory and shallow-water bottom fishes, some invertebrates.

Ringed seal
Phoca (=Pusa) hispida

Circumpolar in arctic and subarctic waters, breeding south to White Sea, Norway, N Iceland, S Greenland, N Gulf of St. Lawrence, Alaska Peninsula, S Sakhalin, with isolates in inner Baltic and nearby Lakes Ladoga, Saima. Has strayed to S Portugal, C California, S Japan. World population 3.5–6 million? Much variation in body and skull measurements expressed as 7–8 subspecies, most doubtful. Male HTL 124–150cm; wt 65–95kg. Female HTL 116–138cm; wt 45–80kg (various populations). Large fast-ice and small pack-ice forms in Canadian

Arctic, Okhotsk and Bering–Chukchi Seas may result from differing lengths of lactation period and local population traditions. Coat: silvery to dark gray below, darker on back, with rings on sides and back. Born with white lanugo. Short muzzle, with fine, cuspid teeth. Female first young 5.8–8.3 years, male maturity 7.1–7.4 years, various populations. Longevity: male 43 years, female 40 years. Births March–April in snow lairs over breathing holes in fast ice, sometimes in open on pack ice. Lactation up to 2.5 months in fast ice, shorter in unstable ice. Males call underwater and may be "territorial." Rests on ice, rarely land. Diet: inshore: polar cod, bottom-dwelling crustaceans; offshore: planktonic crustaceans, some fishes.

Baikal seal
Phoca (=Pusa) sibirica

Lake Baikal (USSR), mainly in deeper parts. Population about 70,000. HTL 122cm; wt 72kg (mean of both sexes). Coat: silver-gray, darker above, and unspotted. Born with white lanugo. Skull foreshortened, with large eye sockets. Claws on foreflippers heavier than in Ringed and Caspian seals, for keeping holes open in freshwater ice? Female first young 5.3 years, male maturity about 5 years. Longevity: male 52 years, female 56 years. Births in late February to early April in solitary snow lairs, as in Ringed seal. Lactation 8–10 weeks. Diet: largely deep-water fishes.

Caspian seal
Phoca (=Pusa) caspica

Caspian Sea, concentrating in north during breeding season, and in cooler, deeper middle and south of the lake during summer. Population about 450,000. HTL about 125cm; wt 55kg (both sexes). Coat: gray, darker on back with fine dark spots. Newborn with white lanugo. Skull like Ringed seal's. Female first young 6.8 years, male maturity 6.6 years. Longevity: male 47 years, female 50 years. Aggregations of females give birth in late January to early February on pack ice north of Kulaly Island. Lactation 2 weeks. After ice melt, occasionally remain on islets and rocks. Diet: wide range of small fishes, crustaceans.

CONTINUED ▶

Harp seal

Phoca (= Pagophilus) groenlandica

Discrete populations breed off NE Newfoundland and in Gulf of St. Lawrence, around Jan Mayen Island and near mouth of White Sea, summering in Kara and Barents Seas and in waters off Greenland and the Canadian Arctic Archipelago. Has strayed to Mackenzie Delta, Virginia, Scotland and France. World population 2.6–3.8 million. HTL 170cm; wt 130kg (mean both sexes in NW Atlantic, slightly larger elsewhere). Coat: light gray with dark brown spots in juveniles, some subadult males becoming very dark, developing dark, U-shaped "harp" on back of gray adult, more slowly and less contrastingly in female. Newborn with white lanugo. A rather slender, active species, with small, cuspid teeth. Female first young 5.5 years in NW Atlantic, about 5 years in White Sea, male maturity 4 years in White Sea. Longevity: male 29 years, female 30+ years. Gregarious females give birth among hummocks near middle of large floes, mid-February to March in White Sea, slightly later at Jan Mayen Island and in NW Atlantic. Lactation 9–12 days. Females then join underwater aggregations of vocalizing, displaying males for mating. Migrate and spend summer in sometimes large and fast-moving groups, sometimes resting on ice. Diet: capelin and other fishes, shrimps and krill (especially by young seals) in south; polar cod, planktonic amphipods in north.

Ribbon seal

Phoca (= Histrophoca) fasciata

Breeds in Bering and Okhotsk Seas, with populations from the former summering in Chukchi Sea. Has strayed to Beaufort and E Siberian Seas, S Hokkaido, C California. World population about 180,000? HTL 160cm; wt 95kg (both sexes; little geographical variation). Coat: in young silvery, dark above, becoming uniformly darker with age, except for distinct bands around neck, hind torso and each foreflipper. Born with whitish lanugo. Skull foreshortened, with small teeth, large eye sockets. Female first young 3.3 years in Okhotsk Sea, 3.8 years in Bering Sea; male maturity 3.1 years in Okhotsk Sea, 3.5 years in Bering Sea. Longevity: male 31 years, female 23 years. Births on heavier pack ice than for Spotted seal, mainly in early April. Lactation 3–4 weeks. Males not seen with scattered females and pups. Stay offshore after melt. Diet: open-sea fishes, shrimps, cephalopods in deeper water; the young eat krill.

Grey seal

Halichoerus grypus

Three populations distinct in breeding seasons and, weakly, in form are: *H. g. grypus* in NW Atlantic from S Greenland (formerly?) and S Labrador to Massachusetts; *H. g. atlanticus* in NE Atlantic from Spitsbergen (formerly) and Murmansk coast to S Iceland, UK, S Ireland; *H. g. balticus* in inner Baltic. Has strayed to New Jersey, S Portugal, N Labrador. World population 120,000–135,000. Male HTL 213cm, wt 270kg; female HTL 183cm, wt 140kg (Northumberland). Male HTL 228cm; wt 330kg; female HTL 200cm, wt 170kg (Nova Scotia). Coat: male heavily dark-spotted, sometimes black, female gray, darker above, with black spots and blotches below. Born with whitish lanugo. Snout elongate and arched, especially in adult male, which also develops heavy, scarred neck region. Large peg-like teeth. Female first young 5.5 years in UK, 5.0 years in Nova Scotia, male maturity about 6 years in Scotland, 4.2 years in Nova Scotia, but does not mate until about 8–10 years old. Longevity: male 31 years (43 in captivity), female: 46 years. Births on land in NE Atlantic group during September–December, on pack ice in Baltic during February–March, and on land or ice in NW Atlantic in January–February. Lactation 2–2.5 weeks. Males territorial or aggressive but mobile among grouped females, perhaps polygynous on ice. At other seasons, often on offshore islets and rocks. Diet: migratory, open-sea and bottom fishes (often large specimens), some invertebrates.

IAM

▶ **Elephant of the oceans.** The massive nose of the Northern elephant seal leaves no doubt as to how it got its name. Elephant seals show the most extreme disparity in form between male and female to be found in true seals. The nasal protuberance of the males is the primary organ of sexual display.

The Krill-eating Crabeater

The world's most abundant large mammal

The Crabeater seal is a creature of superlatives. It numbers 15–40 million, which is at least equal to the total for all the other pinnipeds combined (the total weight of the population is about four times or more that of all other pinnipeds combined); it occupies a range of up to 22 million sq km (8.5 million sq mi), the maximum extent of the antarctic pack ice, but as the pack ice contracts in summer it is confined to six residual pack-ice regions totalling 4 million sq km (1.6 million sq mi); it feeds on the swarming Antarctic krill, the abundance of which has been estimated at 500–750 million tonnes, and which is possibly the most abundant animal species, by weight.

The Crabeater seal is a key species in the Southern Ocean and there is evidence that it has now overtaken the baleen whales as the major consumer of krill, possibly eating up to 160 million tonnes a year. As the commercially sought baleen whales declined during this century due to over-hunting by man (see pp226–227), certain other krill-feeding birds, seals and whales have increased. In the case of the Crabeaters, the body growth-rates appear to have accelerated so that they mature earlier: at 2.5

years now compared with 4 years in 1950; this, together with the fact that up to 94 percent of mature females may be pregnant at any one time, and a life span of up to 39 years, indicates an expanding population.

Despite their huge overall population, Crabeaters seals are fairly sparsely distributed. During the summer, recorded mean group sizes are 1.3–2.2; the densities are 2–7 per sq km (5–18 per sq mi) and they haul-out during the day, with maximum counts around midday. They feed mainly at night when krill are nearer the surface.

The Crabeater pupping season lasts for 4–6 weeks and is highly synchronized, with a peak in early to mid-October. Until recently, very little was known about their breeding behavior because of the difficulty of reaching their breeding populations in the remote southern pack ice, but in 1977 an expedition set out with this objective.

The basic social unit is the mother and the milk-coffee-colored, furry pup, which select a hummocked floe and remain together for no more than a few weeks until the pup is weaned, growing from 25kg (55lb) to 120kg (264lb) solely on the mother's milk. They are joined by an adult male to form a

▲ **Jaws agape,** a young Crabeater seal, displays its elaborately cusped teeth used for straining from the sea, krill, its principal and almost exclusive food.

▶ **Not a nuclear family.** This triad of male, female and pup Crabeaters is not quite what it seems. The male is not the father of the pup, is aggressive to both mother and pup and is merely waiting for the opportunity to mate with the female when the pup has been weaned. Prior to mating, the male drives the mother away from the pup.

▼ **Basking Crabeaters** on an ice floe. The Crabeater seal is almost exclusively a creature of the antarctic pack ice. The spotted animal in the foreground is a Weddell seal.

triad which persists until the pup is weaned. These groups are usually separated by 1–2km (0.6–1.2mi). On average, the female is slightly larger than the male and drives him away from the pup with an agression that fades as the pup grows and her own condition weakens. The male is very aggressive and persistent in trying to stay with the female, and the pup is weaned when the male becomes dominant and drives the female away from it. Other males occasionally approach the family group over the ice, when a fight ensues lasting up to six minutes. The mated pairs are very obvious because the female's back is red where she has been bitten by the male and the rear half of her body is very thin. Mating occurs, it is thought, on the floe, a few days after weaning. Soon the pairs break up and solitary females are seen. As a result of fights with both males and females the old male Crabeaters are heavily scarred about the head and neck.

Many Leopard seals (see pp290–291) occur in the leads (the channels of open water between the floes) and these prey on the Crabeaters. They bob up to look over the surface of floes, turning their heads from side to side in a sinister, questing way. Leopard seals have been seen eating weaned Crabeater pups in the water; one chased a yearling Crabeater with great speed and energy—three times the Crabeater exploded from the water onto a floe, hotly pursued by the Leopard seal, which made a supreme effort but just failed to catch it and gave up the chase. However, young weaned pups must be easy prey for they do not swim with such agility. Leopard seals preferentially take weaned Crabeaters in the spring, but as these pups grow throughout the summer and become more experienced, the probability of escape increases, although up to 84 percent of those escaping receive wounds, which are visible as parallel scars on most adults. When the new crop of weaned Crabeaters appears the Leopard seals switch to this easier prey. The age-composition of the Crabeater population reflects high mortality in the first year, but subsequently annual mortality is relatively low.

Such predation may have played an important role in the evolution of Crabeater behavior, resulting in mating on the floes (although this has yet to be confirmed), because pre-mating behavior underwater would presumably attract these predators and possibly Killer whales. It may also explain widely dispersed family groups, because fewer larger groups would be more vulnerable to predation.   RML

Birth in a Snow-cave
The lairs of the Ringed seal

As the winter pack ice thickens and snow builds up around pressure ridges in the ice, pregnant Ringed seals dig upwards with their foreflippers from the water below, to create a lair or snow-cave. Here the pup is born and spends the first one or two months. This behavior is unique among seals.

The Ringed seal is only about half the size of other true seals. The name derives from its distinctive coat pattern of dark spots surrounded by a white ring, scattered over the gray-brown fur. It is one of the most numerous and successful of northern true seals, with a circumpolar distribution, although the Baltic population is declining.

During the winter, Ringed seals live on land-fast ice, although pack ice may sometimes be used as long as it is well-consolidated and stable. In early winter, they use the open leads and cracks in the ice for access to the air, but as the ice thickens they must claw at the ice with their foreflippers to maintain breathing holes. Around these holes, the accumulating snow is excavated to form a small cave. Both sexes excavate hauling-out lairs, but the pupping lairs, perhaps up to three within 100m (330ft) of each other, are constructed by females alone. This complex of birth lairs probably provides alternative refuges to which a female can move her pup if danger threatens.

The lair is thought to give the pups some protection from predation by Polar bears, Arctic foxes and man. But the lairs are quite conspicuous, and predation rates by Arctic foxes on newborn pups may be as as high as 58 percent. It may be that the benefit the lair confers in keeping the pup warm until its insulating blubber is laid down may outweigh this risk of predation.

In the Baltic, pups are born from late February to late March, about one month earlier than in the Canadian Arctic. Each female's single pup bears a white fluffy coat and weighs about 5kg (11lb). Pups are suckled for 6–7 weeks. It is possible that the female feeds during this time; otherwise the demands of lactation and her own body requirements might deplete her blubber stores too quickly. Females lose up to 40 percent of their body weight during the spring and early summer.

Females become receptive towards the end of the lactation period, and mating occurs under the ice. Little is known of their sexual behavior because of the difficulties of observation beneath the ice, but the Ringed seal appears to be very similar in many ways to the much larger Weddell seal of the Antarctic. Male Weddell seals defend under-

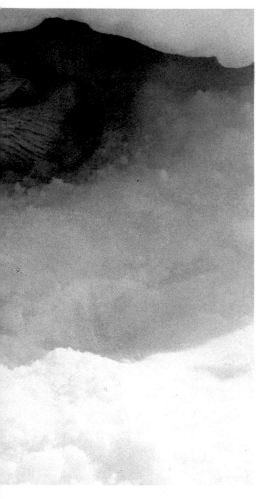

▲ **Pup peering out of a lair.** The pups spend up to two months in the lair before being weaned.

◄ **Birth in a snow-cave.** The Ringed seal exploits the build-up of snow around pressure points in the ice to hollow out a lair in which to give birth.

▶ **Adult Ringed seal** on Lake Saima, Finland, showing the distinctive markings: pale rings scattered over a dark gray coat. The population of this isolated subspecies (*P.h. saimensis*) is estimated at 100–120 individuals and they give birth on ice but not in ice lairs.

water territories and are thought to exhibit a limited form of polygyny, in that they try to prevent access to the females by other males. Male Ringed seals often carry wounds which could well be the result of territorial disputes within a similar social system. However, the sex ratio of adult Ringed seals is equal and birth lair complexes are widely spaced, so it is unlikely that males could defend more than one at a time.

The only time that Ringed seals haul out in large numbers on the ice is immediately after pupping. In the spring sunshine, the ice begins to crack and seals butt and scratch at the snow roof of their haul-out lairs to make an exit. A few mothers may still be suckling their pups, but most of the adults laze on the ice for days or more at a time, doing very little except scratching and being vigilant for predators. The molt occurs during this time on the ice surface, and the seals scratch incessantly. Sun-bathing is also important, in that high skin temperatures help the molting process. The pups have already molted within their lairs, shedding their white birth coat for the first adult coat.

As the ice melts, the seals disperse, adopting an open-sea existence for the short arctic summer. They feed intensively to replace their depleted blubber. By mid-fall thin ice covers the bays and the annual cycle begins again.

In the Canadian Arctic, the Ringed seal is the most numerous marine mammal, but the Baltic population has declined markedly during this century. Because of the difficulties of counting seals in their lairs, estimates of numbers can only be crude, but it appears that a population once numbered in hundreds of thousands is now reduced to about 10,000. Overhunting has been a major cause of decline, but now the species is fully protected.

Recently, a more insidious threat has been implicated—pollution by organochlorine compounds, in particular polychlorinated biphenyls (PCBs). The reproductive rate of Ringed seals in the Baltic has declined sharply: in the Canadian Arctic 80–90 percent of mature females are pregnant in one year, but in the Baltic the figure is now less than 25 percent. Associated with this lack of fertility are abnormalities of the female reproductive tract which have been linked with high levels of PCBs in seal tissue. As fertility has declined, so has the age of maturity. Baltic Ringed seals of both sexes now mature at 3 years of age, whereas 40 years ago the age of maturity was 5. Such a change often occurs when a population declines, thus easing competition for food. A direct causative link between PCBs and reduced fertility remains to be established, but the decline in the population of Ringed seals in the Baltic is giving cause for serious concern.   SSA

Beach Warfare

Sexual conflict among Northern elephant seals

"The battle between the sexes" which is a perennial subject for cartoonists and humorists is a serious and fascinating study for evolutionary biologists, and nowhere is it more vivid than within the society of Northern elephant seals.

The most striking thing about elephant seals is that males and females look and act differently. The disparity in size is so marked that it would be understandable to mistake the sexes for different species. Males are at least three times the weight of the females and they have two outstanding secondary sexual characteristics: a pendulous, elephantine proboscis and a thick shield of wrinkled tissue on the neck and chest. They engage in bloody fights for the dominant status which confers access to groups of females. The few males that achieve the highest status monopolize mating. The alpha male (the dominant of dominants) alone may inseminate 100 females in one breeding season and four times that number in his lifetime.

This is what is known as a polygynous mating system. The male is a father in only the genetic sense, for males exhibit no paternal behavior. Females look like a larger version of the juveniles and, unlike males, they are gregarious, gathering together in groups or harems of up to 1,000 individuals to give birth and nurse their young. Virtually all adult females give birth to a single pup annually throughout their lives. If a female starts reproducing early, at three years old, and lives long, to 14 years, she may produce a maximum of 12 pups in her lifetime.

From the moment that females appear on the sandy island beaches of California and Mexico where they breed, they are hounded by males eager to mate with them. Males not only pursue receptive females, they direct their attention to females that do not want to mate and are not yet capable of being inseminated. These include pregnant females, females giving birth and nursing females.

Male courtship is direct, aggressive and relentless. Without preliminaries, a male moves directly to the side of a female, puts a foreflipper over her back, bites her on the neck, pulls her strongly to him, and attempts to copulate. If the female protests or attempts to move away, as is usually the case, the male pins her down by slamming the full weight of his head and forequarters on her back one or more times and bites her more vigorously.

In these sexual disagreements, the outcome is usually bad for the female. Mounting is harmful for pregnant females: it disrupts the mother-pup bonding process in females giving birth and it interrupts feeding and causes mother-pup separation when nursing mothers are involved. Moreover, in their single-minded efforts to chase subordinates out of the harem or to evade a superior, males trample over pups in their path. Up to 10 percent of the pups born in one season may die in this way. After a four-week nursing period, at the end of which mating occurs with a high ranking male in the harem, females face a more serious peril as they attempt to return to sea. They must run the gauntlet of several peripheral males surrounding the harem. These males intercept departing females and compete fiercely to mate with them. In their zeal to outdo each other, males sometimes injure and kill females inadvertently. All that a female can do in these disagreements is to make it difficult for young, low-ranking males to mate. Females protest vocally at all attempts to mate with them. This signals to all males in the vicinity that a female is being mounted. If a male dominant to the mounter is nearby, he chases him off and usually continues the sexual assault himself.

Clearly, mating in this species is not a cooperative venture where two individuals combine efforts to produce an offspring. Rather, the impression is that the large males dominate the smaller females and selfishly take what they want, being constrained only by energy limitations or by each other. Females do the best they can under the circumstances. How has this strategy evolved?

The differences in form and behavior between the sexes, and their conflict, so apparent in this species, evolved in part because of the disparity in reproductive potential between them. Gestation severely constrains productivity of females and sets the stage for two entirely different reproductive strategies: one emphasizes quantity and the other quality of offspring produced. For males, the mating game is to gain membership of an exclusive breeding club. A one year membership is all that is needed to hit the genetic jackpot, although a male may retain dominant status for up to four years. However, the club has stringent entrance requirements such as great size, fighting ability and sexual prowess, and since a male must become a member or he doesn't breed, he is compelled to take risks to increase his chances. For example, newly weaned male pups risk injury by attempting to steal milk from nursing females in the harem. If successful, they may double their

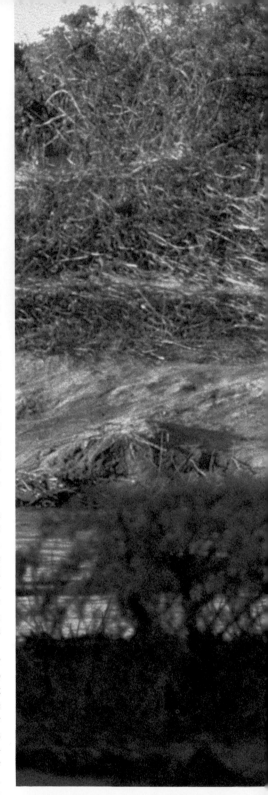

▲ **Battle for dominance.** Rearing their necks, two bull Northern elephant seals strive for mastery of a segment of a breeding beach. The neck, which is toughened, and the huge nasal protuberance bear the brunt of these attacks.

◄ **Irony of reproduction.** In his selfish urge to mate, a lumbering bull elephant seal has trapped a pup between himself and the cow. Many pups are crushed to death by the bulls, but not normally their own kin.

weight and obtain additional nutrients important in development at a time when other weaned pups are losing weight and energy reserves. This early advantage usually leads to increased size in adulthood, which in turn is linked to fighting success and social rank achieved. Female pups do not attempt to steal milk because the potential benefits do not outweigh the risks. The female strategy is to work hard to ensure the survival of the limited number of pups she produces. There is no jackpot here but a small steady flow of winnings.

Why, then, is the difference in size between males and females more extreme in the Northern elephant seal than in any other seal? We can only speculate on this, but it may be that the distribution (in this case, clumping) and relative abundance of resources (either food or suitable breeding sites, or both) provide an opportunity for males to monopolize large numbers of females at these sites, and inter-male competition for the females (requiring great strength and endurance) consequently becomes intense.

BLeB

Culling the Whitecoats
The controversial fate of the Harp seal

The Harp seal is the most numerous pinniped of the North Atlantic Ocean, despite periods of overexploitation. It inhabits the fringes of the pack ice and undergoes extensive migrations necessitated by the seasonal freezing and melting of the ice. The coats of the young—"whitecoats"—have been highly prized and the Harp seal's fecundity has allowed a substantial cull to be taken every year without diminishing the population.

Harp seals are divided into three stocks, pupping in the White Sea, near Jan Mayen Island east of Greenland, and on both sides of Newfoundland. These give birth respectively in late February, late March, and late February to mid-March (in each area, this is the time when daytime melting of the leads begins).

At the time of reproduction in early spring, adult females form aggregations of several tens of thousands on close, one-winter pack ice, which they reach from the leads of open water. They maintain an individual distance, displaying to each other with head pointed vertically, and snarling. The ice may drift at 1.5km/h (1mph) or more and have a subsequent life of a few weeks only; a premium is therefore placed on rapid development, and the whitecoat grows from 8kg (18lb) at birth to 35kg (77lb) at 10–14 days when it is weaned. It then starves for several weeks and sheds its lanugo before beginning to enter the water to feed on krill and small fish. The adult males rest in groups within the whelping patches, but are aggressive to each other and extremely vocal underwater amongst the ice floes. Mating takes place, mainly in the water, when the pup is weaned. Development of the embryo is arrested at an early stage and then resumes in late July or August. At the time of mating, the adults leave the ice floes and the pups soon begin to enter the water among the loose ice floes and start to feed.

The animals haul out on pack ice again about a month after whelping, and are then not aggressive to each other and are highly aggregated. The immature animals and adult males begin to molt, starting in late March at Newfoundland, and the females arrive later, in late April at Newfoundland, after a phase of fattening which follows the heavy drain of food reserves due to lactation.

Each stock of Harp seals probably originally numbered 3 million animals. Each was subject to heavy hunting, beginning in the 18th century, when a number of north European nations, engaged in taking Bowhead whales, added a catch of Harp seals in the spring months. The people living around the White Sea in arctic Russia, and the early settlers of Newfoundland, started sealing from shore and from small craft in order to find a source of revenue in the winter months when fishing was not possible. Although ice and storms protected the seals from rapid overexploitation, each stock eventually became depleted, the Newfoundland stock twice (in the mid-19th and mid-20th centuries, with a phase of recovery between). The hunting of all three stocks has now been controlled by the governments of Norway, the USSR, Denmark (for Greenland) and Canada. Protective measures have included, in succession: a prohibition against shooting adult females at the whelping patches, a closing date for hunting of molters and, finally, a quota on the killing of pups. These measures have allowed recovery of the White Sea herd to a present level of 0.75 million or more, and of the Newfoundland herds to 1.5 million or more, though Norway has kept the Jan Mayen herd at about 0.25 million animals in order to prevent excessive predation by Harp seals on its important fishery for capelin in the Barents Sea. Present pup production at Newfoundland is estimated from capture-recapture tagging at about 400,000 and a recent catch of 180,000, mostly pups and young immatures, is believed to be allowing an increase of the

▲ **Death of a whitecoat.** The Harp seal population is no longer in danger from exploitation, so the case against culling rests on its intrinsic unpleasantness.

▼ **Pack-ice patrol.** Harp seals in an open lead between the pack ice of the Gulf of St. Lawrence, Canada. Harp seal migrations follow the freezing and melting of the pack ice.

▲ **Tearful, large eyes** and creamy coat of a Harp seal pup show just why there is so much public resistance to the practice of clubbing them to death. Even if it is allowed to survive, this stage of life is very short: weaning takes 10–14 days and the birth coat is shed a few weeks later.

population at about 5 percent per annum.

The principal goal of the hunt in recent decades has been pups of all stages, especially the young, fast-haired whitecoats and the fully-molted "beaters," valuable for their hair coats and oil. While a controlled kill of young seals gives a higher production than a kill of the biologically more valuable adults (especially the females), and killing of the pups can be humane, public reaction has set in against the killing of the attractive whitecoats in the presence of their mothers. Public opinion moreover has been skillfully manipulated by confusing the issue of humane killing with the alleged overexploitation of the herds, which is no longer a valid issue, as discussed above. The sealers, who include northern hunters and fishermen-hunters, therefore face economic deprivation at a time when successful management of the seal herds has been achieved, a distressing irony.   DES

The Rarest Seals

Saving the imperiled Monk seals

Monk seals are the only pinnipeds that live in warm, subtropical seas. Of the three species, the Caribbean monk seal is probably extinct; the two remaining species are both imperiled, such that rapid action is required to save them. Overall, numbers have declined by half within the last 30 years because of human interference. There are estimated to be about 500 Mediterranean monk seals, and the number of Hawaiian monk seals may be closer to this than to the figure of 1,000 often quoted.

The Hawaiian monk seal has been described as a "living fossil." Certain anatomical characteristics of the species (eg the bony structure of the ear) are at a more primitive stage developmentally than those found in seal fossils dating back some 14.5 million years (man's first upright ancestors appeared only about 3 million years ago). Over 15 million years ago, the ancestors of today's Hawaiian monk seals left a population of Atlantic-Caribbean seals in the North Atlantic Ocean and swam halfway across the Pacific, through a long-gone channel, the Central American Seaway, separating North and South America, to the Hawaiian Islands.

The Mediterranean monk seal may have given rise to the mythical nymphs and sirens, who lay on the rocks and sang a song so enchanting it lured passing sailors to their doom, and Aristotle's description of it is the first record of a pinniped.

The Hawaiian monk seal colonizes six of the nine atolls and islands that make up the Leeward Hawaiian islands, a low, fragmented chain of coral and rock islets that extends for over 1,600km (1,000mi) northwest from the main Hawaiian islands. Sealing expeditions in the 19th century reduced the population, and later expeditions for guano, feathers and whales further disturbed their environment. However, the species remained isolated from permanent human settlements until World War II, when US naval bases were established.

Monk seals are sensitive to any human intrusion into their habitat, particularly during reproductive periods. Nursing is interrupted, the vital mother-pup bond may be broken, and pup-mortality rates rise. Some 39 percent of pups born at one of the Leeward Islands during a study in the late 1950s died before weaning, most likely from malnutrition after nursing was disrupted. When disturbed, pregnant monk seals may leave their sheltered beach pupping-grounds for exposed sand-spits.

Shark attacks and disease also take their toll. As many as 60 seals died at Laysan Island (the largest of the Leeward chain) in 1978, possibly from ciguatera, a form of fish poisoning thought to originate with infected microorganisms. Ciguatera outbreaks may follow the destruction of coral reefs, such as that caused by extensive harbor dredging in recent years at Midway Atoll.

Unlike the Mediterranean monk seal (whose fate is in the hands of at least 10 countries bordering the Mediterranean and northeast Atlantic) conservation of the Hawaiian monk seal comes under the jurisdiction of just one country. In 1976, the United States government declared the monk seal to be an endangered species. All but two of the Leeward Islands are protected

▼ **Frolicking in the Mediterranean.** Mediterranean monk seals in an idyllic scene from an old print. The modern reality though is far from idyllic. With the increased human presence around the Mediterranean, seals no longer congregate on rocks or beaches. Instead, they shelter and give birth in sea-caves, usually with underwater entrances. Even here, pregnant females are vulnerable to disturbance. Aborted fetuses have been discovered outside cave entrances and newborn pups in caves must contend with sudden flooding during storms. One of the largest Atlantic colonies (at Cap Blanc, consisting of possibly more than 50 seals) was destroyed in 1978 when the cave in which it had found refuge collapsed.

▲ **Exotic contrast.** The Hawaiian monk seal presents a contrast in setting to the other true seals, but its tropical paradise is no more secure than that of the Mediterranean monk seal. The establishment of American naval bases in World War II probably led to the disappearance of one large colony (at Midway Atoll between 1958 and 1968); others appear to be following in its wake: 1,200 seals were counted at the Leeward islands in 1958, less than 700 in 1976. There may now be as few as 500 Hawaiian monk seals.

under the Hawaiian Islands National Wild-life Refuge, and some breeding areas have been placed off-limits. In 1980, the United States National Marine Fisheries Service appointed a 12-member Monk Seal Recovery Team to review all available information on the species and to develop a management program to ensure that future disturbance is kept to a minimum. Despite such measures, the monk seal's future is by no means assured. Population growth is hampered by a low rate of reproduction and high pup mortality. During a four-year observational study, 136 pups were born at Laysan Island, of which 15 died or disappeared before weaning and two were stillborn. Only females older than six years produced offspring. The pregnancy rate of the Hawaiian monk seal has been estimated at 56 percent, over a two-year period.

A proposal has been made to establish a large commercial fishery in the waters surrounding the islands. This would lead to further disturbance of breeding females, seals might become entangled in fishing gear, and would be viewed as competitors for prey species also claimed by man.

Halfway across the world, a similar situation exists. The Mediterranean monk seal survives in tiny, scattered colonies, with the greatest numbers found in the Aegean Sea and along the adjacent Turkish coast. Although once hunted commercially (primarily during the 15th century), the species is now too rare to support sealing, but human pressures persist. Since the 1950s, increased affluence has led to a burgeoning tourist industry, a rapidly expanding human population and the development of the Mediterranean as one of the world's most intensively fished seas.

The Mediterranean monk seal's decline is due mainly to the loss of suitable breeding and resting habitat. A possible solution would be the creation of international coastal marine parks devoted to year-round protection. Such sanctuaries would have to take into account the needs of fishermen and tourists for, clearly, they are not going to abandon this ancient coast. Financial compensation for the fishermen and education for those catering for the tourists are required. If conservation sites are provided for the monk seal which enable it to survive, this will also help a number of endangered species of birds, some endangered and indeed almost unknown plant species, as well as those habitats in which they dwell. Immediate and effective action by the USA and those European countries within whose boundaries the monk seal occurs can provide a future for the species. KR

Hunter of the Southern Ocean
The predatory Leopard seal

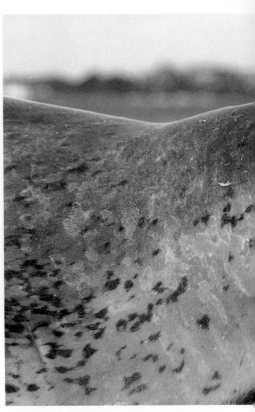

A slender body, spotted like a leopard, a way of craning its neck in an almost reptilian pose, a gaping mouth, and its habit of preying on penguins and other seals, have given the Leopard seal a sinister reputation. There are even stories of explorers reportedly attacked on the ice by Leopard seals. Recent evidence has shown that this reputation is exaggerated.

The largest of the antarctic seals, the Leopard seal is the only seal that regularly preys on warm-blooded animals. Throughout its circumpolar distribution, the Leopard seal is generally closely associated with the edge of the pack ice, but it frequently hauls out on islands near the continent in summer, when the ice melts, and on subantarctic islands during the winter months, when the ice sheets expand.

The Leopard seal is largely solitary, to the extent that it is more likely to haul out on the ice next to a Crabeater seal, its prey, than with another Leopard seal. It is an opportunistic predator, feeding on a wide variety of prey, including krill (37 percent), fish (13 percent), squid (8 percent), as well as penguines (25 percent), other seabirds (3 percent), and seals (8 percent). It is an active predator only in the water; on land it is quite cumbersome and certainly no threat to man unless closely approached.

The proportions of large and small prey in the diet undoubtedly vary according to their seasonal and distributional availability and the maturity of the Leopard seal. Young Leopard seals are dependent largely upon krill initially. The manner in which Leopard seals feed on krill is unknown, but they probably seek out krill swarms and gulp mouthfuls of water containing krill, which are then strained through the sieve-like rows of the ornately shaped post-canine teeth.

Only larger and older Leopard seals ap-

◀ **Built like a tank,** the leopard seal is paradoxically both thick-set and reptilian.

◀ **Jaws.** BELOW LEFT The impressive gaping mouth of the Leopard seal leaves no doubt about its ability to seize large prey such as other seals. Its teeth, however, are very similar to those of the Crabeater seal, which it sometimes eats, in being adapted for catching the small crustacean, krill.

▼ **Predator and prey at rest.** Out of the water, leopard seals are too cumbersome to catch penguins, a fact which enables the two species to coexist, apparently peacefully, on an ice floe.

pear to take larger prey. Although spectacular, predation on penguins in the vicinity of rookeries is seasonal and appears to be the speciality of just a few seals; these individuals may have quite different diets from the bulk of the Leopard seals distributed on the pack ice. Even in the vicinity of rookeries, the mobility of swimming penguins makes them elusive prey.

When preying on penguins, Leopard seals attack from below and presumably by surprise. Accordingly, in the vicinity of penguin rookeries, the seals tend to patrol the deeper inshore waters where penguins are more vulnerable to this mode of attack, rather than the shallow, sloping beach areas. Even when a penguin is captured, the seals often have difficulty in killing and devouring their prey. Penguins repeatedly escape their captors, although sometimes the seals may be "playing" with their quarry in a cat-and-mouse fashion. Leopard seals cannot ingest a whole adult penguin, so portions of flesh are torn from the body by vigorously thrashing the victim about. Once the body skin is ripped open, only the fleshy body parts are normally eaten, leaving the legs, flippers, head, and much of the inner skeleton. Nonetheless, a fair amount of feathers is ingested.

The Leopard seal is unique among seals in habitually feeding on other seal species. Such an attack has never been witnessed, but the high frequency (55 percent) of attack-scarring on Crabeater seals, together with the observed high frequency of seal remains in Leopard seal stomachs, taken from pack-ice areas, indicates a fairly high level of predation. The majority of the seals preyed upon are young animals, but freshly scarred older seals attest to the fact that all age classes are vulnerable. In addition to the Crabeater, seal prey species include the Weddell seal, the pups of elephant seals, fur seals, and presumably also the Ross seal. Unlike the other true seals (but like the eared seals), the Leopard seal has elongated foreflippers which give it an advantage in speed and maneuvrability in the water and on land.

The characteristic scarring on Crabeater seals resulting from Leopard seal attacks consists of slashes, up to 30cm (12in) long, often in parallel pairs, coursing tangentially across the body. Once thought to be caused principally by Killer whales, it now appears that they result from the evasive rolling action which often enables Crabeaters to escape from Leopard seals. When a Crabeater is caught, only the skin and attached blubber are eaten. AWE

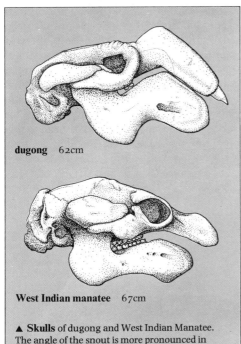

dugong 62cm

West Indian manatee 67cm

▲ **Skulls** of dugong and West Indian Manatee. The angle of the snout is more pronounced in the dugong, which also has a pair of short "tusks" (projecting incisor teeth). Both manatees and dugong only have teeth at the back of the jaw, but in manatees the teeth move forward in the jaw and are then lost.

volume (8–15 percent of their body weight daily) of relatively low quality forage required to obtain adequate energy and nutrients.

Sirenians expend little energy: for manatees, about one-third that of a typical mammal of the same weight. Their slow, languid movements may have reminded early taxonomists of mermaids—sirens of the sea. Although they are capable of more rapid movement when pursued, in an environment without humans they have little need for speed, having few predators. Living in tropical waters, sirenians can afford to have a low metabolic rate, because little energy is expended in regulation of body temperature. Marine mammals which inhabit deeper, colder water require extra energy to add to a thick layer of blubber which functions as insulation, and as an energy store during periods of scarcity of food supply. Sirenia also conserve energy by virtue of their relatively large body size. The cold-tolerant Steller's sea cow weighed about 5–6 times as much as contemporary topical sirenian species.

The large body size dictated by the requirements of nutrition and temperature regulation is associated with traits seen in other large mammalian herbivores as well as large marine mammals. The life span is

long (a 33-year-old manatee is still doing well in captivity), and the reproductive rate is low. Females give birth to a single calf after about a year's gestation, calves stay with the mother for 1–2 years and sexual maturity is delayed (4–8 years). Consequently, the potential rate of increase of population is low. It is possible that rapid reproduction brings no advantage where the renewability of food resources is slow and there are few predators.

Sirenians have few competitors for food. In contrast to the complex division of food resources by grazing and browsing herbivores seen in terrestrial grasslands, the only large herbivores in seagrass meadows are sirenians and sea turtles. Marine plant communities are low in diversity compared with terrestrial communities and lack species with high-energy seeds which facilitate niche subdivision by herbivores in terrestrial systems. It is not surprising that dugongs and manatees dig into the sediments when they feed on rooted aquatics; over half of the mass of seagrasses is found in the rhizomes, which concentrate carbohydrates. In contrast, the cold-blooded sea turtles subsist by grazing on the blades of seagrasses without disturbing the rhizomes, and appear to feed in deeper water. Thus sea turtles probably do not compete signifi-

▲ **Surface browsing.** An Amazonian manatee feeding in a tangle of water weeds. It is this feeding habit which has been used to advantage to clear congested waterways.

◄ **Docile duo.** West Indian manatees are placid, slow-moving creatures.

▷**Manatee mother and calf** OVERLEAF West Indian manatees are slow breeders and the suckling period in West Indian manatees is 12–18 months. The cow-calf bond is the only strong social relationship among manatees, and throughout the period of dependency calves stay very close to females.

▼ **Sea-grass browser.** A West Indian manatee feeding on sea grasses in shallow water.

The eyes of manatees are not particularly well adapted to the aquatic environment, but their hearing is good, despite the tiny external ear openings, and often alerts them to the presence of hunters. They do not use echolocation or sonar, and may bump into objects in murky waters; nor do they possess vocal cords, but they do communicate by vocalizations, which may be high-pitched chirps or squeaks. How these sounds are produced is a mystery. Taste buds are present on the tongue, and are apparently used in the selection of food plants, and also in the recognition of other individuals by "tasting" the scent marks left on prominent objects. Unlike the toothed whales, manatees still possess the parts of the brain concerned with a sense of smell, but since they spend most of their time underwater with the nose valves closed this sense may not be used.

A unique feature of manatees is a constant horizontal replacement of their molar teeth. When a manatee is born, it has both premolars and molars. As the calf is weaned and begins to eat vegetable matter, it seems that the mechanical stimulation of the teeth, by chewing, starts a forward movement of the whole tooth row. Now teeth entering at the back of each row push the row forward through the jawbone, at a rate about 1mm per month, until its roots are eaten away and it falls out. This type of replacement is unique to manatees.

As aquatic herbivores, manatees are restricted to feeding on plants in, or very near, the water. Occasionally, they feed with their head and shoulders out of water, but normally they feed on floating or submerged grasses and other vascular plants. They may eat algae but this does not form an important part of the diet. The coastal West Indian and West African manatees feed on sea grasses which grow in relatively shallow, clear marine waters, as well as entering inland waterways, rivers, lakes etc, to feed on freshwater plants. Amazonian manatees are surface feeders, browsing floating grasses (the murky Amazon waters inhibit the growth of submerged aquatic plants). The habit of surface feeding may explain why the downward deflection in the snout of Amazonian manatees is much less pronounced than that of the bottom-feeding West Indian and African manatees. Some 44 species of plants and 10 species of algae have been recorded as foods of the West Indian species, but only 24 species for the Amazonian manatee.

Many of the manatees' food plants have evolved special anti-herbivore protective mechanisms—spicules of silica in the

cantly for food taken by sirenians.

The four sirenian species are geographically isolated. Dugongs occupy tropical coastlines in east Africa, Asia, Australia and new Guinea. The West African manatee and the similar West Indian manatee have been isolated long enough to become distinct, since their supposed common ancestor migrated to Africa across the Atlantic Ocean. Each can occupy both saltwater and freshwater habitats. The Amazonian manatee apparently became isolated when the Andes mountain range was uplifted in the Pliocene (2–5 million years ago), changing the river drainage out of the Amazon basin from the Pacific to the Atlantic Ocean. Amazonial manatees are not tolerant of salt water and occupy only the Amazon River and its tributaries. JMP/GBR/DPD

Docility, delicious flesh and a low reproductive capacity are not auspicious characteristics for an animal in the modern world. **Manatees** have all three and are consequently among the most threatened of aquatic mammals. They are the only fully aquatic freshwater herbivores, and this role, rather like that of an aquatic cow, has given rise to the names *vaca marinha* (sea cow) in Spanish-speaking countries and *peixe-boi* (fish cow) in Portuguese.

Manatees have the typical sirenian body form and are distinguished from dugongs mainly by their large, horizontal, paddle-shaped tail, which moves up and down when the animal is swimming. They have only six neck vertebrae, unlike all other mammals, which have seven. The lips are covered with stiff bristles and there are two muscular projections that grasp and pass the grasses and aquatic plants that they feed on into the mouth.

grasses, tannins, nitrates and oxalates in other aquatics—which reduce their digestibility and lower their food value to the manatee. The constant replacement of teeth in manatees is an adaptation to the abrasive spicules of silica in the grasses or rooted plants. Microbes in the digestive tract may be able to detoxify some of the plants' chemical defenses.

Manatees can store large amounts of fat as blubber beneath the skin and around the intestines, which affords some degree of thermal protection from the environment. Despite this, in the Atlantic Ocean manatees generally avoid areas where temperatures drop below 20°C (68°F). The blubber also helps them to endure long periods of fasting: up to six months in the Amazonian manatee during the dry season, when aquatic plants are unavailable.

Manatees are extremely slow breeders: at most they produce only a single calf every two years, and calves may be weaned at 12–18 months. Although young calves may feed on plants within several weeks of being born, the long nursing period probably allows the calf to learn from its mother the necessary migration routes, foods, and preferred feeding areas. In highly seasonal environments such as the Amazon and probably at the northern and southern extremes of manatee distribution, the availability of food dictates when the majority of manatee females are ready to mate and this, in turn, results in a seasonal peak in calving. The reproductive biology of male manatees is poorly known, but it is not uncommon for a receptive female to be accompanied by 6–8 males and to mate with several of these within a short time. The age of attainment of sexual maturity of manatees is not known, but based on size it must be between 5 and 8 years of age.

Direct observation and radio-tracking studies have shown that manatees are essentially solitary but occasionally form groups of a dozen or more (see pp300–301).

All three species of manatees are considered by the IUCN to be threatened as a result of both historical and modern overhunting for their meat and skins, as well as more recent threats such as pollution, flood-control dams and high-speed pleasure craft. They are protected under the Convention on International Trade in Endangered Species of Fauna and Flora (CITES), and legally in most countries where they exist, but most underdeveloped countries lack sufficient wardens to implement practical measures such as sparing females. In Florida, signs and posters have been used

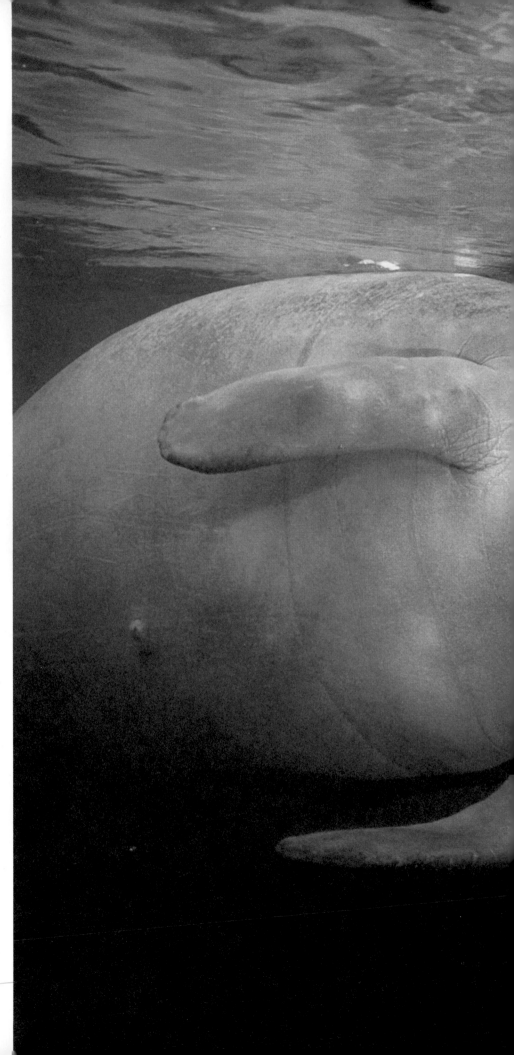

THE PRIMATES

PRIMATES

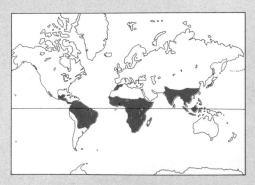

To many people typical primates are the acrobatic monkeys or ponderous gorilla, and most recognize that man himself is a primate. Technically primates are an order—a taxonomic category on the same level as the carnivores, rodents, cetaceans (whales) etc. The order Primates contains a far wider array of animals than just monkeys and gorillas. In addition to the capuchin-like monkeys of South and Central America (family Cebidae) and the Old World monkeys of Africa and Asia (family Cercopithecidae), the primates include four families of lemurs from Madagascar, the bush babies and lorises of Africa and Asia, and the tarsiers of Southeast Asia (all prosimians), the marmosets and tamarins of South America, the gibbons and orang-utan and the African apes, and all fossil and living men.

The prosimians, or "lower primates," are less man-like, or show less advanced primate evolutionary trends, than the anthropoids, the "higher primates" which comprise the monkeys, apes and man. Prosimians tend to have longer snouts, a more developed sense of smell, and smaller brains; anthropoids are short-faced, with a highly developed sense of vision, and large brains,

even allowing for greater body size.

Two other groups, both at different times included in the order Primates, are here considered as separate orders—the tree shrews (order Scandentia, pp440–445) and the flying lemurs (order Dermoptera, pp446–447)—which reflects the present scientific consensus.

The primates occupy a wide range of habitats and show a wide diversity of adaptations to their contrasting environments. The order contains terrestrial species as well as arboreal ones; species active at night as well as those active by day; specialized insectivores as well as fruit- and leaf-eaters. Primates range in weight from less than 100g (3.5oz) in the Dwarf bush baby, to over 100kg (220lb) in the gorilla, both inhabitants of the wet forests of tropical Africa. As a result, virtually all aspects of their biology vary widely from species to species (the following comments relate to primates other than humans). Gestation lengths range from around two months to eight or nine months; the weight of newborn infants from less than 10g (0.4oz) to over 2,000g (4.4lb). Weaning age differs from less than two months to over four years, and age of first breeding from nine

► **Largest and smallest** of the higher primates. Weighing in at some 160kg (350lb), the male African gorilla BELOW is a thousand times heavier than the Pygmy marmoset of South America ABOVE. Some prosimians are even smaller, such as the two lesser mouse lemurs and the Dwarf bush baby.

▼ **Posture and gait.** Some lemurs (a) walk on all fours and the tree-dwelling life-style of most species is reflected in the longer hindlimbs for leaping. Other prosimians, such as the tarsier (b), are "vertical clingers and leapers" adapted for leaping between vertical trunks. Most arboreal monkeys such as the Diana monkey (c), have well-developed hindlimbs and a long tail for balancing; baboons and other ground-dwelling monkeys have forelimbs as long as, or longer than, their hindlimbs. Among apes, the knuckle-walking gorilla (d) is the most terrestrial. The gibbons (e) arm-swing beneath the branches on their long arms and, like the chimpanzee (f), may walk upright, thus freeing the hands.

ORDER PRIMATES

Includes **Night monkey** (*Aotus trivirgatus*), **titis** (*Callicebus* species).

Marmosets and tamarins
Family Callitrichidae
Twenty-one species in 5 genera.
Includes **Common marmoset** (*Callithrix jacchus*), **Emperor tamarin** (*Saguinus imperator*).

Old World monkeys
Family Cercopithecidae
Eighty-two species in 14 genera.
Includes: **Hamadryas baboon** (*Papio hamadryas*), **gelada** (*Theropithecus gelada*), **mandrill** (*Papio sphinx*), **Savanna** or **"Common" baboon** (*P. cynocephalus*), **Barbary macaque** (*Macaca sylvanus*), **Japanese macaque** (*M. fuscata*), **Toque macaque** (*M. sinica*), **Guinea forest red colobus** (*Colobus badius*), **Guinea forest black colobus**

(*C. polykomos*), **guenons** (*Cercopithecus* species), **Hanuman langur** (*Presbytis entellus*), **talapoin** (*Miopithecus talapoin*).

Great apes
Family Pongidae
Four species in 3 genera.
Gorilla (*Gorilla gorilla*), **Common chimpanzee** (*Pan troglodytes*), **Pygmy chimpanzee** or **bonobo** (*P. paniscus*), **orang-utan** (*Pongo pygmaeus*).

Lesser apes
Family Hylobatidae
Nine species of the genus *Hylobates*.
Includes **siamang** (*H. syndactylus*) and **gibbons**.

Man
Family Hominidae
One species, *Homo sapiens*.

[*] The entire order Primates is listed by CITES.

different foods that their diet encompasses.

Even when two species apparently eat the same food at the same levels, close inspection normally shows that they differ in some important aspect of their food choice. For example, the Guinea forest red and Guinea forest black colobus monkeys are both leaf-eaters (folivores) which use the upper levels of many of the same African rain forests, but they specialize in eating leaves at different stages of growth. Similarly, while chimpanzees and guenons are fruit-eaters (frugivores), the chimpanzees take mostly ripe fruit, while the monkeys also eat fruits at earlier stages of their growth.

Differences in feeding affect virtually all aspects of morphology, physiology and behavior. For example, all insectivorous primates are small in size, and the more folivorous species tend to be larger than their frugivorous relatives—thus the folivorous siamang is larger than the frugivorous gibbon and the folivorous gorilla is bigger than the frugivorous chimpanzee.

Species using similar habitats and foods often resemble each other in the structure of the teeth, the proportions of the body, the form and complexity of their digestive tracts, and the relative size of their brains, as well as many aspects of social behavior and ecology. Folivorous primates are usually more sedentary than frugivorous ones—they require smaller home ranges and their population densities are higher. For example, in the Madagascan forests, troops of the omnivorous Ring-tailed lemur have home ranges of around 7 hectares (17.3 acres), whereas those of the leaf-eating Brown lemur seldom exceed 1 hectare (2.4 acres). The extent of a species' home range is also related to body size (bigger primates require more food and have larger home ranges than smaller ones) and also to the nature of the habitat.

The interaction between the primates and the forest is thus a complex one, and easily disrupted by human interference, for example, hunting for food. The collection of primates for use in medical research has made damaging inroads into some populations: during the 1950s, around 200,000 macaques were imported into the USA alone from Asia each year, and even today the USA still imports around 20,000 wild-caught primates each year. But it is habitat destruction, rather than trapping or hunting, that has had the most important influence on primate populations.

The world's rain forests are being felled at an alarming rate to provide timber or to make way for agriculture. In 1981 it was estimated that tropical rain forest was being

LEMURS

Twenty-two species in 12 genera.
Four families: Lemuridae, Cheirogaleidae,
Indriidae, Daubentoniidae.
Distribution: Madagascar.

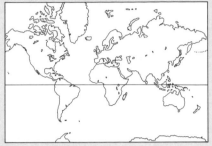

Habitat: forests.

Size: smallest are the lesser mouse lemurs—
head-body length 12.5cm (4in), tail length
13.5–15.5cm (5.3–6.1in), weight 55–65cm
(1.9–2.3oz), and largest is the indri—head-body
length 57–70cm (22.5–27.5in), tail length
5cm (2in), weight 7–10kg (15.5–22lb). Hairy-
eared dwarf lemur may weigh 45g (1.6oz).

Coat: soft in most species, often vividly colored.

Gestation: 60–160 days where known.

Longevity: not known in wild.

Lemurs (family Lemuridae, 10 species in
4 genera).
Typical lemurs (subfamily Lemurinae),
7 species including the **Ring-tailed lemur**
(*Lemur catta*); **Black lemur** (*L. macaco*);
Crowned lemur (*L. coronatus*); **Brown lemur**
(*L. fulvus*) and subspecies including Collared
lemur (*L. f. collaris*), Mayotte lemur (*L. f.
mayottensis*) and Red-fronted lemur (*L. f. rufus*);
Mongoose lemur (*L. mongoz*); and **Ruffed
lemur** (*Varecia variegata*).
Sportive lemur (subfamily Lepilemurinae),
1 species, *Lepilemur mustelinus*.
Gentle lemurs (subfamily Hapalemurinae),
2 species, *Hapalemur griseus* and *H. simus*.

Dwarf lemurs (family Cheirogaleidae),
7 species in 4 genera including the **Gray
lesser mouse lemur** (*Microcebus murinus*),
Brown lesser mouse lemur (*M. rufus*) and
Coquerel's mouse lemur (*M. coquereli*); the
Hairy-eared dwarf lemur (*Allocebus trichotis*);
the **Fat-tailed dwarf lemur** (*Cheirogaleus medius*)
and **Greater dwarf lemur** (*C. major*); and the
Fork-crowned dwarf lemur (*Phaner furcifer*).

Indri and sifakas (family Indriidae),
4 species in 3 genera including the **indri** (*Indri
indri*), **Woolly lemur** (*Avahi laniger*), and the
sifakas (2 species of *Propithecus*).

Aye-aye E (family Daubentoniidae),
1 species, *Daubentonia madagascariensis*.

E Endangered. Status of all lemurs is under review by IUCN.

L EMURS (the name means "ghosts") are
confined to the island of Madagascar and
represent the modern survivors of a spectacular adaptive radiation of primates that
seems to have taken place essentially within
Madagascar. The island, in effect, houses the
results of a gigantic "natural experiment" in
which ancestral lemurs were isolated at
least 50 million years ago and gradually
diversified into the modern array of over 40
species (including several large-bodied
species which are sadly documented only by
their subfossil remains). As such, lemurs
have retained numerous primitive characteristics while at the same time developing
many features in parallel to the monkeys
and apes of the major southern land masses,
especially among the larger day-active (diurnal) species. There is a trend in increasing
body weight from the dwarf lemurs (Cheirogaleidae) through the medium-sized (Lemuridae) and on to the largest extant species in
the family Indriidae. This trend is correlated
with a shift away from predominant night-
time (nocturnal) activity to exclusive diurnal activity, which broadly reflects the
evolutionary trend among primates
generally.

Lemurs

Like all the primates of Madagascar, the
lemurs of the family Lemuridae evolved in
isolation from the monkeys and apes of
Africa, and from most of the competitors and
predators facing primates on the mainland.
Some play ecological roles similar to those of
monkeys in Africa, while others have
evolved in ways unique among the primates. About 2,000 years ago, people arrived on the island. They hunted, modified
the habitat and introduced new species,
particularly cattle and goats. Their evolution in isolation left the Malagasy primates
ill-equipped to confront these new arrivals,
and at least 14 species went extinct, including one whole subfamily of lemurs, the
Megaladapinae, animals the size of orang-
utans that lived in the trees, and moved
about like giant Koala bears. Today, three
subfamilies of Lemuridae persist. The Lemurinae ("typical lemurs") and Lepilemurinae
(Sportive lemur) are widespread, the Hapalemurinae, (gentle lemurs) close to
extinction.

The Lemuridae are squirrel- to cat-sized
and weigh 0.5–5kg (1–11lb). Coat colors
range from a muted gray-brown in the
Sportive lemur and gentle lemurs to the
striking black-and-white or black-and-red of
the Ruffed lemur. Males and females are
about the same size but in "true lemurs"

(*Lemur* species) they differ in color, most
strikingly in the Black lemur in which the
male is jet black, and the female reddish- or
golden-brown with lavish white tufts on the
ears. All have long, often bushy, tails and
have longer hindlimbs than forelimbs, a
feature that is least pronounced in the
Lemurinae (forelimbs measured at 69.7
percent of hindlimb length), somewhat
more pronounced in gentle lemurs (67.1
percent), and most marked in the Sportive
lemur (60.3 percent). These differences
influence the way these generally arboreal
animals move through the trees. "Typical
lemurs" are largely quadrupedal; they move
with agility amongst small branches and
twigs on the periphery of tree crowns, and
are capable of leaping several meters to cross
from one crown to another. An exception is

▼ **Representatives** of the family Lemuridae ("typical lemurs") showing scent marking and sex differences in coat coloration of *Lemur* species. (**1**) Black lemur (*Lemur macaco*) male (ABOVE) and female. (**2**) Mongoose lemur (*L. mongoz*) male (ABOVE) and female. (**3**) Brown lemur (*L. fulvus*) marking its tail with the scent-glands on its wrist. (**4**) A subspecies, the White-fronted lemur (*L. fulvus fulvus*) male (the female has gray in place of white fur). (**5**) Gray gentle lemur (*Hapalemur griseus*) marking a branch with the scent glands on its wrist. (**6**) Sportive lemur (*Lepilemur mustelinus*). (**7**) Ruffed lemur (*Varecia variegata*) engaged in anogenital scent marking.

the Ring-tailed lemur, which habitually travels on the ground and, in the trees, prefers broad horizontal limbs to thin, less stable branches. It is the only primate in Madagascar to make extensive use of the ground, though the little known Crowned lemur may also be partially terrestrial. Gentle lemurs are not well studied, but have been observed moving quadrupedally and by leaping between vertical supports. The Sportive lemur travels almost exclusively by leaping from one vertical support to another; it rests by clinging to a tree trunk, sometimes in a fork but often with no horizontal support at all.

The muzzle is black, pointed, covered with sensitive whiskers and tipped with a naked, moist area of skin (rhinarium) that is linked to olfactory functions. Though all species,

particularly the Sportive lemur, show some reduction in the area of the brain associated with olfaction, the sense of smell is still important: communication by smell is a conspicuous aspect of their behavior and all have scent glands which they use to mark certain branches or even one another. The Ring-tailed lemur's tail serves a double role in this respect. The black and white bands make it a striking visual signal, and during ritualized fights animals also smear their tails with secretions from the scent glands on their arms and wave them over their heads at the opponent. The family shares the typical primate trait of forward-facing eyes and binocular vision, though their binocular field is somewhat smaller (114–130°) than that of the monkeys (140–160°). Whether active by day or by

night, most Malagasy primates have a retina with a reflective layer (the *tapetum lucidum*), a specialization for night vision. Ruffed and "true" lemurs (except the Ring-tailed species) lack this characteristic, even though certain species of *Lemur* in some parts of their range are active by night as well as or instead of by day. Lemurids also communicate by voice. Ruffed lemurs and *Lemur* species use loud calls to draw attention to possible sources of danger and to maintain spacing between social groups; quiet calls help members of a group to stay in contact.

There are members of the Lemuridae in most of the remaining forests of Madagascar; Ring-tailed lemurs and perhaps Crowned lemurs occupy more open, scrubby areas in the south and north respectively. This is the only family of Malagasy primates with representatives in the wild outside Madagascar. The Mongoose lemur occurs on the Comorian islands of Moheli and Anjouan, and the Brown lemur on Mayotte. The date of their introduction (almost certainly by people) is unknown, but it goes back several hundred years. In Madagascar, the "true lemurs" and the Sportive lemur are found almost the length of the island in the east and the west, whereas gentle lemurs occur predominantly, and the Ruffed lemur exclusively, along the east coast. The largely deforested central plateau is devoid of primates today, but 1,000 years ago it contained a wide range of species, including representatives of all three lemurid subfamilies. In coastal areas the ranges of species and subspecies within each genus do not overlap, being broken up by stretches of uninhabitable terrain. The partial differentiation of recently isolated populations can make it difficult to decide whether they are subspecies or different species. The Sportive lemur presents a particular problem, and may be classified as one or as many as seven species. Differences in chromosome number have been used to separate populations of the Sportive lemur into species, but they are also found within populations in the same region. (This variation in chromosome number within a population, rare among primates, has also been observed in the Collared lemur.)

The family is vegetarian. They feed in a wide range of postures and can reach almost any part of a tree. Except for gentle lemurs, they rarely use their hands to manipulate food items but rather pull food-bearing branches to their mouth and feed from them direct. Particularly large items may be held

The Bygone Wealth of Malagasy Lemurs

The evolution of the Malagasy lemurs is poorly understood because of the dearth of fossil evidence from the early and middle Tertiary in both Africa and Madagascar. One theory is that an early primate form, probably resembling in many respects today's Mouse lemur, colonized the recently formed island by clinging to rafts of vegetation as they swept out of river deltas draining eastern Africa some 50–60 million years ago.

Meeting no established mammalian competitors, these founding lemurs radiated to become an array of at least 40 species, evidence of which is preserved in sub-fossil deposits throughout western Madagascar. They spanned a wide range of physical and ecological types. Body size ranged from forms as small as a mouse to others as large as an orang-utan; all types of locomotion were represented: quadrupedal terrestrial, quadrupedal arboreal, slow grasping climber, vertical clinging and leaping, and brachiation (swinging by the arms); and, very likely, the larger-bodied types tended to be highly gregarious leaf-eaters, active chiefly in the daylight hours, like some monkeys in Africa today. The Indriidae alone, it is generally accepted, included (together with the present-day forms) the baboon-like *Archaeolemur*, the gelada-like *Hadropithecus*, the enormous and robust *Archaeoindris*, and the large brachiating *Palaeopropithecus*. Competing with *Archaeoindris* in body size was *Megaladapis*

(ABOVE), koala-like in proportions but with a skull over a foot (25cm) long in one species, proving that the evolutionary diversification involved more than a single family.

There is good evidence that the majority of these large lemurs were still widespread up to about 5,000 years ago and were subsequently devastated by hunting, with the arrival of the first permanent human settlements in Madagascar about 2,000 years ago. Fire and competition with domestic animals may also have accelerated their disappearance. Whichever the case, we have just missed a unique opportunity to observe the extraordinary capacity of evolutionary processes to construct variations on a theme, with the primates isolated on Madagascar evolving in parallel with the monkeys and apes of the Old World.   JIP

while they are being eaten. Gentle lemurs have yet to be studied in detail, but they are reported to feed primarily on young bamboo shoots and leaves, and their front teeth appear specialized to exploit this food. The upper canine is short and broad and the premolar behind it is relatively large and not separated from the canine by a gap as it is in most primates. A gentle lemur will detach a bamboo shoot with its incisors, clamp it between the upper and lower canines and premolars, and pull the shoot sideways with its hands, stripping off the fibrous outer layer. It then pushes the tender interior back into the side of the mouth and chews it.

The Sportive lemur, studied in a spiny forest in the south, devoted 91 percent of its feeding time to leaves, and 6 percent to flowers and fruit together. Over half the food items came from just two plant species. This small, nocturnal animal may make the most of its low-energy diet by digesting its food by fermentation. It excretes the nutrients released by this process in its feces, eats the feces and assimilates the nutrients contained in them.

The diet of *Lemur* species varies from

▲ **The unmistakable tail** of the Ring-tailed lemur is used by this day-active species as a visual signal. In aggressive encounters, the lemur will wave high its scent-smeared tail in the direction of its rival.

◄ **The Mongoose lemur** in Madagascar lives in small groups of male, female (shown here) and young offspring. In the Comoro Islands this nectar-eating lemur lives in larger groups.

▷ **In mid-leap** OVERLEAF, a Ring-tailed lemur prepares to land on an upright branch.

species to species and, within species, according to region and season. For example, the Mayotte lemur eats primarily fruit (67 percent of feeding time) and leaves (27 percent) from a wide range of species, but the proportion of these plant parts in its diet varies seasonally from 48 to 79 percent for fruit and 20–36 percent for leaves. The Red-fronted lemur, in contrast, spends over half its feeding time on the leaves of a few species. The diet of the Mongoose lemur contains a unique component: during the dry season, animals spend 81 percent of feeding time licking nectar from flowers or eating the nectaries themselves.

Social organization and ranging behavior vary widely within the family, and in *Lemur* there is variation within as well as between species. In Madagascar, Mongoose lemur social groups consist of an adult male and female with their immature offspring. They live in small (about 1.15ha/3-acre)

overlapping home ranges, and the bond between the two adults may last several years. Among Mongoose lemurs in the Comoro Islands, however, there is no evidence of pair-bonding; animals live in larger groups of highly variable composition. In Madagascar, social groups of Red-fronted lemurs contain about nine animals (range 4–17) and occupy an extremely small (0.75–1ha/about 2-acre) home range that overlaps extensively with the home ranges of neighboring groups. Groups are stable in composition but, other than grooming, interactions among members are rare and there is no clear social structure. In the Comoro Islands, Mayotte lemurs also spend their time in groups of about nine animals, but the composition of these groups varies from day to day, and they may be subunits of a larger social network. Social group size in the Ring-tailed lemur varies from five to 30 (average 15). The home range is larger than

in other lemurs (6–23ha/15–57 acres), and it may be defended and used exclusively, or partly shared with neighboring groups. Aggressive interactions within the social group are common and there are clear male and female dominance hierarchies. Females are dominant to males. The male hierarchy disintegrates during the mating season and males compete equally for access to females. Females spend their lives in the group into which they were born, whereas males transfer at least once and possibly several times during their lives from one group to another. The Ruffed lemur has yet to be well studied but it appears to live in pair-bonded units. Its pattern of reproduction is unique in the family. The female usually gives birth to twins, and during the postnatal period she "parks" them on a branch or in a nest while she forages.

In contrast to the sociable "typical lemurs," the Sportive lemur spends most of its time alone, though heterosexual or female pairs often share most or all of a tiny home range (0.3ha/1 acre for males and 0.18ha/0.5 acre for females). Meetings occur 1–3 times a night, lasting from five minutes to an hour, during which the pair move, feed, rest and occasionally groom together. The social organization of gentle lemurs has not been studied; however, they have been observed in groups of two to six animals.

All the Lemuridae are threatened by habitat destruction, but differences in ecology may affect the length of time members of the three subfamilies will be able to survive on the island. The "typical lemurs" eat a wide variety of foods; their ranging behavior is flexible and some species are able to be active by day or by night or even both; their social organization also seems to be adaptable. They live at high densities in favorable habitats and occupy many types of vegetation over much of the island. The diet of the Sportive lemur in a given forest is likely to be much narrower than that of the "typical lemurs," but these small, solitary, nocturnal and inconspicuous animals are specialized to exploit one of the most abundant resources in the forest, namely leaves. They are thus able, like "true lemurs" though for different reasons, to survive at high densities in many forests and are widespread on the island. Gentle lemurs, by contrast, are specialized eaters of bamboo shoots, a plant that grows only in a limited range of environmental conditions. Gentle lemurs are thus much less common, their distribution is patchy, and they occur only in the island's moister forests.   AFR

bark or earth (see below) or to cross small treeless areas. The indri may leap up to 10m (33ft), although most leaps are of 3–5m (10–16ft). Movement on the ground is also unique: bipedal hops with arms held at shoulder level or higher, the body inclined somewhat away from the direction of travel.

There are few physical distinctions between the three genera; they include the relatively small size of the Woolly lemur (the only nocturnal species), the near-absence of a tail in the indri, and body coloration differences. Common indriid features include a high leg-to-arm-length ratio (an adaptation to their mode of locomotion), the loss of one premolar tooth from both upper and lower jaws, four rather than six teeth in the tooth-comb, and a single pair of axillary teats. They have short, broad snouts and large hands and feet. There have been field studies of Verreaux's sifaka and of the indri, but little is known of the Diadem sifaka and Woolly lemur.

The diet of indriids is composed entirely of fruit and leaves. A small amount of bark and dead wood is consumed by Verreaux's sifaka (probably to obtain water) and the indri also ingests earth (possibly as an aid to digestion). Indriids generally feed by pulling branches manually to the mouth and biting off the food items. Their grasping hands and feet enable them, despite their size, to hang

from thin branches to reach food items. Over the year, Verreaux's sifaka spends about 43 percent of its feeding time eating young and mature foliage, 38 percent on fruit and the remainder on flowers, bark and dead wood. The proportion of time spent feeding (24–37 percent) varies seasonally. feeding accounts for 35–40 percent of indri's daily period of activity on average and 60–70 percent of this is spent eating leaf shoots and young leaves, 25–30 percent on fruit and seeds and the remainder on flowers and mature foliage. All indriids, especially the indri, possess a well-developed cecum where plant cellulose is presumably fermented with the aid of gut microflora.

Groups of Verreaux's sifaka are composed of 3–12 individuals, often with more than one breeding adult of each sex. Some males transfer between groups before the mating season, apparently according to their social status within the group. Females can reproduce about three years of age and have a very short (up to 42 hours) period on heat in late summer (February–March) which is highly synchronized within and between groups and results in a sharp peak in the birth rate in June and July after a 160-day gestation. The single newborn infant is almost hairless and black-skinned, clutching the lower part of the mother's abdomen to begin with but gradually transferring to

▲ ▶ **The long, muscular legs,** large grasping hands and feet, and long balancing tail of an active leaper. This white Verreaux's sifaka ABOVE on a cactus-like *Didiera* is one of the largest lemurs. Like most larger species it is active during the daytime.

◀ **Limbs outstretched,** this indri's midair posture is that of a "vertical clinger and leaper," the largest in fact, and the largest of all prosimians.

1–9ha (2.5–22 acres) in groups of 1–4 adult females, 1–4 adult males and young of both sexes, with a mean group size of 5.9. In larger ranges, a quarter or half the range is an actively defended territory—in smaller ranges the whole area may be territorial. Population densities of over 100/per sq km (39/sq mi) occur in this species, much more than in the Diadem sifaka, which lives in largely exclusive ranges of at least 20ha (49 acres) in groups of only 2–5 individuals. In both sifaka species females engage in ano-genital scent-marking and males rub glands in the throat region against trees and branches—behavior which increases in frequency in the mating season. Indri groups defend territories of 18–30ha (44–74 acres); population density is estimated at 9–16/per sq km (23–41/sq mi) where the species is abundant. Indri males "cheek mark," and ano-genital marking is performed by both sexes.

Indri may also defend their territory by the groups' loud, modulated series of howls, which occur regularly in infectious fashion throughout the population. These "songs" are emitted 1–7 times a day on 70 percent of days during the year. They serve to recall separated group members and are repeated during the occasional encounters between groups at territory borders. Sifakas also occasionally emit very loud "football-rattle" calls and both the indri and sifakas call distinctively to warn of ground predators ("hoot"—indri; "sifaka"—*P. verreauxi*; "kiss-sneeze"—*P. diadema*) and aerial predators ("roar"—indri; and "football-rattle"—sifakas). Soft calls within the family group consist of hums, grunts and growls. Each species appears to have its own distinct repertoire of 5–6 calls.

Woolly lemurs live in small groups of 2–5 but are frequently encountered alone. Four or five cries, some loud, have been described. Neck glands are developed in both sexes.

All indriids are severely threatened by the destruction of their habitat for fuel, timber or local agricultural development. The eastern species are in most danger because the rain forest of eastern Madagascar is becoming fragmented into a series of thin islands, which is certain to result in extinctions. Both species of sifakas are eaten locally and are commonly trapped and shot. Only Verreaux's sifaka has been satisfactorily maintained in captivity. The few remaining species of the family can only be protected by efficient management, and perhaps by extensions to the 15 protected areas, which currently cover just 1 percent of Madagascar.

her back after 3–4 weeks. Weaning is completed by five months and the young sifaka moves independently of the mother from about seven months.

Indri generally live in small family groups, with only one breeding adult of each sex. Mating occurs in mid-summer and single infants are born in May after a gestation of probably 120–150 days. Compared with the sifaka, development is slow: the infant is carried on its mother's back from 15 to about 28 weeks and moves about independently at 42 weeks, some three months before weaning. Births probably occur at three-year intervals, and reproductive maturity is attained at the age of 8–9 years.

Verreaux's sifaka occupies ranges of

JIP

THE 22 SPECIES OF LEMURS

Abbreviations: HBL = head-and-body length; TL = tail length; wt = weight. Approximate nonmetric equivalents: 2.5cm = 1in; 230g = 8oz, 1kg = 2.2lb.
[E] Endangered. The status of all lemurs is under review by the IUCN.

Lemurs (family Lemuridae)

Subfamily Lemurinae (typical lemurs)

Genus Lemur ("true" lemurs)

Medium-sized primates (2–3.4kg). Mostly arboreal, with a diet of fruit, leaves, and flowers. Somewhat prominent muzzle, tipped with a moist rhinarium. Dental formula I2/2, C1/1, P3/3, M3/3 = 36. Lower canines and incisors form a forward-projecting "comb." Arms shorter than legs, and tail longer than body. Usually move on all four limbs. Often striking male/female differences in coat color. Sexual maturity at about two years of age. Mating seasonal. Usually a single offspring after a gestation of 120–136 days. Several species have received little study.

Ring-tailed lemur
Lemur catta

Madagascar. Deciduous forests, gallery forests, *Euphorbia/Didierea* arid bush/forest. Diurnal. Gregarious, in groups of 5–30 with both male and female dominance hierarchies, but females generally dominant to males. Feeding largely arboreal, but animals often travel on ground. Births in August–November (N hemisphere, March–June). Coat: back gray, limbs and belly lighter, extremities white; top of head, rings about eyes and muzzle black; tail banded black and white. HBL 39–46cm; TL 56–63cm; wt 2.3–3.5kg.

Lemur fulvus

Seven subspecies from E and W coasts of Madagascar and from Comoro Islands. In all types of forest, except in dry S and SW. Highly arboreal with a preference for closed-canopy forests. Little evidence of dominance hierarchies. May live at very high densities (up to 12 per hectare). Group size variable (4–17). Some populations diurnal, others sporadically active through day and night. Some of 7 subspecies becoming very rare. Sometimes included in *L. macaco*.

Brown lemur
L. f. fulvus

Range discontinuous, along NW coast NE of Galoka mountains, and central E coast of Madagascar. Upper parts and tail grayish-brown, cheeks and beard white, muzzle and forehead black, underparts creamy-tan; color paler in females. HBL 43–50cm; TL 50–55cm; wt 2.1–4.2kg. Groups 3–12 individuals, predominantly diurnal (?).

White-fronted lemur
L. f. albifrons

E coast rain forests, N of *L. f. fulvus*. Coat color variable, different between sexes. Males usually brown on upperparts and tail, paler underneath with striking black face and muzzle surrounded by snowy white forehead, crown, beard and throat. Females have gray-brown backs and tails, with lighter underparts; muzzles black, but otherwise heads usually grayish. HBL 38–42cm; TL 50–55cm; wt 1.9–2.6kg.

Red-fronted lemur
L. f. rufus

Forests along much of W coast (S of *L. f. fulvus*) and on central E coast (S of *L. f. fulvus* and N of *L. f. albocollaris*). Coat colors variable, different between sexes. Male upperparts and tail gray, underparts lighter; muzzle black, head hooded in reddish-orange, cheeks and throat grayish-brown. Female upperparts reddish-brown, underparts lighter or grayer; muzzle and center of forehead black, crown gray with pale eyebrows and cheeks. HBL 38–45cm; TL 50–60cm; wt 2.1–3.6kg. Groups of 4–17 animals with small overlapping home ranges. High proportion of mature leaves in diet, also fruit, few flowers. Feeds throughout day with frequent rests. Aggression very rare, dominance hierarchies nonexistent (?). Most abundant subspecies.

Collared lemur
L. f. collaris

Extreme S section of E coast rain forest. Upperparts olive-brown to gray-brown, with darker strip down spine. Underparts paler, tail darker. Face and top of head black, cheeks, orange and bushy in males. Females similar but face grayer, and cheeks have shorter hair. HBL ? TL ? wt 2.1–2.8kg.

Mayotte lemur
L. f. mayottensis

Limited to island of Mayotte, in Comoro Islands NW of Madagascar. Coat very similar to *L. f. fulvus*, but individual variation somewhat greater. HBL about 40cm; TL about 50cm; wt ? Closely related to *L. f. fulvus*. Likely a human introduction to Mayotte. Highly arboreal, active chiefly in early morning and evening, but sporadically at all times. Group size variable (2–29). Aggression rare, dominance hierarchies not apparent.

Sanford's lemur
L. f. sanfordi

Limited to vicinity of Mt d'Ambre in far N of Madagascar. Male upperparts brownish-gray, underparts paler, limbs sometimes reddish; black muzzle, with forehead and upper cheeks whitish; crown and lower cheeks bushy and reddish-brown, ears white and tufted. Females have similar body colors but dark-gray head, no ear tufts, less bushy cheeks. HBL 36–43cm; TL 46–52cm; wt ?

White-collared lemur
L. f. albocollaris

S east coast rain forest, between *L. f. collaris* and *L. f. rufus*. Males similar to *L. f. collaris* males, but beard is white. Females similar to *L. f. collaris* females. HBL 40–44cm; TL 45–59cm; wt ?

Mongoose lemur
Lemur mongoz

NW Madagascar, and Moheli and Anjouan in Comoro Islands. Moist forest, deciduous forest and second growth. Likes nectar, also eats flowers, fruit and leaves. Most populations nocturnal, arboreal, and live in family groups (male, female and immature offspring). Aggressive behavior uncommon. Males gray, with pale faces, red cheeks and beards. Females have browner backs, dark faces, white cheeks and beards. HBL 32–37cm; TL 47–51cm; wt 2–2.2kg.

Black lemur
Lemur macaco

West of N Madagascar. Humid forests. Primarily arboreal, daytime and dusk activity, foraging groups of 5–15 animals may coalesce in evenings. Highly dichromatic: males uniformly black; females light-chestnut brown, with darker faces and heavy white ear tufts. HBL 38–45cm; TL 51–64cm; wt 2–2.9kg.

Crowned lemur
Lemur coronatus

Extreme north. Dry forests and, recently, high-altitude moist forest. Apparently lives in large, multi-male groups. Active in day and at dusk. Travels frequently on ground. Sexually dichromatic. Males have medium-gray backs, lighter limbs and underparts; faces whitish, with V-shaped orange marking above forehead; crown of head black. Female upperparts and head cap lighter in color. HBL 32–36cm; TL 42–51cm; wt about 2kg.

Red-bellied lemur
Lemur rubriventer

Medium to high altitudes in E coast rain forest. Poorly known but probably diurnal, limited to highest strata of forest, always in small groups of up to 5. Upperparts chestnut-brown, tail black, face dark. Males have reddish-brown underparts, females whitish. HBL 36–42cm; TL 46–54cm; wt ?

Genus Varecia

Ruffed lemur
Varecia variegata

Sparsely distributed in E coast rain forest. Largest of Lemuridae. Poorly known: probably fruit-eating, in upper strata of forest. Live in pair-bonded families; high rate of twin births. The only lemurid that leaves young in nest. At least 2 subspecies recognized, primarily on basis of coat color. Both have long, dense fur, especially around neck. Prominent muzzle, face covered by short hair.

Black-and-white ruffed lemur
V. v. variegata

Central and S portion of E coast rain forest. Geographically highly variable coat colors; usually white ruff with black face, extremities and tail; shoulders, back and rump have black and white patches and bands of various extent. HBL 54–56cm; TL 58–65cm; wt 3.3–4.5kg.

Red ruffed lemur
V. v. rubra

N part of species' range. Body deep red, except underparts: extremities, forehead, crown and tail black, white patch at the back of the neck. HBL 51–55cm; TL 56–62cm; wt about 4kg. Exceptionally rare.

Subfamily Lepilemurinae (Sportive lemur)

Sportive lemur
Lepilemur mustelinus

Xerophytic, gallery, deciduous and humid forests of Madagascar. Medium-sized (HBL 24–30cm, TL 22–29cm, wt about 0.5–1kg). Arboreal, nocturnal, usually sleep during day in tree hollows. Diet largely leaves, also fruit, flowers, bark. Move by leaps of up to 5m from trunk to trunk with body in vertical position. Legs much longer than arms, tail always shorter than body. Short face, moist rhinarium, prominent ears, dense, woolly fur. Dental formula $I_0/2$, $C_1/1$, $P_3/3$, $M_3/3 = 32$; lower incisors and canines form a forward-projecting tooth-comb. Single births September–November after gestation of 135 days; sexual maturity attained at about 18 months. Six subspecies.

Weasel lemur
L. m. mustelinus
E coast rain forest. Upperparts brown, underparts paler, face dark, lighter cheeks and beard. Perhaps largest subspecies.

Red-tailed sportive lemur
L. m. ruficaudatus
Didierea/Euphorbia bush, gallery forests in SW. Back light brown, underparts paler, reddish tail, pale face and throat. Large ears.

Gray-backed sportive lemur
L. m. dorsalis
NW, moist forests. Small-bodied. Medium to dark brown above and below, face dark, ears small.

Milne-Edward's sportive lemur
L. m. edwardsi
W deciduous forests. Similar to *L. m. ruficaudatus*, but coat darker, especially on upper part of back. Gray-brown face, underparts gray, ears large.

Northern sportive lemur
L. m. septentrionalis
Extreme N, deciduous forests. Upperparts and crown gray, rump and hindlimbs paler, tail pale brown. Underparts and face gray.

White-footed sportive lemur
L. m. leucopus
S gallery forests and *Didierea/Euphorbia* bush. Small-bodied. Upperparts medium gray, underparts gray-white, tail light brown. Ears large.

Subfamily Hapalemurinac (gentle lemurs)

Genus *Hapalemur*
Madagascar. Similar in size to *Lemur*. Active morning and late afternoon. Specialized diet of bamboo shoots and reeds. Moves quadrupedally, as well as by leaps, often near the ground. Rounded head, with small, furry ears, short muzzle and woolly coat. Dental formula $I_2/2$, $C_1/1$, $P_3/3$, $M_3/3 = 36$, with upper canine and P2 specialized for unsheathing bamboo shoots. Forward projecting tooth-comb. Single births after 140-day gestation. Two living species.

Hapalemur griseus
E coast humid forest and two isolated populations along W coast. Essentially limited to bamboo forests and reed beds. Three subspecies.

Gray gentle lemur
H. g. griseus
Throughout eastern humid forest. Small family (?) groups of 2–6 animals. Coat largely gray to gray-brown with lighter underparts. HBL 27–31cm; TL 32–40cm; wt 0.7–1kg.

Alaotran gentle lemur
H. g. alaotrensis
Only in reed beds and marshes surrounding Lake Alaotra, E Madagascar. Coat similar to *H, g. g.* HBL about 40cm; TL about 40cm; wt probably about 1kg.

Western gentle lemur
H. g. occidentalis
Two small isolated populations in bamboo forests along W coast. Somewhat smaller and lighter colored than *H. g. g.* HBL about 28cm; TL about 38cm; wt probably about 1kg.

Broad-nosed gentle lemur
Hapalemur simus
Extremely limited range in central E coast humid forest. Coat gray to gray-brown with lighter underparts. Larger and more heavily built than *H. griseus*. Total length (HBL + TL) about 90cm. In immediate danger of extinction. AFR

Dwarf and Mouse Lemurs (family Cheirogaleidae)

Fat-tailed dwarf lemur
Cheirogaleus medius
NW, W and S Madagascar in well-established secondary forests and primary forests; nocturnal. HBL 19cm; TL 21cm; wt 200g. Fur short and dense; pale gray above, white to cream below. Gestation: 61 days. Longevity: 18 years in captivity.

Greater dwarf lemur
Cheirogaleus major
E Madagascar in well-established secondary forests and primary forests; nocturnal. HBL 23cm; TL 28cm; wt 450g. Fur fairly short and dense; gray-brown above, white to cream below; black ring around each eye. Gestation: 70 days. Longevity: 15 years in captivity.

Gray lesser mouse lemur
Microcebus murinus
NW, W and S Madagascar, in forest fringes and secondary vegetation; nocturnal. HBL 12.5cm; TL 13.5cm; wt 65g. Fur on back gray to gray-brown; white to cream below. Large membranous ears. Gestation: 60 days. Longevity: 14 years in captivity.

Brown lesser mouse lemur
Microcebus rufus
E Madagascar, in forest fringes and secondary vegetation; nocturnal. HBL 12.5cm; TL 15.5cm; wt 55g. Fur on back brown; white to cream below. Medium-sized membranous ears. Gestation: 60 days. Longevity: 12 years in captivity.

Coquerel's mouse lemur
Microcebus coquereli
Disjunct distribution in well-established coastal forests of W and NW Madagascar; nocturnal. HBL 21cm; TL 33cm; wt 300g. Fur on back gray-brown to pale brown, yellowish below. Tip of tail darker than rest of fur. Large membranous ears. Gestation: 86 days. Longevity: unknown.

Hairy-eared dwarf lemur
Allocebus trichotis
NE Madagascar; very restricted distribution in primary rain forests; nocturnal. HBL 14cm; TL 16cm; wt unknown, probably about 45g. Fur on back pale brown; white to cream below; ears short but with pronounced tufts of long hair. Gestation and longevity unknown.

Fork-crowned dwarf lemur
Phaner furcifer
Disjunct distribution in W, NW and NE Madagascar, in well-established forests in coastal regions; nocturnal. HBL 24cm; TL 36.5cm; wt 300g. Fur gray-brown on back, white to cream below; conspicuous dark line running over back of head and forking to join up with dark rings surrounding the eyes. Gestation and longevity unknown. RDM

Indri and Sifakas (family Indriidae)

Woolly lemur
Avahi laniger
Woolly lemur, woolly indris or avahi.
Two subspecies, in E rain forests, also in secondary growth (*A. l. laniger*) and central NW coastal area (*A. l. occidentalis*). HBL of *A. l. l.* 26.5–29.5cm; TL 28–35.5cm; wt 1kg. Coat thick, dark, usually with white inside thigh patches.

Indri
Indri indri
Indri or indris, endrina or babakoto.
Rain forest along N central part of E coast. HBL 57–70cm; rudimentary tail 5cm; wt 7–10kg or more. Coat variegated black and white, thick, silky; amount of white variable.

Verreaux's sifaka
Propithecus verreauxi
Four subspecies, in deciduous forests of S, W and N. HBL 39–48cm; TL 50–60cm; wt 3.5–4.3kg. Coat varies greatly from all-white to partly or largely brown, black or maroon.

Diadem sifaka
Propithecus diadema
Five subspecies, in evergreen forests in E. HBL of *P. d. candidus* 50–55cm; TL 45–51cm; wt 6–8kg. Coat varies from all-white to all-black, with extensive gold, gray or brown patches in some subspecies. JIP

Aye-aye (family Daubentoniidae)

Aye-aye [E]
Daubentonia madagascariensis
E coast rain forests. HBL about 40cm; TL about 40cm; wt 3kg. Coat thick, dark brown, white-flecked on body, with long guard hairs. Tail bushy. Incisors very large. Fingers and toes very large; thin middle finger. Nocturnal and solitary; eats fruit and insect larvae. (See p 327.)

BUSH BABIES, LORISES AND POTTOS

A crude definition of the family that includes the bush babies, pottos and lorises would be that they are lemurs that do not inhabit Madagascar. Unlike their Madagascan counterparts, these continental species share their habitat with monkeys. However, because their activity is exclusively nocturnal the Lorisidae do not compete ecologically with the monkeys.

Like the lemurs, lorisids have retained a well-developed sense of smell and can be distinguished from the higher primates (and the tarsiers—see p338) by the presence of a moist snout (rhinarium). In addition, unlike the higher primates, their face is covered with hair. The dental formula (I2/2, C1/1, P3/3, M3/3 = 36) is almost the same as in the earliest lemur-like creatures of 50 million years ago, although modern members of the family, like most of the Madagascan lemurs, are characterized by the presence of a tooth-comb formed by the four lower incisors and two canines, which are pointed and project forward. Species that feed on gum and other plant exudates use the comb to scoop out drops held in fissures of the tree bark. During grooming the comb is used to remove any rough material, encrusted mud, tangled hair etc. On the underside of the tongue lies a second, fleshy comb (the

► **Bat-like ears** of the Lesser or Senegal bush baby enable it in the dark to track movements of its insect prey. Some prey (eg arthropods) is taken on the ground, but insects may be snatched as they fly past.

▲ **The nocturnal Slender loris** has large eyes and binocular vision. Not unlike bush babies, lorises and pottos are slow movers and can "freeze" chameleon-like for hours. They locate their slow-moving prey particularly by smell. The Slender loris of India and Sri Lanka is one of just two Asian members of this chiefly African family.

▼ **Thick-tailed bush babies** hang from a branch as they feed on gum trickling down the trunk of an acacia.

baby can cover some 10m (33ft) in less than five seconds, and can effectively evade an intending predator.

Several morphological adaptations are linked to this type of locomotion. The hind limbs are highly developed, the eyes are large for good night vision, and the long tail is important for keeping balance during a leap.

The pottos and lorises (subfamily Lorisinae) are slow climbers. There are two African and two Asiatic species. These four species have a much reduced tail and limbs of less unequal length than in the bush babies. They look like slow and cautiously moving bear cubs. They move along a branch or a liana in a somewhat chameleon-like movement that is smooth and perfectly coordinated, so that they remain unnoticed as they pass through the thick vegetation. This system of concealed or "cryptic" locomotion has been developed to such a degree that they have lost the skills of leaping. One captive potto remained amidst some branches fixed to the ceiling of a room for two years without once falling to the floor 2m (6.6ft) beneath the lowest branches. Only in the case of intense fear, for example when confronted with a large snake, will these animals let themselves drop to earth, an effective means in thick forest of escaping. When a potto or loris is on the move, it will be transfixed by the slightest sound or unexpected occurrence, frozen in mid-movement until the potential enemy has left the scene. This petrified stance can be maintained for hours, so long as the danger lasts, and will frustrate even the most patient watcher! The strategy of cryptic locomotion can only work in luxuriantly leafy surroundings, and, unlike the bush babies, the potto and lorises only inhabit the thickest vegetation.

Should one of these animals be discovered by a small carnivore, certain adaptations enable them to defend themselves and sometimes dissuade the aggressor. The nape and the back of the potto, for example, are protected by a shield of thickened skin overlying hump-like protuberances formed by the spinal processes on the vertebrae projecting through shoulder blades which nearly meet in the middle of the back. The "shield" is covered by fur and by tactile hairs 5–10cm (2–4in) long which detect any attack. In the event of an attack by, for example, an African palm civet, the potto turns toward it, head buried between its hands and presenting its shield. The aggressor's charges are dodged by sideways movements without the potto loosening the

sublingua). This has sharpened and hardened points used to clean the debris from between the teeth of the dental comb.

The fingers and toes all bear nails, except the second toe which is modified as a toilet claw and used to groom the head and neck fur and to clean the ears. Only the first toe of the foot is truly opposable to the other digits.

As in all primates the external sexual organs are clearly visible. However, the clitoris is so developed as to lead to possible confusion between the sexes, especially as the vaginal opening is nearly always obscured by the growth of "scar tissue" between the female's fertile periods. The surest method of sexing individuals is to determine whether a scrotum is present or not.

The best known members of the family are the bush babies of Africa—so called perhaps on account of their plaintive cries and also because of their cute appearance—and the lorises of India and Sri Lanka, which take their name from the acrobatic and "comical" postures adopted as they move about ("loris" means clown in Dutch, language of the seafarers who first brought individuals to Europe).

The different ways in which members of the group move about are one of its most remarkable characteristics. Two subfamilies are recognized, based on modes of locomotion developed along two diametrically opposed evolutionary paths. The bush babies (subfamily Galaginae) are agile leapers, and comprise six species, all in Africa. The bush babies' leaping and fast-running progress is equally effective in the thick foliage of the rain forest and in the trees of the savanna. With a series of leaps between branches or tree trunks a bush grip of its hands and feet on the branch. Then, straightening its body, and maintaining a clamp-like hold on the branch, the potto delivers fearful bites or a violent blow with its shield, toppling the predator to the ground, where it is difficult for the aggressor to find a route back to its prey.

The Golden potto or angwantibo is much more slender than the potto, it has no shield and is incapable of such defense. Faced with a predator it will roll into a ball, completely hiding its head and neck within one arm and its chest. Only the small button-like tail emerges from this motionless, hairy ball, its erectile hairs raised in the form of a ring. The odd posture can puzzle a predator, which may approach carefully and sniff at the tail of the animal. As soon as this happens or it is seized by its rump, the angwantibo directs a bite under its arm at the opponent. The predator's abrupt recoil may throw the angwantibo several meters, where it will once again roll up into a ball.

All members of the family have a mixed diet of small prey, mostly insects, together with fruits and gums. Generally the smaller species feed more on prey (70–80 percent of diet), while the larger species eat more fruit and gums (70–80 percent).

The bush babies as they move rapidly through the foliage disturb many prey animals, whose movements betray them. Their highly developed ears have a series of folds which enable them precisely to orientate the outer ear towards a sound source, much like a bat. Experiments in captivity have shown that a bush baby could follow the movements of a flying or walking insect even through an opaque partition. Many prey items, such as moths and grasshoppers, are taken as they fly past. Keeping its feet clamped fast to the support, the bush baby suddenly extends its body and grabs the prey with one or both hands. These stereotyped hand movements associated with locating the prey by hearing are so precise that a Dwarf bush baby can catch gnats on the wing. Bush babies grasp their prey between the palm and the fingertip of the little finger, the only one with a fleshy pad.

The pottos and lorises, by contrast, have short fingers with soft pads on the tips of all fingers. They catch their prey, which is mostly slow moving and detected by smell, when it is stationary. Typically the prey is foul-smelling or bears hairs that cause irritations; these items are rejected by most predators, particularly bush babies, but pottos and lorises eat them with little problem—irritant caterpillars and butterflies, ants, fleas, foul-smelling beetles and poisonous

millipedes. The angwantibo feeds mainly on irritant caterpillars, holding the head between its teeth as it rubs the insect vigorously with both hands to remove some of the hairs before chewing it up. When it has swallowed the prey it wipes its lips and snout clean on a branch. If an angwantibo is given the choice between such caterpillars and more "edible" items such as grasshoppers or hawk moths, it will reject the caterpillars. The ability to eat prey which is not very palatable yet is easy to locate by its scent seems to be a consequence of the slow, imperceptible movement that is characteristic of pottos and lorises.

Compared with other mammals of similar size, members of the family have a relatively low reproduction rate. With few exceptions they reproduce only once a year, usually giving birth to a single young.

In bush babies, the newborn is covered in a fine down, its eyes are half open and it is unable to move about itself. The mother leaves it in the nest briefly only at the beginning, and after 3–4 days carries her offspring by the flank in her mouth. She then parks the young bush baby on a small branch and goes to feed nearby. As she moves from one spot to another during the night she carries her offspring, returning to the nest only at dawn. After 10–15 days, mother and young rejoin the group (several related mothers with young of different ages). In the largest species, the Thick-tailed bush baby and the Needle-clawed bush baby, at about one month the young is able to cling to its mother's back. It subsequently follows its mother (or other individuals of the same group) at gradually increasing distances.

Pottos and lorises do not make a nest and are more developed at birth. The thickly furred newborn clings to the belly of its mother, who carries it there for several days. Very soon, the mother deposits her young on a branch (baby parking) and only retrieves it later in the night when moving to forage elsewhere or even in the morning when going off to sleep. Later, the offspring follows its mother as she moves about, first clinging to her back, then following her over longer and longer distances, learning from her to recognize different types of food. Weaning is at 40 to 60 days, and the young enters puberty between 8 and 12 months of age.

The bush babies have the most complex social structure of the family. The female occupies a territory whose limits she indicates to her neighbors. The growing offspring accompanies nearly her every move

▶ **Moving about in the trees.** The bush babies are agile leapers with long hindlimbs and bushy tails used for balance when jumping. (**1**) Thick-tailed bush baby (*Galago crassicaudatus*). (**2**) Dwarf bush baby (*G. demidovii*), (**3**) The needle-clawed bush babies (here, *G. elegantulus*) have needle points that help to grip on trees on the nails of all digits except the thumb and big toe.

Lorises and pottos are slow-moving climbers with a strong grip, opposable first digit, and no tail. (**4**) The Slender loris (*Loris tardigradus*) has a particularly mobile hip joint for climbing. (**5**) Slow loris (*Nycticebus coucang*). (**6**) Potto *Perodicticus potto*). (**7**) Angwantibo or Golden potto (*Arctocebus calabarensis*).

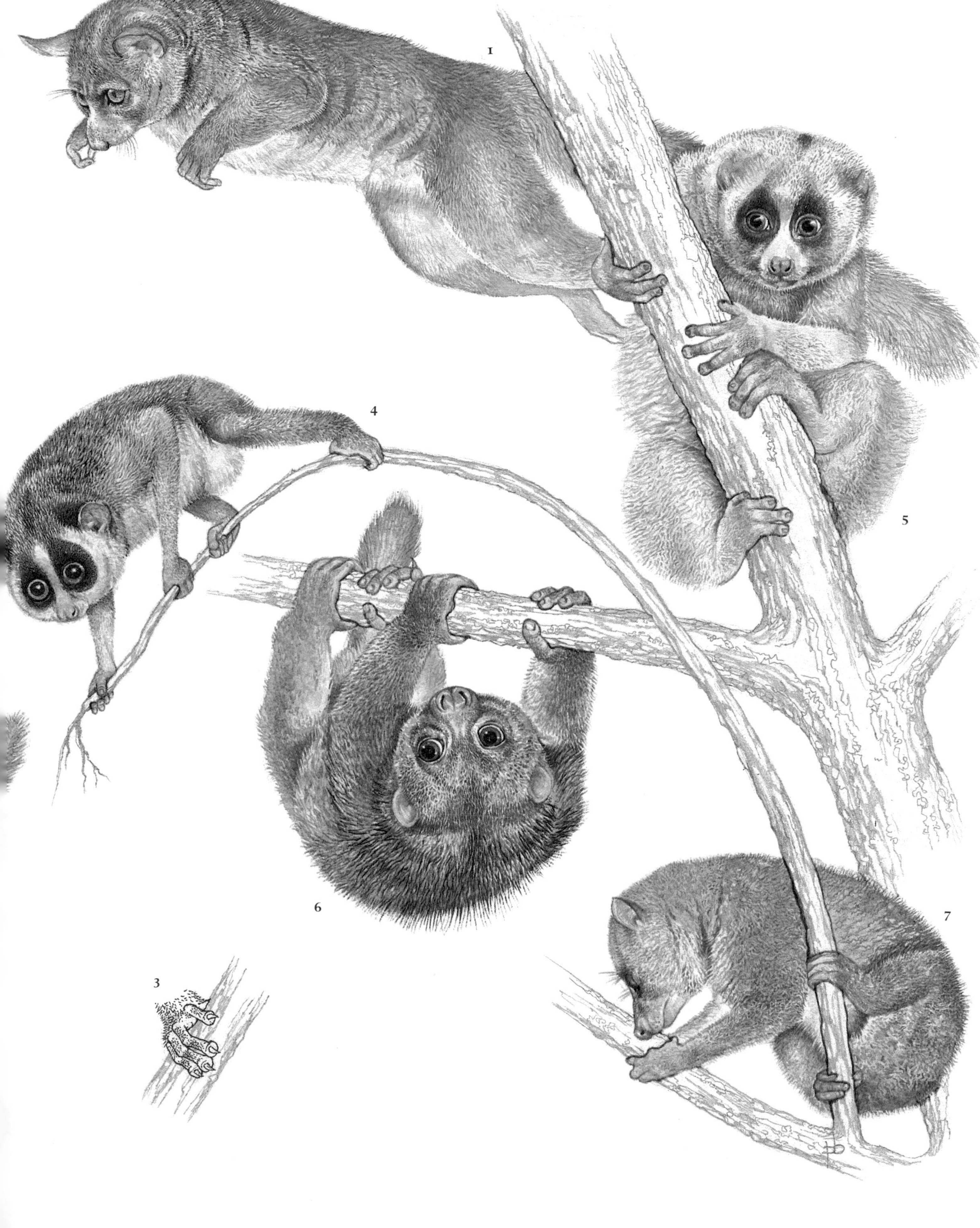
1
4
5
6
3
7

and so occupies the same territory. Males leave the mother's territory after puberty, but a young female maintains the association with her mother. Small social groups are thus formed comprising mothers, daughters and sisters and their young. Females from outside the group are chased off the shared territory, within which there may be areas that are primarily used by one or another group female.

Usually a single adult dominant male mates with the females of a group, but the same male may also control other females outside the group. Male territories are much bigger in area than those of females, and competition between males that are not established is intense. While females remain for years in the same place, dominant males are replaced almost every year. Young adult males that have gone through a period of wandering shortly after puberty establish themselves near the territory of a matriline group, sometimes forming small groups of 2–3 bachelor males awaiting the chance of supplanting a dominant male. Males bear the scars of fights for possession of a female group, and in captivity such struggles may result in death unless the combatants can be separated in time. In some species, such as the Dwarf bush baby, some small adult males remain in the female group, but in such cases they behave towards the females

HBL = head-and-body length; TL = tail length; wt = weight. Approximate nonmetric equivalents: 2.5cm = 1in; 230g = 8oz; 5ha = 12 acres.

Bush babies or galagos
Subfamily Galaginae

Six species, all in Africa. Very large eyes adapted to nocturnal vision; long tail with tuft; large membranous ears which can be folded up; long hind limbs adapted to leaping. Most construct a nest.

Allen's bush baby
Galago alleni

Gabon, N Congo, SE Central African Republic, S Cameroon and S Nigeria. In tropical rain forest. Living chiefly in lower storey, leaping from small trunk to trunk and between bases of lianas. HBL 20cm; TL 25cm; wt 260g. Coat: quite thick, smokey-gray with reddish flanks, thighs and arms; underside pale gray. Coloration of the tail in Gabon populations may range from dark to silver-gray, with or without 1–6cm white tip. Diet: fruits, small prey. One, usually single, birth in a year. Gestation: 133 days; newborn weighs 24g. Female territory about 10ha. Equal numbers of males and females at birth but later ratio 1:4. Density in Gabon 15/sq km. Longevity: to 12 years in captivity.

Lesser bush baby
Galago senegalensis
Lesser or Senegal bush baby.

Most widely distributed species, in a vast area bounding African rain forests from Senegal to N Ethiopia, Somalia to Natal, Mozambique to Angola, in dry forests, gallery forests and savanna with trees. HBL 16cm; TL 23cm; wt 250g. Smaller than Allen's bush baby, with paler gray coat, longer ears and hind limbs. Diet very varied, including small prey, *Acacia* gum, fruits, nectar. Gums provide the basic food in dry periods. Reproduction twice a year; often twins, exceptionally triplets born. Gestation: 123 days; newborn weighs 12g. Density up to 275/sq km in some regions. Longevity: to 14 years in captivity. Subspecies 9: *albipes, braccatus, dunni, gallarum, granti, moholi, senegalensis, sotikae, zanzibaricus.*

Thick-tailed bush baby
Galago crassicaudatus

E and S Africa in dense dry and gallery forests, often in same areas as Lesser bush baby. HBL 32cm; TL

44cm; wt 1.2kg; the largest bush baby and the one least adept at leaping. Coat gray. Accorded separate genus status by some (*Otolemur crassicaudatus*). Diet: similar to Lesser bush baby but prey items often bigger (birds, eggs, small mammals, reptiles), although not in all subspecies. Although area of distribution only half that of *G. senegalensis*, 10 subspecies distinguished based on size and tint of gray: *argentatus, lönnbergi, umbrosus, garnetti* (sometimes accorded species status), *monteiri, badius, crassicaudatus, lasiotis, agysimbanus, kikuyensis.*

Dwarf bush baby
Galago demidovii
Dwarf or Demidoff's bush baby or galago.

In three distinct areas: C Africa, Gabon, Central African Republic, Uganda, W Tanzania, Burundi, Zaire, Congo; Senegal, S Mali, Upper Volta, SW Nigeria, Dahomey to Senegal; very small area on coast of Kenya. In tropical rain forest, in thick foliage and lianas, crowns of tallest trees, beside tracks, in former plantations. HBL 12cm; TL 17cm; wt 60g; smallest lorisid and, with *Microcebus murinus*

of Madagscar, smallest of all primates. Coat: gray-black to reddish, depending on the individual and age (darker in young animals). Accorded separate genus status by some (*Galagoides demidovii*). Diet chiefly small insects but also fruits and gums. In Gabon one, usually single, young per year (1 in 5 births twins); gestation 110 days; newborn weighs 7–12g, reaching adult size at 2–3 months and puberty at 8–9 months. Female territories about 1ha, dominant males' about 1.8ha. Density about 50/sq km. Longevity: to 12 or more years in captivity. Subspecies: 7 based on variation in size and coat color, but some doubtful as variations may occur in some populations: *animurus, demidovii, murinus, orinus, phasmus, poenis, thomasi.*

Needle-clawed bush baby
Galago elegantulus

Gabon, S Nigeria, S Cameroon, N Congo. In forests. HBL 30cm; TL 29cm; wt 300g. Coat: an attractive reddish color on back, with darker line down back, ash-gray underside

▲ **Just 12 grams in weight,** a newborn Lesser bush baby clings in adult posture to the stalk where it has been placed.

◀ **Shining eyes** of this angwantibo, or Golden potto, reflect the photographer's flash. Night vision is aided by the *tapetum,* a layer of cells behind the retina of the eye which reflects the light back through the retina – hence the "eyeshine."

and dominant male as would an immature individual.

The dominant male regularly visits all his females in order to monitor their sexual cycle. When a female comes into heat, the male will not leave her until they have mated.

At night-time bush babies communicate by loud cries and they mark with urine throughout their travels by an unusual method; this "urine washing" involves balancing on one foot, depositing drops of urine in the hollow of the other foot and of the hand on the same side, subsequently rubbing one against the other. The same operation is carried out standing on the other foot. In this way the animal's path is marked with a scent of urine that has important social functions. By means of scent and sound, bush babies can maintain social relations at a distance ("deferred communication"). Not until morning do the bush babies gather again, using a special rallying call, before going to sleep as a group in a hole in a tree, in a clump of branches, or in a round nest made of green leaves piled up in the fork of a tree.

Among pottos and lorises there is a simpler social structure based on the same territorial system. There are no matrilinear groups of females, and social communication is principally by means of the messages contained in urine marking.

Members of the family feature in certain myths of African societies. In the ethnic groups of Gabon, for example, every species has its name. Allen's bush baby is called "Ngok" or "Nogkoué" in onomatopoeic style after the species' alarm call. It is said to warn of the approach of a leopard, a belief not far from the truth since Allen's bush baby lives in the undergrowth and will at once call out in alarm should a "suspicious" animal pass nearby.

A more obscure tale concerns the potto, which is supposed, if caught in a trap, to be able to hold an antelope prisoner in its vice-like grip until the hunter returns to his snare. This widespread myth celebrates the great strength of the potto, one of the largest members of the family.

Because of their small size and nocturnal habits, lorisids are not hunted systematically like monkeys and other vertebrates in the countries where they live. In fact, few people have seen these animals in the wild and apart from zones where their habitat is threatened with destruction, man currently presents little real danger to their survival. Sometimes a loris, bush baby or potto is brought to Europe as a pet, but the temperature of an appartment and the lack of insects sooner or later prove fatal to them.

PC-D

---

and flanks; tail gray always with white tip. Often placed in separate genus *Euoticus* on basis of differences indicated below. Nails elongated to form fine point; branches etc may be held by pad on last joint of digits as in other bush babies, or by digging in nails. Diet 80% gums with corresponding adaptations: second premolar in form of canine, elongated dental comb, longer intestine. The heavier muzzle than other bush babies, and large golden eyes give it a striking appearance. The only bush baby not to make a nest or take refuge in holes in trees. Reproductive biology not studied. Longevity: to 15 or more years in captivity. Subspecies 2: *G. e. pallidus* in North and *G. e. elegantulus* in South.

Needle-clawed bush baby
Galago inustus

In Great Rift Valley in Rwanda, Burundi, E Uganda. HBL 16cm; TL 23cm; wt 250g. Coat: very dark. Separated from Lesser bush baby on basis of coat color, sometimes placed in genus *Euoticus* on basis of nails which are similar to those of *G. e. elegantulus*. Biology unknown.

Lorises and Pottos
Subfamily Lorisinae

Two species in Africa, 2 in Asia. Tail very short, limbs less unequal in length than in bush babies, adapted for climbing. Hands and feet developed into pincers with opposable thumb and much reduced index finger. Do not construct a nest.

Potto
Perodicticus potto

In tropical forests of W African coast from Guinea to Congo and from Gabon to W Kenya. HBL 32cm; TL 5cm; wt 1.1kg. Large, muscular, compact. Coat: reddish-brown to blackish; ears often yellowish within. Processes project from vertebrae between shoulder blades to help form "shield" on nape and back. Diet: chiefly fruits, some gums, small, often irritant prey items (birds, bats, rodents) eaten whole. After 193-day gestation, a single young born dark-colored in Gabon, speckled with white in Ivory Coast, weighing 50g. Young attain puberty at about 1 year. Home range area of females about 7.5ha, of

males about 12.3ha. Density about 8/sq km. Longevity: to 15 or more years in captivity. Subspecies 5: *edwarsi, faustus, ibeanus, juju, potto.*

Angwantibo
Arctocebus calabarensis
Angwantibo or Golden potto.

S Nigeria, S Cameroon, Gabon, Congo, W Zaire. In Gabon, in wet, low forest rich in lianas, also in former scrubby plantations (where it preys chiefly on caterpillars). HBL 24cm; TL 1cm; wt 200–500g. Slender and light compared to the heavier compact *P. potto.* Coat an attractive light reddish color. Gestation 135 days; one young born weighing 24g with white-spotted coat. Mother mates a few days after birth, so weaning occurs a few days before the next birth. Subspecies 2: *calabarensis* in north, 400–500g; more slender and smaller *aureus* in south, 210g.

Slender loris
Loris tardigradus

India and Sri Lanka. HBL 24cm; no tail; wt 300g. Coat gray or reddish, varies according to subspecies. Similar slender build to angwantibo but larger. Eyes surrounded by two black spots separated by narrow white line down to nose. Biology similar to angwantibo's. Subspecies 6: *grandis, lydekkerianus, malabaricus, nordicus, nycticeboides, tardigradus.*

Slow loris
Nycticebus coucang

Bangladesh to Vietnam, Malaysia, Sumatra, Java, Borneo. HBL 30cm; TL 5cm; wt 1.2kg. Anatomy and life-style similar to potto, coat color more varied: ash-gray, darker dorsal line divides on head into two branches which surround eyes. One infant, 45g. Subspecies 10: *bancanus, bengalensis, borneanus, coucang, hilleri, insularis, natunae, javanicus, tenasserimensis, pygmaeus* (this last, in Indochina, is recognized as a separate species by some authorities).

TARSIERS

Family Tarsiidae
Three species of genus *Tarsius*.
Distribution: islands of SE Asia.

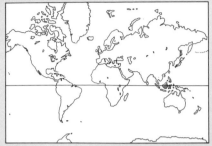

Philippine tarsier Ⓔ

Tarsius syrichta
Distribution: SE Philippine Islands (Samar, Mindanao etc).
Habitat: rain forest and shrub; crepuscular and nocturnal.
Size: head-body length 11–12.7cm (4.3–5in); tail 21–25cm (8.3–10in); weight 110–120g (3.9–4.2oz).
Coat: gray to gray-buff; face more ocher; tail tuft sparse.
Longevity: in captivity 8–12 years.

Western tarsier

Tarsius bancanus
Distribution: Borneo, Bangka, S Sumatra.
Habitat: primary and secondary rain forest, shrubs, plantations; lives in pairs; crepuscular and nocturnal; insectivorous and carnivorous.
Size: head-body length 11.5–14.5cm (4.5–5.7in); tail 20–23.5cm (7.9–9.2in); weight 105–135g (3.7–4.8oz).
Coat: buff, brown-tipped; tail tuft well developed but not bushy.
Longevity: 8 years or more.

Spectral tarsier

Tarsius spectrum
Spectral tarsier, Celebes or Sulawesi tarsier.
Distribution: Sulawesi, Great Sangihe, Peleng.
Habitat: primary and secondary rain forest, shrubs, plantations; lives in pairs or family groups; crepuscular and nocturnal; insectivorous.
Size: head-body length 9.5–14cm (3.7–5.5in); tail 20–26cm (7.9–10.2in); weight probably slightly less than either of the other species.
Coat: gray to gray-buff, sometimes darker than other species; tail tuft long and bushy, scale-like skin at tail.
A small, montane subspecies (*T. s. pumilus*) may be separated as the species *Tarsius pumilus*.

Ⓔ Endangered.

FOR the head-hunting Iban people of Borneo the tarsiers once played an important role as a totem animal, since the head of this small, nocturnal primate was believed to be loose. This belief stemmed from the extraordinary capability for rotation of the tarsier's neck vertebrae. The crucial systematic position of the tarsiers, between other prosimians and monkeys, makes them relevant to many problems of primate evolution.

The three species are of similar size. Tarsiers are buff-gray or ocher, sometimes beige or sand-colored. The coat is softer than velvet. These "vertical clingers and leapers" are famous for their leaping abilities. Head-and-body length is only about half as long as the whole hind limb. All three segments of the leg (thigh, lower leg, and foot) are elongated and roughly equal in length (in the Western tarsier 6–7cm each).

In the Spectral tarsier the long slender tail is covered in "scales" like those of mice and rats, but in the other two species only the surface of the skin shows how such scales were once arranged. In each species the tuft of hairs on the tail has a distinctive form. The second and third toes of tarsiers are equipped with a so-called toilet claw used for grooming, while the other toes bear nails, as do the fingers. The fingers are long and slender, and are used as a kind of cage to trap swift insect prey in the darkness of a forest night. The third finger of the Western tarsier is roughly the same length as the upper arm (about 3cm/1.2in).

The enormous size of the eyes indicates the tarsiers' nocturnal predatory habits. They are directed forward to allow stereoscopic vision and, like those of owls, can hardly be moved within their orbit. In a Western tarsier each eye weighs slightly more than the whole brain (about 3g) and in the brain the visual regions predominate. Tarsiers first locate many of their prey with their sharp ears. In comparison to other primates of their size the tarsiers have needle sharp, rather large teeth.

While fossil relatives have been found in Asia, Europe, and America, the tarsiers of today are restricted to some southeast Asian islands. All three species occur separately. The Spectral tarsier from Sulawesi is the most primitive of modern tarsiers and the one least specialized to both nocturnal activity and to exclusively leaping movement between vertical trunks and branches. Sulawesi is separated from the Philippines and Borneo by Wallace's Line, which marks the division between the Eurasian and the Australasian fauna. *Tarsius* is unusual in that its distribution crosses this zoogeographic border. This is an indication of the tarsiers' long residence in the region, which may go back more than 40 million years. Modern tarsiers may derive from the ancestor of the more primitive Sulawesi species. The Philippine and Western tarsiers share a number of characters, which cannot be found in the Sulawesi tarsiers.

All three species seem to be exclusively insectivorous and carnivorous. All kinds of arthropods are taken, including ants, beetles, cockroaches or scorpions. Variation in diet is great; different individuals may relish or disregard lizards and bats. A Western tarsier can catch and kill a bird larger than itself. Venomous snakes are also sometimes taken. Tarsiers also drink several times each night. Prey is caught invariably by leaping at it, pinning it down by one or both hands, and killing or at least immobilizing it by several bites. The victim, often caught on the ground, is carried in the mouth to a perch, where it is eaten head first. A Western tarsier may eat about 10 percent of its own weight per day (10–14g/0.35–0.50z).

Western tarsiers are sexually mature at about one year. In this species and the Sulawesi tarsier births occur throughout the year, although Western tarsier births peak at the end of the rainy season (February–April).

Courtship in the Western tarsier is accompanied by much chasing around, sometimes with soft vocalizations. During mating, which occurs when sitting in a tree, both partners are silent. The gestation period is about six months. The single young is born fully furred and with its eyes open. It can climb around in its first day of life and at birth weighs almost one quarter as much as its mother. Before hunting, the mother will "park" her offspring, who can call her with soft clicking or sharp whistling calls, depending how far away she is.

In the Western tarsier, one pair per home range, possibly with one young, seems to be the rule. One Sulawesi group has been observed to occupy about 1ha (2.5 acres), giving a density, in a favorable area, of about 250–350 tarsiers per square kilometer (650–900/sq mi). The home ranges overlap to some extent, but core areas seem to be defended, as indicated by frequent injuries (including typical fractures of bitten fingers). However, all three species reduce the risk of open fights by marking with urine and with a secretion from a skin gland on the chest (epigastric gland). In the Sulawesi species a pair or small family group may stay

together, uttering social calls near the sleeping site in the center of the home range. In these spacing calls the male and female perform beautiful duets with very different, high-pitched voices.

On Sulawesi and on Borneo tarsiers are abundant and not endangered, except where the forest is logged—logging certainly kills tens of thousands every year. In Malaysia and Indonesia tarsiers are protected by law. It seems that their only true sanctuaries will be national parks.

The appearance of tarsiers appeals to many people, who sometimes try to keep them as pets. But as these delicate primates require appropriate live food, they usually die within days. All tarsiers examined have had intestinal worms (hookworms, common ascarid worms, tapeworms and others). Man may be susceptible to some of these.

CN

▲ **The three species of tarsier,** showing the extraordinary proportions of the hindlimbs, the toilet claws used for grooming, and differences in tail-tuft patterns. (**1**) Spectral tarsier (*Tarsius spectrum*) or Celebes tarsier. (**2**) Philippine tarsier (*T. syrichta*). (**3**) Western tarsier (*T. bancanus*).

▼ **Vertical clinger and leaper.** The forward-seeing eyes allow the tarsier to judge its safe landing, and each eye may equal the brain in weight.

MONKEYS

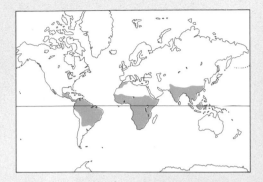

Three families: Cercopithecidae, Cebidae, Callitrichidae.
One hundred and thirty-three species in 30 genera.
Distribution: chiefly within the tropics, in S and C America, Africa and Asia.

Habitat: chiefly forests, some species in grasslands.

Size: ranges from the Pygmy marmoset, with head-and-body length 17.5–19cm (7–7.5in), tail length 19cm (7.5in) and weight 120–190g (4.2–6.7oz), to the drill and mandrill, males of which may measure 80cm overall (31.5cm), and weigh up to 50kg (110lb).

Marmosets and tamarins (family Callitrichidae)
Twenty-one species in 5 genera.

Capuchin-like monkeys (family Cebidae)
Includes **Howler, Woolly** and **Spider monkeys, Night** and **Squirrel monkeys, titis, sakis, capuchins,** and **uakaris.**
Thirty species in 11 genera.

Old World monkeys (family Cercopithecidae)
Guenons, macaques and baboons (subfamily Cercopithecinae), also **mandrills** and **mangabeys.**
Forty-five species in 8 genera.

Leaf monkeys (subfamily Colobinae), including **colobus monkeys** and **langurs.** Thirty-seven species in 6 genera.

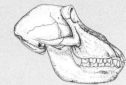

Savanna baboon (female)   16.6cm

Savanna baboon (male)   19.6cm

THE monkeys differ from the prosimians in the detailed structure of their skulls, the structure of their placenta and the relative size of their brains. In general, they show an increased reliance on sight over sound and smell and greater flexibility in their mode of locomotion.

The first monkeys appeared in the Oligocene, around 35 million years ago. Present-day monkeys are divided into two geographically separate lineages—the New World monkeys, sometimes called the platyrrhines, and the Old World monkeys, or catarrhines. These names are derived from the shape of the nose, which provides a reliable way of distinguishing between the two groups: New World monkeys have nostrils that are wide open and far apart (platyrrhine) while in Old World species the nostrils are narrow and close together (catarrhine). Other obvious differences include the development of a prehensile tail in the larger-bodied species of New World monkeys but not in Old World monkeys, and the development of ischial callosities—hard, sitting pads on the lower side of the buttocks—in Old but not New World monkeys.

It used to be thought that the New World and Old World monkeys had developed separately from Eocene prosimians and that their similarities were the result of convergent adaptations to a common way of life. However, more recent biochemical evidence links the two groups more closely, clearly distinguishing them from the prosimians.

The New World monkeys consist of two main groups. The marmosets and tamarins are all small-sized fruit-eaters mostly weighing around 300g (0.6lb). All the 21 species

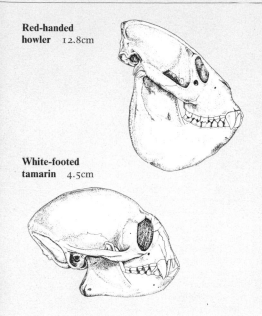

Red-handed howler 12.8cm

White-footed tamarin 4.5cm

Skulls of Monkeys

In all monkeys, the eyes are directed forwards for binocular vision and are contained in bony sockets produced by a virtually complete plate behind the orbit. The frontal bones of the forehead become fused together early in life. The brain-case is quite large and globular, reflecting the relatively large brain size of the monkeys. The two halves of the lower jaw are fused together at the mid-line and the body of the jaw is typically fairly deep.

Monkeys have spatulate (shovel-shaped) incisors, conspicuous canines, and squared-off molar teeth which typically have four cusps. In marmosets, the lower incisors are as tall as the canines (see box p344). Among the New World monkeys, the capuchin-like monkeys (family Cebidae) all have a formula of I2/2, C1/1, P3/3, M3/3 = 36, while both marmosets and tamarins (family Callitrichidae) have I2/2, C1/1, P3/3,

M2/2 = 32 and are the only primates to have reduced the dental formula by loss of molar teeth. As in other respects (see p342), Goeldi's monkey (*Callimico*) is intermediate in that it has the full dental formula of the capuchin-like monkeys but has tiny third molars in both upper and lower jaws. In Old World monkeys there is but a single dental formula (shared with apes and man) which has been attained by losing premolars: I2/2, C1/1, P2/2, M3/3 = 32. The molars of Old World monkeys are distinctive in that the four cusps arc joined in pairs by transverse ridges (bilophodonty, see p308).

Sexual dimorphism, often marked in monkeys, is less pronounced in New World species, among which howler monkeys are the most extreme case: their tendency towards leaf-eating is reflected in the depth of the lower jaw. In the Old World baboons the male can be twice as heavy as the female and the skull is accordingly much larger.

of this family are active in the daytime and arboreal, and the majority live in small groups consisting of a monogamous breeding pair and their offspring. Among monkeys, they are unique in that all their digits, except the first toe which bears a flat nail, end in a sharp, curved claw rather than a flat nail, which helps them to run up the sheer sides of the big trees in the South American rain forests where they live. They are strongly territorial and have shrill, bird-like calls.

In contrast, the capuchin-like monkeys (sometimes, but not here, termed "the New World monkeys") are a much more diverse family. They consist of four principal groups, sometimes classified as subfamilies, which occupy contrasting ecological niches. The howler monkeys are large, leaf-eating animals weighing 6–8kg (13–18lb) which digest their coarse diet with the help of a special extended cecum. They live in groups of 2–30, sometimes including several adult males. The spider monkeys and woolly monkeys are similar in size to howlers but feed on a mixed diet of fruit and leaf shoots and range widely. They have larger brains, relative to body size, than most of the other New World monkeys and very long periods of infant dependence—of all the South American primates they most closely resemble the African apes. They have very large ranges and can travel several miles in a day. The sakis and uakaris are smaller in size and specialize in feeding on the seeds of forest trees. The last group includes the day-active fruit-eating capuchins, the dainty squirrel monkeys and monogamous titis, and the nocturnal Night monkey.

The radiation of Old World monkeys is

probably the most recent among the major primate groups. Like the New World monkeys, the Old World monkeys may be grouped into subfamilies. The larger of the two subfamilies, the Cercopithecinae, is sometimes known as "typical monkeys." It includes the African baboons and the Asian macaques which are mostly large (10–20kg/22–44lb), omnivorous and terrestrial and live in open country. The baboons are replaced in the African rain forests by the terrestrial mandrills and the smaller, arboreal mangabeys. The drills and mandrills live in large troops which vary in size throughout the year and are thought to consist of harem units as in Hamadryas baboons, while the mangabeys occur in stable groups of 10–30 animals. The bare highlands and deserts of Ethiopia are occupied by the Hamadryas baboon and the gelada. In Asia, the macaques replace the baboons and include both arboreal and terrestrial species which are found in forested country as well as in more open areas. One species of macaque extends into North Africa and Gibraltar, where it has been (mis)named the Barbary ape.

The other group of Old World monkeys are the colobine monkeys—which includes nine species of African colobus monkeys and 26 Asian leaf monkeys. The distinctive feature of all these animals is that, unlike any other primates, they all possess a large forestomach which contains populations of microbes that are able to digest the cellulose in the foliage that the animals eat. The colobines are the primate equivalent of ruminants and are specialized folivores, though they will also eat fruit and flowers when these are available.   THC-B

▲ **Shape of the nose** distinguishes New World from Old World monkeys. The White-faced or Guianan saki (above) from north of the Amazon has nostrils that are wide open, far apart and face outward; it is platyrrhine (broad-nosed). In De Brazza's monkey, a guenon from African swamp forests, the nostrils are narrow, close together and point downward (catarrhine = downward-nosed).

◀ **Vivid colors** on the bare face of an adult male mandrill, largest of monkeys. The bright red pigment depends on gonadal hormones, so is absent in juveniles. The blue requires similar hormone but once established becomes structural and permanent.

MARMOSETS AND TAMARINS

Family: Callitrichidae.
Twenty-one species in 5 genera.
Distribution: S Central and N half of South America.

Habitat: chiefly tropical rain forest, also gallery forest and forest patches in savanna.

Size: ranges from Pygmy marmoset, head-body length 17.5–19cm (7–7.5in), tail 19cm (7.5in), weight 120–190kg (4.2–6.7oz), the smallest of all monkeys, to the Lion tamarin, head-body length 34–40cm (13–16in), tail 26–38cm (10–15in), weight 630–710g (22.2–5oz). Most species weigh 260–380g (9.2–13.4oz).

Coat: fine, silky, often colorful. Many species have ear tufts, mustaches, manes or crests.

Gestation: 130–170 days.

Longevity: not known in wild (to 7–16 years in captivity).

Species include:
Pygmy marmoset (*Cebuella pygmaea*).

Marmosets (*Callithrix*, 7 species), including the **Tassel-ear marmoset** ⓥ (*C. humeralifer*), **Bare-ear marmoset,** Silvery, or Black-tailed marmoset (*C. argentata*), **Common marmoset** (*C. jacchus*) and **Black tufted-ear marmoset** or Black-eared marmoset (*C. penicillata*). **Buffy-headed marmoset** Ⓔ (*C. flaviceps*)

Tamarins (*Saguinus*, 11 species), including the **Emperor tamarin** Ⓘ (*S. imperator*), **Red-handed tamarin** or Midas tamarin (*S. midas*), **Cotton-top tamarin** (*S. oedipus*), **Silvery-brown bare-face tamarin** ⓥ or White-footed tamarin (*S. leucopus*), **Geoffroy's tamarin** (*S. geoffroyi*), **Moustached tamarins** (*S. mystax, S. labiatus*), **Saddle-back tamarin** (*S. fuscicollis*), and **Pied tamarin** Ⓘ (*S. bicolor*).

Lion tamarin Ⓔ (*Leontopithecus rosalia*).

Goeldi's monkey Ⓡ (*Callimico goeldii*).

Ⓔ Endangered. ⓥ Vulnerable. Ⓡ Rare.
Ⓘ Threatened, but status indeterminate.

Wᴵᵀᴴ their fine, silky coats, long tails and a wide array of tufts, manes, crests, moustaches and fringes, marmosets and tamarins are the most diverse and colorful of the New World primates. These diminutive, squirrel-like monkeys of the tropical American forests share a combination of features that is extremely unusual among primates, including a monogamous breeding system, with few differences in form between the sexes, multiple birth (usually twins), extensive care of young by the father, and social groups as large as 15 comprised of the breeding pair and their offspring. The latter may remain in the group, even when adult, without breeding but help to care for their younger siblings. Marmosets (but not tamarins) are uniquely specialized gum eaters (see p344).

With one exception, marmosets and tamarins are distinguished from the other monkeys of the New World, the capuchin-like family Cebidae, by their small size, modified claws rather than nails on all digits except the big toe, the presence of two as opposed to three molar teeth in either side of each jaw, and by the occurrence of twin births. These features, together with their simple uterus and their lack of a rear inner cusp on the upper molars, have led to the suggestion that marmosets and tamarins are advanced primates which have again become small during their evolution, as an adaptation to the adoption of an insectivorous diet. Goeldi's monkey—a tamarin—is also believed to have undergone phyletic dwarfism but shares traits with both the Cebidae (three molar teeth in each jaw and single offspring) and the Callitrichidae (small size and claws rather than nails).

The Pygmy marmoset and Goeldi's monkey are the only representatives of their respective genera and both are restricted to the upper Amazon, in Brazil, Peru, southern Colombia and northern Bolivia. Goeldi's monkeys prefer to forage and travel in the dense scrubby undergrowth and, possibly because of this habitat preference, they are rare, with groups in patches of suitable vegetation isolated from one another by several kilometres. The Pygmy marmoset is also a habitat specialist, and populations are at their highest—up to 40–50 groups/sq km (104–130 groups/sq mi)—in the riverside and seasonally flooded forest where their preferred tree gum sources are most abundant. In areas away from rivers and in secondary forest they occur in lower densities of 10–12 groups/sq km (26–31 groups/sq mi).

The Tassel-ear and Bare-ear marmosets

▼ ► **Marmosets and tamarins:** variety in form and color of facial skin and head hair, foraging behavior, scent marking and offensive threat postures. (**1**) Goeldi's monkey (*Callimico goeldii*) in "arch-bristle" offensive threat posture used within the troop. (**2**) Pygmy marmoset (*Cebuella pygmaea*) gouging tree for gum and sap. (**3**) Silvery marmoset (*Callithrix argentata argentata*) and (**4**) Black-tailed marmoset (*C. a. melanura*), the latter presenting its rear with tail raised as an offensive threat posture used between members of different troops. (**5**) Buffy tufted-ear marmoset (*C. aurita*). (**6**) Black tufted-ear marmoset (*C. penicillata*). (**7**) Tassel-ear marmoset (*C. humeralifer intermedius*) eating typical fruit item. (**8**) Golden-rumped Lion tamarin (*Leontopithecus rosalia chrysomelas*) using elongated fingers to probe a bromeliad for insects. (**9**) Geoffroy's tamarin (*Saguinus geoffroyi*) scent marking a branch with glands situated around its genitals. (**10**) Red-chested moustached tamarin (*S. labiatus*) marking with chest glands. (**11**) Saddle-back tamarin (*S. fuscicollis*) marking with glands above pubic area. (**12**) Mottle-faced tamarin (*S. inustus*). (**13**) Emperor tamarin (*S. imperator*). (**14**) Black-chested moustached tamarin (*S. mystax*). (**15**) Cotton-top tamarin (*S. oedipus*).

13

14

15

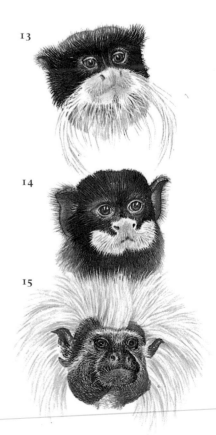

are restricted to Amazonia (except for the dark-coated subspecies of the latter which extends south into east Bolivia and northern Paraguay). The remaining five marmosets occur in southern, central and eastern Brazil. The tamarins, *Saguinus*, are distributed widely through Amazonia, north of the Rio Amazonas and, in the south, west of the Rio Madeira; one subspecies of the Midas tamarin (*S. midas niger*) occurs south of the Amazonas at its mouth. Only three species, the Cotton-top, Geoffroy's, and Silvery-brown bare-face tamarins, occur outside Amazonia, in north Columbia and Central America. These marmosets and tamarins inhabit a wide variety of forest types, from tall primary rain forest with secondary growth patches to semi-deciduous dry forests, gallery forests and forest patches in savanna regions in Amazonia, in the *chaco* of Bolivia and Paraguay and in the *cerrado* of central Brazil. They appear to be most numerous—3–5 groups/sq km (8–13 groups/sq mi)—in areas of primary forest with extensive patches of secondary growth forest, where they feed on fruits of colonizing trees. Bushy vegetation and dense liana tangles of the secondary growth are also their preferred sleeping sites, provide protection from predators such as the marten-like tayra and forest hawks, and probably contain higher densities of their insect foods.

The three subspecies of Lion tamarin survive in widely separated remnant forests in southern Brazil, in low densities of 0.5–1 group/sq km (1–3 groups/sq mi). Although they exploit secondary growth forest, they depend on tall primary forest for sleeping holes in tall tree trunks and for their relatively large animal prey.

Marmosets and tamarins eat fruits, flowers, nectar, plant exudates (gums, saps, latex) and animal prey (including frogs, snails, lizards, spiders and insects). They are generally not leaf-eaters although they infrequently eat leaf buds. The fruits are usually small and sweet, and the genera *Pourouma*, *Ficus*, *Cecropia*, *Inga* and *Miconia* are particularly important. They spend a large portion of their activity time (some 25–30 percent) foraging for animal prey, searching through clumps of dead leaves, amongst fresh leaves, along branches and peering and reaching into holes and crevices in branches and tree trunks. Marmosets also exploit the insects disturbed by Army ant swarm raids. The Pygmy marmoset is primarily an exudate feeder, spending up to 67 percent of its feeding time tree-gouging for gums and saps. Spiders and insects are also important, but fruit is eaten only infrequently. Other marmosets are primarily fruit-eaters, with flowers, animal prey and, particularly at times of fruit shortage, exudates also being important. The remaining members of the family are also fruit-eaters, supplementing their diet with animal prey, flowers and, particularly at times of fruit shortage, nectar. Gums are eaten occasionally when readily available. No marmoset species share the same forest, possibly due to their shared specilization on plant exudates, but a number of tamarin species do (see pp348–349), differing most importantly in the levels and sites at which they habitually travel and forage for animal prey as well as

▶ **Fruit is a major part of the diet** of the white-faced Saddle-back tamarin of Amazonia. As in all marmosets and tamarins, claws rather than nails are borne by all digits except the big toe.

▼ **Endangered species** of Southeastern Brazil, the Buffy-headed marmoset survives only in Atlantic forest remnants.

Gum-eating Monkeys

The Pygmy marmoset and the seven larger marmoset species are uniquely specialized gum eaters. Saps and gums are exuded where the tree is damaged (often from attack by wood-boring insects). The Fork-crowned lemur (p327) uses its tooth-comb to scrape up gums already exuded but marmosets are the only primates which regularly gouge holes irrespective of insect attack. The amount of gum exuded at any such site is usually very small, and they spend only 1–2 minutes licking droplets and gnawing at any one hole. Unlike the tamarins (**a**), the marmosets (**b**) have relatively large incisors, beyond which the canines barely protrude. The marmosets' lower incisors lack enamel on the inner surface, while on the outer surface the enamel is thickened, producing a chisel-like structure. Marmosets anchor the upper incisors in the bark and gouge upwards with these chisel-like lower incisors. The holes they produce are

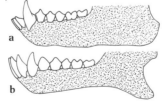

usually oval and about 2–3cm (1in) across at most, but favored trees may be riddled with larger holes and channels as long as 10–15cm (4–6in). The small size and claw-like nails of callitrichids are important adaptations that enable them to cling to vertical trunks and branches. Exudates are a larger part of the diet of the Pygmy marmoset than other marmosets. However, it is an important supplement to their diet, particularly at times of fruit shortage and for such species as the Common and the Black tufted-ear marmosets it is probably vital, allowing them to survive in the relatively harsh environments of northeast and central Brazil.

in their foraging methods. The marmosets and probably the Moustached and Emperor tamarins employ a foliage-gleaning and visual-searching method. The Lion and Saddle-back tamarins are more manipulative foragers, searching in holes, breaking open humus masses, rotten wood and bark, and they possibly exploit larger insects. Lion tamarins have long hands and fingers compared to other callitrichids, an adaptation for this mode of foraging.

Marmosets and tamarins live in extended family groups of between four and 15 individuals. The groups defend home ranges of 0.1–0.3ha (0.2–0.7 acres) in the Pygmy marmoset to 10–40ha (25–100 acres) in the case of *Saguinus* and *Callithrix*, the size depending on availability and distribution of foods and second-growth patches. They visit approximately one-third of their range each day, travelling up to 1–2km (0.6–1.2mi). Range defense involves extended bouts of calling, chasing and, when the groups confront each other, displaying. Marmosets, with their distinct white genitalia, display their rumps with their tail raised and fur fluffed. Lion tamarins raise their manes and tamarins fluff their fur and tongue-flick. Scent marking is also important as a means of registering the group's presence in an area. Marmosets use chest and suprapubic glands for such marking. A third type of scent marking, using the circumgenital glands, is used in communication between group members. This frequently takes place after tree-gouging, when marmosets mark and sometimes urinate in the holes they gouge, possibly as a means of maintaining dominance relations. The most obvious and prolonged social behavior within a group is mutual grooming, most frequently between the adult breeding pair and their latest offspring. Other forms of communication involve a limited number of facial expressions, specific postures and patterns of hair-erection, and complex, graded, high-pitched and bird-like vocalizations.

In the wild only one female per group breeds during a particular breeding season, although she may copulate with more than one adult male in the group. Reproduction is suppressed in other female members of the group, possibly as a result of subordination by the reproductive female as well as chemicals (pheromones) in the scent marks from her circumgenital glands. In Goeldi's monkey groups, there may be two breeding females in a group, although the social organization is otherwise apparently similar; breeding females produce a single young twice a year. In all other species, non-identical twins are born twice a year, at intervals only a few days longer than the gestation period. The birth weights of Pygmy and other marmoset litters are high, 19–25 percent of the mother's weight, which is considerably greater than in other primates. The male parent and other group members help in the carrying of young from birth. Marmoset infants are completely dependent for the first two weeks but by two months can travel independently, catch insects or rob them from other group members, and spend extended periods in play, wrestling, cuffing and chasing each other and other group members. They reach puberty at 12–18 months and adult size at two years of age. In the tamarins, Lion tamarin and Goeldi's monkey, whose newborn are smaller (about 9–15 percent of the mother's weight), males help carry the young only when they are 7–10 days old. Tamarins mature slightly slower than marmosets, becoming independent at $2\frac{1}{2}$ months.

All group members take some part in carrying the young and also surrender food morsels, particularly insects, to them and to the breeding female and infant carriers. So far as is known, this form of cooperative breeding is unique among primates. The adult "helpers" which stay in the family group may gain breeding experience through helping to raise their younger kin, while waiting until suitable habitat becomes available for them to breed or the possibility arises for them to breed in their own or a neighboring group. Once established as breeders, callitrichid monkeys have a higher reproductive potential than any other primate. In suitable conditions a female marmoset can produce twins about every five months.

The variety of species is greatest in the upper Amazon region, where they occur in limited distributions between even quite small river systems. They are therefore extremely vulnerable to extensive habitat destruction. Marmosets and tamarins used to be wrongly considered carriers of yellow fever and malaria and were persecuted in consequence; until 1970–1973 they were captured and exported in large numbers particularly for zoological gardens and for biomedical research. Today only Bolivia, Panama and French Guiana still permit their export. The Lion tamarins (see p350), the marmosets of the south and southeast of Brazil and such forms as the Pied tamarin, which has a minute distribution around the capital of Amazonas in Brazil, face extinction in the near future if habitat destruction continues unchecked. **ABR**

THE 21 SPECIES OF MARMOSETS AND TAMARINS

Abbreviations: HBL = head-and-body length; TL = tail length; wt = weight. Approximate nonmetric equivalents: 2.5cm = 1in; 230g = 8oz; 1kg = 2.2lb.
E Endangered. V Vulnerable. R Rare. I Threatened, but status indeterminate.

Marmosets

Genus *Callithrix*

In primary tropical rain forest mixed with second growth, gallery forest, forest patches in Amazonian-type savanna, Bolivian and Paraguayan *chaco*, NE Brazil and *cerrado* of C Brazil. Diet: fruit, flowers, plant exudates (gums, saps, latex), nectar, insects, spiders, frogs, snails and lizards. HBL 19–21cm; TL 25–29cm; wt 280–350g. Coat: very variable, some species showing subspecific variation from dark to completely pale or white; varying degrees of ear-tufts. Gestation: 148 days. Litter: 2.

Tassel-ear marmoset V
Callithrix humeralifer

Brazilian Amazon between Rios Madeira and Tapajos. Three subspecies: *C. h. humeralifer*—pigmented face, long silvery ear-tufts, mantle mixed silvery and black, back with pale spots and streaks, tail silvery ringed with black, white hip patches; *C. h. intermedius*—face pink, reduced ear-tufts, upper chest and back creamy white, rump and base of tail dark brown, underparts orange; *C. h. chrysoleuca*—face pink, fur near-white, long white ear-tufts, rest of body pale golden to orange.

Bare-ear marmoset
Callithrix argentata
Bare-ear, Silvery or Black-tailed marmoset.

Brazilian Amazon, S of Rio Amazonas, into E Bolivia and N Paraguay. Three subspecies: *C. a. argentata*—predominantly white, pink face and ears, black tail; *C. a. leucippe*—completely pale with orange or gold tip; *C. a. melanura*—predominantly dark brown with a black face, pale hip and thigh patches. No ear-tufts.

Common marmoset
Callithrix jacchus

NE Brazil in states of Piauí, Paraiba, Ceará, Pernambuco, Alagoas and Bahia; introduced in Minas Gerais and Rio de Janeiro. Coat: elongated white ear-tufts; body mottled gray-brown; tail ringed; crown blackish with a white blaze on forehead.

Black tufted-ear marmoset
Callithrix penicillata
Black tufted-ear or Black-eared marmoset.

South C Brazil in states of Goiás, São Paulo, Minas Gerais and Bahia. Two subspecies: *C. p. penicillata*, *C. p. kuhlii*. Coat: body mottled gray; ringed tail; black face. *C. p. kuhlii* (recognized as a species by some), restricted to small area of Bahia, distinguished by brown bases to hairs on outer thighs and flank, extensive pale cheek patches and a buffy-brown crown.

Buffy tufted-ear marmoset E
Callithrix aurita

Remnant forests in SE Brazil in states of Rio de Janeiro, São Paulo and Minas Gerais. Coat: whitish or buffy ear-tufts; forehead ochraceous to whitish; front of crown tawny or pale buff; side of face and temples black; back agouti to dark brown or black striated as in Common marmoset; tail ringed, underparts black to ochraceous.

Geoffroy's tufted-ear marmoset
Callithrix geoffroyi

Remnant forests in SE Brazil in states of Minas Gerais and Espírito Santo. Coat: blackish-brown, with elongated black ear-tufts; forehead, cheeks and vertex of crown white; tail ringed; underparts dark brown.

Buffy-headed marmoset E
Callithrix flaviceps

Remnant forests in SE Brazil in states Espirito Santo and Minas Gerais. Coat: ear-tufts, crown, side of face and cheeks ochraceous; back grizzled striated agouti; underparts yellowish to orange.

Genus *Cebuella*

Pygmy marmoset
Cebuella pygmaea

Upper Amazonia in Colombia, Peru, Ecuador, N Bolivia and Brazil. Prefers floodplain forest and natural forest edge. Diet: exudate, insects, spiders, some fruits. HBL 17.5cm; TL 19cm; wt 120–190g. The smallest living monkey. Coat: tawny agouti; long hairs of head and cheeks form a mane; tail ringed. Gestation: 136 days. Litter: 2.

Tamarins

Genus *Saguinus*

In tropical evergreen primary forests, secondary growth forest and semi-deciduous dry forests. Diet: fruit, flowers, leaf buds, insects, spiders, snails, lizards, frogs and plant exudates, such as gums, and nectar, when readily available. HBL 19–21cm; TL 25–29cm; wt 260–380g. Coat: very variable. Three sections: a) hairy-faced tamarins including white-mouth tamarins (*S. nigricollis* and *S. fuscicollis*), moustached tamarins (*S. mystax*, *S. labiatus* and *S. imperator*) and Midas tamarin (*S. midas*); b) the Mottle-face tamarin (*S. inustus*); and c) the bare-face tamarins (*S. oedipus*, *S. geoffroyi*, *S. leucopus* and *S. bicolor*). Gestation: 140–170 days. Litter: 2.

Black-mantle tamarin
Saguinus nigricollis
Black-mantle or Black-and-red tamarin.

Upper Amazonia, N of Rio Amazonas, in S Colombia, Ecuador, Peru and Brazil. Coat: head, neck, mantle and forelimbs blackish-brown; hairs around mouth, sides of nostrils gray; lower back, rump, thighs and underparts olivaceous, buffy-brown or reddish. Two subspecies: *S. n. nigricollis* with black mantle, *S. n. graellsi* with agouti mantle.

Saddle-back tamarin
Saguinus fuscicollis

Upper Amazonia, W of Rio Madeira to S of Rio Amazonas and S of Rios Japurá-Caquetá and Caguán in Brazil, Bolivia, Peru and Ecuador. Coat: extremely variable amongst 14 subspecies occuring between major as well as minor river systems. All have tri-zonal back coloration which except in palest forms produces a distinct rump, saddle and mantle. The cheeks are covered in white hairs. Fourteen subspecies: *acrensis*, *avilapiresi*, *crandalli*, *cruzlimai*, *fuscicollis*, *fuscus*, *illigeri*, *lagonotus*, *leucogenys*, *melanoleucus*, *nigrifrons*, *primitivus*, *tripartitus* and *weddelli*.

Black-chested moustached tamarin
Saguinus mystax
Black-chested moustached or Moustached tamarin.

South of Rio Amazonas-Solimões between Rio Madeira and Marañon-Huallaga in Brazil, Bolivia and Peru. Three subspecies. Coat: crown and tail black (*S. m. mystax* and *S. m. pluto*) or rusty red (*S. m. pileatus*);

prominent white nose and moustache; mantle blackish-brown; back, rump and outer thighs blackish striped with orange (*S. m. mystax*) or blackish-brown (*S. m. pileatus* and *S. m. pluto*); tail black; *S. m. pluto* distinguished from *S. m. mystax* by base of tail being white.

Red-chested moustached tamarin
Saguinus labiatus
Red-chested moustached or White-lipped tamarin.

Two subspecies widely separated: *S. l. labiatus* S of Rio Amazonas between Rios Purús and Madeira in Brazil and Bolivia; *S. l. thomasi* between Rios Japurá and Solimões in Brazil. Coat: crown with golden, reddish or coppery line and a black gray or silvery spot behind; mouth and cheeks covered by a thin line of white hairs; back black marbled with silvery hairs; throat and upper chest black; underparts reddish or orange.

Emperor tamarin I
Saguinus imperator

Amazonia in extreme SE Peru, NW Bolivia and NW Brazil. Coat: gray; elongated moustaches; crown silvery-brown; tail reddish-orange. Two subspecies *S. i. subgrisescens* has small white beard lacking in *S. i. imperator*.

Red-handed tamarin
Saguinus midas
Red-handed or Midas tamarin.

Amazonia, N of Rio Amazonas, E of Rio Negro in Brazil, Surinam, Guyana and French Guiana. Two subspecies: *S. m. midas* N of Rio Amazonas, *S. m. niger* to S in state of Pará, Brazil. Coat: black face; middle and lower back black marbled with reddish or orange hairs. Hands and feet of *S. m. midas* golden orange, those of *S. m. niger* black.

Mottle-faced tamarin
Saguinus inustus

N of Rio Amazonas between Rio Negro and Rio Japurá in Brazil extending into Colombia. Coat: uniformly black, parts of face without pigment, giving mottled appearance.

Pied bare-face tamarin I
Saguinus bicolor

N of Rio Amazonas between Rio Negro and Rio Parú do Oeste. Coat: head from throat to crown black and bare; tail blackish to pale brown above and reddish to orange below; large ears. Three subspecies: *S. b. bicolor* (Pied tamarin) has white forequarters, brownish-agouti hindquarters and reddish underbelly; *S. b. martinsi* has brown back and *S. b. ochraceus* is more uniformly pale brown.

Cotton-top tamarin
Saguinus oedipus

NW Colombia. Coat: crest of long, whitish hairs from forehead to nape flowing over the shoulders; back brown; underparts, arms and legs whitish to yellow; rump and inner sides of thighs reddish-orange; tail reddish-orange towards base, blackish towards tip.

Geoffroy's tamarin
Saguinus geoffroyi

NW Colombia, Panama and Costa Rica. Coat: skin of head, and throat black with short white hairs; wedge-shaped mid-frontal white crest sharply defined from reddish mantle; back mixed black and buffy hairs; sides of neck, arms and upper chest whitish; underparts white to yellowish; tail black mixed with reddish hairs towards base black at tip.

Silvery-brown bare-face tamarin [V]
Saguinus leucopus
Silvery-brown bare-face tamarin or White-footed tamarin.

N Colombia between Rios Magdalena and Cauca. Coat: hairs of cheeks are long, forming upward and outward crest; forehead and crown covered with short silvery hairs; back dark brown; outer sides of shoulders and thighs whitish; chest and inner sides of arms and legs reddish-brown; tail dark brown with silvery-orange streaks on undersurface.

Genus *Leontopithecus*

Lion tamarin [E]
Leontopithecus rosalia
Lion tamarin, Golden lion tamarin, Golden-headed tamarin, Golden-rumped tamarin.

Non-overlapping and minute distributions, in primary remnant forests in Brazil. Three subspecies (considered separate species by some): Golden lion tamarin (*L. r. rosalia*) in the state of Rio de Janeiro, Golden-rumped tamarin (*L. r. chrysopygus*) in São Paulo, and Golden-headed tamarin (*L. r. chrysomelas*) in Bahia. Diet: fruits, flowers, frogs, lizards, snails, insects and plant exudates (gums and nectar) when readily available. HBL 34–40cm; TL 26–38cm; wt 630–710g. The largest member of the Callitrichidae. Coat: long hairs of crown, cheeks and sides of neck form an erectile mane. Subspecies *L. r. rosalia* is entirely golden; *L. r. chrysomelas* is black with a golden mane, forearms and rump; *L. r. chrysopygus* is black with golden rump and thighs. Gestation: 128 days. Litter: 2.

Genus *Callimico*

Goeldi's monkey [R]
Callimico goeldii

Upper Amazon in Brazil, N Bolivia, Peru, Colombia and Ecuador, in dense undergrowth of non-riverine forests and bamboo forests. Diet: fruits, insects, spiders, lizards, frogs, snakes. HBL 25–31cm; TL 25.5–32cm; wt 390–670g. Coat: black or blackish-brown, with bobbed mane, tiered pair of lateral tufts on back of crown, thick side-whiskers extending below jaws. Gestation: 150–160 days. Litter: 1.

▲ **Unmistakable crest** of the Cotton-top tamarin of Colombia.

Cooperation is Better than Conflict

Why Saddle-back and Emperor tamarins share a territory

Associations between two or more species of monkeys are common in the forests of Africa and tropical America, but why the participants join forces has not been investigated until recently. In the Amazonian region several types of mixed association can be observed, one of which involves two members of the marmoset family, the Saddle-back and Emperor tamarins. Both of these squirrel-sized monkeys live in extended family groups that include from 2–10 individuals.

In parts of southeastern Peru it is common to observe Saddle-back and Emperor tamarins together. But to find out why the two species associate it is necessary to know how contact between the two groups is maintained, and whether just one or both species actively participate in promoting the association. If each species actively joins or follows the other, a mutually beneficial interaction is implied. However, if one actively joins and follows while the other is passive, evasive or hostile, it suggests that the active joiner benefits and that its associate does not.

By following the tamarins through the forest it has been found that the associated groups maintain frequent contact through vocal exchanges and are thus able to coordinate their movements even though they are not always in sight of one another. Following periods of separation, either species may go to join the other, implying that the association is of benefit to both participants.

An unexpected finding in Peru was that the associated groups live within a common set of territorial boundaries which they defend together. Such "co-territoriality" between species had not previously been

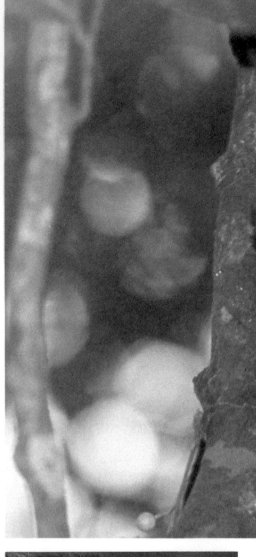

◄ ▲ **Mutual benefit** is the basis of joint use of the same forest area by the Saddle-back tamarin (ABOVE eating fruit of *Leonia*) and the elaborately moustached Emperor tamarin LEFT. also shown FAR LEFT in its natural habitat.

extend the shared territorial boundary. An opportunity to test this idea arose fortuitously when a group of Saddle-back tamarins disappeared, leaving the territory occupied only by Emperor tamarins. The family of Saddle-back tamarins that occupied the adjacent territory with a second group of Emperor tamarins then began to use both territories, switching back and forth from one to the other every few days. Although the two Emperor tamarin groups regularly confronted one another at their common border, the Saddle-back family was on friendly terms with both Emperor tamarin groups, and during clashes rested quietly on the sidelines. This observation appears to rule out the possibility of mutual reinforcement in territorial defense.

The third possibility is that the association somehow leads to more efficient exploitation of food resources. The available evidence supports this idea. Although the Saddle-back tamarin appears to have more manipulative skills and may eat more insects, both species are primarily fruit-eaters and feed on the same species of plants, often together in the same tree crown. The plant species that are most important in their diets are common small trees or vines that ripen their crops gradually over periods of weeks or months. A territory may contain 50 or more plants of a given species, virtually every one of which will be exploited by the resident tamarins. However, each plant is harvested no more than once every several days. By sharing a common territory, traveling together, and keeping in constant contact, tamarin groups can effectively regulate the intervals between visits, allowing sufficient time for the accumulation of ripe fruit, and thereby assuring that each visit will be well rewarded. If they did not share the same territory, or if they traveled independently within it, neither species would know when a given fruit tree had last been harvested, and would make frequent unrewarded trips to trees stripped of ripe fruit by the other species. Through cooperating, both species minimize the number of visits to empty trees and thus reduce their need to travel, consequently lowering their exposure to predators.

The relationship between the two tamarin species thus leads to a most unusual accommodation. In consuming the same types of fruit they are potentially the closest of competitors, yet by cooperating they attain a higher level of efficiency in harvesting the fruit crops in their territory than either species could by ignoring the other.

recorded among South American primates (though it is well documented for species of guenon in Africa). The evidence available clearly suggested that the interaction provides benefits to both associates, but as yet there were no clues as to the nature of the benefits. The most likely areas of mutual advantage fall into three categories: the detection of predators, defense of the territory, or more efficient harvesting of food.

Both species are highly vigilant, and each responds instantly to the alarm calls of the other, so there does appear to be a roughly equal exchange of benefits in the form of anti-predator warnings. However, different species commonly respond to each other's alarms without sharing territories, so there must be some additional factor which accounts for the co-territoriality of the two species.

One possibility is that the associated species may cooperate to defend or even

JWT

On the Brink of Extinction

Saving the Lion tamarins of Brazil

The Jesuit Antonio Pigafetta, chronicler of Magellan's voyage around the world, referred to them as "beautiful simian-like cats similar to small lions." Though not taxonomically accurate, Pigafetta's description, based on observations made in 1519, expresses well one's first impression of a Golden lion tamarin (*Leontopithecus rosalia rosalia*)—one of the most strikingly colored of all mammals and, unfortunately, one of the most endangered.

The Golden lion tamarin has a magnificent pale to rich reddish-gold coat and a long, back-swept mane that covers the ears and frames the dark, almost bare face, and sometimes brown or black markings on the tail. There are two other subspecies (recognized as species by some authorities, see p347), both black with gold markings, and both at least as endangered as their golden relative. All three Lion tamarins are found only in remnant forest patches in the Atlantic forest region of eastern Brazil. This was the first part of Brazil to be colonized over 400 years ago, and it is now the most densely inhabited region of the country as well as its agricultural and industrial center.

The Golden lion tamarin has always been restricted to forests of low-altitude (below 300m/1,000ft) coastal portions of the state of Rio de Janeiro, with several dubious records from adjacent portions of the neighboring state of Espírito Santo. Since they are easily cleared for agriculture and pastureland, low-altitude forests are usually the first to disappear in most parts of the tropics. Habitat destruction in Rio de Janeiro increased greatly in the early 1970s, when a bridge connecting the city of Rio de Janeiro with Niterói across the bay facilitated access to remaining portions of the Golden lion tamarin's range.

Added to the major problem of habitat destruction has been live capture of tamarins for pets and zoo exhibits. Hundreds of animals were exported legally in the 1960s, to be followed by uncounted others in an illegal trade that developed after the enactment of national and international protective measures in the late 1960s and early 1970s. This trade continues to the present day, mainly to serve a local market within eastern Brazil.

On top of this, it is reported that the Golden lion tamarin is sometimes even eaten by local people in Rio de Janeiro, a sad waste of such a beautiful and internationally important little animal.

Very few Golden lion tamarins still exist in the wild. Surveys conducted over the past three years by a joint Brazilian–American

team of personnel from the Rio de Janeiro Primate Center and the World Wildlife Fund–US Primate Program have located wild populations in only two areas, one of them a stretch of forest along the coast to the south of the mouth of the Rio São João and the other the 5,000 hectare (19sq mi) Poço d'Anta Biological Reserve established in 1974 mainly for the protection of this species. The former has already been divided into lots for beachfront housing development and appears to be doomed. The situation in Poço d'Anta is also far from satisfactory. The total population of Golden lion tamarins in the reserve is estimated to be 75–150 animals. The reserve is cut by a railroad and a road, a dam that will flood a portion of it is now being completed, poaching still takes place within its borders, and the guard force in the reserve is not sufficient to patrol it at maximum efficiency. Furthermore, only about 10 percent of the reserve is mature forest and only about 30 percent is suitable habitat for Golden lion tamarins.

A joint program involving personnel from the Rio de Janeiro Primate Center, the Brazilian Forestry Development Institute (which adminsters the reserve), the National Zoo in Washington, DC, and the World Wildlife Fund, is now being developed. Its aims are to provide detailed data on the ecology and population dynamics of the remaining Golden lion tamarins in the reserve, to restore the forest habitat, and eventually to reintroduce Golden lion tamarins into uninhabited portions of the reserve. This program must succeed if this species is to survive in the wild.

▲ **Lion tamarins** are monogamous like other callitrichids, and give birth to more than one young, usually twins.

◄ **The golden mane** is common to all Lion tamarins, but the Golden lion is the only entirely gold subspecies, the others including black in their coloration.

Fortunately, the species seems to be saved in captivity, thanks particularly to the effort of Dr Devra G. Kleiman of the National Zoo in Washington, DC, the Studbook Keeper for the captive colonies. Colonies in the USA and Europe now number more than 300 animals (up from 90–100 in 1972), and they continue to increase. In Brazil, the Rio de Janeiro Primate Center has about two dozen Golden lion tamarins under the supervision of Dr Adelmar F. Coimbra-Filho, Brazil's leading primatologist and the center's director. In 1980, five Golden lion tamarins from the Brazilian colonies were sent to the USA to ensure that genetic diversity is maintained, and future exchanges of animals are planned between the two countries.

The situation of the other two subspecies of Lion tamarin is similar. The Golden-rumped lion tamarin (*L. r. chrysopygus*) has always been restricted to the interior of the state of São Paulo, Brazil's most highly developed state, and is probably the rarest South American monkey. Much of its habitat had already been cleared by the early 1900s and none was seen between 1905 and 1970. In 1970 a remnant population was discovered in the 37,000 hectare (145sq mi) Morro do Diabo State Forest Reserve in extreme southwestern São Paulo. A few years later, a smaller population was also found in the 2,170-hectare Caitetus Reserve in central São Paulo. These widely separate populations are almost certainly the last remaining wild representatives of this subspecies, which probably numbers no more than 100 free-living individuals.

The Golden-headed lion tamarin (*L. r. chrysomelas*) has a tiny range in the southern part of the state of Bahia, one of the few parts of eastern Brazil where reasonably large stands of forest still remain although these are being logged and cleared for various agricultural projects. The one biological reserve there was inhabited by hundreds of squatters in 1980, and the situation continues to deteriorate.

However, there is a thriving colony of about 25 individuals of each of these subspecies in the Rio de Janeiro Primate Center. These are the only colonies of these two subspecies in existence.

Efforts are now under way within Brazil to convince the government and the general public of the importance of these uniquely Brazilian monkeys and to improve protective measures on their behalf. If these efforts fail, then all three Lion tamarins will almost certainly be extinct in the wild by the end of the decade.   RAM

CAPUCHIN-LIKE MONKEYS

Family: Cebidae
Thirty species in 11 genera.
Distribution: America (Mexico) south through S America to Paraguay, N Argentina, S Brazil.

Habitat: mostly tropical and subtropical evergreen forests from sea level to 1,000m (3,280ft).

Size: from head-body length 25–37cm (10–14.6in), tail length 37–44.5cm (14.6–17.5in) and weight 0.6–1.1kg (1.3–2.4lb) in male Squirrel monkey, to head-body length 46–63cm (18.1–24.8in), tail length 65–74cm (25.6–29.1in), and weight to 12kg (26.4lb) or more in the muriqui or Woolly spider monkey. Males often larger than females but not always.

Coat: white, yellow, red to brown, black; patterning mostly around head.

Gestation: from about 120 days to 225 days, depending on genus.

Longevity: maximum in 12–25 years range for most species.

Species include:
Night monkey (*Aotus trivirgatus*).
Titi monkeys (*Callicebus*, 3 species).
Squirrel monkey (*Saimiri sciureus*).
Capuchin monkeys (*Cebus*, 4 species), including **Brown capuchin** (*C. apella*) and **White-fronted capuchin** (*C. albifrons*).
Saki monkeys (*Pithecia*, 4 species).
Bearded sakis (*Chiropotes*, 2 species).
Uakaris (*Cacajao*, 2 species).
Howler monkeys (*Alouatta*, 6 species), including **Mantled howler monkey** (*A. palliata*).
Spider monkeys (*Ateles*, 4 species).
Muriqui or **Woolly spider monkey** (*Brachyteles arachnoides*).
Woolly monkeys (*Lagothrix*, 2 species).

► **Starved-looking** even when in the best of health, the Red or White uakari has almost hairless crown and facial skin whose coloration fades when kept out of sunlight. Uakaris have a short tail.

THE monkeys of the New World have evolved into an extraordinary array of ecological, social and anatomical types, many of them unique. The 30 species of the family Cebidae of which the capuchin monkeys, *Cebus*, are the type genus include the world's only nocturnal monkey, some of the world's brainiest non-human primates, and the only primates with prehensile tails. They feed on everything from insects and fruits to leaves, seeds, and even other mammals. One species occurs only in a small and isolated mountain range (Yellow-tailed woolly monkey), while others have spread throughout tropical South America (eg Night monkey and Brown capuchin). Their social organizations range from strict monogamy to large polygamous groups.

In spite of their broad range of adaptations, cebid monkeys share some common features. The family is set apart from other primates by the wide form of the nose (specifically, of the septum that separates the nostrils), its absence of cheek pouches, and its tooth formula (I2/2, C1/1, P3/3, M3/3 = 36). They are mostly found in tropical and subtropical evergreen forest, although some have adapted to elevations as high as 3,000m (9,900ft) and to forests with marked dry seasons. They live almost exclusively in trees, but some species will descend to the ground to play (White-fronted capuchin), look for food (Squirrel monkey), or travel between patches of woodland. Nevertheless, none of the cebids show obvious specializations for life on the ground, as do so many of the Old World primates. All the cebid monkeys that have

▲ **Prehensile tail** of the Black-handed spider monkey is used as a fifth limb and can support the whole weight of the animal. Spider monkeys have long arms and flexible shoulder joints for swinging along branches (brachiating).

▼ **Male** (RIGHT) **and female Black howler monkeys** have different colored coats.

muscles. The Brown capuchin eats larger fruits and more vegetation than the White-fronted species. The bearded saki monkeys derive most of their diet from the hard seeds inside fruits, which they position in the distinctive gap between the canine and premolar teeth before cracking them open.

These characteristic adaptations of form and ecology are closely related to body size. The smallest and lightest species can most easily leap from branch to branch without risk of injury, which may explain their lack of a prehensile tail. The small species also inevitably have small, weak jaws, which limit the size and hardness of the fruits which they can efficiently eat. Small size also means a low demand for energy and protein, so that small species can afford to live on foods that are relatively scarce but easily processed, such as insects and ripe fruits. Finally, the small gut and short digestive times of the smaller cebid monkeys are adequate for easily digested foods, but not adapted for tough plant materials like mature leaves. Large monkeys of course have the opposite advantages and disadvantages: high risk of injury from falling, strong jaws, high energy demand, and long digestive times.

Although cebid monkeys coexist with many non-primate competitors such as birds and bats, they compete directly with other cebid monkeys. It is common for as many as five species to feed on one tree species or even in the same tree. When several species feed in a single tree, physical clashes determine which has precedence. Usually the smaller or less agile species are evicted. Their vulnerability to being displaced from fruit trees may have contributed to the specialized life-styles shown by the smaller species. Titi monkeys are able to eat green fruit before it is palatable to the larger monkeys. Night monkeys feed at night in the same trees that are dominated during the day by big species. Squirrel monkeys find safety in numbers that are too great for larger monkeys, living in smaller groups, to chase out of a tree.

Even when different species do not share the same fruit trees, it may be as a result of effective competition between them. The species which exploits a given resource most efficiently will generally force other species to choose different foods. Thus the greater ability of large monkeys to eat big fruits and to digest tough leaves may have accelerated the tendency of smaller monkeys to use other resources. These pressures may explain why bearded sakis are specialized for opening the seeds inside fruits, and why

been tested have some color vision, usually fairly acute, although they have poor sensitivity to the red end of the color spectrum. Fur colors tend to be white, yellow, red to brown, and black, and most of the color patterning occurs around the head.

Species such as the Squirrel monkey, which move by leaping, have thighs that are shorter relative to the lower leg, thus allowing more force to be developed in the jump, than species that more commonly clamber, such as the howler monkeys. Others, like spider monkeys, that swing hand over hand below branches have relatively long arms and extra mobility in the shoulder joint. The very flexible, prehensile tail of the larger cebids is used like a fifth limb. They can use it to grab on to branches for safety and can even hang from it to feed near the tips of branches.

Each species has a diet that matches, and may be limited by, its anatomy, in particular the forms of the jaws, teeth and gut. Leaf-eating Mantled howler monkeys have relatively broad flat teeth, very deep lower jaw bones, and a relatively large gut occupying one third of their body volume, because they must process large amounts of tough plant material (see p368). The insect-eating Squirrel monkey has sharp, narrow teeth to macerate insects quickly, and a short, simple gut occupying less than one sixth of its body volume, which is all that is needed to absorb this nutritious food. Even within one genus, the Brown capuchin differs from the White-fronted capuchin in having a deeper lower jaw and more massive jaw

uakaris, which eat many of the same foods as other medium-sized monkeys, are found only in a restricted habitat, flooded swamp forest, where other cebids are absent.

Different species within one genus are likely to compete severely because they are more likely to be similar in anatomy and ecology. That competition for food has influenced the evolution of cebid monkeys is strongly suggested by the fact that in any one place it is rare to find more than one species of the same genus. In the few examples of such overlap, such as between the Brown capuchin and other capuchin species, there is some evidence that they have reduced competition by eating less similar foods where they coexist than where they occur alone.

Each species of cebid monkey also has its

distinctive social structure. Most smaller cebids of 0.7–1.5kg (1.5–3.3lb), including the Night monkey, titi monkeys, and probably also sakis, are monogamous. The pair bond is maintained both by friendly interactions between the adult couple and by active aggression toward other members of the same species and sex. In monogamous species, juveniles may stay with their parents for up to a year or two after the birth of the next infant, so that groups of up to five animals may be seen. An exception among the smaller species is the Squirrel monkey, which lives in large groups, typically containing 30–40 animals, with up to a dozen reproductive females and several adult males. Females tolerate females, but are not very tolerant of males and often gang up on individual males within their group to drive them away from their vicinity. During the breeding season, males may have spectacular fights that leave the loser injured or weakened. A female often mates with several males during her brief period of receptivity.

All the larger cebids (2–9kg/4.4–20lb) typically live in groups of at least five

▲ **Representative species** of capuchin-like monkeys, showing movement among the trees. In most species males are slightly larger than females (shown here); in a few species there are color differences between the sexes.
(1) White-faced or Guianan saki (*Pithecia pithecia*) (male has matt of buff hair on top of head). (2) Red uakari (*Cacajao rubicundus*); the two uakaris are the only short-tailed primates (other than man) in the New World. Both (3) the Dusky titi (*Callicebus moloch*) (4) the Squirrel monkey (*Saimiri sciureus*) move chiefly by leaping and have tails that are not prehensile. (5) Brown capuchin (*Cebus apella*). (6) The Night monkey (*Aotus trivirgatus*). (7) The female Black howler monkey (*Alouatta caraya*) is olive-buff. As in other larger cebids, the tail is prehensile, naked beneath the tip for better gripping. In (8) the Black-handed spider monkey (*Ateles geoffroyi*), the tail may be used for picking up small objects (eg food items). (9) Humboldt's or Smokey woolly monkey (*Lagothrix lagotricha*).

animals and are more or less polygamous. At low population densities, howlers and capuchins often live in harems in which one male monopolizes 1–3 females. At higher population densities, these same species occur in larger groups of 7–20 animals that include several adult and subadult males. Such large, multi-male groups are normal for bearded sakis, uakaris, woolly monkeys and muriqui or Woolly spider monkey. In these species, it seems that females usually mate with the dominant male or males, but solicit and mate with subordinate or subadult males as well. Spider monkeys (and to a lesser extent woolly monkeys and the Woolly spider monkey) have variable social groupings in which individuals daily join and leave subgroups of changing size and composition. Only for a few weeks a year do all 20 or so members of a spider monkey group gather together in one place, but all group members continue to recognize and tolerate one another over long periods.

Group size seems to depend to a large extent on the productivity and abundance of the foods typically eaten by a given species. Most species that live in small groups feed on small, scarce, and scattered resources, such as insects, small fruit crops in vines, and newly emerged leaves of vines and bamboo. Species with large groups typically use large, abundant, and clumped or isolated resources, such as fruits on large fig trees. This relation holds true even within one species of, for example, spider monkey, forming subgroups that vary in size: the smallest subgroups of 1–3 animals occur when food trees are small and scattered, and the largest of 7–20 animals when food trees are large and clumped. The exception to this general pattern is the Night monkey, with small monogamous groups, but feeding in large, clumped food trees.

How a species uses its home range also depends to a large extent on how its food resources are distributed. Titi monkeys, for example, feed in small, scattered food trees and use their home range in a very even fashion, visiting each part of it every few days. Squirrel monkeys and White-fronted capuchins depend on large, clumped or rare trees and their large groups travel their home range in an uneven way, spending most of their time in a small sector until the fruit there is exhausted, then moving on to find new sources.

These patterns of home range use in turn affect how neighboring groups of a species interact. Those cebid monkey species that exploit their home range in a very even way are usually territorial, and may defend their range with loud dawn calls, as given by titi and howler monkeys (see pp366, 368). At the opposite extreme, different groups of Squirrel monkeys seem to overlap completely and usually show no overt aggression toward each other even when feeding in the same fruit tree. Other species show intermediate patterns—Brown capuchins will fight other groups of its species only if a fruit tree is at stake, while White-fronted capuchin groups tend to avoid each other whenever possible.

The relation between large group size and abundant or large food sources may be caused by competition for food between members of a social group. Within their groups of 3–15 or more, Brown capuchins often fight over food (see box). Individuals which cannot win aggressive confrontations, or are not tolerated by other group members, suffer markedly reduced feeding success. Fighting is most common in small fruit trees, or when food is scarce. At these times some group members may forage alone or in smaller groups.

However, there are also compensating benefits to large group size. For instance, individuals in large groups probably suffer less predation. The more eyes and ears there are to watch for predators, the lower the chance that a predator attack will be successful. Throughout Central and South America there are a variety of large hawks and eagles, some of them specialized to eat monkeys. In southeastern Peru, each capuchin group is attacked by an eagle once every two weeks on average, and there are less serious threats up to several times a day. Brown capuchins are so wary that they consistently take alarm at completely harmless birds that fly by.

In the absence of predation, social groups could be relatively small. The lack of major nocturnal predators may allow the Night monkey to live in small groups, even though they feed in large, clumped food trees (see p364). Spider monkeys may be too big for eagles to kill, and this immunity may facilitate the formation of their characteristic small foraging subgroups.

Other advantages to group life include communal finding and defending of food trees. Although individuals of many species know in advance what trees will be in fruit and where they are, some portion of their diet comes from unpredictable or small sources which they find by chance. In either case, extra individuals in the group can increase the pool of food available to the group as a whole by sharing knowledge about fruit trees. In fact, at least one species, the Brown capuchin, his highly distinctive loud whistles which are given when a group member finds or begins to use a rich source of food. Larger capuchin groups also usually win fights for possession of fruit trees.

There are other, more specific advantages to members of large groups. Squirrel monkey females receive no help from males in rearing the young, but they do have other female "friends" that help carry and watch over an infant while its mother forages. The "friends" that do not have their own young are the ones most able to help a mother, and often are her own offspring from previous years. A male howler monkey deciding whether to join a new group may prefer one which has a relatively large number of reproductive females. For a juvenile White-fronted capuchin, having a large number of young group mates to play with may be important to its social and physical development.

Several cebid monkeys actively form mixed groups with members of other species. A great variety of stable associations has been recorded, most notably between Squirrel monkeys and capuchins, Squirrel monkeys and uakaris, even capuchins and spider monkeys. Observations in Peru and Panama suggest that the benefits are often one-sided in such mixed associations. For instance, it is almost always the Squirrel monkeys that join up with the capuchins, and capuchins usually determine the direction of movement of the combined group.

Social Station in Brown Capuchins

As a group of Brown capuchins spreads out in search of food, it is possible to predict which position each monkey will take up as it forages. Each individual's position depends upon its foraging success when food is scarce. If there is squabbling at a food tree it is the most dominant male and those whom he tolerates that almost always feed first and for longest. The subordinate individuals whose

proximity the dominant male will not tolerate must wait until the dominant's entourage has left the tree.

The desirability of a given position in a foraging group can be rated by the extent to which it offers access to food and safety from predators. Individuals securing a central position benefit from the watchfulness of their neighbors whose presence also shelters them from a direct attack. However, success in foraging may be highest at the leading edge of a moving group, where new resources are being discovered. But if an individual can parasitize the efforts of 8–12 members who scout, then the best position is behind the leading edge, but close enough to monitor the success of individuals at the front.

Group members keep a wary eye on the dominant male and adjust their own position according to his tolerance of them. The dominant male occupies the central area just behind the leading edge, where both his feeding success and protection from predators are greatest. He is very tolerant of infants and young juveniles, and these tend to follow him, just behind the center of the group. Females tolerated by the dominant male, plus their older offspring, often form the leading edge of the group, trading off foraging success for exposure to predation. Finally, those females and males not tolerated by the dominant male are found on the periphery of the foraging group, at the trailing edge, or even further away from the rest of the group. Their priority seems to be to avoid aggression, even at the expense of increased time spent looking for food and/or greater risk of attack by predators.

CHJ

◄ **Pair of Guianan or White-faced sakis.** Like many other New World monkeys, these live in monogamous pairs or small family groups. Only the male has the white face.

▼ **The muriqui** or Woolly spider monkey is the largest and most ape-like of the New World monkeys. It also appears to be the most endangered neo-tropical primate species. Found only in the Atlantic forest region of southeastern Brazil (though once abundant in this area) its numbers have fallen to just 200–250 muriquis in seven small remnant forest areas. Three of these forests are government reserves and four are privately protected, but none can be considered entirely secure against further forest destruction over the long term.

Since the muriqui is the largest mammal entirely restricted to Brazil and also a single-species genus with no other close relatives, it is a most appropriate symbol of the Brazilian conservation movement.

Adult muriquis weigh at least 12kg (26lb) and perhaps as much as 15kg (33lb), and can measure almost 1.5m (5ft) from head to tail tip.

Because capuchins have significantly smaller home ranges than Squirrel monkeys—1–2sq km (0.4–0.8sq mi) compared with over 4sq km (1.5sq mi), they probably know better the wheareabout of fruiting trees. The Squirrel monkeys arrive more quickly at local food trees by following the capuchins than if they forage alone. This explains why such associations form only between ecologically similar species, and also why only one of the species actively maintains the mixed group. (For two species of a different family, the marmosets and tamarins, that derive mutual benefit from sharing a territory, see p348.)

Regardless of their social organization, most species have a similar diversity and range of calls. This basic set includes some forms of trills, squeaks, grunts, hoots, barks, and whistles. Nevertheless, distinctive differences arise because each species uses only a certain number of the possible basic call types, which it combines in characteristic ways, and employs in different contexts. A striking example is the different forms of the call used for contacting and intimidating other groups: Night monkeys use low resonant hoots, howlers have loud roars, Brown capuchins give whistles, and titis perform a complex sequence of gobbles and pumping notes.

Some social displays are common to many, if not all, cebid genera. Most species show some form of threat behavior to other members of the same species, and even toward other species and predators. The usual posture is with the mouth opened and teeth bared to expose the canines. Not surprisingly, this display seems to be absent in titi monkeys, which have small canines, and Night monkeys, which fight at night. Along with the open mouth display, a monkey often shakes a nearby branch, bounces on it, or tries to break it off, a hazard to the biologist lurking below.

Grooming is the most common friendly behavior shown by cebids. Often an individual approaches another and lies down in a characteristic posture on the branch next to it, or even right on top of its feet. Occasionally an animal will take the initiative in grooming another. The groomer usually grooms areas difficult for the other monkey to reach or see, such as the back of the neck, crown, and hind limbs. An individual grooms for only a few minutes at a time, then turns around and solicits grooming from its partner. According to the old rule "I'll scratch your back if you scratch mine," the pair usually exchanges grooming bouts several times; the sequence often stops when one of the partners refuses to return grooming.

The behavior of infant monkeys differs from adults' in many ways. They are clearly less coordinated and less aware of the appropriate occasion on which to behave in a particular way. Some juvenile behavior is almost entirely absent from the adult repetoire, and vice versa. It seems that many adult behavior patterns have to be learned, or at least practiced, before an individual can perform them correctly. Since their food supply is assured, infants spend much of their time playing, either exploring their environment or chasing, grappling, wrestling, and jumping on other juveniles. Both within and across species, the more playmates a juvenile has, the more likely it is to play. Monogamous species with small groups tend to show relatively little play for the amount of time they spend resting, whereas in Squirrel monkeys, the infants often form a completely distinct subgroup which plays continuously whenever the group moves slowly (see p362).

A great deal still remains to be learned about cebid monkeys. A number of species in several genera are known only from museum specimens. Opinions on the division of the family into subfamilies, for example, are constantly changing. Only a few species have been studied for over five years, yet long-term studies are essential to understanding the behavioral flexibility and development of individuals and the relation between environment and behavior.

Over one-third of the species of cebid monkeys are listed as endangered or vulnerable to extinction. The Woolly spider monkey (or muriqui) is the most endangered (see LEFT). In the Amazon basin, spider monkeys and woolly monkeys have been shot for food out of large portions of their former rangers. These species are especially vulnerable because of their slow maturation, low reproductive rate, and dependence on mature rain forest that is being cut down for farms and wood pulp at the rate of 14,000 hectares (35,000 acres) a day. Smaller cebids, like the titis, Night monkey and Squirrel monkey, can adapt more easily to habitat loss and change. But even for these the impending destruction of mature rain forest throughout South America will prevent scientists from ever observing them in a truly natural state. Species that are restricted to tiny ranges, like the Yellow-tailed woolly monkey, or are naturally fairly scarce, like all the species of uakaris, may become extinct before mankind can learn of their unique adaptations.

CHJ

THE 30 SPECIES OF CAPUCHIN-LIKE MONKEYS

Abbreviations: HBL = head-and-body length; TL = tail length; WT = weight. Approximate nonmetric equivalents: 2.5cm = 1in; 230g = 8oz; 1kg = 2.2lb.

E Endangered. V Vulnerable. I Threatened, but status indeterminate.

Classification of cebids

The constant revision of the taxomomy of the cebids is a reflection of how little is known about these New World monkeys. Many species have not been studied since they were first discovered, and their distributions are known only from a few collecting localities. The scientific criterion for distinguishing a species—whether it can interbreed extensively with other animals—cannot be applied to many cebids because they do not overlap in range. In other instances, there are important differences in the genetic material between forms that cannot reliably be distinguished by color. There is even debate about whether all the cebids, or just *Saimiri* and *Cebus*, should be united with the marmosets and tamarins in a single family. The treatment here is the more usual one of keeping them separate. Where the species status of a distinct form is debated, this is noted in the introductory remarks to the genus.

Genus *Aotus*

Night monkey

Aotus trivirgatus
Night monkey, Owl monkey, douroucouli.

From 81°W in Panama south to N Argentina, except Guianas, Uruguay, Chile, E Brazil. Savanna and dry to rain forests, from sea level to over 3,000m. Primarily eats fruits, leaves, and insects; vertebrates and eggs eaten occasionally. Chiefly nocturnal. Monogamous, in groups of 2–5. Sexes similar in size. HBL 24–47.5cm; TL 22–42cm; WT 0.8–1.3kg. Coat: grizzled brown, gray, or reddish on back, back of head, and limbs; underside buff-white to bright orange; head distinctive, with triagonal white patches above large eyes, and three black stripes, between and either side of eyes, converging on crown. Populations with similar coats may vary in chromosome number and pattern. (Other authorities recognize 2, 3, even 9 distinct species.) Gestation: 133 days. Litter size: 1, rarely 2. Birth frequency: 1 per year, births seasonal in some areas.

Titi monkeys

Genus *Callicebus*

In disturbed to mature, moist to rain forest; from sea level to about 1,000m. Prefer understorey up to 10m. Feed on fruits, often unripe, insects and leaves. Coat dense and long. Canines short relative to other cebids. Males may be slightly bigger than females. Diurnal. Monogamous, in groups of 2–5. Gestation: not certain, probably over 4 months. Litter size: always 1. Births once a year, usually in early rainy season.

Dusky titi

Callicebus moloch
Dusky or Red titi.

Colombia and W Venezuela south to S Bolivia, E of the Andes to Rio Negro N of the Amazon and to Maranhâo (Brazil) S of the Amazon. Prefers swampy, flooded, disturbed habitats. More leaf-eating than Yellow-handed titi, and can live on leaves and green fruits alone for short periods. HBL 26–41cm; TL 29.5–52cm; WT 0.7kg. Coat: gray to red-brown; belly same as back, or sharply defined orange-red; forehead may contrast, with brighter red, gray, or black band. Tip of tail pale cream or buff.

Yellow-handed titi

Callicebus torquatus
Yellow- or White-handed titi, Widow monkey, Collared titi.

N of Amazon and Rio Marañón (Peru) to Orinoco and the Guianas; S of Amazon to Rio Purus in Brazil. Prefers unflooded, mineral-poor, sandy-soil forests. Eats more insects than Dusky titi, but over 75% of diet is fruit. HBL 31–46cm; TL 38–51cm; WT about 1kg. Coat: red-brown to black; forehead face, throat, and tip of tail may have contrasting white-cream to orange fur; fur on hands pale cream; forearms, legs, and feet black; tail dark brown to black.

CONTINUED ▶

▶ **Humboldt's woolly monkey** (or Smokey woolly monkey) young.

Exploration and Play

Steps to adulthood in the Squirrel monkey

Squirrel monkeys are small, agile and inquisitive New World monkeys that live in thickets, mangrove swamps, and the lower layers and edges of tall forests. They are omnivores that feed mostly on fruit and insects, relying on their inquisitiveness and speed to catch the insects that are their preferred foods. Group sizes of 10 to 35 are common in smaller forests. In large expanses of Amazonian forests, groups may contain several hundred individuals. Adult females with their young travel together and form the core of the group. Adult males intermingle in the group during the several months of mating season, then take more peripheral positions during the remainder of the year. Squirrel monkeys are not territorial and home ranges often overlap extensively; however most groups avoid close contact with neighboring groups. Range size varies—the limited information available suggests day ranges of 15–25 hectares (37–62 acres), possibly up to 60 hectares (150 acres) or even 130 hectares (320 acres) in some areas.

In remote forests that are seldom visited by humans, Squirrel monkeys will appear out of the foliage to peer down at human visitors, cocking their heads and moving from branch to branch for better vantage points. The youngsters usually show the greatest interest and remain the longest. If an unusual bird perches in the trees, nearby monkeys may come up for a closer look. If all appears to be safe, the monkeys may even try to touch or catch the bird. Some birds appear to respond playfully to the monkeys' curiosity, flying just out of the monkeys' reach and waiting for the monkeys to approach again before flying just a few more feet away.

Young infants ride their mothers' backs for the first month of life, then begin venturing off to explore and play for increasing numbers of hours each day.

Both exploration and play involve physical exercise that promotes healthy physiological development, and both propel the young monkey into interaction with many aspects of its physical and social environments, where it learns information and skills that it will need as an adult to survive and to reproduce. During exploration of the physical environment, the young Squirrel monkey learns how to catch flying insects and other prey, open various types of foods, and move safely through the trees. It learns the location of food sources, water holes, wasp nests, and safe arboreal pathways.

Play involves higher levels of activity than does exploration. Active play in the trees gives the young monkey a chance to develop skills for running and jumping through the branches. These skills may be of critical importance if the monkey ever has to flee from a predator (eg a large hawk) or respond quickly in an emergency (eg when a branch breaks under its weight).

Social play helps the young develop bonds with their peers and become integrated members of their group. Various sexual, maternal and aggressive behaviors are practiced and perfected during social play; and this presumably facilitates the acquisition of reproductive skills and appropriate sex and gender roles. During social play, the young gain experience in transmitting and interpreting various communicative signals, such as facial expressions, body postures, intention movements and vocalizations. They often playfully imitate and acquire troop tradition, such as learning the location of trees with water holes and how to dip their hands to obtain water. Most social play involves wrestling, chasing and other forms of play fighting, in which individuals learn skills of sparring, dodging, jumping, pouncing, feinting, chasing and fleeing. Mastery of these self-defense skills can increase an individual's success in coping with predators and social conflicts, such as the fights that are common among adult males in the mating season.

Play among peers also functions to draw the infant away from its mother and help it become increasingly independent. Because play is rewarding and "fun," the maturing infants spend increasing amounts of time with peers, which eases the weaning process. By the end of its first year of life, the young Squirrel monkey spends hours each day with age-mates, almost completely independent of its mother.

In most primates (except humans) play ends by adulthood, though exploration continues in abated form for much longer. By adulthood, the monkeys have learned most of the information and skill that they need for survival; thus the benefits of continued exploration and play cease to outweigh the dangers of rowdy activity in the trees and the costs of high energy expenditure. Once the maturing monkeys have explored all the readily available parts of their home range and tried almost every type of game, they turn increasing attention to other activities. These may include foraging, sexual interactions, care of infants, dominance relations, cuddling together, and other "adult" activities, in which behavior is employed that has been acquired during exploration and play.

JDB

▲ **Juvenile Squirrel monkeys at play.**
(1) Wrestling. (2) Sparring. (3) Exploring hole in tree. (4) Stalking a perched bird. (5) Learning to catch insect prey. Both social and solitary "play" are important in the apprenticeship for adult life.

► **Enterprise and curiosity** of the young Squirrel monkey.

Howling by the Light of the Moon

Why a "day monkey" has become the Night monkey

With the full moon overhead, a small monkey hoots mournfully in the treetops of the Amazon jungle. This is a lone male Night monkey searching for a mate; if his nightly travels of up to 6km (3.7mi) are unsuccessful, he must retire and try again on another moonlit night.

The Night monkey is the only truly nocturnal monkey and inhabits the forests of much of South America, where it feeds mainly on fruits, insects, nectar and leaves—with the occasional lizard, frog or egg. Night monkeys live in small groups of a male, female and young (a single offspring born each year and remaining with its family for two and a half years), occupying territories of up to 10 hectares (25 acres).

Unlike other strictly monogamous primates, only roving subadult male Night monkeys searching for a mate or adult males holding a territory will call, and then only when the moon is full, or nearly so, and the sky is cloudless. Female Night monkeys call rarely, if at all, in the wild. Similar groups of gibbons, siamangs and titis, for example, have daily morning duets to re-affirm territorial possession, males and females calling in unison, but each sex with a different song. Night monkeys do not sing in duets, and calling sessions are restricted to once or twice a month. On a clear night with a full or nearly full moon the adult male will give a series of 2–4 short, low hoots (10–30 hoots a minute) which can be heard for 500m (550 yards). The hooting monkey travels 100–350 meters (330–1,150ft) along or up to its territorial border during a 1–2 hour period, announcing his territorial possession. Night monkeys rarely fight during hoot nights.

But Night monkeys do fight. During a 12-month period the author observed 15 battles (about one each month), all occurring when the moon was bright and overhead, and invariably when a neighboring family group trespassed into a ripe fruit tree near a border. Males and females of each group burst into a low, ascending resonating "war whoop" and attacked. The home team won every time, putting the invaders to flight within 25 minutes. The three times during the year when groups met on a dark night, 5–10 short hoots were exchanged and the monkeys moved apart without fighting.

Why should bright moonlight be important to Night monkeys? Night monkeys can see well at low light levels with their enlarged eyes. They make spectacular three-to five-meter leaps (10–16ft) from tree to tree, adeptly catch insects and locate fruit trees in light levels too low for humans or other diurnal primates to see. Yet even Night monkeys' activity seems to be limited in total darkness. Path lengths average about 550m (1,800ft) on dark nights, as opposed to 850m (2,800ft) on clear moonlit nights. Monkeys never fight or hoot extensively when there is no moonlight, and even rough-and-tumble play is restricted to dawn and dusk on moonless nights.

Night monkeys differ from most nocturnal mammals by having color vision, and the structure of the eye suggests that the ancestor of *Aotus* was active in daytime only. Why then, has a day monkey evolved into a night monkey? Other small South American monkeys, such as titis and marmosets, are hunted by diurnal hawks and eagles such as the Harpy and Crested eagles, and large monkeys, especially capuchins, chase smaller monkeys from fruit trees. The Night monkey avoids these two problems by sleeping, spending each day in the same

▲ **A monogamous family group,** with parents and single young of two annual birth seasons. Color patterning on the head is distinctive, as in many cebid monkeys.

◄ **More owl-like** than this parrot-like pose suggests, the Night or Owl monkey has a low resonant hooting call. Only males call, and then only on moonlit nights.

dense vine tangle or tree hole, only venturing out punctually 15 minutes after sunset, when daytime predators and competitors have roosted. The only nighttime predator big enough to eat a Night monkey is the Great horned owl, which is rare in the tropical rain forest.

In some habitats, however, such as the open forests of the dry *chaco* of Paraguay and Argentina, where diurnal Harpy and Crested eagles are rare, Great horned owls common and capuchin monkeys absent, Night monkeys have partially reverted to daytime activity. They sleep on open branches (one group was observed to use 42

different sleep trees in five months) and are active for between one and three hours in daylight, feeding on fruits and flowers. In fact, in the cold *chaco* winter, during times of the month when there is no moonlight, groups travel nearly as far in the day (280m/920ft) as in the night (330m/1,080ft).

Although changes in ecological conditions modify certain Night monkey behavior, such as sleep, site selection and activity times, much behavior, such as hooting and fighting in the bright moonlight, do not change and are typical of the Night monkey in all habitats. PCW

Titi Monkey Family Life
Father is the primary caretaker of the young

Not all primates live in large social groups. Some, such as the indri, gibbons, siamang, Night monkey, the Mentawi Islands langur, and the three South American species of titi monkey live in small monogamous family units comprising an adult male, an adult female and their immature offspring. Elusive and difficult to observe, titi monkeys (genus *Callicebus*) are unique for the tail-twining posture which family members adopt when at rest, and are particularly notable for the prominent role played by the father in caring for the young.

There are three species of *Callicebus* monkeys. The Dusky titi (*C. moloch*) is found throughout most tropical forests of the Amazon, Orinoco, and Upper Paraná river drainage systems. The Yellow-handed titi (*C. torquatus*) frequently occurs in the same areas, but is found primarily on vegetation growing on white sands drained by black water rivers in Colombia, Venezuela and Peru and along the Rio Negro in Brazil. A third species, the Masked titi (*C. personatus*) is restricted to the dwindling Atlantic coastal forests of eastern Brazil in Bahia, Espírito Santo, Minas Gerais, Rio de Janeiro and São Paulo. All three species are small monkeys of about 1kg (2.2lb) but they differ substantially in coat color and pattern. For example, the hands of the Dusky titi vary from gray to brown to red, while the Masked titi has black hands and the Yellow handed titi, yellow hands. All titi monkeys live in family groups of 2–5 animals, occupy small territories, and regulate intergroup spacing with loud morning calls. About three-quarters of their diet consists of fruits, which they supplement with leaves, flowers and insects. The Dusky and Masked titis appear to obtain most of their protein from young leaves, leaf petioles and young shoots, and usually spend the last few hours of every day feeding on these food items relatively close to the ground. On the other hand, in vegetation growing on white sand soils the leaves are heavily laden with secondary (toxic) compounds, sclerophylous (hard and tough), and difficult to digest. The Yellow-handed titi therefore obtains most of its protein from insects, searching for them high in the forest canopy. The reduced feeding time required appears to allow an increase in the amount of time spent grooming.

Apart from territorial calls at dawn, titi monkeys move virtually noiselessly through the dense jungle except for an occasional soft "swoosh" and the patter of falling water droplets as they jump into the damp, pliable foliage of a neighboring branch. In this way

◄ **Typical social behavior** of titi monkeys. (**1**) Father carrying young. (**2**) Father grooming young. (**3**) Tail-twining when at rest huddled on a "sleep bough."

► **A Dusky titi** takes a meal of young vine leaves. Fruit is the major food of both Dusky and Yellow-handed species, but the Dusky titi may eat substantial amounts of young leaves and shoots, while the Yellow-handed titi takes insects instead.

▼ **Dusky titi with young.**

they hide from the huge Harpy eagle, or the voracious Ornate hawk-eagle.

Often during the day an adult pair stops, rests and grooms each other, usually with tails twined. The Yellow-handed titi has an additional period of extensive grooming just prior to sleeping: the entire group rests on a large "sleep bough," where all members of the family take turns grooming each other, with most time being devoted to grooming the youngest infant, particularly by the father. Finally, as the sun sets, the entire group huddles together to sleep with all their tails entwined. It has been suggested that balance and warmth are enhanced by tail-twining, but the primary function is probably social.

A striking feature of the behavior of titi monkeys is their long early morning bouts of calling which echo throughout the forest for distances of 600–700m (over a third of a mile). Despite similarity in vocalizations, the species of *Callicebus* do not all regulate intergroup spacing with the same vocal mechanisms. Dusky titi groups move to their territorial boundaries and confront each other in vigorous vocal battles. Boundaries are rigidly maintained over the years. In the Yellow-handed species, however, calling is more subtle, as groups do not confront each other at close range. They regulate intergroup spacing by calling from well within the territorial boundary, and over a period of years the boundaries shift. Nobody understands how or why these two patterns have evolved in two closely related species.

Titi monkey fathers are most indulgent and spend much time in the care, carrying and attentive observation of their offspring. Indeed infants have been observed to spend substantially more time in contact with their father than with the mother or siblings, and the father is the primary caretaker of the young. He will, for example, shift his position to cover and protect a young infant in a heavy rain storm. Whenever there is danger, as from strong winds or a falling tree, the father moves closer to his young. On one occasion when a juvenile animal fell to the ground, the father was seen to jump down quickly to within a few feet of the stunned animal to protect it until it was able to recover and move back into the safety of the trees. Most important, the father is responsible most of the time for carrying the infant through the trees—giving it up for the mother to nurse or occasionally for a sibling to carry it—until it is old enough to keep up with the adults on its own, at the age of 4–5 months.

A dawn call, which consists of repeated sequences of loud vocalizations, may last up to seven minutes. Neighboring groups do not call concurrently, but await the termination of the adjacent group's call before initiating their own. Usually an adult pair sits side-by-side and coordinates a vocal duet with each animal contributing a part of the song. If the pair moves apart the coordination breaks down and the male may continue singing alone. Young animals frequently join in with their parents for brief periods and one may even hear, for a few moments, a cacaphony of four animals singing together. In this way a young animal begins to learn the species-specific song sequence. The completely coordinated duet is not fully learned until the animal grows up, leaves its natal family between two and three years of age, finds a mate, and establishes a new monogamous group. It takes up to a year for the newly formed pair to learn to coordinate its duet.   WGK

Leaf-eaters of the New World

Diet and energy conservation in the Mantled howler monkey

The six species of howler monkey (genus *Allouatta*) are capable of producing calls that are among the loudest made by animals. Charles Darwin considered that natural selection favored those males which made the loudest calls to attract females. Others since Darwin have suggested that the howlers' calls are used to defend the troop's rights to particular food trees. In the case of howler monkeys, the latter explanation appears more correct, but it overlooks the probable energetic relationship between the development of loud howling behavior and the feeding patterns of howler monkeys, revealed in recent studies of the Mantled howler monkey of Central America and northwestern South America.

Howler monkeys have the widest geographical distribution of the New World primates; furthermore, where howlers occur, they usually make up the highest percentage of the local primate biomass. One factor contributing to the ecological success of howlers is their ability to use leaves as a major dietary component. Leaves are far more available and abundant in tropical forests than fruits, flowers or insects, so in such habitats leaf-eating primates are apparently faced with fewer problems of food availability than the more strictly frugivorous or insectivorous primates. Most primates, however, do not eat large quantities of leaves, despite their relative availability, because leaves are low in nutrients relative to indigestible fiber. Leaves are also very low in sugars—important energy sources for most primate species. To be a successful leaf-eater, a primate must therefore have some way of circumventing these problems.

In the tropical forests of the Old World, there are many leaf-eating primate species (eg the subfamily Colobinae). Colobine monkeys have specialized, sacculated stomachs similar in many respects to the complex stomachs of cows. Bacteria in the colobine stomach digest the fibrous cellulose and hemicelluloses in leaves. In this process (fermentation) energy-rich fatty acids are produced which, in turn, can be absorbed by the monkey and used to fuel its daily activities. It is only through the intervention of gut flora that monkeys or any mammals can utilize leaf fiber for energy.

Howler monkeys do not have a sacculated stomach but they do have two large sections in the hindgut (cecum and colon) where the necessary cellulolytic bacteria are found. In general, however, hindgut fermentors such as howler monkeys are probably not as efficient at obtaining nutrients and energy

from leaves as the more specialized colobines, since in howlers fermentation takes place in sections of the gut below the small intestine—the major site of nutrient absorption. To improve digestive efficiency, howlers feed very selectively, primarily on tender young leaves that can be rapidly fermented and on a few species of unusually nutritious mature leaves. Howlers also eat sugary fruits and flowers whenever these are available but they can live for weeks at a time only on leaves,

▲ **Advertising its presence,** a male Mantled howler calls in warning to nearby troops. Such calls are thought to be one key to the success of howlers as a group.

▶ **About half of howlers' diet is leaves.** Adaptations in the stomach, a slow-moving life-style and careful selection of food also characterize howlers. This Mantled howler is feeding on leaves in the Panamanian forest; howlers are distributed also south as far as Argentina.

home range lie within an average day's travel time. Howlers also show a "division of labor" between the sexes; males help settle disputes within the troop and defend certain important food trees from neighboring howler troops, whereas females put their efforts into maintenance and reproduction and care of young.

The distinctive vocalization of howlers can be heard for well over a kilometer in their natural forest habitat. The howl is produced by passing air through the cavity within an enlarged bone in the throat, the hyoid, which is much larger in males. Howling itself contributes to economizing on energy; every morning around sunrise, each troop gives a "dawn chorus" that is answered by all other howler troops within earshot. A troop does not maintain an exclusive territory but shares part of its home range with other howler troops. By howling loudly each morning and again whenever it moves on during the day, one troop can inform another of its precise location. When two troops meet, as they occasionally do, there is a considerable uproar, with animals, particularly males, expending much energy in howling, running and even fighting. Thus it pays to avoid meeting another troop; howling is far less expensive in terms of energy expenditure than is patrolling the home range and looking for other howler troops or getting into long intertroop squabbles over food trees. There is a dominance hierarchy between troops and by listening to the various howls, weaker troops know the locations of stronger troops and can avoid meeting them during the day. This helps troops to space themselves more efficiently in terms of exploiting food sources. Thus, through a combination of adaptations in diet-related morphology and in spacing behavior, howler monkeys have surmounted problems that are usually associated with having leaves as a principal food source, and evolved into highly successful leaf-eating primates. KM

providing the leaves are high in quality.

Even with a careful feeding regime, howlers must still conserve energy, and they rely on behavioral and morphological adaptations to help. They are relatively slow-moving and more than 50 percent of the howler day is spent quietly resting or sleeping; during the day the monkeys range over only about 400m (1,300ft) and the home range for a troop of some 20 howler monkeys is just 31 hectares (77 acres). Thus all potential food sources within a howler's

GUENONS, MACAQUES AND BABOONS

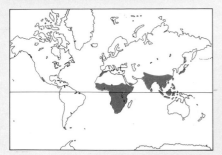

TOUGH, active and gregarious, noisy, imitative, curious—the cercopithecines are the "typical monkeys" best known to legend because their distribution and ways of life bring them into contact with people. Many are adaptable generalists, able to take advantage of the wastefulness or sentimentality of human neighbors to make a living, or to take their share from unwilling human hosts by skilful theft from unharvested crops or food stores.

Previously, when a laboratory scientist referred to "the monkey" he nearly always meant the Rhesus macaque, a cercopithecine which has long borne the brunt of our invasive curiosity.

It is only in recent years that we have begun to appreciate the variety within the subfamily Cercopithecinae. "The monkey" was a useful concept to those looking for a non-human model of human disease, or those who saw the animal kingdom as a static hierarchy with man at the top of the ladder. But the modern comparative approach towards natural history, made possible as we learn more about the anatomy, physiology and behavior of different species, is more exciting: it includes insight into the dynamics of the group, and the possibility of recent, ongoing, and future change in this young and probably most rapidly evolving subfamily of primates.

Anatomy and posture of the "typical monkey"

Cercopithecine monkeys have the same dental formula as man: I2/2, C1/1, P2/2, M3/3 = 32. They have powerful jaws with the muscles arranged to give an effective "nutcracker" action between the back teeth. The face is rather long, except in some of the smaller guenons, the "dog-faced" baboons being the most extreme in this

▲ **Foraging in grass,** a female Olive baboon in Kenya bears her watchful infant on her back. Baboons typically stand on one hand and pluck grass with the other.

◄ **The vervet or grivet** ABOVE LEFT is the most widespread of the guenons, and lives in many local variants throughout African savanna. Other guenons are mostly forest dwellers.

◄ **The White mangabey** is a medium-sized monkey whose large incisor teeth enable it to tackle food (eg palm nuts) that cannot be used by guenons that share the same forest. The red-capped race occurs in Cameroon.

trend: the longer jaw increases the surface area of back teeth available for grinding food. The canine teeth are much longer than the rest in all males, and in female guenons, but not in adult female baboons, mangabeys and macaques. Long upper canines cut against a specially modified "sectorial" premolar in the lower jaw.

Cercopithecines have cheek pouches which open beside the lower teeth and extend down the side of the neck. When both are fully distended, the cheek pouches contain about the equivalent of a stomach's load of food. When competing for food, or foraging in a dangerous place, they cram it hastily, with minimal chewing, into the pouches and retire to a safe place to eat at leisure, leaving the hands and feet free for running and climbing. In a gesture highly characteristic of cercopithecines, the back of the hand is used to push food in the full pouches towards the opening. Food is processed (peeled, scooped out, etc) by hand

and mouth, under close visual scrutiny, so that what is swallowed is selected for high quality and digestibility. The stomach is simple and not very large, and the gut as a whole is unspecialized.

The first digit can be opposed on both the hands and feet, a facility used equally in moving, feeding, and such social activity as grooming. The hind foot is plantigrade (the animal walks on the whole foot, not just the toes) in all cercopithecines, and the hand also is plantigrade in primarily arboreal species. In those other species which move from place to place primarily on the ground, such as baboons and the Patas monkey, the joint between palm and fingers forms an extension of the walking limb, so that the walking surface of the hand is the underside of the four fingers, the palm being held vertically.

In tree-living species the hindlegs are long and well-muscled, used in leaping between branches and bounding along them. When moving slowly in the trees the hind legs are often forward under the body so that the center of gravity is over a line from knees to feet and the hands are almost freed from weight-bearing and are available for manipulation. This posture is especially characteristic of species with a long heavy tail which helps to bring the center of gravity back over the hips. On the ground, aboreal monkeys are "down at the front"— their arms being shorter than their legs. Monkeys which spend more time on the ground have relatively longer front limbs. The most specialized ground walkers, the baboons, have their shoulders higher than their hips when walking, due to the lengthening of the arm bones and the addition of the palm to the effective limb length. The smaller Patas monkey has not achieved the "shoulders higher" posture, so, in order to scan its surroundings, it frequently stands upright.

The stance of a baboon requires support under the shoulders. When foraging, therefore, baboons typically stand on one hand and pluck grass with the other. Gelada baboons typically sit to forage with both hands, before shuffling forward on their bottoms. Ground-walking monkeys do not require tails for counterbalancing, and many have shortened tails or none at all— the absence of a tail does not reliably distinguish apes from monkeys as is popularly supposed (and suggested by the name cercopithecine, "tailed ape"). Monkey tails seem to have very poor circulation and are very susceptible to frostbite, so a shortened tail can be an adaptation to a cold climate, although some short-tailed monkeys live in warm places. Both short and long tails are used to communicate: forest monkeys hold their tail in a position characteristic of the species, but in general the long tails of arboreal monkeys are of limited use in communication, because of the requirements of balance and locomotion. The tails of terrestrial monkeys, on the other hand, are sometimes used to signal the mood of the owner, particularly confidence or fear. Patas females curl up their tails when they are sexually receptive. The first few vertebrae in the tail of the Savanna baboon fuse during the first year to form an upright stalk from which the rest of the tail dangles, at an angle that steepens gradually as the baboon matures.

Coat, changes in skin color and swellings

Cercopithecines have long, dense, rather silky fur, often with longer hair forming a cape or mane over the shoulders which is heavier in adult males. The macaques, baboons and mangabeys have drab brown or gray coats—a few macaques are black. Most guenons have brightly colored coats with vividly contrasting patterns, especially around the face. These colors make the forest-dwelling species easy to identify, even

▼ **Drills and baboons,** largest of the monkeys (adult males shown). (**1**) Mandrill (*Papio sphinx*). (**2**) Drill (*P. leucophaeus*). (**3**) Gelada (*Theropithecus gelada*), showing bare patches on neck and chest. (**4**) Hamadryas baboon (*Papio hamadryas*) with red naked skin on face and rump. (**5**) Guinea baboon (*P. papio*). Three forms of the Savanna or Common baboon (*Papio cynocephalus*): (**6**) Yellow baboon of lowland East/Central Africa asleep in a tree; (**7**) Olive baboon of highland East Africa with hare prey; (**8**) Chacma baboon of southern Africa.

where several live together. In baboons, mangabeys and macaques the bright colors occur on patches of bare skin on the face, rump, and, in the gelada, the chest. The red face color of some macaques depends on exposure to the sun: monkeys in the wild have red faces, those kept indoors have gray-white ones. The black face color of the Patas monkey also fades indoors. Skin color also depends on gonadal hormones, so that adults but not juveniles show the bright red, the color is brighter still during the mating season, and castration causes the color to fade. Mandrills have patches of blue skin as well as red, but the blue is a structural, not a pigment, color. A similar bright blue color appears in the scrotal skin of several guenons at adolescence. This requires gonadal hormone (testosterone), but once formed it is stable, and does not disappear if the male is castrated.

Female baboons, mangabeys, and some macaques and some guenons (see table of species, pp 90–93) develop a perineal swelling which in normal animals increases in size during the first half, or follicular, phase of the menstrual cycle and decreases after ovulation. The swellings of adult females clearly identify a female which is about to ovulate, and adult male baboons, for example, will not normally attempt to copulate with a female unless she has a swelling. The exact site of the swelling differs from species to species, and each individual also has recognizable swelling patterns. The swellings tend to increase in size in successive cycles, so that captive monkeys which are not breeding regularly may grow enormous swellings, up to 10 or 15 percent of their body weight. In the wild, adult females rarely undergo more than one or two successive cycles before conceiving again, so have smaller swellings. Rhesus macaques and some other species show a rather different pattern of swelling, associated with adolescence and sometimes, in the adult, with a return to reproductive activity after a long interval. The adolescent Rhesus female swells around her tail root and along her thighs, the swelling reaching a maximum just before menstruation, in the luteal phase of her cycle. This pattern ends when she is fully mature and ready to conceive. Similarly, adolescent Patas females show vulval swelling, whereas adults usually do not.

In the wild, changes which occur during pregnancy are even more conspicuous in some species than these changes related to the menstrual cycle. Thus the black naked skin over the ischia on the rump of baboons loses its pigment and becomes a glowing red in pregnancy. The vulva of Vervet monkeys and mangabeys also reddens when they are pregnant, sufficiently to be easily recognized at a distance.

Newborn cercopithecines have short velvety fur, often of a color that contrasts with the pelage of the adult: olive-brown Stumptailed macaques have primrose-yellow infants, while yellow-gray baboons have black infants. The infants are even more conspicuous because they have little or no pigment on the naked skin of face, feet, perineum, and ears (which seem to be almost adult sized). The newborn male baboon has a bright red penis, while infant male macaques have a very large, empty scrotum. Infant guenons, on the other hand, are very difficult to sex even when you have them in your hand. Special attention to infants by others than their mother often coincides with the duration of the natal coat; such attention includes frequent inspection of the newborn's genitals, and it is perhaps important for the normal development of social behavior that the sex of the infant is known to its fellow group members as early as possible. The natal coat begins to be replaced in the third month by a juvenile coat which is usually a fluffier, less brightly colored or clearly marked version of the adult pattern.

Evolution

The cercopithecines are a modern group which originated in Africa, their macaquelike forebears appearing in the fossil record towards the end of the Miocene (26–7 million years ago). Macaques spread north and east, to Europe in the Pliocene (7–2 million years ago), and Asia by the Plio-Pleistocene (2 million years ago). At the same time they died out in Africa south of the Sahara, or perhaps evolved and radiated into the modern African genera, the baboons, mangabeys and guenons. The Barbary ape seems to be somewhat separated from the Asian macaques in terms of molecular genetics as well as some anatomical details, perhaps retaining some more primitive features.

The radiation of the guenons in Africa is very recent: the emergence of distinct species (speciation) seems to have occurred during the last main glaciation, when Africa as a whole was colder and much drier, so that the forests retreated to a few scattered areas in equatorial Africa—along the east and west coasts, and around Mount Cameroon and the Ruwenzoris. When the climate became wetter and warmer about 12,000 years ago the forests spread, and with them their now distinct monkeys. Similarly, in Asia, cold dry periods associated with glaciation restricted the habitats of macaques and separated populations, which differentiated. Here the picture is more complicated because variations in sea level allowed macaques to move from one island of Southeast Asia to another.

In Africa, the history of baboon species is the history of grasslands. The earliest baboons were ancestors of today's gelada, specialized to harvest grass seed. Dry grassland spread in dry periods at the expense of forest, encouraged by human habits of burning to control game and later to increase grazing for livestock. The Savanna or "Common" baboon, once probably a forest-edge species, spread with the wooded savannas which resulted, and eventually replaced the geladas except in their Ethiopian highland stronghold.

Species and distribution

All **macaques** are placed in a single genus (*Macaca*) which occupies the whole of Asia except the high latitudes. Most areas are occupied by a single species with characteristics appropriate to local conditions. The one surviving macaque in Africa, the Barbary ape, has thick fur and no tail, traits which help it to survive the snowy winters of the Atlas mountains where it lives. Another shaggy and short-tailed species, the Japanese macaque, survives the snowy winters of northern Japan, and yet another, Père David's macaque, lives in high mountains of Tibet. The sturdily built, medium-tailed Rhesus monkey of the Himalayan foothills, northern India and Pakistan (see p386), is replaced in southern India by the smaller, more lightly built and longer tailed

see p388.

▲ **Facial expressions in macaques** (adult males shown). (**1**) Barbary macaque (*Macaca sylvanus*): "lip-smacking" with infant: see p388. (**2**) Moor macaque (*M. maura*): open-mouth threat. (**3**) Bonnet macaque (*M. radiata*): canine display yawn. (**4**) Crab-eating macaque (*M. fascicularis*); fear grin. (**5**) Stump-tailed macaque (*M. arctoides*): open-mouth threat. (**6**) Pig-tailed macaque (*M. nemestrina*); approach pout-face – can precede copulation or attack or even grooming another individual. (**7**) Rhesus macaque (*M. mulatta*); aggressive stare.

Bonnet macaque which, further south still in Sri Lanka, is in turn replaced by the rather similar Toque macaque. Towards the Equator, in wetter areas which will support rain forest, the number of niches available for monkeys increases, and two species of macaque occur together. Thus the arboreal Lion-tailed macaque lives in the forest of southwest India above the more terrestrial Bonnet macaque. In Sumatra and Borneo the small, long-tailed, Crab-eating macaque lives in the same forests as the large, heavily built, short-tailed, more ground-living Pig-tailed macaque. In Sulawesi (Celebes) a black, stump-tailed group of species has radiated (3, 4 or 7 of them according to different authors) to occupy the different peninsulas of that dissected island, with only one species in any given locality. The Stump-tailed macaque is another short-tailed species which inhabits the high mountains of Southeast Asia, while other macaques occupy the rain forest below.

The **baboons** live everywhere in Africa where they can find drinking water. They have dog-like muzzles, and limb modifications which allow them to walk long distances on the ground. The Savanna or "Common" baboon is the most widespread; individuals from different regions are sufficiently different in appearance to have been given separate species status in the past. They live in grass- and bush-land, and along the edge of forests. The Hamadryas baboon replaces the Savanna baboon in the Ethiopian highlands: male Hamadryas baboons have red faces and rumps instead of black, and a long cape of gray fur, so they look very different (though females are similar to females of the West African Guinea baboon). The two species hybridize along a narrow boundary zone in Ethiopia. The drill and the mandrill are baboons of the forest floor of west central Africa. They have contiguous distributions in Cameroon occupying the forest north and south of the Sanaga river respectively. The largest of the baboons, they are mainly black and have short tails. Their niche is perhaps parallel to that of the Pig-tailed monkey, largest of the macaques. The gelada is a long-haired species living in the highlands of Ethiopia, and specialized in gathering grass seeds.

The **mangabeys** (*Cercocebus* species) may

be thought of as lightly built, long-tailed baboons. They only live in closed-canopy forests. Some, like the Gray-cheeked mangabey, are highly arboreal, while others, like the Agile mangabey, usually move on the forest floor. An arboreal and a terrestrial species may live in the same forest: the author has seen Gray-cheeked and Agile mangabeys in the forest reserve of Dja, southern Cameroon.

The **guenons** are mainly in the genus *Cercopithecus*, but a few of the more eccentric species have been given generic status. The many species of *Cercopithecus*, recognized by differences in coat color, are regional variations of perhaps half a dozen ecotypes. In a given forest one finds only one example of an ecotype, so that in the richest habitats there may be four or five guenons species living together. The Vervet, Grivet, or Green monkey is the most widespread guenon, living in many local variants throughout savanna Africa. It is never far from water, typically inhabiting the acacia trees which grow along water courses. All the other species of *Cercopithecus* are forest species. The most widespread is the Sykes' and Blue monkey (*nictitans-mitis*) group, large guenons which include quite a lot of leaves in their diet and are found wherever there is a patch of closed-canopy forest; next come the red-tailed guenons (*cephus-ascanius* group), smaller monkeys which seem to require a more layered canopy to the forest, with tangles of creepers; then the *mona* group, smaller still, and more insectivorous. These three species commonly form associations of monkeys of more than one species, in rain forests of Gabon for example. De Brazza's monkey inhabits wet patches of forest which include palms. The ground-living L'Hoest's monkey can inhabit quite high altitude forest. Where overlap occurs, some hybridization of species is known (see p396).

Other guenon genera have only a single species each. The Patas monkey is accorded generic status because of its skeletal adaptations to ground living. The largest of the guenons, it is like a long-legged, orange-colored vervet. It lives in the open acacia woodlands and scrub of drier more seasonal areas north of the equatorial forest. Its habitat is often adjacent to that of the vervets and, although much larger, patas avoid vervets when they meet. The talapoin is the smallest of all the Old World monkeys, and lives in floodplain forests of west central Africa; Allen's swamp monkey is another swamp-living monkey from further east, in the Congo basin. Both these are placed in separate genera partly because the females have a perineal swelling, unlike females of other guenons.

Diet and foraging

Cercopithecines are primarily fruit-eaters, but their diet may include seeds, flowers, buds, leaves, bark, gum, roots, bulbs and rhizomes, insects, snails, crabs, fish, lizards, birds, and mammals. They take almost anything which is digestible and not actually poisonous. Most food is caught or gathered with the hands. Selection and preparation of food is learned from observation, initially of the mother. In this way local traditions in food preference develop. Adult baboons will prevent juveniles from eating unfamiliar food. On the other hand, in experimental situations, juveniles have come to recognize new food items and devised new preparation methods; other juveniles and adult females have learned from them, but adult males less readily so. This transmission of information may be the most important foraging-related function of group-living: the troop is primarily an educational establishment.

Species which live near water use aquatic foods. Japanese macaque troops living by the seashore have recently incorporated some seaweeds into their diet. The Crab-eating macaque is so called for good reason; Savanna baboons at the coast in South Africa take shellfish off the rocks; and talapoins are said to dive for fish.

Where several species live in association, for example in a West African forest, the smaller species tend to eat more insects, and

▲ **A Crab-eating macaque** in its typical riverbank habitat. Crabs may indeed be taken by this omnivorous species found from Indonesia and the Philippines to Burma.

▶ **The Patas monkey** RIGHT ABOVE is larger, more long-legged and more terrestrial than its forest guenon relatives. Inhabiting the open acacia woodlands north of Africa's equatorial forests, it runs from one tree to the next in search of the fruit, galls, leaves, flowers and gums that comprise most of its diet.

▶ **"Red, white and blue" display** of the male Vervet monkey. The Vervet monkey is closely related to the Patas monkey and takes a varied diet including fruit, leaves, flowers, insects, eggs, nestlings, rodents and crops. Bright blue scrotum and red penis are characteristics of both Patas and Vervet monkey males.

▼ **Savanna baboon eating gazelle kid.** Baboons may act cooperatively to head off and trap such prey.

more active types of insects (like grass-hoppers), while larger species eat more caterpillars, and more leaves and gum. Mangabeys have powerful incisors, used to open hard nuts which are inaccessible to guenons.

Patas monkeys are adapted for running in grassland between patches of the acacia woods where they feed on fruit, leaves and gum, as well as insects and some small vertebrates. Their diet is not very different from that of other guenons living in forests. Baboons, in contrast, have a diet that includes large quantities of grass, and the large area of molar teeth, made available by the longer jaws, allows them to prepare the tough silicaceous leaves. Their very powerful spoon-shaped hands are strong enough for digging, and they subsist through severe dry seasons by digging up the rhizomes and the leaf-base storage bulbs of grasses and lilies. The small incisors of geladas are suitable for extracting seeds from grass heads, and they are also "close grazers," using a rapid pinching movement of the thumb and forefinger of each arm alternatively to crop a sward as closely as sheep. Baboons take small mammalian herbivores, kill and eat the kids of gazelles which are left hidden in the grass, and hunt hares which they start from their forms. In a simple form of cooperative hunting, a group of baboons will spread out to start and head off such small prey, almost like beaters, although the prey is shared only reluctantly by the eventual captor.

Wherever people and monkeys come in contact (which is relatively frequent, as their ecological requirements are rather similar) the diet of the monkeys expands to include offerings, garbage, or stolen crops. The monkeys' behavior is clear evidence that learning plays an important role in how they acquire food. They time their arrival at feeding stations to coincide with the arrival of food, and raid crops when people are predictably absent, in heavy rainstorms or during the siesta. Baboons will enter a field where woman are working, and even chase them away, but avoid men, who are usually armed. Talapoins will crowd quite close to people who are washing or fishing at a river in the forest, but avoid people setting out to hunt; all of which suggest a sophisticated appreciation of human behavior.

Predators

Monkeys are themselves prey to other animals. Some of the largest eagles feed mainly on forest monkeys, for example the African Crowned hawk eagle which often hunts in pairs. One swoops and perches among a troop of monkeys, and while they mob it, the mate swoops from behind and picks up an unwary monkey. Forest monkeys use a special alarm call when an eagle flies over, and respond by diving into thick cover. The Crowned hawk eagle can, however, fly through forest and hunt on the forest floor, and has been seen to kill a near-adult male mandrill, largest of all the cercopithecines. In open country the Martial eagle may prey on vervets and baboons. Vervets are the prey of phythons, which wait for them at the base of trees. These monkeys make specific alarm calls on sight of poisonous tree snakes. Monkeys are probably only incidental food items for Carnivora. Apart from birds, other primates may be the most important predators of monkeys. Baboons occasionally take vervets at Amboseli in Kenya, and chimpanzees eat baboons, red colobus and guenons at Gombe in Tanzania. Monkey is also the preferred meat of some people in West and Central Africa and in Southeast Asia.

Mating and the raising of young

Cercopithecine monkeys are slow to mature, slow to reproduce, and live long. The Rhesus macaque usually conceives first at $3\frac{1}{2}$ years of age and gives birth at 4, but perhaps 10 percent will mature a year earlier, and another 10 percent a year later than that. Patas, the largest guenons, usually conceive at $2\frac{1}{2}$ years (range $1\frac{1}{2}$–$3\frac{1}{2}$ years). They are thus the fastest-maturing cercopithecine monkeys so far recorded. On the other hand, females of the smallest cercopithecine, the talapoin, do not conceive until 5–6 years old, and the same is true of other forest guenons, such as the Sykes' monkey and De Brazza's monkey. In some species the age at first conception is variable, probably depending on nutrition. Captive baboons, for example, may conceive at $3\frac{1}{2}$ years, but baboons in a deteriorated natural environment, as at Amboseli, not until $7\frac{1}{2}$ years. Vervets at Amboseli conceive first at about 5 years, while in captivity they conceive at about $2\frac{1}{2}$ years. This difference has not been observed in forest guenons or patas. Males begin to produce sperm at about the same age as the females of their species first conceive, but they are not then fully grown and are still socially immature. Males are several years older than females before they begin to breed.

Most cercopithecines conceive in a limited mating season. In high latitudes mating occurs in the fall. In the tropics, conceptions occur in the dry season among guenons in

◀ **Clinging to mother's belly,** this infant Vervet monkey will be nursed up to the arrival of the next single offspring, about a year after its own birth.

▼ **Bonnet macaque mother and young.** The mother/infant bond continues into adulthood with daughters, but sons leave the group on becoming sexually mature. Central whorl growing out sideways on crown gives the species its name.

wet forests, but in the wet season among patas in dry country. Baboons and mangabeys breed at any time of the year, but stress, such as a drought, that causes the death of several infants may have the effect of synchronizing the next pregnancies of the mothers. Other factors that determine mating periods include increased food supply and social facilitation. Mating periods may last for several months, as in vervets, or be concentrated into a few weeks, as in patas and talapoins, in which case the female probably ovulates only once in the annual season. Individual females usually mate in bouts lasting several days; during a species' mating period, females which have already conceived will continue to show bouts of receptivity and to copulate. Male Rhesus macaques also show seasonal changes, with reduced testosterone levels and testis size in the summer months.

Courtship is not elaborate, since mates are usually familiar with each other; signals indicating immediate readiness to mate generally suffice. The courtship of patas females is perhaps the most elaborate, a crouching run with tail tip curled, chin thrust forward, lips pouted. The patas female also puffs out her cheeks, and often holds her vulva with one hand or rubs it on a branch at the same time. Consortships are frequently formed, a pair remaining close together and at the edge of their troop for hours or days. In some species a single mount may lead to ejaculation, in others several mounts precede it. Copulating pairs are often harassed by juveniles, especially by the female's own male offspring, and the disruption may be enough to make repeated mounting necessary before ejaculation is achieved.

A single infant is born after a gestation of 5–6 months (twins are very rare), furred and with its eyes open; it often grasps at the mother's hair with its hands even before the legs and feet are born. Infants cling to the mother's belly immediately and can usually support their own weight, although the mother typically puts a hand to the infant's back, supporting it as she moves about during the first few hours. The newborn usually has the nipple in its mouth and uses it to support its head even when it is not nursing. Most monkeys are born at night, in the tree where the mother sleeps, and she eats the placenta and licks the infant clean before morning. (None of the cercopithecines ever makes a nest.) Patas infants, on the other hand, are usually born on the ground and during the daytime. It seems that timing of births is subject to selection by predation pressures, for Patas monkeys

sleep at night in low trees, where they are vulnerable to predators. Changes in maternal care match the growing ability of the infant to move independently. Nursing becomes infrequent after the first few months, but usually continues until the next infant is born. The next birth usually occurs after about a year in most macaques, vervets and Patas monkeys and talapoins, and after two years or more for forest guenons like the Blue monkey. In baboons the birth interval varies, probably depending on food availability, between 15 and 24 months. If an infant is stillborn or dies, the birth interval may be shortened, although not significantly so in species that breed seasonally.

The mother–daughter bond lasts into adulthood, and the maternal bond with sons lasts until sexual maturity, when juvenile males of most species leave their natal group and enter another one or become solitary. Beyond infancy, the bond is seen in the frequency of grooming or sitting together, and in defense of both juvenile by mother and vice versa. Juveniles also form bonds with their siblings, and where hierarchies are in evidence, a female usually ranks just below her mother and just above her older sisters. Males lose their inherited rank when they leave the troop, but a young rhesus male will often join the same new troop as his older brother, who helps with his introduction.

When more than one female is receptive in a troop, there is some tendency for males to prefer older females, which also have rather longer periods of receptivity. Similarly females tend to prefer older males. Baboons may have preferred mates, spending time together even when the female is not receptive (see Olive baboon, p392). In species where a single adult male lives with a group of females (see below) other males come to the troop when several females are receptive, thus providing the females with a choice of mates.

Matrilines and troops
The basic unit of cercopithecine social oranization is the matriline, in which daughters stay with their mothers as long as they live, while males usually leave the natal group around the time of adolescence; the Hamadryas baboon seems to be the single exception (see p394). Whereas some years ago it seemed possible to identify species-typical group sizes, home ranges, and social organization, recent research has revealed considerable variation within a species, both in time and from place to place.

Under good conditions, a single founding female may be survived by several daughters, each now head of her own matriline, and all still within a single troop. In harsh conditions, survival may be so low that the matrilinear organization can only be detected after several years of study.

An upper limit to troop size may be determined by constraints on foraging; macaque troops that are provisioned with food begin to split into smaller troops, mainly along matrilines, but only after troop numbers have reached the hundreds, more than occurs naturally. Combination or fusion of troops is even rarer. In general, troops retain a defined home range; guenons defend a territory against adjacent troops. The range is the "property" of the females which form the permanent nucleus

of the troop, and in Blue and Redtail monkeys (pp396–397) it is the females, with juveniles, which engage in boundary disputes. The male troop members are transitory. They may remain in a troop for a few weeks, or months, or 2–3 years (rarely more). Adult males make loud calls which are highly species-specific and (where they have been studied) also characteristic of an individual male (see pp390–391). The loud calls serve as a rallying point, and may also locate the troop and identity the male as being in residence. Thus the males' loud calls provide a means of communication between troops which are sub-units of the larger population, while the females tend to keep the troops apart.

Cercopithecines have been categorized into one-male and multi-male group species. Male baboons, mangabeys, and macaques will tolerate each other's presence in a troop; nonetheless, a small troop may still include only a single fully adult male. Males living together in a troop will establish a hierarchy based on the outcome of competitive interactions. The rank order is not very stable, but changes with age, or as males join or leave the troop. In some studies, males that ranked high in the male hierarchy also did most of the mating, while others have found no such correlation.

Among guenons, the vervets and talapoins also live in multi-male groups, but patas and those forest guenons that have been studied have one-male troops. This single male's tenure may be quite short and, in a mating season when more than one

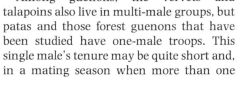

◀ **Adult females** remain with their mothers but males leave the troop. Patas monkeys, like these at a water hole, and forest guenons live in one-male troops.

▼ **Small and medium-sized cercopithecines.**
(1) Gray-cheeked mangabey (*Cercocebus albigena*), western race with double crest.
(2) Allen's swamp monkey (*Allenopithecus nigroviridis*). (3) The Moustached monkey (*Cercopithecus cephus*) bobs its head from side to side when threatening, to "flash" his moustache. (4) Face of Sooty mangabey, a geographical race of the White mangabey (*Cercocebus torquatus*). (5) Talapoin (*Miopithecus talapoin*), the smallest Old World monkey.
(6) Patas monkey (*Erythrocebus patas*): long legs, long feet and strong, short digits are adaptations for running in this fastest-moving of all primates, which may attain 55km/h (35mph).

female is receptive, other adult males join the troop and also copulate.

Newly arrived adult males have been seen to kill infants they find in the troop, leading some observers to regard this as part of the male's reproductive strategy (see p410), though other studies of the same species have not revealed infanticide.

Adult male guenons not in a troop are usually found alone, although patas males will form small temporary parties. In captivity more than one male can be housed together only so long as no females are present. Talapoins live in very large multi-male troops, but outside the mating season the males live in a subgroup whose members interact with each other but very rarely with females. Hamadryas baboons (see p394) and geladas have "harem" groups within troops. Each adult male gelada herds several females, while bachelor males live in a peripheral subgroup. Baboons move in procession, usually with adult males at the front and rear, adult females also towards front and rear (including those carrying infants), and juveniles towards the center of the column.

Conservation
All forest-living monkeys may be considered endangered, because tropical forests are being destroyed at such a high rate and monkey populations are always at risk because of their slow reproductive rate.

Where monkeys are considered a delicacy, the introduction of guns and the increased commercialization of hunting have further greatly reduced populations. As crop-growing areas are extended, the displaced monkeys raid crops: modern cash-oriented economies are less tolerant of such theft than are traditional societies. Monkeys also share many diseases with people—tuberculosis is one human disease to which monkeys are susceptible. Monkeys have been shown to carry yellow fever, to which they are very susceptible, and baboons carry asymptomatic schistosomiasis. There have been occasional suggestions that monkeys be exterminated to control disease, but probably no actual attempts to do so. For several years it seemed as if the increasing demand for monkeys for use in medical research, together with the appallingly high mortality rates in trapping and shipping, would cause the extinction of some "popular" species. Recently, a decline in the research industry, increasing efforts to breed monkeys in captivity for research purposes, and awareness of the need to handle newly caught animals carefully have reduced this threat. But the conservation of monkey species is fundamentally a matter of preserving the ecosystems in which they live, in large enough patches to allow viable populations to survive. Successful management depends upon controlling human encroachment.   TER

THE 45 SPECIES OF "TYPICAL" MONKEYS

Abbreviations: HBL = head-and-body length; TL = tail length; wt = weight. Approximate nonmetric equivalents: 2.5cm = 1in; 230g = 1oz; 1kg = 2.2lb.
[E] Endangered. [V] Vulnerable.

Mangabeys

Genus *Cercocebus*

Medium-sized monkeys restricted to forests and closely related to the baboons. The brownish species (Agile and White mangabeys) are considered to be closely related to each other and rather widely separated from the blackish species (Gray-cheeked and Black mangabeys), for which the genus name *Lophocebus* has been proposed but not widely accepted. All have tails longer than their bodies. Females smaller than males but not as markedly as in guenons. Their large strong incisor teeth allow mangabeys to exploit hard seeds which are not accessible to guenons, with which they share habitats.

Pregnancy lasts about 6 months and there is no evidence of breeding seasonality. Infants are the same color as adults. Mangabeys live in large groups which include several males. They are very vocal, and the adult male has a dramatically loud long-distance call (the whoop-gobble of the Gray-cheeked mangabey, p390), while the adult females of a group also perform loud choruses.

Gray-cheeked mangabey

Cercocebus albigena

SW Cameroon to E Uganda. Primary moist, evergreen forest. Arboreal. Diet: fruit and seeds, also flowers, leaves, insects and occasional small vertebrates. HBL: males 45–62cm, females 44–58cm; wt: males 9kg, females 6.4kg. Coat: black, with some brown in long shoulder hair; short hair on cheeks grayish; hair on head rises to single (eastern races) or double (western races) crest. Female has bright pink cyclic vulval swelling.

Black mangabey

Cercocebus aterrimus

Zaire. Rain forest. Arboreal. Diet: fruit, seeds. HBL 71cm; wt about 10kg (male). Coat: black.

Agile mangabey

Cercocebus galeritus
Agile or Tana River mangabey.

Cameroon and Gabon, Kenya and Tanzania. The recently discovered eastern populations are scattered and separated from the western ones by thousands of kilometers. Rain forest. Terrestrial. Diet: palm nuts, seeds, leaves. HBL 44–58cm; wt 5.5kg (female), 10.2kg (male). Coat: dull yellowish-brown; hair on top of head forms crest. (Includes *C. agilis*.)

White mangabey

Cercocebus torquatus
White, Collared, Red-capped, or Sooty mangabey.

Senegal to Gabon. Primary rain forest. Terrestrial. Diet: palm nuts, seeds, fruit, leaves. HBL 66cm; wt about 10kg (male). Coat: gray; geographical races have color variants: a white collar in Ghana, a red cap in Cameroun. Females have a cyclic vulval swelling.

Guenons

Genus *Cercopithecus*

The African long-tailed monkeys which are mainly forest living. Both sexes have brightly colored coats, but with patterns more pronounced in males. Infants have dark or dull-colored coats, with pink faces at birth which darken later. Tails are considerably longer than bodies. Males are much larger than females, the difference being greater in larger species; females range from two-thirds to half weight of male. Taxonomy is complex: several species groups are recognizable, species from one group replacing each other geographically in the guilds of guenons present in each forest. These species groupings are indicated in the species entries below. Other species occur in suitable habitat over a very large area without obvious racial differentiation. Social organization is varied and is described by species. Adult males give loud species-specific distance calls. Groups of different species may travel together for long periods. Gestation periods have been estimated at around 5 months. Breeding is seasonal where known. Typical birth intervals vary between 1 and 3 years and first births occur between 3–7 years, variation being attributed to species and habitat differences in different cases.

Vervet

Cercopithecus aethiops
Vervet, grivet or Savanna or Green monkey.

Senegal to Somalia and southern Africa. Savanna, woodland edge, never far from water and often on banks of water courses. Semi-terrestrial. Diet: fruit, leaves, flowers, insects, eggs, nestlings, rodents, crops. HBL 46–66cm; wt 3.3kg (female), 4.5kg (male). Coat: yellowish- to olive-agouti, underparts white, lower limbs gray, face black with white cheek-tufts and browband; eyelids white; scrotum bright blue, penis and perineal patch red. Geographical

races have been recognized within their vast range and given specific status according to detail of color and pattern of cheek-tufts, but there is also variation of these characters within one troop. Groups usually include several adult males. Closely related to Diana monkey and Patas monkey.

Redtail monkey

Cercopithecus ascanius
Redtail or Coppertail monkey, Schmidt's guenon.

NE and E Zaire, S Uganda, W Kenya, W Tanzania, SW Rwanda. Mature rain forest and young secondary forest. Arboreal. Diet: insects, fruit, leaves, flowers, buds. HBL 41–48cm; wt 3.3kg (female), 4.2kg (male). Coat: yellow-brown, speckled, with pale underparts; limbs gray; tail chestnut-red on lower end; face black, bluish around eyes, with white spot on nose

and pronounced white cheek fur. Groups often have only one adult male. One of the *C. cephus* species group.

Moustached monkey

Cercopithecus cephus

S Cameroon to N Angola. Rain forest. Arboreal. Diet: fruit, insects, leaves, shoots, crops. HBL 48–56cm; wt 2.9kg (female), 4.1kg (male). Coat: red-brown agouti with dark gray limbs and back; lower part of tail red; throat and belly white; face black with blue skin around eyes, white moustache bar and white cheek fur. Groups may include only one adult male.

▲ **Vervet monkey troop.** Coat patterns are more distinct in the males, which, particularly in such larger species, may be somewhat larger than females.

Red-eared monkey
Cercopithecus erythrotis

S Nigeria and W Cameroon. Rain forest. Arboreal. Diet: fruit, insects, shoots, leaves, crops. HBL 36–51cm; WT 4 5kg male). Coat: brown-agouti with gray limbs; part of the tail red; face blue around eyes, nose and ear-tips red, cheek fur yellow. One of the *C. cephus* species group.

Red-bellied monkey
Cercopithecus erythrogaster

SW Nigeria. Rain forest. Arboreal. Diet: fruit, insects, leaves, crops. HBL 46cm; WT about 6kg (male). Coat: brown-agouti; face black, throat ruff white; belly variable from reddish to gray. A little known species similar to *C. petaurista* and in *C. cephus* species group.

Lesser spot-nosed monkey
Cercopithecus petaurista
Lesser spot-nosed or Lesser white-nosed monkey.

Sierra Leone to Benin. Rain forest. Arboreal. Diet: fruit, insects, shoots, leaves, crops. HBL 36–46cm; WT 3kg (female), 3–8kg (male). Coat: greenish-brown agouti; underparts white, lower part of tail red; face black with white spot on nose, prominent white throat ruff and white ear-tufts. One of the *C. cephus* species group.

Owl-faced monkey
Cercopithecus hamlyni
Owl-faced or Hamlyn's monkey.

Zaire to NW Rwanda. Rain and montane forest. Arboreal. Diet: fruit, insects, leaves. HBL 56cm; WT? Coat: olive-agouti with darker extremities; scrotum and perineum bright blue; face black with yellowish diadem and thin white stripe down nose. Lives in small groups with a single male.

L'Hoest's monkey
Cercopithecus lhoesti

Mt Cameroon and E Zaire to W Uganda, Rwanda. Montane forest. Terrestrial. Diet: fruit, leaves, insects. HBL 46–56cm; WT? Tail hook-shaped at end. Coat: dark gray-agouti with chestnut saddle; underparts dark. The eastern form has a striking white bib, while the western form is less strikingly marked with small bib, light gray cheek fur and whitish moustache markings. Lives in small groups with a single adult male. Includes *C. preussi* (Preuss's monkey).

CONTINUED ▶

Blue monkey

Cercopithecus mitis
Blue, Sykes', Silver, Golden or Samango monkey.

NW Angola to SW Ethiopia and southern Africa. Rain forest and montane bamboo forest. Arboreal. Diet: fruit, flowers, nectar, leaves, shoots, buds, insects; prey includes wood owls and bush babies. HBL 49–66cm; wt 4.2kg (female), 7.4kg (male). Coat: gray-agouti, with geographic variants often given subspecific rank. The **Blue monkey** (*C. m. stuhlmanni*) has a bluish-gray mantle, black belly and limbs, dark face with pale yellowish diadem; **Silver** (*C. m. doggetti*) and **Golden** (*C. m. kandti*) monkeys are variants with lighter and yellowish mantles, respectively, from W Uganda, Rwanda and E Zaire. **Sykes' monkey** (*C. m. kolbi*) has a chestnut saddle and a pronounced white ruff, from Mt Kenya and Nyandarua. The **samango** of more southern areas is a drab rusty-gray. Live in medium-sized groups of about 20–40 often with only a single adult male. *C. mitis* is replaced in W Africa by the closely similar *C. nictitans*.

Spot-nosed monkey

Cercopithecus nictitans
Spot-nosed or Greater white-nosed monkey or hocheur.

Sierra Leone to NW Zaire. Rain forest. Arboreal. Diet: fruit, leaves, shoots, insects, crops. HBL 44–66cm; wt 4.2kg (female), 6.6kg (male). Coat: dark olive-agouti; belly, extremities and tail black, face dark gray with white spot on nose. Habits similar to Blue monkey, which replaces it to the west.

Mona monkey

Cercopithecus mona

Senegal to W Uganda. Rain forest. Arboreal. Diet: fruit, leaves, shoots, insects, crops. HBL 46–56cm; wt 2.7–6.3kg. Coat: back brown-agouti, rump and underparts white; upper face bluish-gray, muzzle pink; hair round face yellowish with dark stripe from face to ear. Lives in fairly large groups which may contain more than one male, or a single adult male. The name comes from the moaning contact call of the females. Similar to Crowned guenon, which replaces it to the south.

Crowned guenon

Cercopithecus pogonias

S Cameroon to Congo basin. Forest. Arboreal. Diet: fruit, leaves, shoots, insects, crops. HBL 46cm; wt 3kg (female), 4.5kg (male). Coat: brown-agouti with black extremities; lower part of tail black; belly and rump yellow; face blue-gray with pink muzzle; prominant black line from face to ear and median black line from forehead-forming crest; fur yellow between black lines. Similar in habits to Mona monkey.

De Brazza's monkey

Cercopithecus neglectus

Cameroon to Ethiopia, Kenya to Angola. Swamp forest. Semi-terrestrial. Diet: fruit, leaves, insects. HBL 41–61cm; wt 4.2kg (female), 7.5kg (male). Coat: gray-agouti with black extremities; tail black; white stripe on thigh and rump white; face black with white muzzle; long white beard and orange diadem; scrotum blue. Lives in small groups, usually a pair with offspring. Freezes when alarmed.

Diana monkey

Cercopithecus diana

Sierra Leone to SW Ghana. Forest. Arboreal. Diet: fruit, leaves, insects. HBL 41–53cm; wt about 5kg (male). Coat: gray-agouti and chestnut back; extremities and tail black; white stripe on thigh; rump fur red or cream in different races; face black, surrounded by white ruff and beard. A wide-ranging species of the high canopy, living in medium-sized groups with a single adult male. This species may be allied to Vervet monkey.

Wolf's monkey

Cercopithecus wolfi
Wolf's or Dent's monkey.

A little known species from Zaire, NE Angola, W Uganda, Central African Republic. Arboreal. HBL 45–51cm. Includes *C. denti*.

Campbell's monkey

Cercopithecus campbelli

A little known species from Gambia to Ghana. HBL 36–55cm; wt 2.2kg (female), 4.3kg (male).

Dryas monkey

Cercopithecus dryas

A little known monkey from Zaire.

Genus *Allenopithecus*

A single species separated from *Cercopithecus* because females have periodic (perineal) swelling.

Allen's swamp monkey

Allenopithecus nigroviridis

E Congo and W Zaire. Swamp forest. Habits unknown. Diet: fruit, seeds, insects, fish, shrimps, snails. HBL 41–51cm; TL 36–53cm; wt? Coat: green-gray agouti with lighter underparts; hair flattened on crown.

Genus *Miopithecus*

A single species, separated from *Cercopithecus* because females have cyclic perineal swelling. Talapoins live in large groups of 70–100 including many adult males. They are sharply seasonal breeders, mating in the long dry season and giving birth 5½ months later. Infants are colored like adults except for the pink face which darkens after about 2 months. The juvenile period is long, with first births occurring at 5 or 6 years.

Talapoin monkey

Miopithecus talapoin

S Cameroon to Angola. Wet and swamp forest, and alongside water courses. Arboreal. Diet: fruit, insects, flowers, crops. HBL 34–37cm; TL 36–38cm; wt 1.1kg (female), 1.4kg (male). Coat: greenish-agouti; underparts and inner sides of limbs pale; scrotum blue; face gray with dark brown cheek stripe.

Genus *Erythrocebus*

A single species separated from *Cercopithecus* because of long limbs and adaptations for running. Patas monkeys live in moderately sized groups, usually with a single adult male. They are seasonal breeders, mating in the wet season and giving birth 5½ months later. Infants are light brown with pink faces which darken by 2 months. The juvenile period is short, with first births occurring at 3 years or even earlier.

Patas monkey

Erythrocebus patas
Patas, Military or Hussar monkey.

Senegal to Ethiopia, Kenya, Tanzania. Terrestrial. Diet: acacia fruit, galls, and leaves; other fruit, insects, crops; gum exudates from trees. HBL 58–75cm; TL 62–74cm; wt 4–13kg. Coat: shaggy, reddish-brown. Underparts, extremities and rump white; scrotum bright blue; penis red; face black with white moustache; cap brighter red, with black line from face to ear. This species seems closely related to the Vervet monkey.

Macaques

Genus *Macaca*

Heavily built, often partly terrestrial monkeys. The coat is generally dull brownish but the naked skin on face and rump may be bright red; some species have sexual swellings. Tails are up to slightly longer than body length (mostly shorter) or totally absent, depending on species. Males are larger than females, sometimes considerably so. Eclectic diets with fruit as the most common item. Seasonal breeders for the most part, mating in the fall and giving birth in the spring after about 5½ months gestation. Infants have a distinctively colored soft natal coat which is replaced after about 2 months. Macaques live in fairly large groups which may include several adult males. Females generally remain throughout life in their natal group, but males emigrate at adolescence and thereafter live alone, in small groups of males, or in other groups with females for varying periods of time.

Stump-tailed macaque

Macaca arctoides
Stump-tailed or Bear macaque.

E India to S China and Vietnam. Forest, particularly montane. Terrestrial and Arboreal. Diet: fruit, insects, young leaves, crops, small animals. HBL 50–70cm; TL 1–10cm; wt 5.1kg (female), 7.9kg (male). Coat: dark brown; face naked, dark red and mottled; rump also naked and dark red. No perineal swelling.

Assamese macaque

Macaca assamensis

N India to Thailand and Vietnam. Forest. terrestrial and arboreal. Diet: fruit, insects, young leaves, crops, small animals. HBL 53–68cm; TL 19–38cm; wt 6.1kg (female), 7.8kg (male). Coat: varying shades of yellowish to dark brown; face and perineum naked, red in adult.

Formosan rock macaque

Macaca cyclopis
Formosan rock or Taiwan macaque.

Taiwan. Terrestrial and arboreal. Diet: fruit, insects, young leaves, crops, small animals. HBL 56cm; tail moderately long; wt? Coat: dark brown.

Crab-eating macaque

Macaca fascicularis
Crab-eating or Long-tailed macaque.

Indonesia and Philippines to S Burma. Forest edge, swamp, banks of water courses and coastal forest. Terrestrial and arboreal. Diet: fruit, insects, young leaves, crops, small animals. HBL 38–65cm; TL 40–66cm; wt 4.5kg (female), 6.2kg (male). Coat: varying shades of brown (grayish or yellowish or darker); underside paler; face skin dark gray; prominent frill of gray hair round face. No perineal swelling.

Japanese macaque
Macaca fuscata

Japan. Forest. Terrestrial and arboreal. Diet: fruit, insects, young leaves, crops, small animals. HBL 47–60cm; TL 7–12cm; wt 8.3–18kg. Coat: brown to gray; face and rump skin naked, red in adult. No perineal swelling.

Rhesus macaque
Macaca mulatta
Rhesus macaque or Rhesus monkey.

India and Afghanistan to China and Vietnam. Forest, forest edge and outskirts of towns and villages. Terrestrial and arboreal. Diet: fruit, insects, young leaves, crops, small animals. HBL 47–64cm; TL 19–30cm; wt 5.4kg (female), 7.7kg (male). Coat: brown with paler underside; face and rump naked, red in adult. No perineal swelling.

Pig-tailed macaque
Macaca nemestrina

E India to Indonesia. Wet forest. Terrestrial and arboreal. Diet: fruit, insects, young leaves, crops, small animals. HBL 47–60cm; TL 13–24cm; wt 4.8kg (female), 8.3kg (male). Coat: varying shades of brown, with paler underside and darker brown areas around face. Females have large cyclic perineal swelling.

Bonnet macaque
Macaca radiata

S India. Forest, forest edge and outskirts of towns and villages. Terrestrial and arboreal. Diet: fruit, insects, young leaves, crops. HBL 35–60cm; TL 48–69cm; wt 3.7kg (female), 6.3kg (male). Coat: grayish-brown with paler underparts; hair on head grows out in whorl from central crown. No perineal swelling.

Lion-tailed macaque [E]
Macaca silenus

S India. Wet forest. Terrestrial and arboreal. Diet: omnivorous. HBL 46–61cm; TL 25–38cm; wt 6.8kg (male). Coat: black with gray around face, in outstanding ruff; tail with slight tuft at tip. Females have cyclic perineal swelling.

Toque macaque
Macaca sinica

Sri Lanka. Wet forest, edges of watercourses, scrub. Terrestrial and arboreal. Diet: fruit, insects, young leaves, crops. HBL 43–53cm; TL 47–62cm; wt 3.6kg (female), 5.7kg (male). Coat: reddish or yellowish-brown with paler underparts; hair on top of head grows out from central crown. No perineal swelling.

Barbary macaque [V]
Macaca sylvanus
Barbary macaque, Barbary ape, Rock ape.

N Algeria and Morocco, introduced to Gibraltar. Mid and high altitude forest, also scrub and cliffs. Terrestrial and arboreal. Diet: fruit, young leaves, bark, roots, occasionally invertebrates. HBL 50–60cm; tail absent; wt 11–15kg. Coat: yellowish-gray to grayish-brown, with paler underparts; face dark flesh colored. Females have dark gray-red cyclic perineal swelling.

Père David's macaque
Macaca thibetana
Père David's or Tibetan stump-tailed macaque.

Tibet to China. Montane forest. Semi-terrestrial. Diet: omnivorous. HBL 60cm; TL 6cm; wt about 12kg (male). Coat: brown.

Moor macaque
Macaca maura

Sulawesi. Forest. Diet: omnivorous. HBL 66cm; tail absent; wt ? Coat: brown or brownish-black; ischial callosities large and pink. Females have cyclic perineal swelling.

Celebes macaque
Macaca nigra

Sulawesi. Forest. Diet: omnivorous. HBL 55cm; tail absent; wt 10kg (adult male). Coat: black, with prominent pink ischial callosities; face black, prominent ridges down side of nose; hair on head rises to stiff crest. Females have cyclic pink perineal swelling.

Tonkean macaque
Macaca tonkeana

Sulawesi. Forest. Diet. omnivorous. HBL about 60cm; tail absent; wt ? Coat: black, lighter brown rump, cheeks; ischial callosities prominent. Females have cyclic pink perineal swelling.

Baboons

Genus *Papio*
The classification of baboons is controversial and several systems have been proposed. Here the Savanna or "Common" baboon is considered to be one species containing three races previously considered separate species. The status of the Guinea baboon is not clear and on behavioral grounds it may be regarded as a western race of the Hamadryas baboon. In fact some latest classifications group all the open country species ("Common", Hamadryas and Guinea baboon) under one species, *Papio hamadryas*.

The drill and mandrill are here included in *Papio* (not *Mandrillus* as formerly). Baboons live in large groups. Hamadryas baboons have a hierarchical group structure based on the one-male unit or harem, and this structure may also be present in groups of Guinea baboons, drills and mandrills. The "Common" or Savanna baboons have more informal groups including several adult males. Gestation is about 6 months and breeding is not seasonal. Birth intervals vary around 2 years, depending on the food supply, and first births occur when females are from 4 to 8 years old. Infants have a black natal coat and pink skin for the first 2 months.

Savanna baboon
Papio cynocephalus
Savanna, Chacma, Olive, Yellow or "Common" baboon.

Ethiopia to S Africa, Angola. Savanna woodland and forest edge. Terrestrial. Diet: grass, fruit, seeds, insects, hares and young ungulates, crops. HBL 56–79cm; TL 42–60cm; wt 12–14kg (female), 21–25kg (male). Coat: gray-agouti, with longer hair over shoulders, especially in adult males; shiny black patch of bare skin present over hips. Females have cyclic perineal swelling. First 3 or 4 tail vertebrae fused in adult giving hook-shaped base to tail. Coat color varies geographically, giving recognizable races which have been previously accorded specific status. The lowland East and Central African form is yellowish (**"Yellow baboon"**), the highland East African form is olive-greenish (**"Olive baboon"**), and the southern African race is dark gray (**Chacma baboon**). The face is naked and black with prominent lateral ridges on the long muzzle especially in adult males. The nose varies geographically, the "Olive" baboon having a pointed nose extending beyond the mouth a little, while the "Yellow" and "Chacma" baboons have retroussé noses.

Hamadryas baboon
Papio hamadryas

Ethiopia, Somalia, Saudi Arabia, S Yemen. Rocky desert and subdesert with some grass and thorn bush. Terrestrial. Diet: grass seeds, roots, bulbs. HBL 76cm; TL 61cm; wt 9.9kg (female), 16.9kg (male). Coat: females and juveniles brown, adult males with silvery-gray cape over shoulders with red naked skin on face and perineum.

Guinea baboon
Papio papio

Senegal to Sierra Leone. Savanna woodland. Terrestrial. Diet: grass, fruit, seeds, insects, small animals, crops. HBL 69cm; TL 56cm in adult male; wt ? Coat: brown with red naked skin on rump; face brownish red.

Drill [E]
Papio leucophaeus

SE Nigeria and W Cameroon. Rain forest. Terrestrial. Diet: fruit, seed, fungi, roots, insects, small vertebrates. HBL 70cm; TL 12cm; wt up to 50kg. Coat: dark brown with blue to purple naked rump; face black with white fringe of hair around it. Muzzle long, with pronounced lateral ridges along it. Females much smaller than males.

Mandrill
Papio sphinx

S Cameroon, Gabon, Congo. Rain forest. Terrestrial. Diet: fruit, seeds, fungi, roots, insects, small vertebrates. HBL 80cm; TL 7cm; wt 11.5kg (female), 25kg (male). Coat: olive-brown agouti with pale underparts; blue to purple naked rump in adult males, duller in females and juveniles. Face very brightly colored in adult male, with red median stripe on muzzle, ridged side of muzzle blue, beard yellow. Females and juveniles similarly colored but duller. Females much smaller than males.

Genus *Theropithecus*
A single species, the only survivor of an important fossil group. Commonly referred to as a baboon, but very different in vocal and visual communication patterns from *Papio*. Geladas live in large herds within which adult males have harems of several females. Other males live in bachelor groups at the periphery.

Gelada
Theropithecus gelada
Gelada or Gelada baboon.

Ethiopia. Grassland. Terrestrial. Diet: grass, roots, bulbs, seeds, fruit, insects. HBL 50–74cm; TL 32–50cm; wt 14kg (female), 21kg (male). Coat: brown, fading to cream at end of long hairs; mane and long cape over shoulders; naked area of red skin around base of neck, surrounded by whitish lumps in the female which vary in size with the menstrual cycle. Rump of both sexes also red and naked and rather fat. Muzzle with concave upper line, longitudinal ridges along side of snout. Upper lip can be everted, used in flash display.

Monkeys in Clover

How Rhesus macaques manage to survive in the Himalayas

Most primates inhabit warm tropical and subtropical regions. The macaques, however, have a distribution that includes China, Japan, the Himalayas, North Africa and Gibraltar.

One of the 15 macaques, the Rhesus macaque or Rhesus monkey (*Macaca mulatta*)—well known for the important role it has played in medical research—ranges from Afghanistan through much of India and Indochina to the Yangtze in China, with an isolated population near Pekin.

In northern Pakistan, rhesus live in the mountains up to 4,000m (13,000ft) in temperate forest that is dominated by pines and firs, though deciduous trees such as the maple, horse-chestnut and elm sometimes mingle with the conifers. The climate is highly seasonal. A warm, dry spring gives way to a three-month monsoon season, when about 38cm (15in) of rain falls. Sunshine and clear weather return in the fall, but winter brings freezing temperatures and snow, up to 6.5m (22ft) of it between January and March. How do the monkeys survive in this area?

Himalayan rhesus live in groups of 20–70, each group's home range including 3–6 sq km (1.2–2.3 sq mi) of rugged terrain. The animals sleep in the trees but spend much of the day on the ground, eating the leaves and roots of herbaceous plants. Clover, in particular, makes up a large proportion of their annual diet. Clover grows only in patches from which the trees have been cleared, either by natural events like avalanches or, nowadays more often, by people. These patches are quite rare, but the monkeys seek them out. They also take advantage of sudden abundances of food items, so that over the year they eat a wide range of foods even though at any one time their diet is narrow. For instance, in spring and early summer they eat young fir tips, wild strawberries and the berries of viburnum, a shrub that grows only in open areas; in summer they relish mushrooms and cicadas; fall brings the cobs of jack-in-the-pulpit and pine seeds buried on the ground in a carpet of dead pine needles. With the onset of winter, snow covers up many potential foods and the monkeys resort to poorer items such as the tough, barely digestible leaves of the evergreen oak, but they still manage to find a few nutritious foods. For example, sweet, sticky sap collects on the needles of some pines trees and they lick it off, probably for its sugar content. Where the snow has melted or blown away, they search for plants with fat roots, which they pull up and eat. In February, the viburnum comes into bloom and they feed heavily on the flowers until the spring thaw. The monkeys are insulated from the cold by a heavy coat that grows in late fall and is shed in the spring. Most animals lose weight, a kilogram or so, but most winters few die.

In many respects, the social life of Himalayan rhesus is like that of rhesus in

▲ **On the northern edge** of the species' range in Nepal, this temple-dwelling Rhesus macaque is protected by monks against some of the rigors faced by its cousins in the wild. Patterns of breeding, social life and individual life-history are different from those of Rhesus macaques in the tropics.

◄ **Surviving snowy winters** of northern Japan, the Japanese macaque, another hardy species, is protected by the thick gray coat covering its heavy frame. It is the largest of all macaques.

frequently and support each other in fights with other females.

The males, which are somewhat larger than the females and dominant to them, can also be ranked in a hierarchy but their relationships are much less stable. Before reaching sexual maturity at about 7 years, most males leave the group into which they were born and join another, usually neighboring, group. As adults they may transfer again. Genetic studies show that in Pakistan Rhesus monkey social groups are not inbred; this pattern of male emigration helps to prevent it. Some males join a new group by loitering on its periphery, cowering to all the resident males. Others directly challenge the highest ranking male in the group and fight fiercely to establish their position. Serious wounds may be inflicted, and some males possibly die as a result.

Some distinctive features of the Himalayan rhesus' social system reflect the seasonality of their environment compared with the equable climate enjoyed by their southern relatives. In the Himalayas Rhesus monkeys mate only in the fall and most male transfers between groups occur in the preceding three months and, particularly, just before the monsoon. In this dry season, several groups with overlapping home ranges will crowd into valleys which still have running water, and groups often move and feed side by side for hours or days on end. Males seize this chance to transfer. Females give birth every other spring at most, a longer minimal interval between the births of surviving offspring than in Rhesus populations further south (2 years compared to about 8 months). In the Himalayas, the monkeys take about two years longer to mature and probably die younger. Females reach sexual maturity at 5–6 years instead of 3–4 years. In provisioned colonies, animals may live for 28 years, but evidence suggests that in the Himalayas few live beyond the age of 20 years. These aspects of their life history mean that females in the Himalayas usually have few (ic 4 or 5) close living relatives and do not form the large matrilineal groups (20 individuals or more) reported for some rhesus populations. The population's capacity for rapid growth is also reduced.

The survival of Rhesus monkeys in the temperate forests of northern Pakistan depends heavily upon access to plants that grow plentifully only in forest clearings. It is ironic that forest clearance—which if continued will lead ultimately to the disappearance of these monkeys—may in the short run increase their abundance. AFR

the tropics. Groups contain 11–70 animals, about half of them adult. Adult females outnumber adult males two to one, though they are born in equal numbers (the death rate is higher in young males than females).

Females spend their lives in the group into which they were born. They can be ranked in a hierarchy, each female's position determined by the number of individuals to whom she cowers in submission. Her daughters all rank immediately below her and above all other females to whom she is dominant. Normally, daughters do not outrank their mothers even when the latter grow old. The rank order of the daughters is determined by their birth order, with the eldest ranking lowest and the youngest achieving highest rank about the time she reaches sexual maturity at about 5 years. Thus changes in the hierarchy usually occur only as daughters approach maturity and outrank their elder sisters. A female's kinship affiliations influence many aspects of her social life. Closely related females move and sit together, groom one another

Baby Care in Barbary Macaques

Infants as instruments of harmony between adult males

As the one-week-old baby nervously tottered away from its mother, a watchful adult male rushed in and picked it up. Holding it upside down in mid-air, the male "teeth-chattered" and "lip-smacked" at the squealing infant. The noisy exchange drew the attention of three other males (of varying ages), who scrambled to the scene. Huddled together, arms over shoulders, they joined in what seemed to be mutual adulation of the young animal. Grimacing and teeth-chattering, often making purring sounds, they passed the bewildered baby from one of the four to the other. After a few minutes the group interaction ended with one of the adult males grooming the baby nonchalantly as the others resumed their feeding and grooming.

Such infant-directed behavior is quite common in the Barbary macaque. Babies are the focus of a rich repertoire of behaviour among troop members of both sexes and all ages. This male care of babies and "use" of babies in social interactions is notable because males of this species interact more with unweaned youngsters than do males of other Old World monkeys. In common with other macaques, male Barbary macaques protect babies from predators, but unlike other species they also undertake "maternal" chores such as grooming and carrying infants. Among Barbary macaques it is usual to observe close groupings of males (adult, subadult and juveniles) in the presence of babies. Such groupings involve either males taking babies and directly presenting them to other males or males without babies approaching those holding one. The infants themselves are passive participants and males will even use a dead baby or sometimes even an inanimate object during their "group huddling" encounters.

The mating system of these macaques is not very different from that of other macaque species. Because males regularly emigrate from their natal groups at puberty, macaque groups are centered around females who form the permanent core of the social unit. These matrilineal female kin form distinct and cohesive units within the larger group and are usually ranked above or below each other in a hierarchy. Kinship and rank clearly influence the nature of social interactions in the group. Among males normally one is dominant to all the others and is thus able to monopolize copulations with all group females. Babies will then generally be fathered by the leader male. During "group huddling" events he is able to withdraw any infant without any

opposition, but males will not choose an infant at random for care-taking or huddling. In fact, two males tend to be involved with each other through their common care-taking relationship with an infant. Whether this relationship is promoted by kinship ties or associations that develop during the breeding season is still not clear. On Gibraltar it appears that those males engaging in care-taking and huddling with particular infants belong to the same matriline as the infant. Males of different matrilines normally use babies in a more random fashion and employ them as "buffers" in a potentially aggressive situation.

The use of babies as buffers is also seen among baboons and other macaques. The form it takes in Barbary macaques follows the same pattern as the non-aggressive huddling encounters. For example, when threatened by another male, a male will pick up a baby and present it to the aggressor. Seemingly appeased, the aggressor will abandon his threatening intentions and join the submissive male in huddling and teeth-chattering over the infant. This very complex behavior is habitual among males when babies are available. When there are no babies nearby, other appeasement behavior, eg socio-sexual mounts (mock copulation between dominant and submissive males), become more frequent.

Proponents of the theory of "agonistic buffering," as this behavior is known, claim

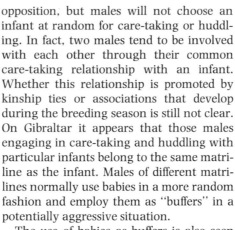

▲ **Adult males** will carry, groom and care for babies, especially if they are related, such behavior often involving two males and an infant. (1) Adult male picks up unweaned infant by hind leg and turns it (2) to sniff genitals, teeth-chattering and lip-smacking as he does so. He holds the infant up to the second male (3) who sniffs, chatters and lip-smacks also. Finally (4) the second male grooms the infant. Mutual grooming between the two adult males may follow.

◄ ▲ **The most famous "Barbary apes"** are on Gibraltar. Barbary macaques have lived on the Rock since at least 1740 when they were imported by the British garrison for game hunting. Numbers have since fluctuated, falling from 130 in 1900 to just four in 1943, when following Mr. Churchill's instructions 24 more were imported from North Africa. Today's population is descended from these individuals and kept at between 30 and 40 in two troops.

that such appeasement interactions allow subordinate animals to gain access to dominant ones and better their chances of "social climbing." But whatever the ultimate consequences may be for the individual's social rank, the behavior is certain to promote a more harmonious social environment. Perhaps the fact that Barbary macaque groups can contain up to 10 adult males as opposed

to a few in other macaques is a direct measure of the success of such appeasement rules.

Baby care-taking is an important feature of troop life in any monkey. It has been elaborated in the Barbary macaque not only to promote survival of the infants by giving them constant attention but also to lower the level of tension between animals.   JEF

What Does "Whoop-gobble" Mean?

Long-distance communication among mangabeys

The familiar "whoop-gobble" sound heard in the rain forests to the north of the Zaïre River is as stereotyped and distinctive a call as any mammal produces—a low-pitched tonal "whoop," followed by a four- to five-second silence that always ends with a series of loud staccato, "gobbling" pulses—the number and timing of which will identify him individually.

Not until it attains sexual maturity does the male Gray-cheeked mangabey produce for the first time his full-fleged "whoop-gobble" call. To produce his call the male employs both the larynx and additional resonant air sacs. In consequence, the volume of the whoop-gobble easily matches that of most other loud mammal vocalizations, for instance those produced by opera singers, and approaches even that of the sonar pulses of echo-locating bats.

Many forest monkeys have calls analogous to the whoop-gobble: loud, low-pitched, carrying over distances of a kilometer or more, and, in some species, given only by adult males. The howls of New World howler monkeys, the whoops of Asian leaf monkeys, the roars of the African Black-and-white colobus, and the booms and pyows of African forest guenons are examples. These calls, though superficially very different in form, are specialized in similar ways to the whoop-gobble and to similar ends. By broadcasting tape-recorded mangabey calls through a speaker and re-recording them some distance away, it has been shown that the whoop-gobble is attenuated less by passage through tropical forest vegetation than is any other mangabey call. One reason is its low pitch, as low-frequency sounds travel well through such a medium. Its stereotyped, distinctive form (other mangabey calls are much more variable than the whoop-gobble) also makes it easy for a monkey's ear to pick out against the inevitable background of tropical bird and insect noises. Over half of mangabey whoop-gobble calls made from 0.5km (500 yards) away are audible to the much less sensitive and attuned human ear. Other monkey species' "loud calls" tend to share the characteristics of low pitch and high stereotypy, presumably for the same reasons.

Most mangabeys give the whoop-gobble call only a few times a day, early in the morning when many birds and other monkeys also call, producing a "dawn chorus." At this time of day the much cooler air below the crowns of the trees tends to focus sounds within the forest canopy. Furthermore, gray-cheeked mangabeys and other species (even those that, unlike these mangabeys, normally live on the ground) tend to give their loud calls from high perches; this is because the further above the sound-absorbent ground low-frequency sounds are

▲ **Air sac inflated** for extra resonance, a male Gray-cheeked mangabey begins his long-distance dawn call. Such "whoop-gobbles" enable neighboring troops to minimize aggressive encounters over food trees.

◄ **Perched high under the forest canopy,** the leading male (**1**) gives his whoop-gobble. Other troop members continue their activities, foraging for insects or other food (**2**) or in social activity –(**3**) female presenting to male. An outsider's whoop-gobble reply from too nearby may elicit a nervous response – (**4**) male yawning – and the caller will be confronted by the troop leader.

▶ **Shape of mangabey calls.** Sonograms of the whoop-gobbles of three Gray-cheeked mangabeys (**a–c**). The characteristic whoop-pause-gobble pattern can clearly be seen, as can the differences between individuals.

If recordings of whoop-gobbles are broadcast near a mangabey group in the field, the mangabeys distinguish between the whoop-gobble calls of males within their group, and can also tell the calls of their "own" males from those of males in other groups. A group of Gray-cheeked mangabeys usually approaches the call of only one of its males, showing no response (except for momentary attention and answering calls) to the whoop-gobbles of its other males. In contrast, the group tends to move away from calls of all outside males. The male whose calls are approached tends to be the most frequent winner of aggressive encounters within the group, and is the most sexually active male; he is also the male most likely to give whoop-gobbles. This individual answers all experimentally broadcast whoop-gobbles (including his own) in kind and may run up to a kilometer through the forest to confront the source of a call.

These responses suggest that group members use the call to congregate if they become scattered, and that both males and females can use it to monitor the number and status of adult males in the vicinity. However, the most important listeners are members of neighboring groups: the call is the basic mechanism whereby one group of mangabeys maintains its distance from the next.

The means by which mangabey groups divide the forest among themselves can also be investigated systematically by field playback of tape-recorded whoop-gobbles. A Gray-cheeked mangabey group moves over and feeds in a large home range which, over a year, may cover some 4.1 square kilometers (1.6 sq mi) for a 16-member group. The group's response to an intruder is the same—avoidance—whether the intruder's call is from the center of its home range or near its edge. Thus, Gray-cheeked mangabeys do not recognize boundaries or "ownership" of the forest; they are not territorial. However, by advertising their location over long distances and by moving away from the whoop-gobbles of any neighboring group within a few hundred meters, each group maintains a buffer area around itself. As a result, only one group, the group that finds it first, will generally have access to a concentrated food source such as a fruiting tree. Occasionally, due usually to accidents of bad weather or topography, groups encounter one another without hearing each other's calls. In this situation, fighting occurs between the two groups: if the convention of avoidance is broken it is backed up by a threat of real conflict. PMW

produced, the further they carry.

Gray-cheeked mangabeys are social animals, living in groups of around 15 individuals (range 6–28) including several adult males and a stable core of 5–6 adult females. Unlike some monkeys of more open habitats, they lack a repertoire of more visual signals—bright colors or visual displays would be of limited use in the relatively dark, dense forest canopy where they live. Instead, mangabeys are highly vocal, communicating with each other through a wide variety of grunts, barks, and other acoustic signals as they forage through the trees. The whoop-gobble stands out in the mangabey repertoire by both its audibility and its spontaneity; though sometimes given following a disturbance within the group, it is generally produced without apparent provocation.

Frequency in 1000Hz

Time in seconds

A Close-knit Society

Alliances in an Olive baboon troop

The Olive baboons (the name refers to the dark green cast to the grizzled gray-brown coat) of the East African highlands are among the most social of all primates. They live in large troops that occupy home ranges of up to 40sq km (15.4sq mi). The 30 to 150 troop members remain together all the time, as they travel, feed, and sleep as a cohesive unit. It was once thought that it was sexual attraction that kept baboons together, while later observers thought that leadership and authority provided by the adult males formed the basis of group life. It is now known that the enduring relationships formed by females with one another, with young, and with adult males are what lie at the heart of baboon society.

As in many other social mammals, female baboons remain in their natal groups, while males voluntarily leave to join new troops, one by one as they near adulthood. Females and their female offspring often maintain close bonds after the offspring grow up. These associations between maternal kin

result in a network of social relationships extending down through three generations and out to include first cousins. Within this female kin group (or matriline, as it is known) each female ranks just below her mother. When a troop of Olive baboons takes a break during the day, relatives will gather around the oldest female in the family to rest and groom. At night relatives usually sleep huddled together, and they will come to one another's aid if a member of the kin group is threatened by another baboon. Females and young from different kin groups within the troop also form close bonds with one another based on years of familiarity. These bonds are developed in play groups, and in nursery groups, associations between females that have infants of similar ages.

A male immigrant who is unfamiliar to members of his new troop therefore has to penetrate a dense network of relatives and friends. He usually begins by cultivating a relationship with an adult female. He will

▲ **Olive baboon troop** feeding on acacia flowers. Although baboons are the most terrestrial and herbivorous Old World monkeys they can and will enter trees in search of food.

◄ **This male appears to be well-established** in the troop and to have been accepted as their friend by three, probably related, females.

▼ **A "foot-back" submissive greeting.** In addition to presenting her foot-palm, the female on the left acknowledges inferior social status by a "fear-grin" and the vertically raised tail. Fights between females are rare. Relative status in the female dominance hierarchy that is the basis of Olive baboon society is routinely expressed by such gestures.

follow her about, making friendly faces at her when he catches her eye, lipsmacking and grunting softly, and, if she permits, he will groom her. After many months the male may succeed in establishing a stable bond with a female. If so, their relationship will serve as a kind of "passport," allowing him to gradually extend his ties to her friends and relatives. Although the newly arrived male's ability to compete effectively against other males is an important determinant of his status, if he fails to form such bonds he is unable to stay in the troop for long.

Relationships with females continue to be important for long-term resident males. When female baboons are in heat they mate and interact with many different males, but females spend most of their adult lives either pregnant or nursing. At these times they will not mate. Observation of one large troop of Olive baboons revealed that most of the 35 pregnant or nursing females had a special relationship or "friendship" with just one, two, or three of the 18 adult males (a 1:2 adult sex ratio is typical of this subspecies of *Papio cynocephalus*), and different females tended to have different male friends. Pregnant and nursing females remained near their friends, avoiding all other males, while foraging for grasses, bulbs, roots, leaves, and fruits. While resting during the day or sleeping on the cliffs at night, "friends" often huddled close together. Nearly all of the females' amicable interactions with males, including grooming, were restricted to their "friends."

The main reason why a female develops such "friendships" seems to be the aid the male gives her and the investment that he makes in her offspring. He will sometimes (not invariably) defend the female or her accompanying juvenile offspring from aggression by other troop members. Here the males' strength, powerful canines and size—at 22–35kg (48–80lb) they are twice as heavy as the females—come into play. Male friends also usually help and care for and protect the female's infant. The male will groom and occasionally carry the infant, protecting it from predators as well as troop members. Such bonds between the young and the friend of its mother sometimes persist for years.

Why, for their part, do males form and maintain "friendships" with certain females? In some instances the male friend mated with the female around the time she conceived, in which case he may be the father of her current infant. But close relationships between infants and males who were unlikely to be the infant's father have also been observed. Once a male has demonstrated his willingness and ability to attach himself to a female and her infant, he seems to become more attractive to the female: when a female comes back into heat she prefers to mate with those males who were her friends when she was pregnant and, later, nursing. The male probably befriends the female who is not in heat in order to increase his opportunities for mating when she once again becomes receptive (usually about one year after giving birth).

In the troop discussed here, most females, regardless of age or dominance rank, had just 2 male friends. But older males who had lived in the troop for several years had 5 or 6 female friends, while younger resident males had only 2 or 3, and males who had lived in the troop for less than six months had none. When a male had several female friends they were often from the same matriline. In several troops of Olive baboons some old males mate more often than younger, more dominant males, perhaps because of the older males' greater number of female friends. However, males do compete actively for access to receptive females, and fights are common. Male dominance relationships are less stable than those of linear hierarchies of females in which each kin group has a clear-cut position. Fights between females are rare, status being routinely expressed by submissive gestures.

Natural selection has favored competitive behavior in baboons, but at the same time it has also favored the capacity to develop close and enduring bonds with a few others. The fact that humans share this capacity with other primates suggests that it is a very ancient and fundamental aspect of human nature.

BS

A Male-dominated Society

The Hamadryas baboons of Cone Rock, Ethiopia

It is an hour before sunset in the semidesert of the southern Danakil plain in Ethiopia. The long column of Hamadryas baboons, brown females and young interspersed with large, gray-mantled males, crosses the dry river bed and threads its way up through a steep gravel slope. It heads for a cliff where it will pass the night in safety from leopards. Suddenly, a male near the front runs back along the column at full speed. A female separates from the last group in the line and hurries towards him as if she knew that she had lagged too far for his tolerance. Upon reaching her, the male gives her a shaking bite on the back of the neck. Squealing, she follows him closely up to the cliff where his other females are waiting. He then leads his family to a ledge where they settle for grooming.

Hamadryas males herd their females by threats and, in severe cases, by neck bites. Four-fifths of the troop's adult males own harems, which range in size from one to 10 females and average about two. Whereas males of other baboon species consort with only one female at a time and only for hours or days when she is in heat, 70 percent of hamadryas pair bonds last longer than three years and continue uninterrupted through the periods of pregnancy and lactation, when the female is not sexually accessible. They show that primate pair bonds are not necessarily sexually motivated.

The troop which lives at Cone Rock in northeastern Ethiopia numbers several hundred and is organized into groups of four levels—harem families, clans, bands and troop—a structural complexity that is not matched by any other known primate populations apart from man (see RIGHT). Members of the same social unit interact about 10 times more often with each other than they do with "outsiders" belonging to next largest unit.

The reproductive career of a young hamadryas male is successful if he obtains possession of a harem. His difficulty is that all reproductive females in a troop belong to some male who will fight any encroaching rival. Indeed, experiments have demonstrated that males have an inhibition against taking over females from another male in the same band, even when the latter is a *less* powerful fighter. In the band referred to above the subadult follower's standard solution is to court a juvenile female, always in his own clan. Having not reached puberty, she is only moderately defended by her father, and other fully grown males are not interested in her at all. Thus, the subadult may closely precede the juvenile female

► **Hamadryas clan on the move.** The gray mantles of the males (clan leader on RIGHT) stand out among the brown females and young.

► **Intensely possessive towards his harem** BELOW, a male threat-gapes at an opponent during a band fight. The rival turns away, grasping his nearest female around the hip. This possessive frenzy is accompanied by a strong inhibition in the male even to look at another female.

▼ **Smallest social unit is the harem family.** One to three *families*, each with its adult male leader, his females (1–10 in number, but averaging 2) and their young, are escorted by several male followers. The families and their followers form a *clan* of 10–20 baboons, who forage and sleep as a group.

Several clans are united in a *band* of about 70 animals. In the morning at the sleeping cliff, the band's adult males communicate about the direction of the day's foraging march; these interactions may last more than an hour, but eventually band members leave the sleeping site together and later reassemble to drink at noon. The band is also a unit of defense against males of other bands attempting to appropriate some of its females.

The *troop* is an unstable set of bands that use the same sleeping cliff.

The male follower (M) of one family is courting a daughter for his first mate.

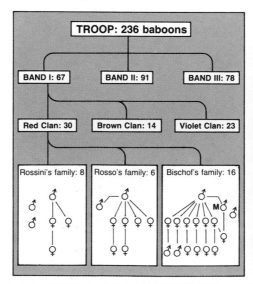

TROOP: 236 baboons		
BAND I: 67	BAND II: 91	BAND III: 78
Red Clan: 30	Brown Clan: 14	Violet Clan: 23
Rossini's family: 8	Rosso's family: 6	Bischof's family: 16

when she follows her mother, and so habituate her to follow *him*. During such maneuvers he must not make her squeal, which might provoke her father to chase him away. With skill, and profiting from the tolerance he enjoys as a clan member, the subadult will extract her from her family in a few month's time. In contrast to this subtle procedure, males in another band always waited till they were young adults and then abducted their juvenile female suddenly and by force: obviously there are diverging band styles of social behavior, even in the same troop. By acquiring a prepubertal female the subadult male avoids the competition of adult males. Once mature she will become his first mate, and the other males will continue to respect the pair bond.

When fully grown, male followers in one band attacked the ageing family leaders in their clan and took some of their females by force. Grown males of other clans joined and sometimes obtained females from the disrupted harem. The winning males were younger than the losers. Whereas the clans of the loser's band shared about equally in the lost adult females, only a third of them were lost to other bands. The three defeated old leaders were left with one or no female. Within weeks, they lost weight and their long mantle hair had changed to the hair color of females, in response to what is presumably a very traumatic experience. Only one defeated leader lived on for several years in his clan; he remained most influential in the clan's decisions on travel directions. The other two disappeared: they either left the troop or died.

It appears that the male's reproductive career depends on his association with his clan and band. Clan and band males obtain most of their females from one another and cooperate in their defense against outsiders. In fact, a male remains in his natal clan to the end of his reproductive period. He first becomes one of its followers and finally, with luck, one of its harem leaders. When two mothers of juvenile sons were taken over by males from outside the clan, the sons actually abandoned their mothers and rejoined their fathers' clans, which is an extraordinary preference in a juvenile primate.

Females, however, are frequently transferred to other clans or even bands. Theoretically a juvenile may be expected to join the parent from which he will profit more in his reproductive career. In the more promiscuous baboon species a son does not know who is his father, but may profit from a high rank of his mother. In the hamadryas, he "inherits" females from his father's clan. The hamadryas from Cone Rock are exceptional in imposing something like a patrilineal system on the ancient and widespread matrilineal organization that is typical of related species (see p392).

Nevertheless, females are not merely passive merchandise in hamadryas society. Experiments were necessary to show that a female prefers certain males, and that a rival male heeds her preference: the less a female favors her male, the more likely it is that a rival will overcome his inhibition and rob her. Females, being of far inferior strength and size (some 10kg as opposed to the males' 20kg), must choose more subtle ways to reach their goals, and research naturally first discovered the conspicuous, aggressive stratagems of males. HK

Hybrid Monkeys of the Kibale Forest

Successful mating between Redtail and Blue monkeys

Hybridization between mammal species in the wild is extremely uncommon. Normally, it is avoided or prevented by isolating mechanisms, such as geographical barriers (eg rivers), preference for different habitats in the same region, or differences in the anatomy, physiology, ecology and behavior of species. Most hybridization in the wild occurs where geographical barriers have broken down and two closely related but previously isolated species are able to interact. When there is a breakdown of isolating mechanisms and interbreeding does occur, it is usually disadvantageous, both to the hybrid and the parent species. Most often the offspring are infertile. If not, they may be ill-adapted to their habitat or be unable to find mates.

In Africa the Redtail monkey or Schmidt's guenon (*Cercopithecus ascanius*) and the Blue monkey (*C. mitis*) (see also p384) occur together over much of their geographical ranges without hybridization. However, hybrids have been found in four forests, one of which is the Kibale Forest of western Uganda. This hybridization is of special interest because it occurs between species whose ranges do normally overlap; because the offspring are fertile, and because the female hybrids, at least, seem to have distinct social advantages.

Physically, blues and redtails differ considerably in size and weight (Blue monkeys are larger, often considerably so), color, and markings. Behaviorally, however, they share many similar calls, gestures, and food items, as well as the same type of social system. They both live in harems which consist of a permanent group of adult females with their young, and one temporary adult male. While females usually remain in their natal group for life, males leave before reaching maturity. They become solitary and apparently monitor other social groups, looking for an opportunity to take over a harem. Because adult males are intolerant of one another, there is usually much aggression during takeovers. Male tenure in a harem can last from a few days to several years.

Interactions between these two species in the Kibale Forest are relatively infrequent, despite the fact they are often found together while traveling to and aggregating at food trees. When they do interact, it is usually aggressively, concerning competition over food: the Blue monkey generally supplants the smaller redtail. Behavior that establishes and cements amicable relations, such as grooming and play, is common within each species but not between them. Why then does hybridization occur?

In Kibale, hybridization is confined to the study area of some 6sq km (2.3sq mi) located about half way up the forest's north-south slope. It is here that the distribution of the Blue monkey population suddenly stops for unknown reasons even though redtails are found throughout the forest. At this southern extreme of the Blue monkey range, their density is only one-seventh of what it is further north, where there are about 35–40 blues per sq km (14–16/sq mi). In fact, there is only one blue social group at Ngogo, but a very high concentration of solitary blue males (at least six, whereas at the same time, in another area further north in the forest, none was observed). Thus, competition by these males for females is extremely intense, resulting not only in a higher rate of male takeovers in this area (six in the Ngogo group and none in four groups further north during the same period) but, apparently, in hybridization.

If a male blue is unable to mate with a female blue, then it seems that the "next best" strategy is to copulate with a closely related species—a female redtail. That this is what has occurred is borne out by the fact that all three known hybrids (one adult

▲ **Confrontation between Redtail monkey troops.** Adult females and juveniles cluster together to face and threaten members of a neighboring troop. A Blue-Redtail hybrid female ABOVE CENTER joins defending the territory of the troop into which she was born. She is larger and more Blue-like than her female relatives. During the tension, individuals often take time out to groom one another RIGHT, perhaps to enhance the strength of the coalition binding the troop. Although threat gestures and vocalizations are intense, physical contact between troops is rare. Harem males are seldom involved in such encounters, and the solitary male Blue monkey TOP, father of the hybrid, adheres to this pattern.

male and two adult females) live in different redtail groups. Presumably they were born and raised in redtail groups as offspring of redtail females and blue males. Both female hybrids have produced offspring and, judging by their appearance, two of the three backcrosses were probably sired by a redtail male, the third by a blue.

In the last case, an adult male Blue monkey joined a redtail group, sharing the "sole" harem male position with a male redtail, for more than two and a half years! Although the Blue monkey has successfully mated with the hybrid female in the group (who looks more like a blue), so far the redtail females have tended to avoid him. It is possible that there must be a long period of familiarization before a redtail female would willingly copulate with a particular male blue, especially because she is apparently conditioned to avoid interactions with this species.

The fact that hybrid females are fertile supports the suggestion that hybridization can be a viable "investment" for male blues when competition for females is unusually intense. However, what advantages are there for a redtail female in mating with a blue? For their part, female hybrids appear to be fully integrated into the redtail groups in which they live. They groom and receive grooming and are allowed to handle the small young infants of redtail mothers. In other words, they are not ostracized, but are treated like redtails. Furthermore, their larger size means that they are likely to be dominant to the redtails and therefore have priority of access to food. When assisting the other females in territorial defense against neighboring redtail groups, both size and a

blue-like appearance are distinct advantages. Furthermore, hybrids benefit from being able to feed on a wider variety of foods than either of the parental species. They not only eat the foods typical of redtails and blues, but also consume items that neither of them take. And, most importantly, the female hybrids appear to have no trouble mating with either redtail or blue males and producing healthy hybrids.

With all these advantages, why do redtail females not hybridize more frequently? The answer may well lie in the reproductive potential of hybrid males. In leaving his natal group at adolescence, the hybrid male also leaves the redtails most familiar with him. In seeking another redtail harem to take over, the hybrid's large size and Blue-monkey appearance will be an enormous disadvantage: redtail females will no doubt treat him with the fear or indifference they would a solitary male blue. As a result, his chances of reproductive success may be considerably lower than those of a redtail male.   TTS

COLOBUS AND LEAF MONKEYS

Subfamily: Colobinae
Thirty-seven species in 6 genera.
Family: Cercopithecidae.
Distribution: S and SE Asia; equatorial Africa.

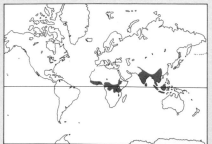

Habitat: chiefly forests; also dry scrub, cultivated areas and urban environments.

Size: from head-body length 43–49cm (17–19.5in), tail length 57–64cm (22.5–25in) and weight 2.9–5.7kg (6.4–12.5lb) in Olive colobus to head-body length 41–78cm (16–31in), tail length 69–108cm (27–42.5in), weight 5.4–23.6kg (12–52lb) in Hanuman langur.

Gestation: 140–220 days depending on species.

Longevity: about 20 years (29 in captivity).

Genus *Nasalis* (2 species): **Proboscis monkey** [v] (*N. larvatus*); **Pig-tailed snub-nosed monkey** [E] (*N. concolor*).

Genus *Pygathrix* (6 species): **Brelich's snub-nosed monkey** (*P. brelichi*); **Tonkin snub-nosed monkey** (*P. avunculus*); **Biet's snub-nosed monkey** (*P. bieti*); **Red-shanked douc** [E] (*P. nemaeus*); **Golden monkey** [R] (*P. roxellana*); **Black-shanked douc** (*P. nigripes*).

Genus *Presbytis* (7 species), including **Mentawai Islands sureli** [I] (*P. potenziani*); **Grizzled sureli** [I] (*P. comata*); **Maroon sureli** (*P. rubicunda*); **Mitered sureli** (*P. melalophos*); **Pale-thighed sureli** (*P. siamensis*); **Banded sureli** (*P. femoralis*).

Genus *Semnopithecus* (13 species), including **Barbe's leaf monkey** (*S. barbei*); **Hanuman langur** or **Common langur** (*S. entellus*); **Dusky leaf monkey** (*S. obscurus*); **Golden leaf monkey** [R] (*S. geei*); **Nilgiri langur** or **Hooded black leaf monkey** [v] (*S. johnii*); **Purple-faced leaf monkey** (*S. vetulus*); **Capped leaf monkey** (*S. pileatus*); **Silvered leaf monkey** (*S. cristatus*).

Black colobus monkeys (4 species of *Colobus*): **Guinea forest black colobus** (*C. polykomos*); **guereza** (*C. guereza*); **Satanic black colobus** [v] (*C. satanas*); **White-epauletted black colobus** (*C. angolensis*).

Red and olive colobus monkeys (5 species of *Procolobus*), including **Olive colobus** [R] (*P. verus*); **Pennant's red colobus** (*P. pennantii*); **Guinea forest red colobus** (*P. badius*).

[E] Endangered. [v] Vulnerable. [R] Rare.
[I] Threatened, but status indeterminate.

Colobus and leaf monkeys—the sub-family Colobinae—exhibit a great diversity of form, and despite an "image" as highly arboreal long-tailed leaf-eating monkeys, less than half regularly subsist on a diet of mature leaves. This diverse assemblage includes the Proboscis monkey, with its haunting appearance and anachronistic display of terrestrial adaptations in an arboreal environment; and the Red-shanked douc monkey, with its ethereal facial skin pigmentation contrasted against the intricate arrangement of four basic coat colors. Equally striking, but less audacious, are the black colobus, notably the guereza. Less dramatic are the Asian leaf monkeys and surelis whose wizened faces have earned one of the genera the name *Presbytis*, meaning "old woman" in Greek.

The Old World monkeys (family Cercopithecidae) are anatomically homogeneous, and few consistent differences distinguish the two subfamilies. The Colobinae are principally distinguished from the subfamily Cercopithecinae by the absence of cheek pouches, and by the presence of large salivary glands and a complex sacculated stomach. The molar teeth have high pointed cusps, and the inside of the upper molars and the outside of the lower molars are less convexly buttressed than they are in the Cercopithecinae. The enamel on the inside of the lower incisors is thicker than in the cercopithecines, and there is a lateral process on the lower second incisor. The sequence of dental eruption differs. Underjet (protrusion of the lower incisors beyond the upper incisors) is common in the colobines, but rare in the cercopithecines.

The majority of living colobines are of slender build compared to the cercopithecines. The two *Nasalis* and six *Pygathrix* species are more thickset and include some of the largest, but perhaps not the heaviest of monkeys; their fore and hindlimbs are also more equal in length than in other living species. An important feature in the colobines is the trend towards a reduction of the thumb length, least pronounced in the snub-nosed monkeys, the Proboscis monkey and the fossil genus *Mesopithecus*, and most prominent in the colobus, where the thumb is either absent or represented by a small phalangeal tubercle which sometimes bears a vestigial nail. The ischial callosities are separate in females and contiguous in males except in male *Pygathrix* and male *Procolobus*, where the callosities are separated by a strip of furred skin.

The present stronghold of the subfamily is Asia with four genera and 28 species, compared to only two genera and 9 species in Africa. Its fossil representation is strongest in Africa, and two of the earliest fossil genera. *Mesopithecus* and *Dolichopithecus* are European. In Asia, *Pygathrix* and *Nasalis* occupy a zone extending from southern China through eastern Indochina to the Mentawai Islands and Borneo, but curiously are absent from the Malay Peninsula and Sumatra. The rest of the Asian species range from about latitude 35.5°N at the Afghanistan-Pakistan border to the Lesser Sunda Island of Lombok; they are absent from the Philippines and Sulawesi. The living African species are distributed from the Gambia through the Guinea forest belt and the central African forest to Ethiopia, with outlying populations in East Africa and on the islands of Macias Nguema (formerly Fernando Póo) and Zanzibar. Fossil African colobines inhabited northern and southern Africa.

An increasing proclivity for leaves and other plant parts that are less susceptible than fruits to seasonal fluctuations in availability equipped the ancestors of Old World monkeys for survival in open woodland and savanna, which would be inhospitable to frugivores such as hominoids. The cercopithecine diet became more varied, while the colobine diet became more folivorous.

Colobine genera are primarily distinguished on the basis of cranial characters. Variation in newborn (neonatal) coat color is also important and in some genera, dental and visceral anatomy, and external features such as the position of the ischial callosities can be taken into account.

At species level colobines are separated

▲ **Tongue-shaped pendulous nose** of the male Proboscis monkey from Borneo contrasts with the snub nose of the female. Males are almost twice the weight of females and are the largest Asian colobines.

◄ **Guinea forest red colobus,** a three-year-old male photographed in the Gambia, westernmost point in the distribution of colobine monkeys. The stump-like reduction of the thumb, a colobine monkey characteristic most marked in colobus species, can just be seen.

only on wild cherries, wild pears and cucumbers—which attract it down from its 2,300m (7,500ft) habitat when they are seasonally available. The general preference is for young rather than mature leaves, and some species may be unable to cope with the latter. Leaves are so far the only items recorded in the diets of the Tonkin snub-nosed monkey, the Mentawai Islands sureli, Barbe's leaf monkey and the Guinea forest black colobus. Fruits form part of the diet of all the remaining studied species with the exception of Biet's snub-nosed monkey, which apparently feeds almost exclusively on the green parts of coniferous trees, and the possible exception of the Olive colobus. Even the guereza, which can tolerate up to 32 percent mature leaf blades, normally eats over a third fruits. Most species eat flowers, buds, seeds and shoots. The Hanuman langur, the better studied leaf monkeys, the guereza and red colobus have all been observed to eat soil or termite clay. Golden leaf monkeys specifically eat salty earth or sand, and the Bornean Grizzled sureli churns up the mud at salt springs, and may eat it. Insects occur as a small proportion of the diet of some surelis, of the Hanuman langur and the Hooded black leaf monkey or Nilgiri langur, and probably also of other leaf monkeys, and of Pennant's red colobus. Hanuman langurs and red colobus monkeys eat insect galls and fungi, and African colobines eat lichen and dead wood. Pith occurs in the diets of the Hanuman langur and the Maroon sureli, and roots in those of the Hanuman langur and the Mitered sureli. The latter digs up and eats cultivated sweet potato. The Hanuman langur eats gum and sap, and this species can eat with impunity quantities of the strychnine-containing fruit of *Strychnos nux-vomica* that would kill a Rhesus macaque. It also eats repulsive and evil-smelling latex-bearing plants such as the ak (*Calotropis*) which are avoided by most animals, including insects. Colobines generally get water from dew and the moisture content of their diet, or rainwater held in tree trunk hollows.

Colobines have an unusual stomach whose essential feature is that its sacculated and expanded upper region is separated from its lower acid region. The upper region's neutral medium is necessary for the fermentation of foliage by anaerobic bacteria. The enlargement of the salivary glands indicates their probable role as one of providing a buffer fluid between the two regions of the stomach. The large stomach capacity accomodates the large volumes of

chiefly by coat color, but also by length and disposition of the hair (especially on the head, where crests, fringes and whorls may be present) and by vocalization.

The greatest concentrations of colobine species are in Borneo with six species, although not more than five in any one part of the island; and in northeastern Indochina and West and Central Africa, each with three species.

With one exception, all species for which information is available include leaves in their diet. The apparent exception is Brelich's snub-nosed monkey which feeds relatively unnutritious food and the slow passage essential for fermentation. The stomach contents may constitute more than a quarter of the adult body weight, and as much as half in a semi-weaned infant. The bacterial gastric recycling of urea may be the crucial factor enabling colobines such as the Hanuman langur to survive in arid regions without water sources.

The sacculated stomachs of colobines allow them to digest leaves more efficiently than any other primates. Firstly, the bacteria can break down cellulose (a major component of all leaves) and release energy; primates without such bacteria cannot do this. Secondly, the bacteria can deactivate many toxins and allow the colobine to eat items containing them.

Plant defense compounds are found in all trees, but occur in higher concentration in forests on nutrient-poor soil where it is costly for trees to replace leaves eaten by herbivores. Therefore, in forests growing on good soil, the colobines find the leaves easy to digest and nutritious and they eat mostly leaves of common trees (for example, the red colobus and guereza in Kibale Forest, Uganda). On poor soil, however, the colobines are forced to be more selective; they avoid many common leaves, but eat other plant parts instead, particularly seeds (for example the Satanic black colobus in Cameroon, and the Southeast Asian Pale-thighed and Maroon surelis from Malaya and Borneo respectively).

Female colobines reach sexual maturity at about four years of age, males at four to five years. Copulation is not restricted to a distinct breeding season, but there tends to be a birth peak, timed so that weaning coincides with the greatest seasonal abundance of solid food. Sexual behavior is usually initiated by the female. Receptive female Proboscis monkeys purse the lips of the closed mouth when looking at the male. If he returns her glance she (like the female in *Semnopithecus* species) rapidly shakes her head. If a Hanuman langur female is ignored by the male, she may hit him, pull his fur, or even bite him. The Proboscis male responds by assuming a pout-face and either he approaches the female or she him, presenting her anogenital region. A female Red-shanked douc will characteristically adopt a prone position, and over her shoulder eye the male. He in turn may signal his arousal by intently staring at the female and then turning his gaze to indicate a suitable location where copulation will take place. Soliciting in female *Colobus* is similar but emphasized by tongue smacking. During copulation douc and *Colobus* females remain prone, whereas Proboscis monkey and *Semnopithecus* females adopt the normal cercopithecid quadrupedal stance. The Proboscis female continues to head-shake, and both partners show the mating pout-face.

At birth infants are about 20cm (8in) in head-body length and weigh about 0.4kg (0.9lb). The eyes are open and the infant can cling to its mother strongly enough to support its own weight, although the Olive colobus infant may be carried in its mother's mouth. Body hair is present, but is shorter, more downy, and usually of a different color than in adulthood. There is usually less pigment in the skin and ischial callosities than in the adult, but in the facial skin of the Proboscis monkey and the Red-shanked douc, the opposite is the case. Births are single or, rarely, twin. Parental care in all species so far studied, except for the Pale-thighed sureli and the red colobus, involves toleration by the mother of her offspring being carried off by

▶ **Hanuman langur mother and young.** Adult size is attained at about five years of age. The single newborn infant may be cared for by temporary female "baby-sitters" and the mother may even nurse infants other than her own.

▼ **The Golden leaf monkey** of Assam and Bhutan. Orange coloration, more marked on the underside, and in adult males and in winter, the crown tufts and the all-black face are characteristic.

other females. Soon after birth, the infant is usually handled and carried by several females to as far as 25m (75ft) from its mother. A mother may even suckle the infant of another female and her own simultaneously, and one has even been observed carrying three infants. Often, a "babysitting" female will abandon her charge and move off, leaving the screaming infant to find its way back to its mother. In *Semnopithecus* active rejection of the young has been observed at the early age of about five weeks. One suggestion is that these behavior patterns accelerate the infant's independence, enhancing its chances of survival during the high infant mortality which often accompanies the violent replacement of the adult male in the one-male troops which occur in some populations. They may also allow the mother to concentrate on time-consuming foraging. Transition from neonatal to adult coat occurs at 5–10 months of age; adult size is attained at about the fifth year.

Compared with macaques, the social relationships of the colobines are typified by a generally lower level of aggressive, sociosexual, vocal and even gestural interactions. Their "grave and serious" demeanor, which prompted the generic name *Semnopithecus* (Greek for "sacred ape"), is probably related partly to their predominantly arboreal habitat which demands less troop coordination for the evasion of predators; and perhaps primarily to their foraging behavior which, owing to the more homogeneous distribution of their food, is less nomadic, requires less acquired experience of choice food sources, and entails prolonged periods of sedentary feeding. Entry into, or movement within a feeding tree is characterized by meticulous care to avoid close encounters with companions already stationed there. Once a feeding position is attained, its very nature, facing towards the periphery of the tree where the bulk of the food is located, enables the colobine to feed for long periods without interacting with its neighbors. Although commonly there is a feeding peak in the morning and another in the late afternoon, the low nutritional content of their diet usually necessitates intermittent feeding throughout the day, thus minimizing opportunity for complex social behavior.

Group sizes range from solitary animals, usually males, to a group of over 120 langurs (possibly a temporary aggregation of troops seeking water). There are reported groups of a hundred or more Golden snubnosed monkeys, but such group sizes exceed the maximum recorded for the Satanic black and Pennant's red colobus by only about

20. Groups of 60 or so have been reported for the Proboscis monkey, the Red-shanked douc and the Guinea forest red colobus; and troops of up to 40 for most genera. However, with the exception of Pennant's red colobus, where the typical number is probably 50, the average troop size is lower, ranging from 3.4 in the Mentawai Islands sureli, which is unique in apparently being exclusively monogamous, to 37 in one Hanuman langur population. In the Pig-tailed snub-nosed monkey and the White-epauletted black colobus it is about five; in most of the surelis, the Hooded black, Purple-faced, and Capped leaf monkeys and the guereza it ranges from 6 to 9; and in most of the remaining species from 10 to 18. The representation of adult males in a bisexual troop is roughly proportional to its size, and is equalled or exceeded in number by adult females. The Pig-tailed snub-nosed monkey commonly practices monogamy (possibly owing to human predation); the Black-shanked douc in eastern Cambodia is invariably encountered in (presumably bisexual) pairs; and the Bornean Grizzled sureli often occurs in "family parties" of three. The presence of all-male troops has been confirmed only in the Grizzled and Banded surelis, the Hanuman langur, and the Hooded black and the Golden leaf monkeys.

Home range size in most of the species for which it has been estimated is about 30ha (74 acres). It has been estimated for the Capped leaf monkey at 64ha (158 acres), and for the Proboscis monkey at about 130ha (320 acres) which is also the upper limit for Pennant's red colobus. In the Hooded black leaf monkey it ranges from 6 to 260ha (15–642 acres), and the Hanuman langur from 5 to 1,300ha (12–3,200 acres). On the basis of defense and exclusive use of at least the major part of their home range, the Grizzled and the Pale-thighed surelis, the Purple-faced, the Silvered and the Dusky leaf monkey, and some Hanuman langur populations are considered territorial. Ceylonese langur troops often temporarily desert their home range in order to attack an adjacent troop; while the adult male Purple-faced leaf monkey has such a fastidious sense of territory that it has been seen to chastise fellow troop members for transgressions into other territories. Other Hanuman langur populations, and other species such as the Mentawai Islands sureli, the Hooded black and the Capped leaf monkey, have exclusive core areas which include important sleeping and feeding trees, and which occupy one 20 to 50 percent, or in a red colobus troop studied in the Gambia, 83 percent of the home range. Within its home range the guereza has a preferred area from which other troops are readily chased, but not permanently excluded. In contrast, three Pennant's red colobus troops were found to have very extensive, if not complete, home range overlap. Relations between these three troops were usually aggressive, involved only the adult and the subadult males, and no matter where an encounter occurred within their home ranges, one dominant troop usually supplanted the other, although there were indications that the outcome of such an encounter might also depend on which males were involved. Other red colobus troops entered the area very infrequently and were usually chased out immediately.

Surelis, langurs and black colobus in

◄ **High in the Himalayas,** this large, white-fronted Hanuman langur inhabits the Helenbu Valley 90km north of Katmandu, Nepal. Langurs and leaf monkeys are the largest, most widespread and diverse group of Asian colobines.

▼ **A troop of guerezas** or White-mantled black colobus feeding in the trees on the shore of Lake Naivasha, Kenya. The U-shaped mantle of long white hairs over glossy black, and the white tail tip distinguish the species.

particular are characterized by their loud calls which are generally most intense and most contagious at dawn, but may also be heard during the day, especially during preparation for troop movement, finalization of night-time sleeping positions and, in some species, during the night. These calls are believed to promote troop cohesion and to enable prediction of the following day's movement by adjacent troops so that inadvertent encounters can be avoided. During an intertroop encounter or sometimes on detection of a predator, these calls may be preceded or accompanied by a dramatic leaping display in which the protagonist plunges onto branches and then ascends and repeats the performance, producing both a visual and an auditory effect from the swaying and the cracking of branches.

Population densities are very variable, both within and between species. In the surelis, they range from 3 to 48 animals/sq km (7–125/sq mi); in the Pig-tailed snub-nosed monkey and the leaf monkeys, 8–220 animals/sq km (20–570/sq mi); in the Hanuman langur 3–904 animals/sq km (7–2,340/sq mi); and in the colobus 30–880 animals/sq km (70–2,280/sq mi). In the Hanuman langur lower densities are most typical of populations living in open grassland or agricultural fields where troops have large home ranges. Intermediate densities appear typical of populations living in close association with towns and villages, and higher densities typical of forest-dwelling populations where the troops have small, sometimes overlapping, home ranges.

In 1819, a single ship's crew visiting Da Nang, Vietnam, killed more than 100 douc between 5am and breakfast-time. Apparently unmolested by the local people, the monkeys lacked respect for firearms and were actually drawn to their deaths by the cries of their wounded companions. Depredations by visiting Europeans were such that by 1831 doucs had learnt to flee from gunfire. In 1974, after depletion of habitat and the ravages of war, only 30–40 doucs were found during 10 weeks in the same locality.

The Guinea forest black colobus was seriously threatened by the European fur trade at the end of the 19th century, and the guereza is still threatened by a tourist demand for rugs and wall-hangings made from their pelts. Other species hunted for their beautiful coats are the Hooded black leaf monkey and the Golden snub-nosed monkey. The coat of the latter was said to protect the wearer from rheumatism, but fortunately only officials and members of the

Chinese Imperial family were allowed to wear it. Both species are now protected, and the former is said to have increased in numbers since 1960. Most species are hunted by local people for their flesh which in many species is reputed to have medicinal value, as are the besoar stones (intestinal concretions resembling those found in ruminants) reported in all the Bornean colobines except for the Banded sureli and the Silvered leaf monkey. Nevertheless, even with the wider availability of firearms, the most insidious threat to the future survival of the colobines is the relentless destruction of habitat for timber and for agriculture. It is essential that at least part of the remaining

▲ **White "spectacles"** and bluish face with pinkish lips and chin are characteristic of the lively Dusky leaf monkey from northeast India to the Malay Peninsula and neighboring islands.

▶ **Leaping a canal** in Gujarat state, Western India, this Hanuman langur is at home in town and temple, revered by Hindu and Buddhist alike.

China's Endangered Monkeys

One of the most endangered and least-known of China's primates is the Golden monkey (*Pygathrix roxellana*) first described in the late 19th century. Mainland China has three *Pygathrix* species. The most endangered is the Black snub-nosed golden monkey or Biet's snub-nosed monkey (*P. bieti*), inhabiting Yunnan Province. Its estimated population is 200 animals. The White-shoulder-haired snub-nosed golden monkey or Brelich's snub-nosed monkey (*P. brelichi*) inhabits the Fan-Jin Mountains in Kweichow Province and totals 500 animals. The Golden monkey is the most numerous and widely distributed species and inhabits Gansu, Hubei (notably Shen Nong Jia), Shaanxi and Szechwan Provinces and totals 3,700–5,700 animals.

Golden monkeys inhabit mountain forests in some of the largest troops known for arboreal primates. Troops of over 600 animals have been reported. In ecologically disturbed areas troops may number 30–100 animals. Larger troops are organized around polygynous subgroups of 1 adult male, 5 adult females and their off-spring. There are also peripheral and solitary males, but within the troop adult females outnumber adult males. Males defend the troop against predators (chiefly Yellow-throated martens).

Golden monkeys are basically leaf-eaters, supplementing their diet with fruit, pine-cone seeds, bark, insects, birds, and birds' eggs. Because they lack cheek pouches and eat leaves, they feed often and in large quantities. In zoos they are fed 850–1,380g (2–3lb) daily. There are difficulties in providing a balanced diet, and they fare poorly in captivity. No Golden monkeys are kept in captivity outside China.

Humans have valued the species' decorative shoulder and back hair (up to 10cm /14in long) for making coats for over a thousand years, and herbal medicines are made from the meat and bones. But the major threat to the Golden monkey's survival was vast destruction to their limited habitat. The Chinese government has taken steps to preserve this rare and beautiful primate. Preservation areas have been established, although there is no reserve for the most endangered species, Biet's snub-nosed monkey; hunting was banned in 1975 and forest destruction has been stopped. Anyone breaking the law is fined and may be imprisoned. As a result, births are increasing in preservation areas, allowing guarded optimism, but long-term studies are urgently needed.   **FEP**

habitat should be protected by the establishment of secure reserves; the areas at present most critically requiring protection are the Mentawai Islands and north Vietnam.

There is little contact between colobines and man, excepting the Hanuman langur which in some areas obtains 90 percent of its diet from agricultural crops, and is considered sacred by Hindus and, like all animals, is unmolested by Buddhists. Its sacred status stems from its identification with the monkey-god Hanuman who played the major role in assisting the incarnate god Vishnu in the search for the recovery of his wife, who had been kidnapped by Ravana of Sri Lanka. While in Sri Lanka, Hanuman stole the mango, previously unknown in India. For this theft he was condemned to be burnt, and while extinguishing the fire he scorched his face and paws which have remained black ever since. Many Hindus regularly feed langurs, generally every Tuesday, which is Hanuman's traditional day. The frustration experienced by those whose crops are decimated or have their shops pilfered was well expressed by the town which in desperation dispatched a truckload of langurs to a destination several stations down the railway line.   **DB-J**

THE 37 SPECIES OF COLOBUS AND LEAF MONKEYS

Abbreviations: HBL = head-and-body length. TL = tail length. wt = weight. Approximate nonmetric equivalents: 2.5cm = 1in; 230g = 8oz; 1kg = 2.2lb.
E Endangered. V Vulnerable. R Rare. I Threatened, but status indeterminate.

Genus *Nasalis*

Thickset build; macaque-like limb proportions, skull shape, and coat color; nose prominent.

Proboscis monkey V
Nasalis larvatus

Borneo, except C Sarawak. Tidal mangrove nipapalm-mangrove and (mainly riverine), lowland rain forest. Swims competently. HBL 54–76cm; TL 52–75cm; wt 8.2–23.6kg; Adult male about twice weight of adult female. Coat: crown reddish-orange with frontal whorl and narrow nape extension flanked by paler cheek and chest ruff; rest of coat orange-white or pale orange, richer on lower chest, variably suffused with gray flecked with black and reddish on shoulders and back; triangular rump patch adjoining tail; penis reddish-pink; scrotum black. Elongated nose in adult male is tongue-shaped and pendulous. Newborn have vivid blue facial skin.

Pig-tailed snub-nosed monkey E
Nasalis concolor
Pig-tailed snub-nosed monkey or langur, or Pagai Island langur or simakobu.

Mentawai Islands. Rain forest; mangrove forest. Also known as *Simias concolor*. HBL 45–55cm; TL 10–19cm; wt 7.1kg. Coat: blackish-brown, pale-speckled on nape, shoulder and upper back; white penal tuft. Face skin black bordered with whitish hairs. Tail naked except for a few hairs at tip. 1 in 4 individuals are cream-buff, washed with brown.

Genus *Pygathrix*

Large with arms only slightly shorter than legs; face short and broad; shelf-like brow ridge; region between eyes broad; nasal bones reduced or absent; nasal passages broad and deep; small flap on upper rim of each nostril.

Golden snub-nosed monkey R
Pygathrix (Rhinopithecus) roxellana
Golden or Orange or Roxellane's monkey or snub-nosed monkey, or Moupin langur.

In Chinese provinces of Hubei, Shaanxi, Gansu and Szechwan. High evergreen subtropical and coniferous forest and bamboo jungle which is snow clad for more than half the year; migrates vertically biannually. HBL 66–76cm; TL 56–72cm; wt ? Coat: upperside and tail dark brown or blackish, darkest on nape and longitudinal ridge on crown; underside, tail tip and long (10cm) hairs scattered over shoulders whitish-

orange; legs, chest band and face border richer orange; orange suffusion throughout increases with age in adult male. Muzzle white; areas above eyes and round nose pale blue; colors in young paler.

Biet's snub-nosed monkey
Pygathrix (Rhinopithecus) bieti
Biet's or Black snub-nosed monkey.

Yun-ling mountain range (26.5–31°N), Yunnan and Tibet. High coniferous forest (3,350–4,000m) with frost for 280 days per annum. HBL about 74–83cm; TL about 51–72cm; wt ? Coat: blackish-gray above as in *P. roxellana*, but including paws (paler), brow, inside of limbs below elbow across chest and from hip across abdomen; long yellowish-gray hairs with black-brown tips scattered on shoulders; longitudinal crest, paws, 2/3 of tail and some hairs on upper lip blackish; rest of coat whitish. Placed by some in *P. roxellana*.

Brelich's snub-nosed monkey
Pygathrix (Rhinopithecus) brelichi
Brelich's or White-shoulder-haired snub-nosed monkey.

Fan-jin Mountains, Kweichow Province, China. Evergreen subtropical forest. HBL about 73cm; TL about 97cm; wt? Coat: upperparts grayish-brown, pale gray on thigh; tail, paws, forearm and outside of shank more blackish; tail tip and blaze between shoulders yellowish-white; nape and vertex whitish-brown suffused with blackish, especially at front and sides; underside pale yellowish-gray; ridge of brow hair round face; midline parting from brow to crestless vertex; tail hairs sometimes long with midline parting.

Tonkin snub-nosed monkey
Pygathrix (Rhinopithecus) avunculus
Tonkin or Dollman's sub-nosed monkey.

Bac Can and Yen Bai, N Vietnam. Bamboo jungle. HBL 51–62cm; TL 66–92cm; wt? Coat: upperside blackish; brown between shoulders; occasionally sprinkled with white; nape and rear of crown brown or yellowish-brown with narrow blackish-brown border at front and sides; paws blackish-brown; yellowish-white to orange underside, throat and chest band, almost encircling ankle and hip; tail blackish-brown with whitish-yellow or orange-gray tip; tail hairs without parting, or long with midline parting or helical parting; crown hairs flat. Penis black; scrotum white-haired.

Red-shanked douc monkey E
Pygathrix nemaeus
Red-shanked douc or Cochin China monkey.

C Vietnam and E C Laos. Tropical rain and monsoon forest. HBL 53–63cm; TL 57–67cm; wt? Coat: white lips, cheeks and throat, inside of thigh, perineum, tail and small triangular rump patch; white areas surrounded by black often with intervening deep orange band, most conspicuously between throat and chest; crestless crown, upper arms and trunk between black areas black-speckled gray, forearm white, rest of shank deep orange-red. Penis reddish-pink; scrotum white; skin of muzzle white, ears, nose and rest of face orange.

Black-shanked douc monkey
Pygathrix nigripes
Black-shanked or Black-footed douc monkey.

S Vietnam, S Laos and E Cambodia. Tropical rain forest; gallery and monsoon forest. HBL 55–72cm; TL 67–77cm; wt? Distinguished from *P. nemaeus* by anatomy of palate and black-speckled gray forearm and blackish shank. Penis red; scrotum and inside of thigh blue. Facial skin blue, with reddish-yellow tinge on muzzle. Placed by some in *P. nemaeus*.

Surelis

Genus *Presbytis*

Forearm relatively long; brow ridges usually poorly developed or absent; bridge of nose convex; muzzle short; 5th cusp on lower 3rd molar usually reduced or absent; cusp development on upper 3rd molar variable; projection on inner face of relatively broad, underjetted lower incisors; longitudinal crest; coat of newborn whitish.

Mentawai Islands sureli I
Presbytis potenziani
Mentawai Islands or Red-bellied sureli.

Mentawai Islands. Rain, mangrove forest. HBL 44–58cm; TL 50–64cm; wt 5.4–7.3kg. Coat: small ridge-like crest; upperside and tail blackish; pubic region yellowish-white; brow band, cheeks, chin, throat, upper chest and sometimes tail tip whitish; rest of underside and sometimes collar reddish-orange, brown or occasionally whitish-orange.

Grizzled sureli
Presbytis comata
Grizzled or Gray or Sunda Island sureli.

W Java, N and E Borneo and N Sumatra. Tropical rain forest. Also

named (wrongly) *P. aygula*. HBL 43–60cm; TL 55–83cm; wt 5.7–8.1kg. Coat: paws blackish; crown blackish or brownish; in Borneo adult sexual dimorphism in crest shape and extent of white on brow; rest of upperside pale gray speckled with blackish or brownish; underside whitish. Includes *P. thomasi*, *P. hosei*.

White-fronted sureli
Presbytis frontata

E, SE and C Borneo. Tropical rain forest. HBL 42–60cm; TL 63–79cm; wt 5.6–6.5kg. Coat: paws, cheeks and brow blackish; forearm, shank and sometimes tail base and crest blackish-brown; trunk pale grayish-brown, yellowish below, tail yellowish, speckled with dark gray. Tall, compressed crest raked forward, with 1–2 whorls at base, flanked by laterally directed fringe.

Banded sureli
Presbytis femoralis

Malay Peninsula, C Sumatra, Batu Islands, NW Borneo. Rain forest, swamp and mangrove swamp. HBL 43–60cm; TL 62–83cm; wt 5.9–8.1kg. Coat: dark brown or blackish with variation in spread of whitish underside. 0–2 frontal whorls. Placed by some in *P. melalophos*.

Pale-thighed sureli
Presbytis siamensis

Riau Archipelago, S Malay Peninsula, E C Sumatra, Great Natuna Island. Tropical rain and swamp forest. HBL 41–61cm; TL 58–85cm; wt 5–6.7kg. Coat: limb extremities and brow blackish; outside of thigh grayish/whitish; rest of upperparts and tail pale grayish or blackish brown; underparts whitish; horizontal fringe radiates from 0–2 whorls at front end of crest. Placed by some in *P. melalophos*.

Mitered sureli
Presbytis melalophos
Mitered or Black-crested sureli or simpai.

SW Sumatra. Tropical rain and swamp forest, village centers; HBL 42–57cm; TL 61–81cm; wt 5.8–7.4kg. Coat: back (occasionally broad midline band only) brownish-red to pale orange, or gray, variably suffused with blackish or gray; brow reddish to whitish, often delineated by blackish, brown or gray crest and brow hairs which may extend to ear; frontal whorl; underside whitish or whitish suffused with yellow or orange, especially chest and limbs.

Maroon sureli
Presbytis rubicunda
Maroon or Red sureli.

Karimata Island and Borneo, except C Sarawak and lowland NW Borneo. Rain forest. HBL 45–55cm; TL 64–78cm; WT 5.2–7.8kg. Coat: blackish-red or reddish-orange, paler underside, more blackish or brownish on tail tip and paws; horizontal fringe radiates from 0–2 frontal whorls; 1–2 nape whorls sometimes present.

Langurs and leaf monkeys

Genus *Semnopithecus*
Included in *Presbytis* by some. Brow ridge shelf-like and coat of newborn blackish in Malabar and Hanuman langurs (subgenus *Semnopithecus*). Brow ridges resemble raised eyebrows, newborn's coat orange or whitish suffused with gray, brown or black in all other species (subgenus *Trachypithecus*).

Malabar langur
Semnopithecus hypoleucos

SW India between W Ghats and coast to 14°N. Evergreen forest, cultivated woodland and gardens. HBL 61–70cm; TL 85–92cm; WT 8.4–11.5kg. Coat: paws and forearm blackish; leg blackish or grayish-brown; tail blackish or dark gray at base, tip blackish, yellowish-gray or white; midline of back dark brown or dark gray; flanks and rear of thigh pale yellowish-gray; crown orange-gray or yellowish-white; throat and underside orange-white. Frontal whorl.

Hanuman langur
Semnopithecus entellus
Hanuman or Common or Gray langur.

S Himalayas from Afghanistan border to Tibet between Sikkim and Bhutan; India NW of range of Malabar langur to Aravalli Hills and Kathiawar, and NE to Khulna province, Bangladesh; N, E and SE Sri Lanka. Reported in W Assam. Forest, scrub, cultivated fields, village and town centers (0–4,080m). HBL 41–78cm; TL 69–108cm; WT 5.4–23.6kg. Coat: upperparts gray or pale grayish-brown, often tinged with yellowish; in Bengal gray almost replaced by pale orange; crown, underparts and tail tip whitish or yellowish-white; paws often, and forearms occasionally blackish or brownish; in Sri Lanka and SE India crown usually crested. Frontal whorl.

Purple-faced leaf monkey
Semnopithecus vetulus
Purple-faced leaf monkey or wanderoo.

SW, C and N Sri Lanka. Forest, swamp, rocky, treeless, coastal slopes, parkland. Formerly known as *S. senex*. HBL 47–70cm; TL 62–92cm; WT 4.3–10kg. Coat: brown, darkest at limb extremities and sometimes with yellow to brown tail tip and crown, or blackish with pale brown crown and yellowish tail tip; white to yellow throat and sideways-directed whiskers; rump patch sometimes whitish or yellowish; tail base, thighs and back sometimes gray-speckled.

Hooded black leaf monkey ⓥ
Semnopithecus johnii
Hooded or Leonine or Gray-headed black leaf monkey, or Nilgiri langur.

W Ghats of India and Cat Ba Island, N Vietnam. Evergreen and riverine forest; deciduous woodland; on Cat Ba stunted tree-clad limestone hills. HBL 51–74cm; TL 69–97cm; WT 9.5–13.6kg. Coat: yellowish vertex grades (further in Cat Ba) through brown to glossy brown-tinged black of rest of body; gray-speckled short-haired rump coloration sometimes extends to thigh and tail.

White-headed black leaf monkey
Semnopithecus leucocephalus

SW Kwangsi Province, China. Tropical monsoon forest on limestone hills. HBL 47–62cm; TL 77–89cm; WT 7.7–9.5kg. Coat: glossy black; head and shoulders white; paws and distal part of tail whitish; pointed coronal crest. Placed in *S. francoisi* by some.

White-rumped black leaf monkey
Semnopithecus delacouri
White-rumped or Pied or Delacour's black leaf monkey.

N Vietnam. Limestone mountains. HBL 57–58cm; TL 82–86cm; WT? Coat: glossy black with white from end of mouth to nape whorl; sharply demarcated white area on hindpart of back and outside of thigh; tail base hairs long; pointed coronal crest. Placed by some in *S. francoisi*.

White-sideburned black leaf monkey
Semnopithecus francoisi
White-sideburned or François's black leaf monkey.

NE Vietnam, Kwangsi and Kweichow. Tall riverside crags, tropical monsoon forest on limestone mountains. HBL 51–67cm; TL 81–90cm; WT 6kg. Coat: glossy black with white from

end of mouth to ears; pointed coronal crest; 2 nape whorls.

Ebony leaf monkey
Semnopithecus auratus
Ebony or Moor or Negro leaf monkey.

NW Vietnam, Java, Bali and Lombok. Forest; plantations. HBL 46–75cm; TL 61–82cm; WT? Coat: glossy black, tinged with brown, especially on underside and cheeks; whitish sometimes on paws. Treated by some as same species as *S. cristatus*.

Silvered leaf monkey
Semnopithecus cristatus

Sumatra, Riau-Lingga Archipelago, Bangka, Belitung, Borneo, Serasan, W coastal W Malaysia, S C Thailand, Cambodia and S Vietnam. Forest swamp, bamboo, scrub, plantations, parkland, village centers. HBL 40–60cm; TL 58–84cm; WT 5.2–8.6kg. Coat: brown, brownish-gray or blackish-brown, darker on paws, tail and brow; color masked by grayish or yellowish hair tips; groin and underside of tail base yellowish; coronal crest variably developed.

Barbe's leaf monkey
Semnopithecus barbei

S China, N Indochina into Burma. Forest. HBL 43–60cm; TL 62–88cm; WT 4.6–8.7kg. Coat: gray to blackish-brown; paws and brow black or blackish-brown, upper arm and sometimes underside, leg, tail, nape or back suffused with silvery gray or yellow; coronal crest variably developed. Formerly divided between *S. cristatus* and *S. phayrei*.

Dusky leaf monkey
Semnopithecus obscurus
Dusky or Spectacled leaf monkey.

Tripura (NE India), adjacent Bangladesh, N Shan and lowland SW and S Burma, Malay Peninsula and neighboring small islands (not Singapore). Forest, scrub plantations, gardens. HBL 42–68cm; TL 57–86cm; WT 4.2–10.9kg. Coat: dark gray to blackish-brown; nape paler, occasionally yellowish-white; back centerline usually paler and sometimes with orange sheen; elbow, legs and base of tail often paler than back, occasionally pale grayish-yellow; paws and brow black or blackish-brown; underside yellowish-brownish or blackish-gray, dark brown or occasionally pale orange; coronal crest usually present in NW; frontal whorl in Shan subspecies. Includes *S. phayrei* (part).

Capped leaf monkey
Semnopithecus pileatus
Capped or Bonneted leaf monkey.

Bangladesh and Assam E of Jamuna and Manas rivers, N and highland W Burma. Forest, swamp, bamboo. Overlaps with Dusky leaf monkey in Tripura and adjacent Bangladesh. HBL 49–76cm; TL 81–110cm; WT 8.9–14kg. Coat: upperparts gray, darkest on anterior of back and occasionally tinged with orange; paws and base of tail black or dark gray; paws sometimes partially orange-white; cheeks and underside gray, whitish to orange; crown hairs semi-erect and project over cheek hairs. Scrotum absent.

Golden leaf monkey ⓡ
Semnopithecus geei

Bhutan and Assam W of Manas river. Forest, plantations. HBL 49–72cm; TL 71–94cm; WT 9.5–12kg. Coat: orange-white; underside and sometimes cheeks, rear of back, orange; blackish hair tips on cap; faint gray tinge on forearm and shank, sometimes on rear of back and upperside of tail; crown hairs semi-erect and project over cheek hairs. Pubic skin pale. Scrotum absent.

Black colobus monkeys

Genus *Colobus*
Stomach 3-chambered; larynx large; sac below hyoid bone; facial skin black.

Satanic black colobus ⓥ
Colobus satanas

Macias Nguema, E and SW Cameroon, Rio Muni, NW Gabon and probably W Congo. Forest, meadows. HBL 58–72cm; TL 60–97cm; WT 6–11kg. Coat: entirely glossy black; crown hairs semi-erect and forward directed on brow.

White-epauletted black colobus
Colobus angolensis
White-epauletted or Angolan black or black-and-white colobus.

NE Angola, SW, C and NE Zaire, SW Uganda, W Rwanda, W Burundi, W and E Tanzania, coastal S Kenya, possibly Malawi, vagrant in NW Zambia. Forest, woodland maize cultivation. HBL 47–66cm; TL 63–92cm; WT 5.9–11.3kg. Coat: glossy black with white or whitish-gray cheeks, throat, long-haired shoulder epaulettes and tip or occasionally major part of tail;

CONTINUED ▶

narrow brow band sometimes, and chest region occasionally, white; brow fringe, frontal whorl or nape parting sometimes present.

Guinea forest black colobus
Colobus polykomos
Guinea forest or Regal or Ursine black colobus, or Western black-and-white colobus.

Guinea to W Nigeria, with hiatus at Dahomey Gap. Forest; scrub-woodland in Guinea savanna. HBL 57–68cm; TL 72–100cm; WT 6.1–11.7kg. Coat: glossy black; tail white; face border and throat sprinkled with white extending to long-haired shoulders, or wholly white which is absent or only sparsely sprinkled on shoulders; if absent is replaced by white outside to thigh; Point of nose reaches, or protrudes beyond, mouth.

Guereza
Colobus guereza
Guereza, or White-mantled or Magistrate black colobus or Eastern black-and-white colobus.

N Congo, E Gabon, Cameroon, E Nigeria, Central African Republic, NE Zaire, NW Rwanda, Uganda, S Sudan, Ethiopia, W Kenya and adjacent Tanzania. Forest, woodland, wooded grassland. HBL 45–70cm; TL 52–90cm; WT 5.4–14.5kg. Coat: glossy black; face and collosities surrounded by white; U-shaped white mantle of varying length on sides and rear of back; outside of thigh variably whitish; tail variably bushy and whitish or yellowish from tip towards base. Albinism common on Mt Kenya. Point of nose nearly touches mouth.

Red colobus monkeys

Genus *Procolobus*
Equatorial Africa. Limb proportions similar to *Pygathrix*; stomach 4-chambered; larynx small, no sac below hyoid. Sexual swelling in female and sometimes in immature male. Male skull usually with sagittal crest. Most, or all, placed in genus *Colobus* by some.

Guinea forest red colobus
Procolobus badius
Guinea forest red or Bay colobus.

Senegal, Gambia to SW Ghana. Forests, savanna woodland, savanna. HBL 47–63cm; TL 52–75cm; WT 5.5–10kg. Coat: crown, back, outside of upper arm and sometimes brow, outside of thigh and tail gray or blackish; pubic area white; rest of body whitish-orange to orange-red.

Cameroon red colobus [E]
Procolobus preussi
Cameroon or Preuss's red colobus.

W Cameroon. Lowland rain forest. HBL 56–64cm; TL 75–76cm; WT? Coat: crown and back pale-stippled dark gray; cheeks, flanks, outside of limbs reddish-orange; tail blackish-red; underparts whitish-orange.

Pennant's red colobus
Procolobus pennantii

Macias Nguema, E Congo, W, N and E Zaire, SW Uganda, Rwanda, Burundi, Tanzania, Zanzibar, Forest. Exceptional polymorphism, especially in N Zaire, indicates more than one species may be involved. HBL 45–67cm; TL 58–80cm; WT 5.1–11.3kg. Coat: paws, crown, nape, anterior of back and tip of tail usually blackish-red or blackish-brown, sometimes paler or more orange; base of tail, rear of back blackish-brown to reddish-orange, occasionally black-flecked, and tail base occasionally orange-white below; flanks reddish-orange some-times tinged with blackish, gray, brown or whitish or black-flecked, arm similar or whitish-black; leg reddish-orange, whitish-orange, gray or blackish-white, often tinged with brown; thigh brownish-black sometimes tinged with blackish, or yellowish; brow whitish, orange or reddish-orange to blackish-brown; cheeks and underside usually whitish or yellowish-white; cheeks and chest often tinged with orange. Whorl sometimes present, or behind ears. Subspecies include *P. p. kirkii*.

Tana River red colobus [E]
Procolobus rufomitratus

Lower Tana river, Kenya. Gallery forest. Dimensions not known. Coat: crown orange; back and tail dark gray; cheeks, limbs and paws pale gray; underparts yellowish-white. Whorl behind ears. Skull small.

Olive colobus [R]
Procolobus verus
Olive or Van Beneden's colobus.

Sierra Leone to SW Togo; C Nigeria, S of Benue River. Forest, abandoned cultivation. HBL 43–49cm; TL 57–64cm; WT 2.9–5.7kg. Coat: upper-parts black-stippled grayish-orange, grayer towards limb extremities; pale gray below, grayish occasionally much reduced, so more orange above, and more whitish below. Short-haired longitudinal coronal crest flanked by whorl on either side.

▶ **Feeding on flowers** of white rhododendron, a Hanuman langur in the Himalayas.

Infanticide

Male takeovers in Hanuman langur troops

The Hanuman or Gray langur is the most terrestrial of all the colobines, and the most widespread primate other than man throughout the varied habitats of the Indian subcontinent and Sri Lanka. These elegant monkeys with steel-gray coats, black faces, hands and feet have long been considered sacred by the Hindu inhabitants of India, and Hanuman langurs may be found in close association with humans in villages and temples. The Hanuman langur is the largest of its genus of "leaf-eating monkey," measuring 60–75cm (24–30in) high when seated, with a tail up to 100cm (39in) long (the word langur derives from the Sanskrit for "having a long tail"). Fully adult males weigh around 18.4kg (40lb), females substantially less (11.3kg/24.5lb), except in the Himalayan portion of the langurs' range where females weighing more than 16kg have been reported. Troops range in size from six to as many as 70 animals. The stable core of each troop is composed of female relatives who remain together in the same 36-hectare or so (90 acres) home range throughout their lives. Females as well as males play an important role in defending these feeding areas from exploitation by other troops. Use of the territory passes from mother to daughter.

Whereas females remain in the same location, young males leave the troop of their birth and join nomadic all-male bands containing from two to 60 or more males of various ages. These flexible assemblages travel over large areas, traversing the ranges of a number of troops, perpetually in search of breeding opportunities. Since most breeding troops contain only one fully adult male, competition between males for this position is fierce. Encroaching males are chased away from the troop. But occasionally one or more invaders will be successful at driving out the resident male and usurping his troop. In a number of cases, unweaned infants have been attacked, sometimes fatally, by incoming males. Some 32 takeovers by invading males have been reported, and at least half of these were accompanied by the disappearance of infants. Whether the occurence or non-occurence of assumed infanticide is due to genetic differences between males, local circumstances, or some interaction between the two remains unknown.

In areas like Mount Abu in Rajasthan, or Dharwar in Mysore state in south India, where food is plentiful, langurs live at densities up to 133 animals per square kilometer (344/sq mi). Encounters between male bands and troops are frequent and takeovers common. Elsewhere, at sites such as Solu Khumbu and Melemchi high in the Himalayas, at the margin of this species' range, densities may be as low as one langur per square km (0.4/sq mi). Fighting among males does occur, but it is more subdued. Typically several adult males coexist in the same troop, and changes in male membership occur gradually over time. Only in the areas with frequent male takeovers (that is, where a takeover might be expected to occur on average once every two or three years) are male membership changes accompanied by assumed infanticide.

High takeover rates place males under considerable pressure to compress as much as possible of their harem's reproductive activity into their own brief tenure in the troop. Since mothers who lose their offspring become sexually receptive sooner than do mothers who rear their infants to weaning age, it has ben suggested that the killing of infants by incoming males is an evolved reproductive strategy. While eliminating the offspring of his competitors, the usurping male enhances his own opportunities to breed. Infanticide in langurs has only been observed when males enter the troop from outside it. Similar patterns of male takeover accompanied by infanticide have recently been reported for the Sri Lankan Purple-faced leaf monkey and the Malaysian Silvered leaf monkey, as well as for more distant species of monkeys among the African cercopithecines, such as the Redtail

▲ **In the Himalayan foothills,** a Hanuman langur troop in Jammu and Kashmir state, northern India. Mixed troops have a stable core of related females and usually just one breeding male.

▼ **Border incident.** When two troops meet at the boundary between their ranges, both males and females join in defending their territory. Chases and hand-to-hand grappling look ferocious but animals are rarely injured in such encounters. It is after a male outsider has chased out a troop's breeding male that infants may be killed.

▲ **Before reaching maturity** males leave or are driven out of the troop and join other unattached males. These nomadic all-male bands monitor the strength of breeding troops, waiting for the opportunity for one of their number to usurp the resident adult male.

and Blue monkeys in the Kibale forest of Uganda, and in several species of howler monkeys in Central and South America. Because of the relationship between high population densities and the occurrence of infanticide, some have argued that infanticide may be a pathological behavior brought about through crowding. It is of special interest therefore that among howler monkeys and the cercopithecine monkeys in the Kibale forest, high population densities were not a factor.

The presence of infanticidal males creates peculiar challenges for females in the same population. However advantageous for the individual who increases his own reproductive success by eliminating an infant, infanticide is clearly disadvantageous from the point of view of the infant and its mother. Confronted with a population of males competing among themselves, often with adverse consequences for females, natural selection should have favored those females inclined and best able to protect their own interests. When an alien male approaches a

troop, he is chased away by females as well as the resident male (or males). After a new male takes over, females may form temporary alliances to prevent him from killing infants. In the short term, females are often able to obstruct an infanticidal male, but the male has the option to try again and again, and often he eventually succeeds. (However, some males simply do not exhibit the infanticidal trait; others have been observed to make dozens of attacks on infants, yet never succeed.)

Given that the greater body size and strength of the male favor his eventual success, one of the most effective counter tactics may be a form of female deceit. If, as has been suggested, males are inhibited from attacking infants associated with former consorts, it may be because females already pregnant at the time of the takeover exhibit "pseudo-estrous" behavior (as they have been observed to do) and thus induce a male to tolerate her subsequent offspring by sexually soliciting a male at times when they could not ordinarily conceive. SB-H

APES

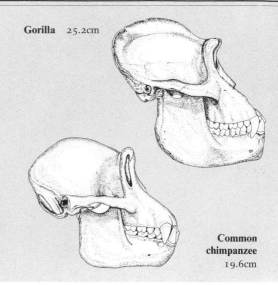

Gorilla 25.2cm

Common chimpanzee 19.6cm

Families: Hylobatidae, Pongidae.
Thirteen species in 4 genera.
Distribution: E India to S China and south through SE Asia to Malay Peninsula, Sumatra, Java, Borneo, W and C Africa.

Habitat: chiefly rain forests; also deciduous woodland, savanna.

Gibbons or lesser apes (family Hylobatidae)
Nine species of the genus *Hylobates*, including **siamang** (*H. syndactylus*), **Hoolock gibbon** (*H. hoolock*), **Pileated gibbon** (*H. pileatus*), **Concolor gibbon** (*H. concolor*) and **Kloss gibbon** (*H. klossi*).

Great apes (family Pongidae)
Four species in 3 genera:
Common chimpanzee (*Pan troglodytes*) and **bonobo** or **Pygmy chimpanzee** (*P. paniscus*).
Orang-utan (*Pongo pygmaeus*).
Gorilla (*Gorilla gorilla*).

THE apes are man's closest relatives, and with man comprise the primate super-family Hominoidea. There is a fairly sharp distinction between the medium-sized lesser apes (gibbons and siamang, family Hylobatidae) and the considerably larger great apes (orang-utan, gorilla and chimpanzees, family Pongidae). The great apes and man are quite closely related and are the largest living primates. Fossil relatives of both the lesser apes and the great apes are known from the early Miocene, some 20 million years ago. Indeed the lesser apes may have become distinct as long ago as the early Oligocene (about 35 million years ago), but the fossil record is fragmentary.

The apes have no tail and their forelimbs, prominent in locomotion, are longer than the hindlimbs. The chest is barrel-shaped (rather than flattened from side to side as in monkeys) and the modified wrist structure permits greater mobility. Gibbons and siamang display the most spectacular pattern of movement, known as "true brachiation," in which the body is swung along beneath the branches with the arms taking hold alternately. The great apes, by contrast, are far less athletic in their movements through the trees. The orang-utan, the largest living arboreal mammal, moves slowly and deliberately, suspending the great weight of its body from all four limbs in a quadrumanous (four-handed) progression.

In contrast to their Asiatic relative, the great apes of Africa generally travel along the ground. Both chimpanzees and gorillas "knuckle-walk" with the knuckles of the hands providing the points of contact with the ground (orang-utans, particularly old heavy males, may descend to the ground and "fist-walk" on the outer margins of the hands—a more rudimentary pattern of fore-limb support). Chimpanzees spend between a quarter and a third of their time in the trees, but gorillas only about 10 per cent.

The apes are all essentially vegetarian, though chimpanzees eat some animal food as well. Only the gorilla, the most terrestrial of the apes, is predominantly a leaf rather than a fruit-eater. In the remaining apes, particularly in gibbons and siamang, their "suspensory" movements while feeding are linked to adaptations for feeding in the terminal branches. Although animal food represents a small part of its diet, the chimpanzee's feeding activity has attracted much interest because of its possible relevance to the emergence of hunting behavior in early humans. At Gombe Stream in Tanzania, male chimps prey upon other primates (eg Red colobus and baboons) and other medium-sized mammals (eg Bush pig); the chimpanzees show a limited tendency to hunt cooperatively and they share food. Chimpanzees, mainly females, also feed on termites, using a "tool," a carefully selected twig (see p424).

Among the apes can be found almost every major pattern of social organization known among primates. The lesser apes are all monogamous and it appears that the mated pair remain together for life. The interval between births in gibbons and siamang is typically 2–3 years, sexual maturity is reached at about six years of age in both sexes, and sexually mature adults emigrate from the parents' home range. Consequently the maximum size of gibbon and siamang groups is about five individuals. Orang-utans feed in ones or twos, adult males typically avoid one another, and the only common social unit is the mother/offspring group, although adult

► **Face-flanges and throat sac** of the male orang-utan become swollen with fat in overweight captive individuals. These secondary sexual characteristics are acquired (like the silverback coloration of male gorillas) at 12–14 years, some 5 years after sexual maturity. By contrast the chimpanzees (males 15–20 percent heavier), siamang and gibbons show little or no size difference between the sexes and breed in monogamous pairs.

▼ **Size difference between sexes** is extreme in the orang and gorilla—mature males outweigh adult females almost twice over. In the tree-dwelling orang-utan BELOW this is all the more surprising since extreme sexual dimorphism is usually associated with a terrestrial life-style.

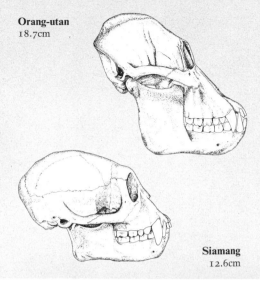

Orang-utan
18.7cm

Siamang
12.6cm

Skulls of Apes

Apes have relatively well-developed jaws, a flattened face with forward-pointing eyes and a globular brain-case, reflecting the fairly large brain in relation to body size. As in monkeys, each eye is enclosed in a complete bony socket formed by development of a plate of bone that separates the orbit from the jaw musculature behind it. The dental formula, as in Old World monkeys and man, is I2/2, C1/1, P2/2, M3/3 = 32, with spatulate (shovel-shaped) incisors and squared-off cheek teeth bearing relatively low cusps which reflect the predominance of plant food in the diet. The canine teeth are prominent and the rear edge of each upper canine hones against the front edge of the first lower ("sectorial") premolar. The lower jaw is fairly deep, and the two halves of the jaws are fused at the front as in monkeys and man. Similarly, in common with monkeys and man, the frontal bones of the skull are fused at the midline.

In association with their much smaller body size, the skulls of lesser apes (gibbons and siamang, family Hylobatidae) have relatively lightly built skulls, and there is relatively little difference between males and females (sexual dimorphism). In the much heavier great apes (orang-utan, chimpanzees, gorilla, family Pongidae), the skull is robustly built and sexual dimorphism in body size is reflected in the considerably heavier build of male skulls. Indeed, the powerfully developed jaw and neck muscles of male gorillas and orang-utans have required the development of substantial midline (sagittal) and neck (nuchal) crests to provide additional surfaces for the attachment of muscles. The orang's skull slopes back markedly more than skulls of other great apes.

females and/or immature orangs may form small temporary groups. Nevertheless, the orang-utan probably has some kind of social system based on overlapping ranges, perhaps broadly comparable to the "extended harems" of many nocturnal lemur and loris species (see pp320–337). The great apes of Africa have quite well defined social groups. The gorilla is essentially harem-living, and groups average about 12 members consisting of a single mature silver-back male, a small number of younger ("black-back") males, several adult females, and immature animals. Lone silver-back males are also common. In chimpanzees there are at least two different levels of grouping. The fundamental social unit seems to be a community of 40–80 individuals including numerous adults of both sexes, but it is rare to find the whole community together in one place.

Clear cut territorial behavior seems to be restricted to the lesser apes and the chimpanzees. Gibbons and siamangs are well known for their loud territorial calls (see p420). In chimpanzees territorial demarcation seems to be more discreet, though encounters between members of neighboring communities can lead to death.

The lesser apes, like most monogamous mammals, show very little difference in body size between sexes, though there are some differences in coat coloration between sexes. In chimpanzees there is relatively little size difference, but in both orang-utans and gorillas there is extreme sexual dimorphism in body size.

The apes, particularly the great apes, are very similar to human beings in their reproductive biology, and in all apes maternal care of infants is prolonged, ranging from some 18 months in gibbons to almost three years in great apes.   RDM

GIBBONS

Family: Hylobatidae.
Nine species of the genus *Hylobates*.
Gibbons or Lesser apes.
Distribution: extreme E of India to far S of
China, south through Bangladesh, Burma and
Indochina to Malay Peninsula, Sumatra, W
Java and Borneo.

Habitat: evergreen rain forests (Southeast Asia)
and semi-deciduous monsoon forests (mainland
Asia).

Size: head-body length 45–65cm (18–26in)
in most species, and weight 5.5–6.7kg
(12.1–14.7lb). The siamang has a head-body
length of 75–90cm (30–35in) and weighs
some 10.5kg (23lb). Sexes similar in size.

Coat: color distinguishes species (and
sometimes sexes and age group within
a species), as do calls.

Gestation: 7–8 months.

Longevity: in wild, siamang to 25–30 years,
Lar gibbon to 25 years or more.

▶ **Leaping to the next branch,** this Lar or
White-handed gibbon shows the long arms, the
thumb well distant from the grasping fingers,
and broad feet with long opposable big toe of a
true brachiator. Gibbons arm-swing (brachiate)
beneath the branches, swinging the body along
with alternate hand-holds.

▷ **"Suspensory" posture** of gibbons INSET is
employed to reach ripe fruit in terminal
branches as well as for locomotion.

THE gibbons are distributed throughout
the mainland and islands of Southeast
Asia forming the Sunda Shelf and, being
virtually confined to a life in the trees, depend on the evergreen tropical rain forests.
It is the rapid clearance of these forests
that places their future in such jeopardy.
They have a spectacular arm-swinging form
of locomotion (brachiation) and habitual
erect posture, which are key adaptations for
their unique suspensory behavior. They
utter loud and complex calls of considerable
purity in a stereotyped manner, which capture the spirit, both joyful and melancholic,
of the jungles of the Far East. These beautiful
calls, mainly given as duets, serve to develop
and maintain pair bonds and to exclude
neighboring groups from the territory of the
monogamous family group. The gibbons'
key attributes—monogamy, territoriality, a
fruit-eating diet, "suspensory" behavior and
elaborate songs—are a blend that is unique
among primates.

Contrary to popular belief, the apes and
man do not share an ancestor that habitually swung through the trees by its arms.
While all apes have long arms, mobile
shoulders and stand erect, only the gibbons
have developed powerful propulsive abilities
in their upper limbs.

While the great apes have developed
sexual dimorphism in body size, adult male
and female gibbons are more or less the
same size. They are relatively small, slender
and graceful apes with very long arms,
longer legs than one would expect, and
dense hair; they are more efficient at bipedal
walking than the great apes, and do so on
any firm support, such as branches too large
to swing beneath, not just on the ground as
is commonly supposed. Coat color and
markings, especially on the face, clearly
distinguish the species and, in some cases,
age and sex. Some species have developed
throat (laryngeal) sacs, which act as
resonating chambers to enhance the carrying capacity of calls. These calls, especially
those of the adult female, provide one of the
easiest ways of identifying species.

In terms of diversity and abundance the
gibbons are the most successful of the apes.
From an adept climbing and fruit-eating
ancestor, they have diversified throughout
the forests of Southeast Asia over the last
million or so years, maintaining the same
body form and size (with the chief exception
of the siamang) for hanging to feed from the
terminal branches and for brachiating
through the forest canopy. It was the frequent periods of isolation in different parts of
the Sunda Shelf during the Pleistocene

► **Gibbon species are geographically separated,** except the siamang which overlaps both Lar and Agile gibbons. Within most species (not in the siamang, Kloss or Moloch gibbons) coat color varies according to sex and/or geographical population. (**1**) Siamang. (**2**) Concolor gibbon (**a**) black-cheeked and (**b**) white-cheeked phases. (**3**) Hoolock gibbon (**4**) Kloss gibbon. (**5**) Pileated gibbon. (**6**) Müller's gibbon. (**7**) Moloch or Silvery gibbon. (**8**) Agile gibbon (sexes similar in one population: (**a**), (**b**) forms in Malay Peninsula and southern Sumatra; and (**c**) southwest Borneo. (**9**) Lar gibbon (sexes similar in same population): Thailand, dark phase (**a**) and (**b**) light phase: (**c**) south of Malay Peninsula: (**d**) northern Sumatra.

Abbreviations: HBL = head-and-body length; TL = tail length: wt = weight. Approximate nonmetric equivalents: 2.5cm = 1in: 230g = 8oz; 1kg = 2.2lb. E Endangered. V Vulnerable. I Threatened, but status indeterminate.

Siamang
Hylobates syndactylus

Malay Peninsula, Sumatra. HBL 75–90cm; wt 10.5kg. Male, female and infants black; throat sac gray or pink. Calls: male screams; female—bark-series lasting about 18 seconds.

Concolor gibbon I
Hylobates concolor
Concolor, Crested or White-cheeked gibbon.

Laos, Vietnam, Hainan, S. China. HBL 45–64cm (as all other gibbons); wt 5.7kg. Coat: male black with more or less whitish (or reddish) cheeks; female buff or golden sometimes with black patches; infant whitish. Calls: male grunts, squeals, whistles; female—rising notes and twitter, sequence of about 10 seconds.

Hoolock gibbon
Hylobates hoolock
Hoolock or White-browed gibbon.

Assam, Burma, Bangladesh. wt 5.5kg (female), 5.6kg (male). Coat: male black, female golden with darker cheeks, both with white eyebrows; infant whitish. Calls: male—di-phasic, accelerating, variable; female—similar to but lower than, and alternating with, male's.

Kloss gibbon V
Hylobates klossi
Kloss gibbon or beeloh (incorrectly Dwarf gibbon, Dwarf siamang).

Mentawai Islands, W Sumatra (Siberut, Sipora, N and S Pagai). wt 5.8kg. Coat: overall glossy black, in male, female and infant—the only gibbon so. Calls: male—quiver-hoot, moan; female—slow rise and fall, with intervening trill or "bubble" or not, sequence lasts 30–45 seconds.

Pileated gibbon E
Hylobates pileatus
Pileated or Capped gibbon.

SE Thailand, Kampuchea W of Mekong. wt ? Coat: male black with white hands, feet and head-ring; female silvery-gray with black chest, cheeks and cap; infant gray. Calls:

male—abrupt notes, di-phasic with trill after female's; female—short, rising notes, rich bubble; 18 seconds.

Müller's gibbon
Hylobates muelleri
Müller's or Gray gibbon.

Borneo N of Kapuas, E of Barito rivers. wt ? Coat: mouse-gray to brown, cap and chest dark (more so in female), pale face-ring (often incomplete) in male. Calls: male—single hoots; female—as Pileated gibbon but notes shorter; sequence 10–15 seconds.

Moloch gibbon E
Hylobates moloch
Moloch or Silvery gibbon.

W Java. wt 5.9kg. Coat: silvery-gray in male and female, all ages; cap and chest darker. Calls: male—simple hoot; female—like Lar gibbon at first, ends with short bubble; 14 seconds.

Agile gibbon
Hylobates agilis

Malay Peninsula, Sumatra (most), SW Borneo. wt 5.9kg. Coat: variable (but same in both sexes in one population), light buff with gold, red or brown; or reds and browns; or brown or black; white eyebrows and cheeks in male, brows only in female. Calls: male—di-phasic hoots; female—shorter than Moloch gibbon, lighter-pitched, rising notes to stable climax, sequence lasts 15 seconds.

Lar gibbon
Hylobates lar
Lar or White-handed or Common gibbon.

Thailand, Malay Peninsula, N Sumatra. wt 5.3kg (female), 5.7kg (male). Coat: variable but same in both sexes in one population; Thailand: black or light buff; white face-ring, hands and feet. Malay Peninsula: dark brown to buff. Sumatra: brown to red, or buff. Calls: male—simple and quiver hoots; female—longer notes than Moloch gibbon, climax fluctuates, duration (Thailand) 18, (Malay Peninsula) 21, (Sumatra) 14–17 seconds.

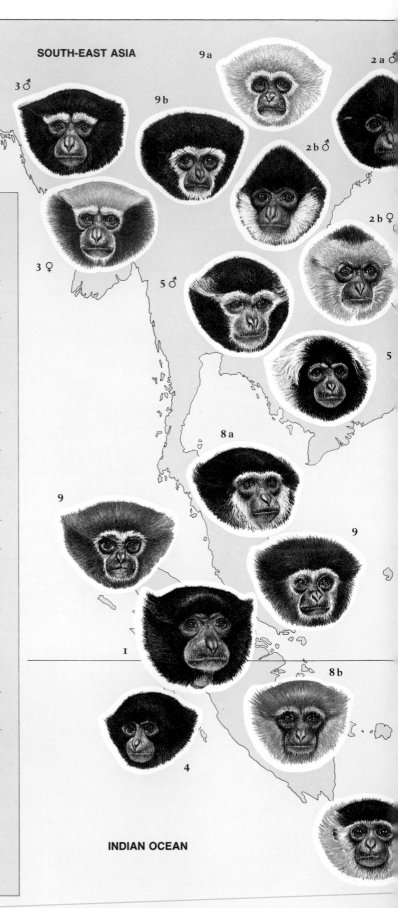

SOUTH-EAST ASIA

INDIAN OCEAN

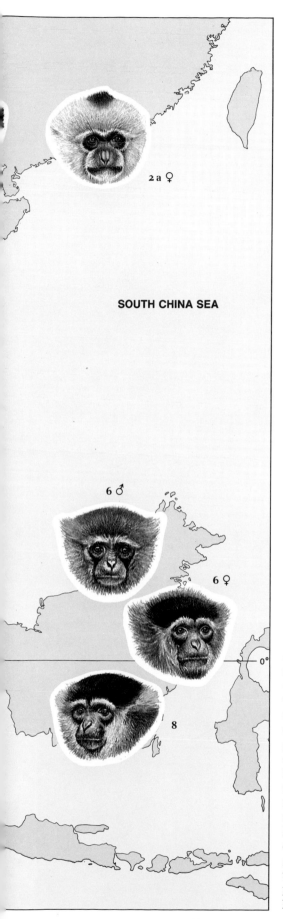

SOUTH CHINA SEA

2a ♀

6 ♂

6 ♀

8

0°

changes in sea level (7–2 million years ago) which stimulated differentiation of gibbons into present species.

It seems that about one million years ago the ancestral gibbon spread down into Southeast Asia to become isolated in the southwest, northeast and east (the Asian mainland would have been uninhabitable during the early glaciations). These three lineages respectively gave rise to the siamang, the Concolor gibbon, and the rest. The greatest changes occurred subsequently in the eastern group, which spread back towards the Asian mainland during the interglacial periods, giving rise first to the Hoolock gibbon (and the Kloss gibbon in the west), then to the Pileated, and finally, during and since the last glaciation to Agile and Lar, with Müller's and Moloch gibbons evolving on Borneo and Java, respectively. The range of gibbons has contracted southwards in historic time— 1,000 years ago, according to Chinese literature, they extended north to the Yellow River. Curiously, gibbons are sexually dichromatic across the north of their range (males are mainly black, females buff or gray), black in the southwest, very variable in color in the center of their distribution, and tending to gray in the east.

The nine species are separated from each other by seas and rivers, except for the much larger siamang which is sympatric with the Lar gibbon in peninsular Malaysia and with the Agile gibbon in Sumatra. Although otherwise similar in size and shape, as a result of their common adaptation to a particular forest niche, they are readily identified by coat color and markings and by song structure and singing behavior. The siamang used to be placed in a separate genus, but the gibbons are best considered as monogeneric, with the siamang in one subgenus (*Symphalangus*) (50 chromosomes, diploid number) the Concolor gibbon of the northeast as a second (*Nomascus*), with 5–6 subspecies spread from north to south across the seas and rivers of Indochina (52 chromosomes), and the Lar gibbon group in a third (*Hylobates*) in the center and east (44 chromosomes). The concolor gibbon is as different from the Lar group as is the siamang. The Hoolock gibbon is the most distinctive of the third and largest subgenus, and it has now been found to have only 38 chromosomes; it is sexually dichromatic, like the Concolor and Pileated gibbons. The Kloss gibbon used to be called the Dwarf siamang because it is also completely black. The "gray" gibbons are the Moloch and müller's gibbons. The most

widely distributed and variable in color are the Agile gibbon, with at least two subspecies, and the Lar gibbon which can both be described as polychromatic, although the Lar gibbon in Thailand shows extreme dichromatism apparently not related to sex.

Gibbons generally show preferences for small scattered sources of pulpy fruit, which brings them into competition more with birds and squrrels than with other primates. Unlike the monkeys which feed in large groups and can more easily digest unripe fruit, gibbons eat mainly ripe fruit; they also eat significant quantities of young leaves and a small amount of invertebrates, an essential source of animal protein.

The structural complexity of the gibbons' habitat buffers the effects of any limited seasonality. Within as well as between plant species (climbers as well as free-standing trees) fruiting occurs at different times of year, ensuring year round availability of fruit. Since such plant species rely on animals for dispersal of seeds, this is an important example of co-evolution between plants and animals.

About 35 percent of the daily active period of 9–10 hours is spent feeding (and about 24 percent in travel). Feeding on fruit occupies about 65 percent of feeding time, on young leaves 30 percent, except for the siamang which eats 44 percent fruit and 45 percent leaves, and the Kloss gibbon (72 percent fruit, 25 percent animal matter and virtually no leaves). The larger the proportion of leaves in a species diet, the relatively larger are the cheek teeth and their shearing blades; the voluminous cecum and colon indicate an ability to cope with (and even ferment) the large leaf component of the diet in these simple-stomached animals. Fruit, even small ones, are picked by a precision grip of thumb against index finger, which permits unripe fruit to be allowed to ripen.

The adult pair of a gibbon family group usually produce a single offspring every 2–3 years, so that there are usually 2 immature animals in the group, but sometimes as many as 4. Thus, copulation is not seen very often; it is usually dorso-ventral with the female crouching on a branch and the male suspended behind, but occasionally the animals copulate facing each other. Gestation lasts 7–8 months and the infant is weaned early in its second year. The siamang is unusual in the high level of paternal care of the infant; the adult male takes over daily care of the infant at about one year of age, and it is from him that it gains independence of movement (by three years of age). Juveniles of either sex are

relatively little involved in group social interactions. By about six years the immature animal appears fully grown, and, as a subadult, tends to interact with siblings in a friendly manner, with the adult male in both friendly and aggressive ways, and avoids the adult female. Conflict with the adult male helps to ease the now socially mature animal out of the group by about eight years of age.

Subadult males often sing alone, apparently to attract a female, but they may also wander in search of one. Thus, either sons or daughters may end up near their parents, although sons perhaps more often. It is clear, however, that the first animal that comes along is not necessarily a suitable mate for life.

The siamang is unusual among gibbons in the high cohesion of the family group throughout daily activities—group members are 10m (33ft) apart on average, and rarely is one animal separated by more than 30m (100ft). In other gibbons the family feeds together only in the larger food sources; for the rest of the day they forage individually across a broad front of about 50m (165ft) coming together occasionally to rest and groom and, in some cases, to sleep at night.

Social interactions are infrequent; there are few visual or vocal signals, even in siamang, despite the "expressive" faces and complex vocal repertoire. Grooming is the most important social behavior, both between adults and subadults, and between adults and young; play, centered on the infant, is the next most common.

The most dramatic and energetically costly social behavior is singing, which mostly involves the adult pair. While it is most commonly explained as a means of communicating between family groups on matters of territorial advertisement and defense, there is increasing evidence that singing is crucial not only in forming a pair bond, but in maintaining and developing it. The elaborate duet which has evolved in most species is given for 15 minutes a day on average and from twice a day to once every five days, according to the species and to factors relating to fruiting, breeding and social change. The Kloss gibbon and possibly the Moloch gibbon do not have duets, but female Kloss gibbons have an astonishing "great call" (see p420) and male solos are given at or before dawn in Kloss, Lar, Agile, Pileated and perhaps Moloch gibbons.

This near-daily advertisement of the presence of a group and its determination to defend the area in which it resides is augmented by confrontations at the territorial boundary about once every five days, for an average 35 minutes. Altogether there are perhaps five levels of territorial defense—calls from the center, calls from the boundary, confrontation across the boundary, chases across the boundary by males, and, very rarely, physical contact between males.

The song bouts of most gibbon species conform to the same basic pattern: an introductory sequence while the male and female (and young) "warm up," followed by alternating sequences of organizing (behaviorally and vocally) between male and female, and of "great calls" by the female, usually with some vocal contribution from the male, at least at the end as a

▲ ◀ **In the Sumatran jungle** ABOVE, a siamang couple call in unison, the female (left) giving a series of barks while the male (center) screams. The song cycle lasts some 18 seconds while the subadult offspring (right) looks on. The throat-sac LEFT acts as a resonator to enhance the carrying quality of the call. Gibbon species can be distinguished by their songs, especially the great call of the female.

◀ **The Moloch or Silvery gibbon** TOP LEFT inhabits the western end of the island of Java. About twice as much time is spent feeding on ripe fruit, the staple diet, as on leaves. (The larger siamang eats more leaves than fruit.)

acres), but about 15 hectares (37 acres) for Lar in Thailand and for Moloch gibbons, and about 60 hectares (148 acres) for Lar gibbons in Malaysia sympatric with siamang. Most gibbon species defend about three-quarters of this home range (25 hectares) as the group's territory. (About 90 percent of the home range is defended by Moloch and Müller's gibbons, and only about 60 percent by siamang and Kloss gibbons.) It is difficult to define territorial boundaries in siamang, however, since disputes are rare; it seems that they use their much louder calls to create a "buffer zone" between territories. Even though twice the size of other gibbons, siamang live in rather smaller home ranges, moving about less and eating more of more common foods such as leaves.

In 1975 there were estimated to be about 4 million gibbons. It was predicted that at prevailing rates of forest clearance (which still show little sign of abating) by 1990 these numbers would be reduced by 84 percent to about 600,000 with only the siamang, Müller's, Agile and Lar gibbons remaining in viable numbers. But thousands of gibbons (millions of animals in all) are still being displaced annually and die as a result.

The highest priority must be given to protecting adequate areas of suitable habitat for each species and subspecies. In the long term it would pay humans better, for economic reasons alone, to maintain rain forests rather than to clear them. As a further immediate step, displaced animals should be rounded up and either returned to unpopulated forests, if such schemes can be proved viable, or serve to establish breeding centers, preferably in the countries of origin, for research beneficial to the species and its conservation (eg nutrition and reproduction), for education and, if absolutely essential, for biomedical research of benefit to both humans and the captive maintenance of gibbons.

The gibbons hold a special place in the society of forest peoples, because of their resemblance to man (lack of tail, upright posture, intelligent expression). They tend not to be hunted by such people, but to be revered as a good spirit of the forest home. It is the more recent arrivals to these oriental countries who shoot anything that moves, but gibbons are very elusive to hunters. As forest dwellers they are neither pests nor effective carriers of disease. It is the human tendency to clear the jungles of the Far East which threatens the survival of every inhabitant.

coda. Only in the Kloss gibbon are the songs of male and female completely separated into solos and these are discussed in the following pages. In Lar, Agile, Moloch, Müller's and Concolor gibbons, male and female contributions are integrated sequentially into the duet, whereas in Hoolock and Pileated gibbons and in the siamang, the male and female call together at the same time, even during the female's great call.

There are usually 2–4 gibbon family groups, each of 4 individuals, to each square kilometer (0.45sq mi) of forest with a total body weight of 45–100kg per sq km (40–90lb/sq mi), but there may be less than one group or more than six. These groups travel about 1.5km a day (siamang, Pileated and Müller's gibbons have mean annual day ranges of about 0.8km) around a home range usually of 30–40 hectares (74–99

DJC

Defense by Singing

Great calls and songs of the Kloss gibbon

Kloss gibbons are restricted to the Mentawai Islands west of Sumatra. Here the tropical rain forest contains several hundred potential food species, many of which flower and fruit in response to different cues. In such a complex environment it would be grossly inefficient for a monogamous group of primates such as these gibbons simply to wander the forest in search of food. The key to survival for a family group of Kloss gibbons is therefore to have an area of rain forest over which they have exclusive rights. Within its home range of 20–35 hectares (50–85 acres) the group can monitor the location and development of fruit, learn pathways between different points, and establish boundaries between its own and neighboring ranges.

A walk in the forest just before dawn gives a clue to how the Kloss gibbon defends its territorial rights. About two-thirds of the home range—the territory—receives particularly heavy use and all the trees used by the gibbons for sleeping at night lie within this area. Members of other groups will not be tolerated within the territory and the resident male will actively defend it if a

▲ **Launched into mid air** a female brings her great call to a climax, and serves notice on others to steer clear of her mate. She may also ABOVE run upright along branches tearing off leaves and be joined by other family group members shaking branches to enhance the display and giving calls of their own. like the clinging infant RIGHT.

second male comes too close. Such conflicts are rare, however, and this is due largely to the messages of passive defense that the adult males communicate when they sing. An adult male Kloss gibbon usually sings in the last hour before dawn and sometimes after dawn too. He will sing, on average, every other day and a song bout can last anything from 10 minutes up to two hours. It starts as simple whistling notes but, in longer bouts, is gradually elaborated into complex phrases containing about 12 notes and a trill. The male is relaxed when singing and often finds time to forage for insects or even eat fruits. His song's basic message is "I'm here" but, of course, it is hardly necessary to sing for two hours for his neighbors to understand just that. Comparative size is commonly used by animals to settle a territorial dispute instead of resorting to blows, but gibbon males in tropical rain forest could not be any larger because their feeding niche—that of exploiting the terminal branches—would then be unavailable. The very limited range of visibility also makes a show of size inappropriate. So, a male is able to "demonstrate" his confidence or willingness to defend his territory by the duration and complexity of his song. Unlike the simple "I'm here" message, this second message of a long, complex song, need not be declared every day and makes it possible to minimize the time spent in conflicts with any particular neighbor.

All the trees he uses as platforms from which to sing are on or near the territory boundary and, since he uses a number of trees, his neighbors are able to get some impression of the area he is prepared to defend.

The song of the female Kloss gibbon has been described as "the finest music uttered by any land mammal" and comprises about twenty 30-second phrases consisting of long rising notes, a loud ringing trill and long falling notes. Her song, usually sung about two hours after dawn, is performed every third or fourth day, from large trees anywhere in the home range. The performance is one of the most dramatic events in the forest. She climbs to the upper boughs of a tall emergent tree to begin and at the climax of the "great call"—the trill—she launches herself into the air, swinging from bough to bough, tearing leaves off branches and frequently causing rotten branches to crash to the ground. During this climax the infant or juvenile will often cling to its mother's belly and attempt to sing as well, and the male and other juveniles race round shaking branches and generally making the

performance as conspicuous as possible.

Unlike other gibbons, an adult pair of Kloss gibbons does not perform a vocal duet and the climax of the female's "great call" is essentially the only activity involving the whole group. While the female and her offspring interact in many ways, the male only rarely has contact with the other group members; he sleeps alone, and often travels around the home range some way behind or to the side of the female or offspring. The "great call" display is important therefore in maintaining the adult pair bond and the general cohesiveness of the group, but it is also a form of defense. Whereas the male's song is directed towards other males with designs on his home range, the female's song is directed towards other females and declares that any stray females who might have been attracted by the male's song should be aware that he already has a mate. Should a young female find an unattached, territory-holding male she will attempt to sing as soon as possible to stake her claim on him and his defended area.

Thus both sexes sing for defense—the male to defend his territory so that his mate and offspring can maintain themselves, and the female to defend her mate—the defender of the territory she occupies—from other females.   AJW

▲ **From a platform on the edge of his territory,** a male begins a bout of singing that may last up to two hours. He is answered TOP LEFT by his adult male neighbor on the adjoining mountain ridge. Meanwhile, supplementing a diet chiefly of fruits, the female searches for insects in foliage and the couple's offspring picks up ants on the back of its hand.

CHIMPANZEES

Common chimpanzee [v]

Pan troglodytes
Distribution: W and C Africa, north of River Zaïre, from Senegal to Tanzania.

Habitat: humid forest, deciduous woodland or mixed savanna; presence in open areas depends on access to evergreen, fruit-producing forest; sea level to 2,000m (6,560ft).

Size: head-body length 70–85cm (28–33in) (female), 77–92cm (30–36in) (male). No tail. Weights (poorly known in wild) in Tanzania 30kg (66lb) (female), 40kg (88lb) (male). Zoo weights up to 80kg (176lb) (female), 90kg (198lb) (male).

Coat: predominantly black, often gray on back after 20 years. Short white beard common in both sexes. Infants have white "tail-tuft" of hair, lost by early adulthood. Baldness frequent in adults, typically a triangle on forehead of males, more extensive in females. Skin of hands and feet black, face variable from pink to brown or black and normally darkening with age.

Gestation: 230–240 days.

Longevity: 40–45 years.

Pygmy chimpanzee [v]

Pan paniscus
Pygmy chimpanzee or bonobo
Distribution: C Africa, confined to Zaire between Rivers Zaïre and Kasai.

Habitat: humid forest only; below 1,500m (4,925ft).

Size: head-body length 70–76cm (28–30in) (female), 73–83cm (29–33in) (male). No tail. Weights (rarely measured in wild): 31kg (68lb) (female), 39kg (86lb) (male). Body lighter in build than Common chimpanzee, including narrower chest, longer limbs and smaller teeth.

Coat: as Common chimpanzee, but face wholly black, with hair on top of head projecting sideways. White "tail-tuft" commonly remains in adults.

Gestation: 230–240 days.

Longevity: unknown.

[v] Vulnerable.

AMONG the apes, it is the chimpanzees that can tell us most about the natural history of our common ancestors. In chimpanzee behavior we see many similarities to people—such as their tool-making, and their aggressive raiding parties of males—which show that several traits once thought to be uniquely human are not in fact so. Common chimpanzees live not only in humid closed-canopy forests but also in relatively dry areas, such as flat savanna where evergreen trees are confined to a few protected gullies. It was in open habitats such as these that our ancestors probably lived. Now, because of the impact of human activities on chimpanzee populations, the race is on to find out how chimpanzees live in their different habitats, before they or their habitats are destroyed.

Both species have stout bodies with backs sloping evenly down from shoulders to hips, a result of their relatively long arms (reaching just below the knee when standing erect). The top of the head is rounded or flattened (there is no sagittal crest), and the neck appears short. Their ears are large and projecting, while the nostrils are small and lie above jaws that project beyond the upper part of the face (prognathous muzzle). All their teeth are large compared to human teeth, but compared to gorillas chimpanzees have small molars, appropriate for their fruit diet. Bonobos, or Pygmy chimpanzees, have particularly small molars. Despite their name, however, their body size is not markedly different from Common chimpanzees.

Males are larger and stronger than females, and have bigger canine teeth which they use in severe fights with occasionally deadly results. Body proportions are otherwise similar, but both sexes have prominent genitals. Females in heat have prominent swellings of the pink perineal skin, lasting 2–3 weeks or more, every 4–6 weeks. Males have relatively enormous testes (120g/4.2oz).

Chimpanzees have similar sensory abilities to people; possibly they are better able to distinguish smells. Their large brains (300–400cc/18.3–24.4cu in) reflect a consistently high performance on all intelligence tests devised by humans, including the ability to learn and use words defined by hand signals in languages used by the deaf. In the wild, however, there is no evidence of linguistic abilities. Thirteen categories of chimpanzee calls have been recognized, from soft grunts given while feeding, to loud pant-hoots, consisting of shrieks and roars audible at least 1km (0.6mi) away.

Chimpanzees travel mostly on the ground, where they "knuckle-walk," like

gorillas. Like the other great apes, chimpanzees sleep in "nests," leafy beds normally made fresh each night. Adults sleep alone, infants with their mothers until the next sibling is born.

The Common chimpanzee, found north of the River Zaïre, has been known since the 17th century. There is much variation in body size and proportions, and even in coat and skin color. As many as 14 species were classified in the early years of this century, but only three subspecies are now recognized, in western, central and eastern populations. However, no distinctive traits have been established for the three subspecies, whose validity remains uncertain. Bonobos were first described as a separate species from museum collections in 1929. Their restriction to closed-canopy forests south of the River Zaïre has protected them from most collectors, and little is known in detail of their distribution or variation.

In all habitats chimpanzee diets are composed mainly of ripe fruits, which they eat for at least four hours a day. One to two hours daily are spent eating young leaves, particularly in the late afternoon. In long dry seasons tree seeds partly replace fruit, and flowers, soft pith, galls, resin and bark are also taken. Chimpanzees eat from as many as 20 plant species a day and 300 species in a year. Whenever possible they eat large "meals" from single food sources, which allows them to rest for an hour or two before walking on to the next fruit tree. They do not store food, and almost all food is eaten where it is found.

Animal prey make up as much as 5 percent of the diet by feeding time. Social

▲ **Adult chimp's black face** and ears are usually pink in younger animals.

◄ **Riding on the mother's back** begins at about six months of age and continues for several years. Earlier the single offspring clings to its mother's underside from within a few days of birth.

► **A Pigmy chimpanzee or bonobo** in captivity. Despite its name this species is no smaller than its relatives on the northern banks of the Zaïre river.

insects provide the largest amounts and are collected either by hand (eg aggregating caterpillars) or with tools (see LEFT). Females spend twice as much time as males eating insects. Birds are caught only occasionally, but mammals are regular prey in some areas and are known to be eaten particularly by males, wherever there have been long-term studies of chimpanzees. Monkeys, pigs and antelope are the principal prey, especially young animals. Hunting occurs irregularly, typically only when prey is surprised in appropriate circumstances. Monkeys, for example, are ignored in continuous canopy forest but are chased if encountered in broken canopy, with few escape routes.

Feeding is essentially an individual activity, and during periods of food scarcity most chimpanzees travel alone or in small family groups (mother with one or two offspring). Larger parties, often formed when individuals meet at food trees, give no advantages in obtaining food and can sometimes lead to competition for feeding sites. Even when hunting mammalian prey, chimpanzees show little cooperation; more than one chimpanzee may take part in the chase, but once a kill is made there is intense competition for the carcass. Both at kills and at trees with a few large fruit individuals with food in their hands are surrounded by others trying to take morsels. This leads to "food-sharing," where scrounging is tolerated apparently because it gives the possessor some peace.

Females raised in captivity begin mating at 8–9 years and give birth for the first time at 10–11 years. Wild females mature 3–4 years later. There is no breeding season. Common chimpanzee females are not receptive for 3–4 years after giving birth, then resume sexual activity for 1–6 months until conception. Female bonobos continue sexual activity during much of pregnancy and lactation. A single young is born after a gestation of 8–9½ months: twins are rare.

The newborn chimpanzee is helpless, with only a weak grasping reflex and needing support from the mother's hand during travel. Within a few days it clings to the mother's underside without assistance and begins riding on her back at 5–7 months. By 4 years the infant travels mostly by walking, but stays with its mother until at least 5–7 years old. Weaning occurs well before this, starting in the third year. Mothers groom and play with their offspring, and allow younger juveniles to take from them foods which only adults can get easily.

Males show precocious sexual behavior,

Tool Use

Chimpanzees use tools to solve a greater range of problems, both in the wild and captivity, than any animal apart from humans. Two kinds of food are commonly obtained with tools, though chimpanzee populations vary in their use of them.

Most social insects have potent defenses which are overcome by the use of sticks or soft stems. For instance, chimpanzees prepare smooth, strong wands 60–70cm (24–28in) long for feeding on Driver ants: they lower the wand onto an open nest, wait for ants to crawl up it, then sweep them off and into their mouths before the ants have time to bite. They strip grass stems to make them supple, poking them into holes on termite mounds: soldiers bite the stem, and cling on long enough for the chimpanzee to extract and eat them. Sticks are also used to enlarge holes, so that honey or tree-dwelling ants can be reached.

A second food type eaten with tools is fruits with shells too hard to bite open. Sticks or rocks weighing up to 1.5kg (3.3lb) are used to smash these fruits, sometimes against a platform stone. Platform stones have been found with a worn, rounded depression, suggesting they have been used for centuries.

Tools are not used only when feeding. Adult males elaborate their charging displays by hurling sticks, branches or rocks of 4kg (8.8lb) or more: in a long display as many as 100 rocks are thrown, and other individuals have to watch out to avoid being hit. Missiles have once been seen in the context of hunting: a male hit an adult pig from five metres (over 16ft), startling it so that it ran off and allowed the chimpanzee to seize its young.

Fly-whisks, sponges (of chewed bark or leaves), leaf-rags and other tools are used irregularly in different areas. Why do chimpanzees use, and even make, so many types? Their upright sitting position, opposable thumb and precision grip are only part of the answer: other primates have them too. Nor are they unique in having large brains: gorillas and orang-utans are large-brained, but rarely use tools. Chimpanzees are inventive problem-solvers, and their habits may simply offer more tool-using opportunities than those of other great apes.

▲ **Two young chimps at play** while their mothers sit nearby. Mother and young continue to travel together for years after weaning and the bonds last into adulthood, reached at 13–15 years of age.

▼ **Rehabilitation of chimps** displaced by logging in the Gambia. A slow rate of reproduction makes chimpanzee populations especially vulnerable to destruction of their habitat. Rehabilitation centers reintroduce captured chimps to the wild.

including full intromission of adult females by the age of 2. Complete courtship patterns, however, develop slowly, from 3–4 years onward. They are normally directed towards females in heat (estrus), and consist of nonvocal attention-getting displays by the male sitting with penis erect: displays include hair erection, branch-shaking and leaf-stripping, some of this behavior varying between populations. Females respond by approaching and presenting for mating. Juveniles of both sexes commonly follow the female, and approach and touch the male after mating begins. These interfering juveniles make submissive gestures to the mating male, who responds with aggression only to older juvenile males.

Females mate only when in heat (when their sexual skin is swollen) and for the first week or more female Common chimpanzees are promiscuous and mate on average six times a day. Towards the last week of estrus, near the time of her ovulation, high-ranking males compete for mating rights, by threatening or attacking subordinates who approach the female. Alternatively, an exclusive "consortship" is formed, a female and male eluding other members of the community for days or weeks. Though 75 percent of matings occur in the promiscuous phase, pregnancies are most likely to result

from consortships. The sexual behavior of bonobos is less well known. They are often promiscuous and, unlike Common chimpanzees, sometimes mate from the front.

All chimpanzee individuals are members of a community 15–120 strong, and travel sometimes with other community members. Neighboring communities have partially overlapping ranges, within which they show either resident or migratory traveling patterns. Resident communities occupy ranges of 10–50 sq km (4–20 sq mi), and have population densities of 1–5/sq km (0.4–2/sq mi). Within these community ranges individuals have their own dispersed "core" areas and spend 80 percent of their time within 2–4 sq km (0.8–1.5 sq mi). Common chimpanzee mothers often travel alone except for their offspring, covering 2–3 km (1.2–1.9 mi) per day. Males are more gregarious, traveling further than mothers and being attracted both to other males and to females in heat.

Party sizes average 3–6 for Common chimpanzees and 6–15 for bonobos. Parties of bonobos tend to have equal sex ratios and persist for longer than those of Common chimpanzees.

Less is known about migratory communities, which occur in open habitats in the extreme west and east of the chimpanzee's range, where population density falls to 0.5–1.00/sq km (0.02–0,4/sq mi). Communities migrate within large ranges of 200–400sq km (77–154sq mi) or more, settling for a few weeks in areas where food is temporarily abundant. When they settle they appear to behave like a resident community, with females more dispersed and more often alone than males.

Membership of communities is determined by sex. Males seldom or never leave the community where they are born, whereas most females migrate to a new community during an adolescent estrous period. For the young female a successful transfer occurs when she establishes her own core area within the range of another community where she can feed without aggression from other females. She travels in the company of males for much of the time in her first few months in a new community, and thereby obtains protection from hostile females. Females typically make a successful transfer only once, but repeated movements are known.

Within communities relationships between established females are poorly understood, but known to range from aggressive to friendly. Female bonobos associate more than Common chimpanzees, and rub their genital areas together in contexts of social excitement. Male relationships are more overt; tension is routinely expressed in dominance interactions when parties meet (see RIGHT), and males also spend much time grooming each other. Males tend to associate with their maternal brothers, but close associations between other male pairs are also common.

There are an estimated 50,000–200,000 chimpanzees and bonobos in 15 countries. In a further nine countries they were known in historical times but are now probably extinct. The main threat comes from habitat destruction, particularly commercial logging, eg in Ivory Coast and central Zaire. Commercial exploitation for overseas trade and hunting for bushmeat have severely reduced populations in some areas, eg Sierra Leone and eastern Zaire, respectively. About 10 national parks contain chimpanzees but most are small. Given their low reproductive rate, chimpanzees are highly vulnerable to loss of habitat or populations. Common chimpanzees are abundant in captivity but bonobos have no viable breeding populations outside the wild.

In several areas chimpanzees are protected by local custom (eg parts of Guinea, Zaire, Tanzania) and they visit fields or even markets. RWW

Gang Attacks
Cooperative fighting in chimpanzee society

Male chimpanzees are commonly aggressive to each other, in common with the males of many other species. But they are unusual because for much of the time adult males not only tolerate male company but seek out, groom and follow each other. This mixture of hostility and relaxed association occurs because familiar males form alliances and support each other in conflicts. Since the composition of male parties shifts unpredictably at any time, the presence of particular allies is never certain. Social relationships are therefore complex.

Males form a loose dominance hierarchy. Subordinates greet dominants by bobbing or crouching in front of them, giving "pant-grunt" vocalizations. Dominant males commonly approach others with a charging display, running with hair erect, perhaps dragging a branch. Reunions between familiar males are the principal context of these displays, which test whether any change has occurred in the dominant's confidence or the subordinate's willingness to challenge. Occasionally, of course, a reversal occurs, normally after several weeks of tension. Chases, physical attacks (hitting, rolling on the ground, stamping) and screams are frequent.

Displays are not restricted to such contexts of social uncertainty. They can also be prompted by heavy rain or strong winds, or by coming to a stream or waterfall. These displays are given both by lone males and by parties. The male begins by rocking gently where he sits, perhaps rhythmically swaying a branch. Movements become larger and more exaggerated until he swaggers or charges, on the ground or through trees and vines, sometimes at a slow tempo for up to 15 minutes. Wind, rain and rushing water all interrupt the quiet of the normal environment, but why chimpanzees respond with displays is unknown.

The importance of other displays is clearer. Given primarily by males, they lead to reduced tension because one male has acknowledged the other's competitive superiority. After reunions a typical sequence is for males to groom each other for several minutes before traveling together. If subsequently any competition is initiated, such as for mating rights, the subordinate abandons his challenge quickly.

But why do males travel together? Though they sometimes follow the same receptive female, or exploit the same productive food trees, they may also travel as an all-male party when food is abundant throughout the community's range. At such times the air is often full of long-distance calls as individuals gauge where others are and join to form large parties, 8–40 strong. This is only possible when food is abundant but provided that it is, chimpanzees (especially males) tend to congregate.

Male congregation is particularly striking on the borders of community ranges, and functions in both defense and attack. When parties from different communities meet by chance they give calls which reveal their relative size: smaller parties retreat faster. Provided there are several males they are not attacked. However, such interactions can lead to the loss of preferred feeding areas, and seasonal changes in food

hold him down while others hit or bite him. The injuries inflicted can lead to death within a few days. These are rare interactions, of course, but more than 10 deaths from such raids have been seen or suspected in relationships involving five different communities. If lone males are so vulnerable to attack by a larger party it is not surprising that males seek each other's company, and that dominant males tolerate the presence of subordinates.

Females are vulnerable also if alone, though in different ways. Mothers who migrate to a neighboring community risk attacks and infanticide by resident males, who sometimes cannibalize their victims. Even residents are not necessarily safe. Mysterious cases have been observed of resident males killing infants conceived within their own community. Other mothers too are a potential threat. One female led her adolescent daughter in killing several infants of resident females. This behavior may have increased the daughter's chances of establishing a core area near her mother; whatever the cause, it emphasizes the vulnerability of the young. Mothers with offspring less than a year old spend more time with males than those with older juveniles, perhaps for protection. Even the mother herself can be attacked. At least two old females have been seen to die as a result of gang attacks by males from neighboring communities.

The brutality and effort put into gang attacks implies they have important rewards. In one case a community with a few females lost all its males in a four-year period. Individuals from neighboring communities occupied the almost empty range, and in subsequent years both flourished. Whether competition for feeding space or mating rights is more important remains to be discovered.

▲ **Aggression and coalitions** between male chimps. (1) Display: a male chimp swaggers bipedally, begins a charge beating its chest, then stops to stamp on and slap the ground, picks up and charges with a stick. (2) A subordinate male bobs and "pant-grunts" in front of another's dominant status, while in the background two other males engage in the mutual grooming which may follow such an encounter. (3) A "border patrol" turns on a lone male, then chases him and finally beats and bites him in a joint effort.

distribution mean that small communities may be regularly jostled by their neighbors. Even more important, parties meet not only by chance but also by design. Common chimpanzees form "border patrols," male parties which visit the boundary of their range and sit for up to two hours, listening and looking toward neighboring areas. If nothing is heard or seen, the patrol may return or advance. If a large party is detected calls are exchanged. And if a lone male is seen he may be stalked, chased, and attacked in a cooperative effort: some males

ORANG-UTAN

Pongo pygmaeus [E]
Sole member of genus.
Family: Pongidae.
Distribution: N Sumatra and most of lowland Borneo.

Habitat: lowland and hilly tropical rain forest, including dipterocarp and peat-swamp forest.

Size: head-body length (male) 97cm (38in); female 78cm (31in); height (male) 137cm (54in); female 115cm (45in); weight (male) 60–90kg (130–200lb); female 40–50kg (88–110lb).

Coat: sparse, long, coarse red hair, ranging from bright orange in young animals to maroon or dark chocolate in some adults. Face bare and black, but pinkish on muzzle and around eyes of young animals.

Gestation: 260–270 days.

Longevity: up to about 35 years (to 50 in captivity).

Subspecies: 2. *Pongo p. pygmaeus* from Borneo; *P. p. abelii* from Sumatra, thinner, longer faced, longer haired and paler colored than *P. p. pygmaeus*.

[E] Endangered.

▶ **Mother and young** ABOVE, one of perhaps three or four the female orang raises on her own during 20 years of active reproductive life in the wild.

▷ **The only truly arboreal ape,** the orang-utan swings on its long arms, grasping branches by its hook-like hands and feet in search of its chief food, fruit. The male's impressive size, cheek flaps, throat pouch and long hair enhance his display in confrontations with males that attempt to encroach too far in his home range.

THE shy orang-utan or "Man of the Woods" is Asia's mysterious great red ape. It lives in the remote steamy jungles of Borneo and Sumatra and for a long time was known more from fabulous native stories and for his reputation as an abductor of pretty girls than from documented scientific accounts. In recent years, however, several extensive studies of this fascinating animal have been made and although some mysteries still remain the orang-utan is now one of the better known primates.

The orang-utan is a large, red, long-haired ape of very striking appearance. It is active in the daytime and spends most of its time in the trees. Adult males are about twice the size of females and have cheek flanges of fibrous tissue that enlarge their face and very long hair which enhance their aggressive displays. Orang-utans have very long arms for arboreal locomotion and hook-shaped hands and feet. They use their heavy weight to swing trees back and forth until they can reach across gaps between one tree and the next. Most orang-utans only occasionally descend from the trees to travel on the forest floor, though large males do so more. On the ground they use their strong arms to bend and break branches to obtain food and to make sleeping nests for the night. Their teeth and jaws are relatively massive for tearing open and grinding coarse vegetation, spiny fruit shells, hard nuts and tree bark. Orang-utans have a large throat pouch, most fully developed in adult males, which is inflated during calling and adds resonance to vocalizations, part-icularly the territorial "long call" of the adult male (see p430). The orang-utan has a large brain and is as highly intelligent as the other great apes.

Orang-utans are clearly descended from one of the Miocene *Sivapithecus* fossil apes but their exact ancestry is not known. Pleistocene orang-utans of giant size are known from China and subfossil orang-utans about 30 percent larger than present size are known from caves in Sumatra and Borneo. During the Pleistocene, a small form occurred on Java but is now extinct. It would seem that ancestral orang-utans were more terrestrial than those of today but the degree of anatomical and functional adaptation of orang-utans to tropical rain forest suggests a very ancient co-evolution. Biochemical relationships indicate that the orang-utan is a rather more distant relative of man than are the African apes, the gorilla and chimpanzee.

The orang-utan has a huge capacity for food and will sometimes spend a whole day sitting in a single fruit tree, gorging. About 60 percent of all food eaten is fruit, including such well-known tropical species as durians, rambutans, jackfruits, lychees, mango-steens, mangoes and figs. The remainder of the diet is mostly young leaves and shoots, but they regularly eat insects, mineral-rich soil, tree bark and woody lianas and oc-casionally eggs and small vertebrates, raid-ing nests of birds and squirrels. Water is drunk from tree holes; the ape dips in a hand and sucks the water-drops falling from its hairy wrist.

Orang-utans range slowly but widely, and usually singly, in search of fruit and they have an uncanny ability to locate it. In the efficiency of their travel routes they show great knowledge of the forest, its seasons, and the relative positions of individual trees and they can deduce where food is from observing the movements of other animals, especially hornbills and pigeons, which share items of diet. They find travel hard work and only travel a few hundred meters a day through the trees.

Orang-utans are long-lived, slow-breeding animals. Their breeding strategy is based on producing a few high-quality, well-cared-for young rather than mass production with high mortality. Females become sexually mature at about 10 years and consort for several days at a time with adult males during periods of sexual receptivity over several months until they become pregnant. They then live alone to bear and rear their infants, which are not weaned for three years. Infants ride on the mother's body and sleep in her nests until she has another infant. The interval between births can be as little as three years, but in fact in most wild populations adult females average only one infant every six years and remain fertile until about 30 years of age. The adult male's reproductive strategy consists of developing a range which takes in as many sexually responsive females as possible. He consorts with these females when they are receptive and until they are pregnant and is aggressive towards other adult males encroaching on his range. Once the females within his range are pregnant or caring for infants, they are sexually uninteresting for several years, so high-dominance males then sometimes move to another area of activity to include more females.

Orang-utans are rather solitary animals. Apart from occasional sexual consortships, adult animals travel and forage independently, each animal occupying an individual though non-exclusive home range of several square kilometers. Infants remain with their mothers. Juveniles (3–7 years old) become increasingly independent, sometimes traveling alone, and by adolescence (7–10 years old) they have usually completely left their mothers. Juveniles and adolescents are the most social, as in other apes, and sometimes come together to play for a few hours or even travel around in pairs or tag onto family units. When several adult orang-utans meet, as when attracted to the same major food source such as a fruiting fig tree, they show almost no social interaction and depart separately when they have eaten their fill. It is nevertheless clear that despite this apparent lack of interest in each other wild orang-utans do recognize individually all the animals whose ranges they regularly overlap, and they have a good knowledge of the location of other individuals nearby in the forest. Subadult males (10–15 years of age) are mainly solitary, do not call and sometimes secretly consort with females.

Adult males in particular are very conscious of one another's movements and give loud "long call" vocalizations to advertise their whereabouts. Encounters between males are avoided but when they occasionally do meet they indulge in violently aggressive displays when they stare at each other, inflate their pouches or charge about, shaking and breaking branches and sometimes calling. Usually one male backs down and flees along the ground but occasionally fights occur and antagonists grab and bite their rivals. Most adult males carry the scars, cut facial flanges or stiff broken fingers, from past battles. Orang-utan populations which are becoming condensed and overcrowded, or otherwise socially disturbed, as a result of habitat loss to logging operations, exhibit increased levels of aggression between males, reduced level of consortship and reduced reproductive rate. Such changes may be adaptive in enabling populations to restabilize with minimal conflict and minimal risk to infants.

There is also evidence that adult males continue their aggressive territorial behavior even after they have ceased to be sexually active after about 30 years of age. This suggests that longevity has been selected to enable males to defend space until their eldest offspring are old enough to take over the same space. More long-term field data are needed to test these theories.

Man has been a serious competitor of the orang-utan since his ancestors moved into the Asian rain forest over 9 million years ago. Orang-utans prefer just those fruits that man also enjoys eating, and man has consistently destroyed the apes' forests and even hunted orang-utans for food.

The Dayak and Punan people of Borneo show orang-utans great respect. Some feel spiritually related to orang-utans, others think of orang-utans as descended from a disgraced man who fled into the forest. Many native stories concern sexual relationships between man and ape and woman and ape. Indeed captive orang-utans are extremely precocious sexually, and pet orangutans were sometimes used for ribald games at the end of a good longhouse party.

Orang-utans make sensitive, gentle pets

The Long Call of the Male

From time to time the peace of the jungle morning is broken by a curious noise: a loud crash as a weak branch is broken off and hurled to the ground, followed by a series of loud roars which rise to a crescendo of bellowing then die back to repetitive bubbling groans. The whole sequence may last for a minute or two; this is the male orang-utan's long call.

According to native legend it is the male orang-utan expressing his anguish for the loss of his human bride when she escaped from the treetop nest that was her prison. Scientists still argue as to the call's exact function. Is it territorial to drive away other males, a primarily sexual display to attract receptive females, or a social signal to inform the whole community of the whereabouts of the patriarch? Probably the call serves all these functions. Observations on calling males show there is an increased tendency to call in bad weather, when other males are calling, when the caller meets other males or when he is close to sexually receptive females.

The response of orang-utans on hearing the call varies. Most give no visible reaction. Intruding or subadult males tend to move away quietly whereas other dominant males call in reply and advance to challenge the caller. Some females with young hide in the top of a tree if they hear a calling male near by; other females are attracted to the caller and consort with him.

It seems clear that the long call does have a

spacing function among adult males at least. Large males keep their distance and calls seem a likely way for them to monitor one another's movements. Long calls probably attract receptive females and may also act as a coordinating signal for the whole orang-utan population in the area. Coordinated seasonal movements of whole communities over several kilometers have been noted and could be guided by the males' calls.

and were very popular in that role before it was made illegal in Malaysia and Indonesia to own or sell one. Captive males sometimes became rather bad-tempered and some apparently docile animals have turned viciously on their keepers, biting off fingers etc.

Captive orang-utans score very highly in comparative intelligence experiments, which is somewhat surprising in view of their relatively simple life-style and social relationships. The orang-utan's high intelligence is probably related to its extraordinary ability to find fruit in the tropical rain forest, where fruit is usually scarce and on isolated trees. A good memory for time and place and an ability to make deductions are essential in predicting the whereabouts of food.

Since they are closely related to man, orang-utans are of interest as carriers of several human diseases (such as malaria, other blood fevers and viral infections) and parasites but contact in the wild is so rare that this is not considered a serious health problem.

Great concern has been shown for the plight of the orang-utan. This spectacular ape has already vanished from several of its former haunts and its home, the tropical rain forest, is disappearing at a frightening rate due to logging for timber and land clearance for agriculture.

At one time the species was seriously threatened by the trade in orang-utan babies for zoos and as pets. Mothers were shot to capture their young and many young died during capture and transport. The elimination of this dreadful trade and improvements in the protected status of the animal have greatly relieved the situation.

Research has shown that orang-utans are not as rare as was formerly thought—density varies between 1 and 5 animals per square kilometer (0.4–2/sq mi) depending on habitat quality—but the future of the rain forest remains as uncertain as ever. Eventually, more rational utilization and management of the rain forests may come about, but in the short term the only way to save the orang-utan is to protect as much of its habitat as possible within the boundaries of nature reserves and national parks. Fortunately, conservationists in Indonesia and Malaysia have been very successful in establishing such reserves, and major populations are now protected in the Gunung Leuser National Park in Sumatra, Tandjung Puting and Kutai National Parks and Gunung Palung and Bukit Raja reserves in Kalimatan (Indonesian Borneo), Lanjak Entimau reserve in Sarawak and the proposed Danum Valley reserve in Sabah.

Several rehabilitation stations have been established in Malaysia and Indonesia to train confiscated young pet orang-utans to return to the wild. Some success has been achieved, particularly in drawing local attention to the plight of this superb ape. It has, however, been generally agreed that returning human-oriented animals, capable of carrying human diseases, into healthy wild populations is not a useful exercise. Instead rehabilitated animals should be released in areas where wild orang-utans no longer occur, in order to establish new populations.   JMacK

◄ **Young orangs differ from adults** in the upright hairs on the crown and pink coloration on the muzzle and round the eyes. In adults the darker coat is flat on top of the head and the facial skin is all black.

▼ **Young Bornean orang-utan** (the individual opposite is from Sumatra). A quadrupedal climber, the orang progresses slowly through the trees, using its body weight to bend trunks or branches in the desired direction.

GORILLA

Gorilla gorilla
Sole member of genus.
Family: Pongidae.
Distribution: C Africa.

Habitat: tropical secondary forest.

Size: male average height 170cm (5.6ft), occasionally up to 180cm (5.9ft); weight 140–180kg (310–400lb). Female height up to 150cm (5ft); weight 90kg (200lb). Often very obese in captivity—one male weight of 340kg (750lb) recorded.

Coat: black to brown-gray, turning gray with age; males with broad silvery-white saddle. Hair short on back, long elsewhere. Skin jet black almost from birth.

Gestation: 250–270 days.

Longevity: about 35 years in wild, 50 years in captivity.

Three races:

Western lowland gorilla (*G. g. gorilla*). Cameroon, Central African Republic, Gabon, Congo, Equatorial Guinea. Coat brown-gray, and male's silvery-white saddle extends to the rump and thighs.

Eastern lowland gorilla (*G. g. graueri*). E Zaire. Coat black, with male's saddle restricted to the back. Jaws and teeth larger, face longer, and body and chest broader and sleeker than Western lowland gorilla.

Mountain gorilla [E] (*G. g. beringei*). Zaire, Rwanda, Uganda at altitudes of about 1,650–3,790m (5,450–12,500ft). Similar in coat and form to Eastern lowland gorilla, but with longer hair, especially on arms. Jaws and teeth even longer, but arms shorter.

[E] Endangered. [V] Vulnerable.

► **Coat colour varies** between subspecies of gorilla. In the Western lowland gorilla ABOVE the hair has a brownish-gray tinge whereas in the Eastern lowland gorilla RIGHT it is a more uniform black.

THE gorilla is the largest of living primates and, along with the two species of chimpanzee, the ape most closely related to man. Indeed, fossils and biochemical data indicate that the chimpanzees and gorilla are more closely related to man than they are to the orang-utan, the fourth of the "great apes," and are probably the most intelligent land animals on earth, apart from humans, at least as judged by human standards. They can learn hundreds of "words" in deaf-and-dumb sign language and even string some together into simple grammatical two-word "phrases." Nevertheless, the gorilla's formidable appearance, great strength and chest-beating display have given it an otherwise unfounded reputation for untameable ferocity. Field studies show that wild gorillas are no more savage than any other wild animal. In Rwanda thousands of tourists every year approach on foot to within a few metres of totally unrestrained wild gorillas, and not one of these visitors has ever been hurt. Threatened by man alone, adult males are dangerously aggressive only in defense of their breeding rights and family groups.

There are three races of gorilla found in two widely separated areas of Africa. Although obviously connected in the past, the western and eastern populations are kept apart by the Zaïre river–gorillas do not readily swim—and the nature of the intervening terrain. This is primary forest where, because it is so dark beneath the high, closed canopy, very little ground vegetation grows—certainly not enough to support the predominantly terrestrial gorilla.

Gorillas are mainly terrestrial and quadrupedal—they walk on the soles of their hind limbs, but pivot on the knuckles of their forelimbs. However some individuals, particularly the young, spend much time in trees and occasionally adults make foraging trips into the forest canopy. Lightweight individuals can be seen swinging from tree to tree by their arms (brachiation).

▲ **Most endangered** of the gorilla subspecies is the Mountain gorilla. Only a few hundred survive in the mountains of East Africa.

▷ **Kasimir the silverback** OVERLEAF rests his huge bulk in dense undergrowth of secondary forest in Kahusi-Beiga National Park, eastern Zaire. Some of the best studied gorilla groups are to be found in this park.

The gorilla differs from its close relative the chimpanzee in being very much larger and in the different proportions of its body (longer arms, shorter and broader hands and feet) and a different color pattern. The build is much heavier, and many of the proportional differences are connected with this. In particular, the much larger teeth (especially the molars) needed to sustain a huge hulk must in turn be worked by much bigger jaw muscles, especially the temporal muscles which in male gorillas meet in the midline of the skull, where they are attached to a tall bony crest—the sagittal crest. A small sagittal crest may occur in female gorillas or in chimpanzees, but a big one, meeting a big shelf of bone (the nuchal crest) at the back of the skull, is a distinctive characteristic of male gorillas and considerably alters the external shape of the head. In addition, male gorillas have canines that in relation to body size are far bigger than those of chimpanzee males and bigger also

than females' canines. The gorilla has small ears and the nostrils are bordered by broad, expanded ridges (naval wings) which extend to the upper lip.

Gorillas are predominantly folivorous, feeding mainly on leaves and stems rather than fruits. The species of herbs, shrubs and vines that make up the gorilla's diet grow best in secondary and montane forests where the open canopy allows plenty of light to reach the forest floor. Although found over a small area of Africa, gorilla habitat includes a wide range of altitudes, from sea level in West Africa to 3,790m (12,500ft) in the east.

Of the great apes (family Pongidae), the gorilla shows the most stable grouping patterns. The same adult individuals travel together for months and usually years at a time. It is because gorillas are mainly leaf-eating that they can afford to live in these relatively permanent groupings. Apes, un-like most monkeys, cannot digest unripe fruit, and in East Africa ripe fruits, in contrast to leaves, are far too thinly distributed to support a large permanent grouping of frugivorous (fruit-eating) animals even half as big as gorillas. It does appear that fruit-eating limits group size in the gorilla. In West Africa, where fruit forms a far higher proportion of the gorilla's diet than in the east, group sizes are about half those recorded for East Africa. (The predominantly frugivorous chimpanzee and orang-utan are mostly solitary.)

The gorilla's large size and folivorous habits mean that the animals cannot regularly travel long distances and still find time to forage and digest their bulky diet. In fact, because of the abundance of their food supply, under natural conditions they do not need to move very far in any one day to find enough to eat. Although the home ranges of gorilla groups cover 5–30sq km (2–11.5sq mi) depending on the region, the normal rate of travel is only 0.5–1km (0.3–0.6mi) per day. Even with a range as small as 5sq km, a circumference of 8km would have to be patrolled were the area to be defended. Gorillas are too large and travel too slowly to do this and thus there is no territorial defense. Consequently there is considerable overlap of the ranges of neighboring groups and even overlap of the most-used "core areas."

Gorillas never stay long enough at one feeding site to strip it completely: rather, they crop the vegetation leaving enough growth for rapid rejuvenation to occur. They normally feed during the morning and afternoon and rest for a few hours around midday. At night they make "nests"— platforms or cushions of branches and leaves pulled and bent under them, that keep them off the cold ground, prevent them sliding down a steep hill slope, or support them in a tree for the night. At higher altitudes in East Africa, gorillas defecate in their nests during the night, perhaps because it is too cold to leave them. However, the lack of fruit in the diet means that the dung is dry and does not foul their coats. By contrast, in West Africa, where the diet includes fruit, nests with dung in them are extremely rare.

Gorillas do not have a distinct breeding season. Births are usually single (as in the chimpanzees and orang-utan). In the very rare cases of twins, they are usually so small when born, and the mother, who has to carry the infants for the first few months of life, finds it so hard to care for two, that at least one always dies. Newborn infants weigh 1.8–2.3kg (4–5lb) and their grayish

pink skin is sparsely covered with fur. They begin to crawl in about nine weeks and can walk from 30–40 weeks. Gorillas are weaned at 2½–3 years of age, and females give birth at about four-year intervals. However a 40 percent mortality rate in the first three years means that a surviving offspring is produced only about once every 6–8 years in the breeding life of a female.

Female gorillas mature sexually at 7–8 years of age but usually do not start to breed until they are 10 or so. Males mature a little later, but because of competition among them for mates, very few will start to breed before 15–20 years of age.

The size of gorilla groups varies from two to about 35 animals but usually numbers five to 10. An average group in the east (Rwanda, Uganda and eastern Zaire) contains about three adult females, four or five offspring of widely different ages, and one fully adult male—called the "silverback" because of its silvery white saddle. Groups in West Africa average about five animals. Because groups effectively always contain

▲ **Midday rest for a gorilla group.** As if drawn by a magnet, most individuals gather round the silverback LEFT. Females with very young infants FAR LEFT tend to be closest, with the result that infants rapidly become used to the silverback's presence, and he becomes a focus for them as well – even at play ABOVE FOREGROUND infants keep within his sphere of protection. Females without infants remain in the background on the edge of the gathering TOP, while subadult males RIGHT are tolerated until they leave on reaching maturity to lead solitary lives before setting up their own harems.

◄ **Silverback male** is the only fully adult male in the group and may be twice the weight of the adult females who with their offspring make up the rest of the group.

► **Mountain gorilla nursing her young.** Births are 3½–4½ years apart and infant mortality reduces the female's successful raising of young to about one every seven years.

a silverback male, the difference is the number of females and offspring. But the main contrast between the regions is seen not in average, but maximum group size. In the west, groups of over 10 animals are rare, but in the east 15–20 members is not uncommon and some groups of over 30 animals have been recorded in Zaire.

The silverback is the most important individual for the cohesiveness of the group. Unlike the females of most other social mammals, female gorillas leave the natal group at puberty to join other troops. Having mostly originated from different

groups, the adult females in any one silverback's harem are therefore mostly unrelated, the social ties between them are weak, and little difference of social status among the females is noticeable. In contrast to many other primates it is bonds between each female and the silverback, rather than bonds among females, that hold the group together. The attractiveness of the silverback to the females is most apparent during the midday rest period (see LEFT), when animals play (primarily youngsters), sleep or groom one another. Mutual grooming, which keeps fur free from dirt and parasites and is an expression of affinity, is not as frequent in gorillas as in other social primates. When it does occur, it is usually between mother and offspring, adult female and silverback, and sometimes immature and silverback, especially if the youngster is an orphan. Social grooming among adult females is rare. Most young adult males leave the group and travel alone—sometimes for years—until they acquire females from other groups and establish their own harem. These young silverbacks leave of their own accord rather than being driven out by the leading male. Aggression in gorillas is extremely rare and serious fights occur only when a group leader meets either another group leader or, more usually, a lone silverback. Then, the two males perform elaborate acts of threat—the famous chest-beating display may be accompanied by hoots, barks and roars, tearing of vegetation and sideways dashes—all designed to intimidate the rival male and possibly also to impress and attract some of his nubile females.

In general, females leaving their natal group seem to prefer to join lone males or small groups, rather than large, established groups. Lone males appear to be prepared to work harder for females than do leaders of established groups, and therefore pose more of a threat to "resident" leaders.

When females leave their natal group, they generally do not stay with the first male to whom they transfer. Many factors probably influence their choice. One could be the quality of the habitat in the male's range, but another is almost certainly the male's prowess in fights, which provide some indication to a female of the male's ability to protect her and her offspring against predators and other males. Protection against other males is important: about a quarter of infant deaths are due to infanticide by a male that is not the infant's father. The most likely explanation for this is that an intruder male that kills a female's young offspring can mate with her, and so begin to reproduce, sooner than a male that does not practice such infanticide.

It appears that once a male has established a successfully breeding harem, he stays with it for life. With some males in near-permanent possession of females, while others have none, competition among males for females is intense: the severity of fights between males bears witness to this. Clearly, to some extent, large size is an advantage in these fights, and in the displays that precede them. Inter-male competition is thus almost surely one explanation for the sexual dimorphism (difference of body form between the sexes) in body size, canine size and jaw musculature shown by the gorilla. In this, the gorilla matches most other polygamous mammal species. Given the competition between males and the necessity for the male of this slow-moving terrestrial species to defend females and offspring, it is very probable that natural selection favors the survival of males with large canines: certainly the gorilla is one of the most sexually dimorphic of all primate species, the males being almost twice as large as the females and, moreover, differently colored.

The number of gorillas surviving in the wild today is not accurately known—far too little of their range has been surveyed. We have to make informed guesses, and the best available estimate (1980) has at least 9,000 in west-central Africa and 4,000 in the east, of which only about 365 are Mountain gorillas. Most of these are in danger; they and their habitat are disappearing and will continue to do so at an ever-increasing rate. Gabon, with three-quarters of its land surface still covered by forest and its very low, only slowly increasing, human population, contains about half the Western lowland gorilla population and Zaire almost all the Eastern one.

Throughout the gorilla's range in Africa the forests on which it depends are being cut down for timber and to make way for agricultural and, in some cases, industrial development. Formerly, deforestation did not matter because the human population was at a low enough density to practice shifting agriculture, and the abandoned fields with their regenerating secondary-growth forest provided abundant food for the gorilla. As time passes, however, more clearings are becoming permanent. Twenty-five years ago, gorillas lived in Nigeria. Now they are almost certainly extinct there and cattle ranches cover what used to be gorilla habitat.

Another threat is hunting, although it poses a minor problem compared to deforestation. Except in Uganda and Rwanda, gorillas are killed for food and because they raid crops. In West Africa gorillas are considered a crop pest throughout much of their range and firearms are common. Gorilla meat is consumed not only by the rural people but in Gabon, for example, it is served in the restaurants of main towns.

Zoos have also taken their toll. By the end of 1976, of 497 gorillas reported to be alive in captivity, 402 were caught in the wild; at

▲ **This orphaned gorilla "Julie"** was returned to the wild by Adrien Deschryver in 1974. Sadly, the adoptive gorilla group contained no lactating females and she died soon afterwards.

▼ **Less of a threat** to gorilla's survival than deforestation, hunting for sale of skulls and skins, and capture for export to zoos, are nonetheless enough in themselves to bring the gorilla to the edge of extinction, unless more protective steps are taken.

▲ **Mountain gorilla** in its natural habitat. National Parks and conservation areas need further protection themselves to ensure gorillas' future.

tain gorillas exist in all countries except the Central African Republic, only about one-third of the roughly 29,500 sq km (11,400 sq mi) of these conservation areas is suitable gorilla habitat. Less than 5,000, and probably only about 3,000 gorillas, actually live in national parks or reserves. Even in them, the gorilla cannot be considered safe. The trade in gorilla skulls (sold to tourists as souvenirs) from the Virunga Volcanoes National Parks of Rwanda and Zaire, and the presence of villages and logging yards within Gabon's Okanda National Park, illustrate this. Nor can the continued existence of the conservation areas themselves be guaranteed: in 1968, almost one-fifth of the Virunga Volcanoes National Park, one of only two refuges for the rare Mountain gorilla, was appropriated for pyrethrum cultivation.

In all countries harboring gorillas, it is extremely difficult for governments to fund major conservation programs given their other urgent priorities. Long-term ecological stability is usually sacrificed for short-term economic gain, often with the active encouragement of international development organizations. If the gorilla is to be saved, international conservation agencies must support existing reserves and fund extensive surveys in West Africa and Zaire to pinpoint the most important areas of gorilla concentration which might then be turned into reserves. Ultimately, the local people must come to value gorillas and the forests in which they live. For this reason, the funding of programs for conservation, education and the development of tourism (whereby live wild gorillas become a source of income) are particularly important. Such programs have recently been established successfully in Rwanda.

All this, however, is a rather desperate rearguard action. In the long run, the well-being both of the gorilla and of its human neighbors must depend on curbing human population growth and increasing the productivity of agricultural land now available. Only these will check the increasing need for yet more land and the consequent destruction of the gorilla's habitat.

The story of man's relationship with gorillas is shrouded in myth and legend (and horror movie: *King Kong*, 1933). It was in 1959 that the Americans George and Kay Schaller began the first thorough investigation of gorillas by observing them from close quarters over a two-year period. This work set a pattern for future studies of these peaceable creatures and effectively buried the gorilla myth for good. **AHH**

least one-third and probably more than half of these came from Cameroon. Since for every gorilla reaching a zoo at least two have died on the way, this figure represents at least 1,200 taken from the wild. Although the trade has decreased markedly in recent years, the current price paid for a young gorilla is enough to keep going the trade in animals for zoos.

Legislation to control hunting and capture of gorillas exists in all eight countries with wild gorilla populations, but in only one—Zaire—is the species totally protected by law and in none are the laws adequately enforced. At the time of writing, infant gorillas for sale are still coming out of Zaire. While national parks or reserves that con-

TREE SHREWS

ORDER: SCANDENTIA

One family (Tupaiidae); 6 genera; 18 species.
Distribution: W India to Mindanao in the
Philippines, S China to Java, including most
islands in Malayan Archipelago. Habitat:
tropical rain forest.

Subfamily Tupaiinae

Genus *Tupaia*: 11 species including **Pygmy tree
shrew** (*T. minor*), **Belanger's tree shrew**
(*T. belangeri*) and **Common tree shrew** (*T. glis*).

Genus *Anathana*: 1 species, the **Indian tree
shrew** (*A. ellioti*).

Genus *Urogale*: 1 species, the **Philippine tree
shrew** (*U. everetti*)'

Genus *Dendrogale*: 2 species, the **smooth-tailed
tree shrews.**

Genus *Lyonogale*: 2 species, including the
Terrestrial tree shrew (*L. tana*).

Subfamily Ptilocercinae

Genus *Ptilocercus*: 1 species, the **Pen-tailed tree
shrew** (*P. lowii*).

TREE shrews are small, squirrel-like mammals found in the tropical rain forests of southern and southeastern Asia. The first reference to them is in an illustrated account in 1780 by William Ellis, a surgeon who accompanied Captain Cook on his exploratory voyage to the Malay Archipelago. It was Ellis who coined the name "tree shrew," a somewhat inappropriate term since these unusual mammals are quite different from the true shrews and, as a group, are not particularly well adapted for life in trees—indeed some tree shrew species are almost completely terrestrial in habit.

Most tree shrew species are semiterrestrial, rather like the European squirrels, a resemblance that is emphasized by the fact that both tree shrews and squirrels are covered by the Malay word "tupai," from which the genus name *Tupaia* is derived. At first classified as insectivores, tree shrews were for a time thought to be primates, but recent research distinguishes them from both orders and they are here considered as the only members of the order Scandentia (see p443).

None of the six genera covers the entire geographical range of the order, though the genus *Tupaia* is the most widespread of all. The greatest number of species is to be found on Borneo, where 10 of the 18 recognized species occur. This concentration is partly a consequence of the large size of the island and the resulting wide range of available habitats, but it is also possible that Borneo was the center from which the adaptive radiation of modern tree shrew species began.

Tree shrews are small mammals with an elongated body and a long tail which, except in the Pen-tailed tree shrew, is usually covered with long thick hair. Their fur is dense and soft. They have claws on all fingers and toes; the first digits diverge slightly from the others. Their snouts range from short to elongated. The ears have a membranous external flap, which varies in size from species to species, and is usually covered with hair. In the Pen-tailed tree shrew the ear flaps are bare and larger than in any other tree shrews, doubtless because this nocturnal species relies more heavily on

▶ **Representative species of tree shrews.**
(**1**) The largely arboreal Pygmy tree shrew (*Tupaia minor*) "sledging" along a branch and leaving a scent trail from its abdominal gland. (**2**) The arboreal Pen-tailed tree shrew (*Ptilocercus lowii*) holding a captured insect in both hands while devouring it. This is the only nocturnal species and the only living representative of the subfamily Ptilocercinae. (**3**) The semi-terrestrial Common tree shrew (*Tupaia glis*) "chinning" to leave a scent trail from the sternal gland on its chest. (**4**) The mainly arboreal Northern smooth-tailed tree shrew (*Dendrogale murina*) snatching an insect from the air with both hands. (**5**) The Terrestrial tree shrew (*Lyonogale tana*) is a large-bodied species that finds most of its food in litter on the forest floor, rooting with its snout and turning over objects such as stones. (**6**) The Philippine tree shrew (*Urogale everetti*) is the largest species and it too spends most of its time at ground level rooting through debris.

Skulls of Tree Shrews

The skull of a tree shrew is that of a strictly quadrupedal mammal. The foramen magnum (the opening through which the spinal cord passes) is directed backward, whereas in the more upright living primates it is directed more or less downward. The skull is longest in terrestrial species which root in leaf-litter. Arboreal species have shorter snouts, larger brains and more forward facing eyes that give binocular vision. Compared here are the terrestrial Philippine and Terrestrial tree shrews (**a**, **b**), the semi-arboreal Common tree shrew (**c**) and the tree-dwelling Pygmy tree shrew (**d**). Common skull features include the post-orbital bar and an auditory bulla.

The dental formula is $I2/3$, $C1/1$, $P3/3$, $M3/3 = 38$. The canine teeth are relatively poorly developed compared with most mammals; the primitive sharp-cusped molars reflect an insectivorous diet and the forward-projecting lower incisors are used in grooming.

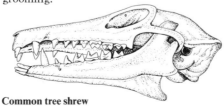

Common tree shrew

(a)

(b)

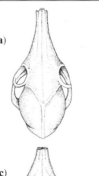
(c)

(d)

ORDER SCANDENTIA

its hearing to find insect prey and avoid predators at night. Species that are mainly arboreal, such as the Pygmy tree shrew, are small, have short snouts, more forward facing eyes, poorly developed claws, and tails longer than the combined head and body length. Terrestrial species, such as the Terrestrial tree shrew, are large, have elongated snouts, well-developed claws for rooting after insects, and tails shorter than head-and-body length. Their terrestrial habits permit greater body size with less need for a long tail to balance in the trees.

In most anatomical features, tree shrews show little obvious specialization, though there are some unusual features in the skull and dentition (see above). Except for the Pen-tailed tree shrew, tree shrews generally have laterally placed eyes, which are large and give good vision relative to body size. There is a well-developed subtongue (sublingua) beneath the tongue.

Like European squirrels, most tree shrews spend more time foraging on the ground than in trees. They scurry up and down tree trunks and across the forest floor with characteristic jerky movements of their tails, feeding on a wide variety of small animal prey (especially arthropods) and on fruits, seeds and other plant material. All except the most arboreal species spend a great deal of time rooting in leaf litter with the snout and hands. Tree shrews typically prefer to catch food with their snouts and only use their hands when food cannot be reached otherwise. However, flying insects may be caught with a rapid snatch of the hand and all tree shrew species hold food between their front paws when eating. The larger tree shrews probably eat small vertebrates in the wild, for example small mammals and lizards, since in captivity they have been seen to overpower adult mice and young rats and to kill them with a single bite to the neck.

Most tree shrews (like squirrels) are exceptions to the general rule that small mammals are nocturnal. The Pen-tailed tree shrews, however, is exclusively nocturnal, and many of its distinctive features (larger eyes and ears, large whiskers, gray/black coloration) can be attributed to this difference. It has been suggested that the Smooth-tailed tree shrews might be intermediate in exhibiting a crepuscular pattern, with peaks of activity at dawn and dusk.

Most tree shrew species nest in tree hollows lined with dried leaves. The gestation period is 45–50 days, according to species, and the 1–3 young are born without fur, with closed ears and eyes. The ears open within 10 days and the eyes in 20 days.

Tree shrews are unusual among placental mammals for the extremely rudimentary nature of their parental care. Laboratory studies have shown that in at least three species (the Pygmy, Belanger's and Terrestrial tree shrews) the mother gives birth to her offspring in a separate nest which she visits to suckle them only once every two days (early attempts to breed tree shrews in captivity failed largely because only one nest was provided). The visits are very brief (5–10 minutes), and in this short space of time she provides each infant with 5–15g (0.18–0.53oz) of milk to provision it for the following 48 hours. The milk contains a large amount of protein (10 percent), which permits the young to grow rapidly, and an unusually high fat concentration (26 percent) which enables them to maintain their body temperature in the region of 37°C (98.6°F) despite the absence of the mother from the nest. However, the infants are relatively immobile in the nest, so the milk contains only a small proportion of carbohydrate (2 percent) for immediate energy needs.

In all three shrew species so far studied, the infants have been found to stay in the nest for about a month, after which they emerge as small replicas of the adults. The young continue to grow rapidly and sexual maturity may be reached by the age of four months. Between the birth of her offspring and their eventual emergence from the nest, the mother spends a total of only one-and-a-half hours with the infants, and her brief suckling visits are accompanied by no toilet care. Indeed, maternal care in tree shrews is so limited that if an infant tree shrew is removed from its nest and placed just beside it, the mother will completely ignore it. She only recognizes her offspring in the nest because of a scent mark which she deposits

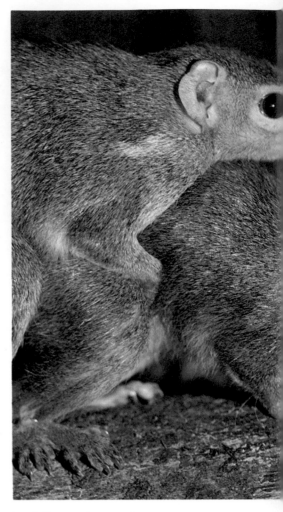

▲ **Indian tree shrews mating.** The gestation period is about 45 days, which is longer than that of insectivores of similar size, but much shorter than for comparable primates. Tree shrews therefore have a more rapid reproductive turnover than primates.

▶ **Rudimentary parental care** of tree shrews is unusual among placental mammals. The mother only suckles her young every 48 hours, leaving them completely alone in the nest between feeds. Because of this widely spaced feeding the young have to take in large quantities of milk at each session and consequently become extremely bloated, as can be seen from this litter.

◀ **Diet of tree shrews** mainly comprises insects and arthropods, but most species will feed on any available small invertebrate prey, such as the earthworms shown here or small mammals such as rats and mice.

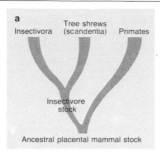

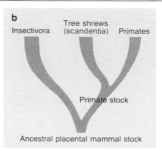

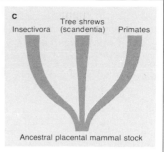

a

Insectivora   Tree shrews (scandentia)   Primates

Insectivore stock

Ancestral placental mammal stock

b

Insectivora   Tree shrews (scandentia)   Primates

Primate stock

Ancestral placental mammal stock

c

Insectivora   Tree shrews (scandentia)   Primates

Ancestral placental mammal stock

Insectivores, Primates—or Neither?

Misleadingly named, and originally placed within the order Insectivora along with the tree shrews, tree shrews would probably have remained in obscurity but for the suggestion made by the anatomist Wilfred Le Gros Clark in the 1920s that these relatively primitive mammals might be related to the primates. Comparing the structure of the skull, brain, musculature and reproductive systems, he concluded that the tree shrews should be regarded as the first offshoot from the ancestral primate stock. This interpretation was accepted by George Gaylord Simpson, who included the tree shrews in the order Primates in his influential classification of the mammals, published in 1945.

Thereafter, numerous studies of tree shrews were conducted in the hope of clarifying the evolutionary history of the primates (including man), and the tree shrews became widely regarded as present-day survivors of our primate ancestors. Today's consensus is that tree shrews are not specifically related to either primates or insectivores, but represent a quite separate lineage in the evolution of the placental mammals.

This view has been reached by several means. The first objection to the "primate" interpretation is that tree shrews may have come to resemble primates through entirely separate (convergent) evolution of certain features because of similar functional requirements. For instance, primates are typically arboreal while insectivores (eg shrews, hedgehogs, moles, tenrecs etc) are typically terrestrial, so it is possible that tree shrew/primate similarities have evolved through convergent adaptations for arboreal life. Various apparently primate-like features—relative shortening of the snout, forward rotation of the eye-sockets and greater development of the central nervous system associated with large eyes—are largely confined to the most arboreal of the tree shrew species, such as the Pygmy tree shrew. So these special characters cannot reliably be regarded as vestiges from a common ancestral stock of tree shrews and primates, particularly since the ancestral tree shrew was probably closest to the modern semi-terrestrial species.

The second, and most important, objection is based on drawing a distinction between similarities that are shared because they derive from a specific ancestral stock and similarities shared merely because of retention of characters from the more ancient ancestral stock of placental mammals. This second kind of similarity does not itself indicate any specific relationship between tree shrews and primates. A particularly good example is the presence of the cecum, a blind sac in the digestive tract at the junction of the small and large intestines, housing bacteria which assist in the breakdown of plant food. Tree shrews and primates typically possess a cecum, whereas it is absent from most insectivores. However, it has recently been shown that the cecum is widespread among mammals, both placentals and marsupials, and is even present in reptiles. It therefore seems likely that the cecum was already present in the earliest placental mammals, so its retention provides no evidence whatsoever for a specific ancestral connection between tree shrews and primates.

It has also emerged that in some respects tree shrews are very different from primates, particularly in reproductive characters, since the development of the placenta in tree shrews is quite unlike that in any primate species and the offspring are born in a naked, helpless condition that contrasts markedly with the advanced condition of newborn primates. In tree shrews, parental care is very rudimentary and also far removed from the elaborate parental care of the primates.

A major difficulty in reconstructing the evolution of tree shrews is the lack of fossil evidence, a gap that has now been filled to some extent by the discovery in Siwalik deposits of the Indian Miocene of tree shrew fossils (*Palaeotupaia sivalensis*) dating back some 10 million years. These support the interpretation that tree shrews derive from a semi-terrestrial ancestral form with moderate development of the snout.

It is probably best to regard the tree shrews as an entirely separate order of mammals which branched off very early during the radiation of placental mammal types. This view is also supported by biochemical evidence recently derived from the immunological cross-reactions of proteins from tree shrews, insectivores and primates, and from comparison of amino acid sequences in proteins from these species.

It now seems that rather than being survivors from early primate stock, the tree shrews may well be closer to the common ancestors of placental mammals in general.

THE 18 SPECIES OF TREE SHREWS

Abbreviations: HBL = head-and-body length; TL = tail length; wt = weight. Approximate nonmetric equivalents: 2.5cm = 1in; 230g = 8oz; 1kg = 2.2lb.

Tree Shrew Classification

In the classification of tree shrews particular emphasis is placed on coat coloration patterns, tail length and shape, form of the ears, development of the snout and claws, and the number of teats in females (the number of pairs of teats being the same as the number of offspring typical for the species).

Tupaia contains the least specialized tree shrews, distinguished primarily by the absence of special features. The wide geographical distribution of the genus is associated with considerable speciation and at least 11 distinct species are recognized.

The single species of the genus Anathana occurs in India south of the River Ganges, which divides it from T. belangeri to the east from which it differs in having relatively larger ear flaps and more complex molar tooth cusp patterns.

The two predominantly ground-living species now placed in the genus Lyonogale have elongated snouts and robust claws on the forefeet.

Urogale is quite distinct in many ways. The single known species is the largest of living tree shrew species and the sole representative on the island of Mindanao. The dentition is striking in that the second pair of incisors in the upper jaw are prominent and canine-like (completely dwarfing the actual canines), while in the lower jaw the third pair of incisors show great reduction.

The two species of the genus Dendrogale are distinguished by their fine tail fur, dimunitive body size and characteristic facial markings.

The Pen-tailed tree shrew (Ptilocercus lowii) is placed in a separate subfamily. It is the only nocturnal tree shrew and appears to be almost exclusively arboreal. The eyes are relatively forward facing, giving marked binocular overlap. The hands and feet are relatively large and in the upper jaw the anterior incisors are enlarged in a distinctive fashion. Pen-tailed tree shrews lack a shoulder stripe, in contrast to all except Dendrogale species.

The Smooth-tailed tree shrews are in many ways intermediate between the other tree shrews and Ptilocercus, for example in the sparseness of the hair on their tails and in reportedly showing a crepuscular pattern of activity.

Subfamily Tupaiinae

Active in daytime (Dendrogale perhaps at twilight). Eyes laterally placed. Five genera.

Genus Tupaia
S Malay Peninsula, Indonesia, Philippines, Indochina. Semi-terrestrial or arboreal; medium-sized (160g) or small (45g). Conspicuous cream or buff shoulder stripes always present; snout short (arboreal forms) or slightly elongated (semi-terrestrial forms); canine teeth moderately well developed. Ear flaps small. Females with 1, 2 or 3 pairs of teats.

Belanger's tree shrew
Tupaia belangeri
Indochina. Semi-terrestrial. Tail equal to length of head and body combined. wt 160g. Coat: ranging from olivaceous to very dark brown above, and from creamy-white or orange-red below. Females with 3 pairs of teats.

Common tree shrew
Tupaia glis
S Malay Peninsula, Sumatra and surrounding islands. Habit, weight, coat and tail features as T. belangeri. Females with 2 pairs of teats.

Long-footed tree shrew
Tupaia longipes
Borneo. Habit, weight, coat and tail features as T. belangeri. Females with 3 pairs of teats.

Montane tree shrew
Tupaia montana
Montane or Mountain tree shrew.
N Borneo (mountains). Habit, weight, coat and tail features as T. belangeri. Females with 2 pairs of teats.

Nicobar tree shrew
Tupaia nicobarica
Nicobar Islands. Semi-terrestrial to arboreal. Tail longer than length of head and body combined. Weight and coat as T. belangeri. Females with 1 pair of teats.

Painted tree shrew
Tupaia picta
N Borneo (lowlands). Habit, weight, coat and tail features as T. belangeri, except that a dark stripe runs length of back. Females with 2 pairs of teats.

Palawan tree shrew
Tupaia palawanensis
Philippines. Habit, weight, coat and tail features as T. belangeri. Females with 2 pairs of teats.

Rufous-tailed tree shrew
Tupaia splendidula
SW Borneo, NE Sumatra. Habit weight, coat and tail features as T. belangeri. Females with 2 pairs of teats.

Pygmy tree shrew
Tupaia minor
Borneo, Sumatra, S Malay Peninsula and surrounding islands. Arboreal TL greater than HBL. wt 45g. Coat: olivaceous above, off-white below. Females with 2 pairs of teats.

Indonesian tree shrew
Tupaia javanica
Indonesian or Javan tree shrew.
Java, Sumatra. Habit, weight, coat, tail and teats as T. minor.

Slender tree shrew
Tupaia gracilis
N Borneo and surrounding islands. Habit, weight, coat, tail and teats as T. minor.

Genus Anathana
Semi-terrestrial. Medium sized (160g). Coat: brown or gray-brown above, buff below; shoulder stripe light buff or white; pale markings around eyes. Tail equal in length to head and body combined. Snout short. Canine teeth poorly developed. Ear flaps well developed. Females with 3 pairs of teats.

Indian tree shrew
Anathana ellioti
India south of the Ganges.

Genus Urogale
Terrestrial. Large (350g). Coat: dark brown above, yellowish or rufous below; shoulder stripe pale. Tail much shorter than length of head and body combined, and covered in closely set rufous hairs. Snout elongated. Second pair of incisors enlarged. Females with 2 pairs of teats.

Philippine tree shrew
Urogale everetti
Mindanao.

Genus Dendrogale
Arboreal. Small (50g). No shoulder stripes present. Tail slightly longer than length of head and body combined, covered with fine smooth hair. Snout short. Ear flaps large. Females with 1 pair of teats.

Southern smooth-tailed tree shrew
Dendrogale melanura
Southern or Bornean smooth-tailed tree shrew.
N Borneo. Coat: dark brown above, pale buff below; facial streaks inconspicuous, but orange-brown eye rings prominent. Claws sharp.

Northern smooth-tailed tree shrew
Dendrogale murina
S Vietnam, Cambodia, S Thailand. Coat: light brown above, pale buff below; dark streak on each side of face running from snout to ear and highlighted by paler fur above and below. Claws small and blunt.

Genus Lyonogale
Terrestrial. Large (300g). Conspicuous black stripe along back; shoulder stripe pale. Tail bushy and shorter than length of head and body combined. Snout elongated. Canine teeth well developed. Claws robust. Females with 2 pairs of teats.

Terrestrial tree shrew
Lyonogale tana
Borneo, Sumatra and surrounding islands. Coat: dark red-brown above, orange-red or rusty-red below; front of dorsal stripe highlighted by pale areas either side; shoulder stripe yellowish. Claws robust and elongated.

Striped tree shrew
Lyonogale dorsalis
NW Borneo. Coat: dull brown above, pale buff below; shoulder stripe creamy buff or whitish. Claws less robust and shorter than in L. tana.

Subfamily Ptilocercinae

Nocturnal. Eyes forward-facing, giving binocular vision. One genus.

Genus Ptilocercus
Arboreal. Small (50g). Coat: dark gray above, pale gray or buff below; dark facial stripes running from snout to behind eye; no shoulder stripe present. Tail considerably longer than combined length of head and body; covered for entire length with scales, except for tuft of hairs at tip. Snout short. Upper incisors enlarged. Ear flaps large, membranous and mobile. Females with 2 pairs of teats.

Pen-tailed tree shrew
Ptilocercus lowii
S Malay Peninsula, NW Borneo, N Sumatra and surrounding islands.

▲ **Insect prey in mouth,** the Common tree shrew of Southeast Asia. This semi-terrestrial species has a snout of medium length. Exclusively tree-dwelling species are short-nosed, terrestrial species long-nosed for rooting in leaf-litter.

a territory, since there is very little overlap between adjacent home ranges and since fights have been observed on their boundaries. Tree shrews engage in extensive scent-marking behavior. The details vary from species to species, but in all cases scent marking involves special scent glands, urine and perhaps even feces. Belanger's tree shrew possesses two glandular areas on the ventral surface of the body: the sternal gland is used in "chinning," the tree shrew standing with stiffened legs and rubbing the gland over the object to be marked, which may be a branch or another tree shrew; the abdominal gland is used in "sledging," in which the tree shrew slides down a branch while pressing its abdomen against the surface. Tree shrews also scent mark by depositing droplets of urine while walking along branches, and the Terrestrial tree shrew has been reported to perform a kind of dance in which the hands and feet are impregnated with urine previously deposited on a flat surface. In captivity, at least, the products of these various scent-marking activities accumulate to form an orange-yellow crust with a fatty consistency and an extremely pungent smell. Captive tree shrews also deposit their feces in a few specific places in the cage, suggesting the droppings may play a role in territorial demarcation in the wild.

Tree shrews have a rather limited range of calls. All species, when surprised in the nest or during attacks on other tree shrews, produce a hoarse, snarling hiss with the mouth held wide open. Infants produce a similar sound when disturbed in the nest. A variety of squeaks and squeals is produced during fights, culminating in really piercing squeals when one combatant is beaten. *Tupaia* species also produce a continued chattering call when mildly alarmed, and there is some evidence that this acts as a mobbing call announcing the presence of potential predators.

Tree shrews are relatively inconspicuous mammals and their contacts with man are restricted. They may be pests in fruit plantations, and they occasionally occur in and around human habitations, but they do not seem to occupy any important place in the human economy or in mythology. Because of their high breeding potential, they can recover rapidly from population decline and quickly colonize new areas, so they are not obviously threatened by man at present. Rare species such as the Pen-tailed tree shrew and the Smooth-tailed tree shrews may be vulnerable in the wild, but firm information is lacking.   RDM

on them with her sternal gland; if the scent is wiped off she will devour her own infants!

The number of pairs of teats is characteristic of each species and is directly linked to the typical number of infants (one, two or three pairs of teats corresponding to one, two or three offspring).

Tree shrews tend to breed over a large part of the year, though a definite seasonal peak of births has been reported in some cases. The short gestation period and rapid maturation of the offspring mean that tree shrews can breed rapidly if the conditions are right, and they are able to colonize new areas quite quickly.

Of all the tree shrews the Common tree shrew has been most closely observed in the wild. This species forms loose social groups typically composed of an adult pair and their apparent offspring. The members of each group occupy all or part of a common home range covering approximately one hectare (2.5 acres), but they usually move around independently during the daytime, predominantly on or near the forest floor. The home range of each group seems to be defended as

FLYING LEMURS

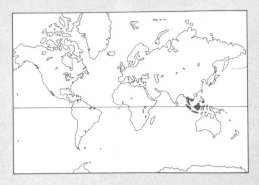

ORDER: DERMOPTERA

One family, the Cynocephalidae.
Two species of the genus *Cynocephalus*.

Malayan colugo

Cynocephalus variegatus
Malayan colugo or Malayan flying lemur.

Distribution: Tenasserim, Thailand, S
Indochina, Malaya, Sumatra, Borneo, Java and
adjacent islands.
Habitat: tropical rain forests and rubber
plantations.
Size: head-body length 34–42cm (13–16.5in);
tail length 22–27cm (8–11in); "wingspan"
70cm (28in); weight 1–1.75kg (2–4lb).
Coat: females slightly larger than males. Upper
surface of flight membrane mottled grayish-
brown with white spots (an effective
camouflage on tree trunks), underparts paler;
females tend to be more gray, males more
brown or reddish.
Gestation: 60 days.
Longevity: not known.

Philippine colugo

Cynocephalus volans
Philippine colugo, Gliding or Flying lemur.

Distribution: Philippine Islands of Mindanao,
Basilan, Samar, Leyte, Bohol.
Habitat: forests in mountainous and lowland
regions.
Size: head-body length 33–38cm (13–15in);
tail length 22–27cm (8–11in); weight 1–1.5kg
(2–3.5lb).
Coat: darker and less spotted than Malayan
colugo.
Gestation and longevity: as Malayan colugo.

THE order Dermoptera includes only two known families, the extinct Plagiomenidae from the late Paleocene and early Eocene of North America 60–70 million years ago and the modern family Cynocephalidae, the colugos or flying lemurs of Southeast Asia. The famous Singapore naturalist Ivan Polunin always refers to colugos as non-flying, non-lemurs, an apt description, as they do not fly but glide and are not lemurs. In the past dermopterans have also been included with the insectivores and bats, and to confuse matters further colugos were known for many years by the family name Galeopithecidae ("cloaked monkeys"). Such problems in classification arise because the family Cynocephalidae has no fossil record. Today it is recognized that colugos are probably remnants of an ancient specialized mammalian side-branch and, because of their unique appearance and habits, they are placed in a separate order—the Dermoptera ("skin-wing").

The order name refers to the flying lemurs' most distinctive characteristic, the gliding membrane or patagium, which stretches from the side of the animal's neck to the tips of the fingers and toes and continues to the very tip of the tail. No other gliding mammal has such an extensive membrane; in the flying squirrels and marsupial phalangers the patagium stretches only between the limbs. With the patagium outspread, the colugo assumes the shape of a kite and can execute controlled glides of 70m (230ft) or more, with the membrane acting as a parachute. During a measured glide of 136m (450ft) between trees one colugo lost only 12m (39ft) in height.

The flying lemurs' spectacular gliding habits are a remarkable adaptation to the environment in which they live: the multi-layered rain forest where trees reach great heights and much of the food is in the canopy. In consequence, many rain forest animals have adopted an arboreal way of life, but this poses the problem of how to get from one tree to the next. Birds and bats fly, squirrels jump and monkeys leap; few animals choose to descend to the ground, cross the gap and climb the next tree, a way of travel that is costly in terms of energy and leaves them vulnerable to a host of ground predators. So the flying lemur has found another solution: it glides.

Although flying lemurs are usually found in primary and secondary forests in both lowland and mountain regions, the Malayan colugo is equally at home in rubber estates and coconut plantations, where it is regarded as a pest because it eats budding coconut flowers. Among the well-spaced trees in a plantation, the colugo's flight can be seen to best advantage.

Flying lemurs are so distinctive in appearance and behavior that they can hardly be mistaken for anything else. They are about the size of a cat and so arboreal in habit that a colugo on the ground is almost helpless. The Philippine colugo is smaller than the Malayan colugo and seems to be more primitive, with less specialized upper incisors and canines. A flying lemur's limbs are of equal length, with strong sharp claws for climbing, and the toes are connected by webs of skin, an extension of the distinctive flight membrane. The head is broad, somewhat like a greyhound's in appearance, with rounded short ears and a blunt muzzle. Flying lemurs have large eyes, as befits a nocturnal animal, and their stereoscopic vision gives them the depth perception necessary for judging accurate landings.

Flying lemurs are herbivores and they have teeth unlike those of any other mammal. Like ruminants, they have a gap

at the front of the upper jaw with all the upper incisors at the side of the mouth, but the second upper incisor has two roots, a feature unique among mammals. The most interesting aspect of their dentition, however, is the fact that all the incisors are comb-like, with as many as 20 comb tines arising from one root. The function of these unique comb tines is not fully understood; they may be used as scrapers, to strain food or for grooming the animal's fur.

Flying lemurs' diet seems to consist mainly of leaves, both young and mature, shoots, buds and flowers, and perhaps soft fruits, which captive animals will accept reluctantly. When feeding, the colugo pulls a bunch of leaves within reach with its front foot, then picks off the leaves with its strong tongue and lower incisors. The stomach is specialized for ingesting large quantities of leafy vegetation and has an extended pyloric digesting region, the part near the exit to the intestines. The intestines are long and convoluted, with the large intestine longer than the small intestine, the reverse of most mammals. Flying lemurs probably obtain sufficient water by licking wet leaves.

A single young is born at a time, rarely two, after a gestation of 60 days. Lactating females with unweaned young have been found to be pregnant, so it is possible that births may follow in rapid succession. The infant is born in an undeveloped state like a marsupial and until it is weaned it is carried on the belly of the mother, even when she "flies." The patagium can be folded near the tail into a soft warm pouch for carrying the young. When the female rests beneath a bough with her patagium outstretched the infant peers out from an exotic hammock. Young flying lemurs emit duck-like cries and the cry of the adult is said to be similar, although it is rarely used.

Flying lemurs spend the day in holes or hollows of trees or hanging beneath a bough or against a tree trunk with the patagium extended like a cloak. In coconut plantations they curl up in a ball among the palm fronds.

Night falls quickly in the tropics and the colugo usually emerges before dusk and climbs to the top of its tree. It ascends by a series of clumsy bounds, grasping the trunk with its outspread limbs and moving both front feet together then both hind feet. The colugo halts at the top of the tall, straight trunk beneath the tangle of branches at the crown and cranes its head to look down. It does not turn its whole body to do this as a squirrel would. Having chosen its flight path it launches into a long controlled glide to another tree, where it lands low on the trunk, sometimes only 3–4m (10–13ft) above the ground, and climbs slowly upwards, often pausing to rest. The colugo again moves to the top of the trunk (this type of locomotion would be impossible in low-branching temperate woods) and glides off again. The animal may pass quickly from tree to tree, covering considerable distances to reach its feeding trees. Flying lemurs use regular gliding trees and several animals may use the same tree, following each other in rapid succession up the trunk, but choosing different glide paths. Animals move about singly, apart from mothers with young, but several cover the same area and use the same feeding trees. Six independent animals were found in an area of less than 0.5ha (1.2 acres) in a coconut plantation in Java. Flying lemurs forage through the night and return to their sleeping trees at dawn.

Like many other rain-forest species, they are endangered by loss of their habitat to timber-felling or agriculture.   KMacK

Bibliography

The following list of titles indicates key reference works used in the preparation of this volume and those recommended for further reading. The list is divided into four categories: general mammology and those titles relevant to each of the three main sections: carnivores, sea mammals and primates.

General

Boyle, C. L. (ed) (1981) *The RSPCA Book of British Mammals*, Collins, London.

Corbet, G. B. and Hill, J. E. (1980) *A World List of Mammalian Species*, British Museum and Cornell University Press, London and Ithaca, N.Y.

Dorst, J. and Dandelot, P. (1972) *Larger Mammals of Africa*, Collins, London.

Grzimek, B. (ed) (1972) *Grzimek's Animal Life Encyclopedia*, vols 10, 11 and 12, Van Nostrand Reinhold, New York.

Hall, E. R. and Kelson, K. R. (1959) *The Mammals of North America*, Ronald Press, New York.

Harrison Matthews, L. (1969) *The Life of Mammals*, vols 1 and 2, Weidenfeld & Nicolson, London.

Honacki, J. H., Kinman, K. E. and Koeppl, J. W. (eds) (1982) *Mammal Species of the World*, Allen Press and Association of Systematics Collections, Lawrence, Kansas.

Kingdon, J. (1971–82) *East African Mammals*, vols I–III, Academic Press, New York.

Morris, D. (1965) *The Mammals*, Hodder & Stoughton, London.

Nowak, R. M. and Paradiso, J. L. (eds) (1983) *Walker's Mammals of the World* (4th edn), 2 vols, Johns Hopkins University Press, Baltimore and London.

Vaughan, T. L. (1972) *Mammalogy*, W. B. Saunders, London and Philadelphia.

Young, J. Z. (1975) *The Life of Mammals: their Anatomy and Physiology*, Oxford University Press, Oxford.

Carnivores

Bekoff, M. (1978) *Coyotes: Biology, Behavior and Management*, Academic Press, New York.

Bertram, B. C. (1978) *Pride of Lions*, Charles Scribner, New York.

Dominis, J. and Edey, M. (1968) *The Cats of Africa*, Time-Life, New York.

Eaton, R. L. (1974) *The Cheetah: the Biology, Ecology, and Behavior of an Endangered Species*, Van Nostrand Reinhold, New York.

Ewer, R. F. (1973) *The Carnivores*, Weidenfeld & Nicolson, London.

Fox, M. W. (ed) (1975) *The Wild Canids: their Systematics, Behavioral Ecology, Evolution*, Van Nostrand Reinhold, London and New York.

Frame, G. & L. (1981) *Swift and Enduring: Cheetahs and Wild Dogs of the Serengeti*, Dutton, New York.

Guggisberg, C. A. W. (1961) *Simba: the Life of the Lion*, Howard Timmins, Cape Town.

Carnivores continued

Herrero, S. (ed) (1972) *Bears: their Biology and Management*, IUCN Publ. New Series no. 23, Morges, Switzerland.

Hinton, H. E. and Dunn, A. M. S. (1967) *Mongooses: their Natural History and Behaviour*, Oliver & Boyd, Edinburgh and London.

Kruuk, H. (1972) *The Spotted Hyena: a Study of Predation and Social Behavior*, University of Chicago Press, Chicago.

Lawick, H. van and J. van Lawick-Goodall (1970) *The Innocent Killers*, Collins, London.

Mech, L. D. (1970) *The Wolf: the Ecology and Behavior of an Endangered Species*, Natural History Press, Garden City, New York.

Mountfort, G. (1981) *Saving the Tiger*, Michael Joseph, London.

Neal, E. G. (1977) *Badgers*, Blandford, Poole, Dorset.

Pelton, M. R., Lentfer, J. W. and Stokes, G. E. (eds) (1976) *Bears: their Biology and Management*, IUCN Publ. New Series no. 40, Morges, Switzerland.

Powell, R. A. (1900) *The Fisher: Life History, Ecology and Behavior*, University of Minnesota Press, Minneapolis.

Schaller, G. B. (1967) *The Deer and the Tiger*, Chicago University Press, Chicago.

Schaller, G. B. (1972) *The Serengeti Lion: a Study of Predator-Prey Relations*, University of Chicago Press, Chicago.

Verts, B. J. (1967) *The Biology of the Striped Skunk*, University of Illinois Press, Urbana.

Wrogemann, N. (1975) *Cheetah Under the Sun*, McGraw-Hill, Johannesburg.

Sea Mammals

Allen, K. R. (1980) *Conservation and Management of Whales*, Butterworths, London.

Bonner, W. N. (1980) *Whales*, Blandford, Poole.

Bonner, W. N. and Berry, R. J. (eds) (1981) *Ecology in the Antarctic*, Academic Press, London.

Ellis, R. (1983) *Dolphins and Porpoises*, R. Hale, London.

Gaskin, D. E. (1972) *Whales, Dolphins and Seals*, Heinemann Educational Books, London.

Gaskin, D. E. (1982) *The Ecology of Whales and Dolphins*, Heinemann, London.

Harrison Matthews, L. (1978) *The Natural History of the Whale*, Weidenfeld & Nicolson, London.

Harrison Matthews, L. (1979) *Seals and the Scientists*, P. Owen, London.

Sea Mammals continued

Herman, L. M. (1980) *Cetacean Behavior: Mechanisms and Functions*, John Wiley & Sons, Chichester.

King, J. E. (1983) *Seals of the World*, Oxford University Press, Oxford.

Martin, R. M. (1977) *Mammals of the Seas*, Batsford, London.

Ridgeway, S. H. and Harrison, R. J. (eds) (1981) *The Handbook of Marine Mammals*, vols I & II, Academic Press, London.

Slijper, E. J. (1979) *Whales*, Hutchinson, London.

Watson, L. (1981) *Sea Guide to Whales of the World*, Hutchinson, London.

Winn, H. E. and Olla, B. L. (1979) *The Behavior of Marine Mammals*, vol 3, *Cetaceans*, Plenum, New York.

Primates

Altmann, S. A. and Altmann, J. (1970) *Baboon Ecology*, University of Chicago Press, Chicago.

Altmann, J. (1980) *Baboon Mothers and Infants*, Harvard University Press, Cambridge.

Bramblett, C. A. (1976) *Patterns of Primate Behaviour*, Mayfield Publishing Co., Palo Alto.

Chalmers, N. (1979) *Social Behaviour in Primates*, Edward Arnold, London.

Charles-Dominique, P. (1977) *Ecology and Behaviour of Nocturnal Primates: Prosimians of Equatorial West Africa*, Duckworth, London.

Charles-Dominique, P. et al. (eds) (1980) *Nocturnal Malagasy Primates: Ecology, Physiology and Behavior*, Academic Press, New York.

Chivers, D. J. (ed) (1980) *Malayan Forest Primates*, Plenum, New York.

Clutton-Brock, T. H. (ed) (1977) *Primate Ecology*, Academic Press, London.

Clutton-Brock, T. H. and Harvey, P. H. (eds) (1978) *Readings in Sociobiology*, W. H. Freeman, Reading.

Coimbra-Filho, A. F. and Mittermeier, R. A. (1981) *Ecology and Behavior of Neotropical Primates*, Academia Brasileira de Ciencias, Rio de Janeiro.

Devore, I. (ed) (1965) *Primate Behavior: Field Studies of Monkeys and Apes*, Holt, Rinehart & Winston, New York.

Doyle, G. A. and Martin, R. D. (eds) (1979) *The Study of Prosimian Behavior*, Academic Press, New York.

Hrdy, S. B. (1977) *The Langurs of Abu: Female and Male Strategies of Reproduction*, Harvard University Press, Cambridge.

Primates continued

Jay, P. C. (1968) *Primates: Studies in Adaptation and Variability*, Holt, Rinehart & Winston, New York.

Jolly, A. (1972) *The Evolution of Primate Behavior*, Macmillan, New York.

Jolly, A. (1966) *Lemur Behavior: A Malagasy Field Study*, University of Chicago Press, Chicago.

Kleiman, D. G. (ed) (1977) *The Biology and Conservation of the Callitrichidae*, Smithsonian Institution Press, Washington.

Kummer, H. (1971) *Primate Societies: Group Techniques of Ecological Adaptation*, Aldine Atherton, Chicago.

van Lawick-Goodall, J. (1971) *In the Shadow of Man*, Collins, London.

Lindburg, D. G. (ed) (1980) *The Macaques: Studies in Ecology, Behavior and Evolution*, Van Nostrand Reinhold, New York.

Martin, R. D., Doyle, G. A. and Walker, A. C. (eds) (1974) *Prosimian Biology*, Duckworth, London.

Michael, R. P. and Crook, J. H. (eds) (1973) *Comparative Ecology and Behaviour of Primates*, Academic Press, London.

Milton, K. (1980) *The Foraging Strategy of Howler Monkeys*, Columbia University Press, New York.

Moynihan, M. (1976) *The New World Primates*, Princeton University Press, Princeton.

Napier, J. R. and Napier, P. H. (1967) *A Handbook of Living Primates*, Academic Press, New York and London.

Napier, J. R. and Napier, P. H. (1970) *Old World Monkeys*, Academic Press, New York.

Rainier III, H. S. H. and Bourne, G. H. (1977) *Primate Conservation*, Academic Press, New York.

Schaller, G. B. (1963) *The Mountain Gorilla: Ecology and Behaviour*, University of Chicago Press, Chicago and London.

Short, R. V. and Weir, B. J. (eds) (1980) *The Great Apes of Africa*, Journals of Reproduction and Fertility, Colchester.

Simons, E. L. (1972) *Primate Evolution*, Collier Macmillan, London.

Struhsaker, T. T. (1975) *The Red Colobus Monkey*, University of Chicago Press, Chicago.

Sussman, R. W. (ed) (1979) *Primate Ecology: Problem-oriented Field Studies*, John Wiley, New York.

Szalay, F. S. and Delson, E. (1979) *Evolutionary History of the Primates*, Academic Press, New York.

GLOSSARY

Adaptation features of an animal which adjust it to its environment. Adaptations may be genetic, produced by evolution and hence not alterable within the animal's lifetime, or they may be phenotypic, produced by adjustment on the behalf of the individual and may be reversible within its lifetime. NATURAL SELECTION favors the survival of individuals whose adaptations adjust them better to their surroundings than other individuals with less successful adaptations.

Adaptive radiation the pattern in which different species develop from a common ancestor (as distinct from CONVERGENT EVOLUTION process whereby species from different origins became similar in response to the same SELECTIVE PRESSURES).

Adult a fully developed and mature individual, capable of breeding, but not necessarily doing so until social and/or ecological conditions allow.

Aerobic deriving energy from processes that require free atmospheric oxygen, as distinct from ANAEROBIC processes.

Agouti a grizzled coloration resulting from alternate light and dark barring of each hair.

Air sac a side-pouch of the larynx (the upper part of the windpipe), used in some primates and male walruses as resonating chambers in producing calls.

Alloparent an animal behaving parentally towards infants that are not its own offspring; the shorthand jargon "HELPER" is most commonly applied to alloparents without any offspring of their own and it can be misleading if it is used to describe any non-breeding adults associated with infants, but which may or may not be "helping" by promoting their survival.

Alveolus a microscopic sac within the lungs providing the surface for gaseous exchange during respiration.

Amphibious able to live on both land and in water.

Amphipod a CRUSTACEAN of the invertebrate order Amphipoda. Includes many freshwater and marine shrimps.

Anaerobic deriving energy from processes that do not require free oxygen, as distinct from AEROBIC processes.

Anal gland or sac a gland opening by a short duct either just inside the anus or on either side of it.

Antarctic Convergence the region between 50°–55°S where the antarctic surface water slides beneath the less-dense southward-flowing subantarctic water.

Anthropoid literally "man-like;" a member of the primate suborder Anthropoidea (monkeys, apes and man). Also, a great ape.

Aquatic living chiefly in water.

Arboreal living in trees.

Arteriole a small artery (ie muscular blood vessel carrying blood from the heart), eventually subdividing into minute capillaries.

Arterio-venous anastomosis (AVA) a connection between the ARTERIOLES carrying blood from the heart and the VENULES carrying it back to the heart.

Association a mixed-species group (polyspecific association) involving two or more species; relatively common among both Old and New World monkeys, but the most stable associations are found in forest-living guenons.

Axilla the angle between a forelimb and the body (in humans, the armpit).

Baculum (*os penis* or penis bone) an elongate bone present in the penis of certain mammals.

Baleen a horny substance, commonly known as whalebone, growing as plates from the upper jaws of whales of the suborder Mysticeti, and forming a fringe-like sieve for extraction of plankton from seawater.

Bends the colloquial name for caisson disease, a condition produced by pressure changes in the blood as a diving mammal surfaces. Too rapid an ascent results in nitrogen dissolved in the blood forming bubbles which cause excruciating pain.

Benthic the bottom layer of the marine environment.

Binocular form of vision typical of mammals in which the same object is viewed simultaneously by both eyes; the coordination of the two images in the brain permits precise perception of distance.

Biomass a measure of the abundance of a life-form in terms of its mass, either absolute or per unit area (the population densities of two species may be identical in terms of the number of individuals of each, but due to their different sizes their biomasses may be quite different).

Biotic community a naturally occurring group of plants and animals in the same environment.

Bipedal walking on two legs. Only human beings exhibit habitual striding bipedalism. Some primate species may travel bipedally for short distances, and some (eg indri, bush babies, tarsiers) hop bipedally on the ground.

Blastocyst see IMPLANTATION.

Blowhole the opening of the nostril(s) of a whale, situated on the animal's head, from which the "spout" or "blow" is produced.

Blubber a layer of fat beneath the skin, well developed in whales and seals.

Boreal region a zone geographically situated south of the Arctic and north of latitude 50°N: dominated by coniferous forest.

Brachiate to move around in the trees by arm-swinging beneath branches. In a broad sense all apes are brachiators, but only gibbons and siamangs exhibit a free-flight phase between hand-holds.

Breaching leaping clear of the water.

Brindled having inconspicuous dark streaks or flecks on a gray or tawny background.

Bursa (plural: bursae) a sac-like cavity (eg in ear of civets and Madagascan mongooses).

Cache a hidden store of food: also (verb) to hide for future use.

Canopy a fairly continuous layer in forests produced by the intermingling of branches of trees; may be fully continuous (closed) or broken by gaps (open). The crowns of some trees project above the canopy layer and are known as emergents.

Carnassial (teeth) opposing pair of teeth especially adapted to shear with a cutting (scissor-like) edge: in extant mammals the arrangement is unique to Carnivora and the teeth involved are the fourth upper premolar and first lower molar.

Carnivore any meat-eating organism; alternatively, a member of the order

Carnivore contd.
Carnivora, many of whose members are carnivores.

Catarrhine a "drooping-nosed" monkey, with nostrils relatively close together; term used for all Old World monkeys, apes and man in contrast to PLATYRRHINE monkeys of the New World.

Caudal gland an enlarged skin gland associated with the root of the tail. Subcaudal: placed below the root; supracaudal: above the root.

Cecum a blind sac in the digestive tract of a mammal, at the junction between the small and large intestines, particularly well developed in some specialized leaf-eaters.

Cephalopod a member of an order of mollusks including such marine invertebrates as squid, octopus and cuttlefish.

Cerebral cortex the surface layer of cells (gray matter) covering the main part of the brain, consisting of the cerebral hemispheres.

Cerrado (central Brazil) a dry savanna region punctuated by patches of sparsely wooded vegetation.

Cetacea mammalian order comprising whales, dolphins and porpoises.

Chaco (Bolivia and Paraguay) a lowland plains area containing soils carried down from the Andes; characterized by dry deciduous forest and scrub, transitional between rain forest and pampas grasslands.

Cheek pouch a pouch used for the temporary storage of food, found only in the typical monkeys of the Old World.

Chromatin materials in the chromosomes of living cells containing the genes and proteins.

Class taxonomic category subordinate to a phylum and superior to an order (see TAXONOMY).

Clavicle the collar-bone.

Clupeid a bony fish of the family Clupeidae, including herrings and similar fish, with soft fin-rays, a scaly body and four pairs of gills.

Coniferous forest forest comprising largely evergreen conifers (firs, pines, spruces etc), typically in climates either too dry or too cold to support deciduous forest. Most frequent in northern latitudes or in mountain ranges.

Consort, consortship in certain primates (eg Rhesus monkey, Savanna baboon, chimpanzee, orang-utan) males form temporary associations (consortships) with the females, ensuring priority of mating at the appropriate time.

Convergent evolution the independent acquisition of similar characters in evolution, as opposed to possession of similarities by virtue of descent from a common ancestor.

Copepod a small marine CRUSTACEAN of the invertebrate order Copepoda.

Crepuscular active in twilight.

Crustaceans members of a class within the phylum Arthropoda typified by five pairs of legs, two pairs of antennae, head and thorax joined, and calcareous deposits in the exoskeleton, eg crayfish, crabs, shrimps.

Cryptic (coloration or locomotion) protecting through concealment.

Cusp a prominence on a cheek-tooth (premolars or molar).

Cyamids amphipod CRUSTACEANS of the family Cyamidae that parasitize the skin of the whales; hence the popular name "whale lice."

Deciduous forest temperate and tropical forest with moderate rainfall and marked seasons. Typically, trees shed leaves during either cold or dry periods.

Delayed implantation see IMPLANTATION.

Den a shelter, natural or constructed, used for sleeping, for giving birth and raising young, and/or in winter; also the act of retiring to a den to give birth and raise young, or for winter shelter.

Dental formula a convention for summarizing the dental arrangement whereby the numbers of each type of tooth in each half of the upper and lower jaw are given; the numbers are always presented in the order: incisor (I), canine (C), premolar (P), molar (M). The final figure is the total number of teeth to be found in the skull. A typical example for Carnivora would be $I3/3$, $C1/1$, $P4/4$, $M3/3 = 44$.

Dentition the arrangement of teeth characteristic of a particular species.

Desert areas of low rainfall, typically with sparce scrub or grassland vegetation or lacking vegetation altogether.

Digit a finger or a toe.

Dichromatic in dichromatic species, males and females exhibit quite different color patterns (eg certain day-active lemurs, some New World monkeys, some Old World monkeys and certain gibbons).

Digital glands glands that occur between or on the toes.

Digitgrade method of walking on the toes without the heel touching the ground (cf PLANTIGRADE).

Dimorphism the existence of two distinct forms (polymorphism = several distinct forms); the term "sexual dimorphism" is applied to cases where the male and female of a species differ consistently in, for example, shape, size, coloration and armament.

Disjunct or **discontinuous distribution** geographical distribution of a species that is marked by gaps. Commonly brought about by fragmentation of suitable habitat, especially as a result of human intervention.

Dispersal the movements of animals, often as they reach maturity, away from their previous home range (equivalent to emigration). Distinct from dispersion, that is, the pattern in which things (perhaps animals, food supplies, nest sites) are distributed or scattered.

Display any relatively conspicuous pattern of behavior that conveys specific information to others, usually to members of the same species; can involve visual and/or vocal elements, as in threat, courtship or "greeting" displays.

Distal far from the point of attachment or origin (eg tip of tail).

Diurnal active in daytime.

Dominant see HIERARCHY.

Dormancy a period of inactivity; many bears, for example, are dormant for a period in winter: this is not true HIBERNATION, as pulse rate and body temperature do not drop markedly.

Dorsal on the upper or top side or surface (eg dorsal stripe).

Echolocation the process of perception, often direction finding, based upon

Echolocation contd.

reaction to the pattern of reflected sound waves (echoes).

Ecology the study of plants and animals in relation to their natural environmental setting. Each species may be said to occupy a distinctive ecological NICHE.

Ecosystem a unit of the environment within which living and nonliving elements interact.

Ecotype a genetic variety within a single species, adapted for local ecological conditions.

Elongate relatively long (eg of canine teeth, longer than those of an ancestor, a related animal, or than adjacent teeth).

Emigration departure of animal(s), usually at or about the time of reaching adulthood, from the group or place of birth.

Enzootic concerning disease regularly found within an animal population (endemic applies specifically to people) as distinct from EPIZOOTIC.

Epizootic a disease outbreak in an animal population at a specific time (but not persistently, as in ENZOOTIC): if an epizootic wave of infection eventually stabilizes in an area, it becomes enzootic.

Erectile capable of being raised to an erect position (eretcile mane).

Esophagus the gullet connecting the mouth with the stomach.

Estrus the period in the estrous cycle of female mammals at which they are often attractive to males and receptive to mating. The period coincides with the maturation of eggs and ovulation (the release of mature eggs from the ovaries). Animals in estrus are often said to be "on heat" or "in heat." In primates, if the egg is not fertilized the subsequent degeneration of uterine walls (endometrium) leads to menstrual bleeding. In some species ovulation is triggered by copulation and this is called **induced ovulation**, as distinct from spontaneous ovulation.

Exudate natural plant exudates include gums and resins; damage to plants (eg by marmosets) can lead to loss of sap as well. Certain PROSIMIANS and other primates (eg marmosets) rely heavily on exudates as a source of food.

Family a taxonomic division subordinate to an order and superior to a genus (see TAXONOMY).

Fast ice sea ice which forms in polar regions along the coast, and remains fast, being attached to the shore, to an ice wall, an ice front, or over shoals, generally in the position where it originally formed.

Feces excrement from the bowels; colloquially known as droppings or scats.

Feral living in the wild (of domesticated animals, eg cat, dog).

Fermentation the decomposition of organic substances by microorganisms. In some mammals, parts of the digestive tract (eg the cecum) may be inhabited by bacteria that break down cellulose and release nutrients.

Fin an organ projecting from the body of aquatic animals and generally used in steering and propulsion.

Fissipedia (suborder) name given by some taxonomists to modern terrestrial carnivores to distinguish them from the suborder Pinnipedia which describes the marine carnivores. Here we treat both as

Fissipedia contd.

full orders: the Carnivora and the Pinnipedia.

Fitness a measure of the ability of an animal (with one genotype or genetic make-up) to leave viable offspring in comparison to other indivuduals (with different genotypes). The process of NATURAL SELECTION, often called survival of the fittest, determines which characteristics have the greatest fitness, ie are most likely to enable their bearers to survive and rear young which will in turn bear those characteristics. (See INCLUSIVE FITNESS.)

Flehmen German word describing a facial expression in which the lips are pulled back, head often lifted, teeth sometimes clapped rapidly together and nose wrinkled. Often associated with animals (especially males) sniffing scent marks or socially important odors (eg scent of estrous female). Possibly involved in transmission of odor to JACOBSON'S ORGAN.

Flense to strip blubber from a whale or seal.

Flipper a limb adapted for swimming.

Floe a sheet of floating ice.

Fluke one of the lobes of a whale's tail; the name refers to their broad triangular shape.

Folivore an animal eating mainly leaves.

Follicle a small sac, therefore (a) a mass of ovarian cells that produces an ovum, (b) an indentation in the skin from which hair grows.

Forestomach a specialized part of the stomach consisting of two compartments (presaccus and saccus).

Fossorial burrowing (of life-style or behavior).

Frugivore an animal eating mainly fruits.

Furbearer term applied to mammals whose pelts have commercial value and form part of the fur harvest.

Gadoid cod-like fish of the suborder Gadoidei.

Gallery forest luxuriant forest lining the banks of watercourses.

Gamete a male or female reproductive cell (ovum or spermatozoon).

Gene the basic unit of heredity; a portion of DNA molecule coding for a given trait and passed, through replication at reproduction, from generation to generation. Genes are expressed as ADAPTATIONS and consequently are the most fundamental units (more so than individuals) on which NATURAL SELECTION acts.

Generalist an animal whose life-style does not involve highly specialized strategems (cf SPECIALIST); for example, feeding on a variety of foods which may require different foraging techniques.

Genus (plural genera) a taxonomic division superior to species and subordinate to family (see TAXONOMY).

Gestation the period of development within the uterus; the process of **delayed implantation** can result in the period of pregnancy being longer than the period during which the embryo is actually developing (See also IMPLANTATION.)

Glands (marking) specialized glandular areas of the skin, used in depositing SCENT MARKS.

Great call a protracted series of notes, rising to a climax, produced by the female

Great call contd.

as part of the group song in lesser apes.

Grizzled sprinkled or streaked with gray.

Guard hair an element of the coat of seals consisting of a longer, stiffer, more bristle-like hair which lies outside and supports the warmer, softer underfur.

Harem group a social group consisting of a single adult male, at least two adult females and immature animals; the most common pattern of social organization among mammals.

Haul-out behavior of sea mammals pulling themselves ashore.

Helper jargon for an individual, generally without young of its own, which contributes to the survival of the offspring of others by behaving parentally towards them (see ALLOPARENT).

Hemoglobin an iron-containing protein in the red corpuscles which plays a crucial role in oxygen exchange between blood and tissues in mammals.

Herbivore an animal eating mainly plants or parts of plants.

Hibernation a period of winter inactivity during which the normal physiological process is greatly reduced and thus during which the energy requirements of the animal are lowered.

Hierarchy (social or dominance) the existence of divisions within society, based on the outcome of interactions which show some individuals to be consistently dominant to others. Higher-ranking individuals thus have control of aspects (eg access to food or mates) of the life and behavior of low-ranking ones. Hierarchies may be branching, but simple linear ones are often called peck orders (after the behavior of farmyard chickens).

Higher primate one of the more advanced primates, known as ANTHROPOIDS.

Holarctic realm a region of the world including North America, Greenland, Europe, and Asia apart from the southwest, southeast and India.

Home range the area in which an animal normally lives (generally excluding rare excursions or migrations), irrespective of whether or not the area is defended from other animals (cf TERRITORY).

Hybrid the offspring of parents of different species.

Hydrophone a waterproof microphone held in position under the sea surface and used to detect the sounds emitted by sea mammals.

Hyoid bones skeletal elements in the throat region, supporting the trachea, larynx and base of the tongue (derived in evolutionary history from the gill arches of ancestral fish).

Implantation the process whereby the free-floating blastocyst (early embryo) becomes attached to the uterine wall in mammals. At the point of implantation a complex network of blood vessels develops to link mother and embryo (the PLACENTA). In **delayed implantation** the blastocyst remains dormant in the uterus for periods varying, between species, from 12 days to 11 months. Delayed implantation may be obligatory or facultative and is known for some members of the Carnivora and Pinnipedia.

Inclusive fitness a measure of the animal's FITNESS which is based on the number of genes, rather than the number of its offspring, present in subsequent generations. This is a more complete

Inclusive fitness contd.

measure of fitness, since it incorporates the effect of, for example, alloparenthood, wherein individuals may help to rear the offspring of their relatives (see KIN SELECTION: ALLOPARENT).

Induced ovulation see ESTRUS.

Infanticide the killing of infants. Infanticide has been recorded notably in species in which a bachelor male may take over a HAREM from its resident male(s).

Insectivore an animal eating mainly arthropods (insects, spiders).

Ischial callosities specialized, hardened pads of tissue present on the buttocks of some monkeys and apes. Each overlies a flattened projection of the ischium bone of the pelvis. Known also as "sitting pads," they are found in Old World monkeys and lesser apes.

Jacobson's organ a structure in a foramen (small opening) in the palate of many vertebrates which appears to be involved in olfactory communication. Molecules of scent may be sampled in these organs.

Juvenile no longer possessing the characteristics of an infant, but not yet fully adult.

Kin selection a facet of NATURAL SELECTION whereby an animal's fitness is affected by the survival of its relatives or kin. Kin selection may be the process whereby some ALLOPARENTAL behavior evolved: an individual behaving in a way which promotes the survival of its kin increases its own INCLUSIVE FITNESS, despite the *apparent* selflessness of its behavior.

Knuckle-walk to walk on all fours with the weight of the front part of the body carried on the knuckles; found only in gorillas and chimpanzees.

Krill shrimp-like CRUSTACEANS of the genera *Euphausia, Meganyctiphanes* etc, occurring in very great numbers in polar seas, particularly off Antarctica, where they form the principal prey of baleen whales.

Lactation (verb: lactate) the secretion of milk from MAMMARY GLANDS.

Laminar flow streamline flow in a viscous fluid near a solid boundary: the flow of water over the surface of whales is laminar.

Lanugo the birth-coat of mammals which is shed to be replaced by the adult coat.

Latrine a place where FECES are regularly left (often together with other SCENT MARKS); associated with olfactory communication.

Lead a channel of open water between ice floes.

Lesser apes the gibbons and siamang.

Liana a climbing plant. In rain forests large numbers of often woody, twisted lianas hang down like ropes from the crowns of trees.

Lob-tailing a whale beating the water with its tail FLUKES, perhaps to communicate with other whales.

Lower primate one of the more primitive primates known as PROSIMIANS.

Lumbar a term locating anatomical features in the loin region, eg lumbar vertebrae are at the base of the spine.

Mammal a member of a CLASS of VERTEBRATE animals having MAMMARY GLANDS which produce milk with which they nurse their young (properly: Mammalia).

Mammary glands glands of female mammals that secrete milk.

Mangrove forest tropical forest developed on sheltered muddy shores of deltas and estuaries exposed to tide. Vegetation is almost entirely woody.

Marine living in the sea.

Mask colloquial term for the face of a mammal, especially a dog, fox or cat.

Matriline a related group of animals linked by descent through females alone.

Melanism darkness of color due to presence of the black pigment melanin.

Menstrual cycle an approximately monthly cycle involving alternation of ovulation and menstruation (loss of blood from the vulva at monthly intervals) until pregnancy intervenes; found in humans, great apes, Old World monkeys and, to varying degrees, in New World monkeys.

Metabolic rate the rate at which the chemical processes of the body occur.

Migration movement, usually seasonal, from one region or climate to another for purposes of feeding or breeding.

Monogamy a mating system in which individuals have only one mate per breeding season.

Mutation a structural change in a gene which can thus give rise to a new heritable characteristic.

Myoglobin a protein related to HEMOGLOBIN, found in the muscles of vertebrates; like hemoglobin, it is involved in the oxygen exchange processes of respiration.

Myopia short-sightedness.

Mysticete a member of the suborder Mysticeti, whales with baleen plates rather than teeth as their feeding apparatus.

Nasolacrimal duct a duct or canal between the nostrils and the eye.

Natal range the home range into which an individual was born (natal = of or from one's birth).

Natural selection the process whereby individuals with the most appropriate ADAPTATIONS are more successful than other individuals, and hence survive to produce more offspring. To the extent that the successful traits are heritable (genetic) they will therefore spread in the population.

Niche the role of a species within the community, defined in terms of all aspects of its life-style (eg food, competitors, predators, and other resource requirements).

Nocturnal active at nighttime.

Odontocete a member of the suborder Odonticeti, the toothed whales.

Olfaction, olfactory the olfactory sense is the sense of smell, depending on receptors located in the epithelium (surface membrane) lining the nasal cavity.

Omnivore an animal eating a varied diet including both animal and plant tissue.

Opportunist (of feeding) flexible behavior of exploiting circumstances to take a wide range of food items: characteristic of many species of Carnivora. See GENERALIST; SPECIALIST.

Order a taxonomic division subordinate to class and superior to family (see TAXONOMY).

Ovulation (verb ovulate) the shedding of mature ova (eggs) from the ovaries where

Ovulation contd.

they are produced (see ESTRUS).

Pack ice large blocks of ice formed on the surface of the sea when an ice field has been broken up by wind and waves, and drifted from its original position.

Pampas Argentinian steppe grasslands.

Papilla (plural: papillae) a small nipple-like projection.

Parturition the process of giving birth (hence *post partum*)—after birth.

Patagium a gliding membrane typically stretching down the sides of the body between the fore- and hindlimbs and perhaps including part of the tail. Found in colugos, flying squirrels, bats etc.

Pelagic the upper part of the open sea, above the BENTHIC zone.

Pelvis a girdle of bones that supports the hindlimbs of vertebrates.

Perineal glands glandular tissue occurring between the anus and genitalia.

Perineal swelling a swelling of the naked area of skin in the region of the anus and vulva of a female primate, found in chimpanzees and some Old World monkeys.

Phytoplankton minute plants floating near the surface of aquatic environments (cf ZOOPLANKTON).

Pinna (plural: pinnae) the projecting cartilaginous portion of the external ear.

Pinniped a member of the order Pinnipedia, aquatic carnivorous mammals with all four limbs modified into flippers; the true seals, eared seals and walrus. Sometimes classified as a suborder of Carnivora.

Placenta, placental mammals a structure that connects the fetus and the mother's womb to ensure a supply of nutrients to the fetus and removal of its waste products. Only *placental mammals* have a well-developed placenta; marsupials have a rudimentary placenta or none, and monotremes lay eggs.

Plantigrade way of walking on the soles of the feet, including the heels (cf DIGITIGRADE).

Platyrrhine a "flat-nosed" monkey with widely separated nostrils. Term commonly used for all New World monkeys in contrast to CATARRHINE monkeys of the Old World.

Pod a group of individuals, usually applied to whales, with some, at least temporary, cohesive social structure.

Polyandrous see POLYGYNOUS.

Polygamous a mating system wherein an individual has more than one mate per breeding season.

Polygynous a mating system in which a male mates with several females during one breeding season (as opposed to polyandrous, where one female mates with several males).

Population a more or less separate (discrete) group of animals of the same species within a given BIOTIC COMMUNITY.

Prairie North American steppe grassland between 30°N and 55°N.

Predator an animal which forages for live prey; hence "anti-predator behavior" describes the evasive actions of the prey.

Prehensile capable of grasping (eg of the tail).

Primary forest forest that has remained

Primary forest contd.

undisturbed for a long time and has reached a mature (climax) condition; primary rain forest may take centuries to become established.

Primate a member of an order comprising the apes, monkeys and related forms, including man.

Process (anatomical) an outgrowth or protuberance.

Promiscuous a mating system wherein an individual mates more or less indiscriminately.

Prosimian literally "before the monkeys"; a member of the relatively primitive primate suborder Prosimii (lemurs, lorises and tarsiers).

Proximal near to the point of attachment or origin (eg the base of the tail).

Puberty the attainment of sexual maturity. In addition to maturation of the primary sex organs (ovaries, testes), primates may exhibit "secondary sexual characteristics" at puberty. Among higher primates it is usual to find a growth spurt at the time of puberty in males and females.

Purse seine a fishing net, the bottom of which can be closed by cords, operated usually from boats (cf SEINE).

Quadrumanous using both hands and feet for grasping.

Quadrupedal walking on all fours, as opposed to walking on two legs (BIPEDAL) or moving suspended beneath branches in trees (SUSPENSORY MOVEMENT).

Race a taxonomic division subordinate to SUBSPECIES but linking populations with similar distinct characteristics.

Radiation see ADAPTIVE RADIATION

Radio-tracking a technique used for monitoring an individual's movements remotely; it involves affixing a radio transmitter to the animal and thereafter receiving a signal through directional antennae, which enables the subject's position to be plotted. The transmitter is often attached to a collar, hence "radio-collar."

Rain forest tropical and subtropical forest with abundant and year-round rainfall. Typically species rich and diverse.

Receptive state of a female mammal ready to mate or in ESTRUS.

Reduced (anatomical) of relatively small dimension (eg of certain bones, by comparison with those of an ancestor or related animals).

Reproductive rate the rate of production of offspring; the net productive rate may be defined as the average number of female offspring produced by each female during her entire lifetime.

Retractile (of claws) able to be withdrawn into protective sheaths.

Rhinarium a naked area of moist skin surrounding the nostrils in many mammals.

Rookery a colony of PINNIPEDS.

Rorqual one of the six species of baleen whales of the genus *Balaenoptera*.

Rostrum a forward-directed process at the front of the skull of some whales and dolphins, forming a beak.

Ruminant a mammal with a specialized digestive system typified by the behavior of chewing the cud. Their stomach is modified so that vegetation is stored,

Ruminant contd.

regurgitated for further maceration, then broken down by symbiotic bacteria. The process of rumination is an adaptation to digesting the cellulose walls of plant cells.

Savanna tropical grasslands of Africa, Central and South America and Australia. Typically on flat plains and plateaux with seasonal pattern of rainfall. Three categories—*savanna woodland, savanna parkland* and *savanna grassland*—represent a gradual transition from closed woodland to open grassland.

Scapula the shoulder-blade. Primates typically have a mobile scapula in association with their versatile movements in the trees.

Scent gland an organ secreting odorous material with communicative properties; see SCENT MARK.

Scent mark a site where the secretions of scent glands, or urine or FECES, are deposited and which has communicative significance. Often left regularly at traditional sites which are also visually conspicuous. Also the "chemical message" left by this means; and (verb) to leave such a deposit.

Scombroid a bony marine fish of the family Scombridae, with two small dorsal fins, small scales and smooth skin, eg mackerel and tunny.

Scrub a vegetation dominated by shrubs—woody plants usually with more than one stem. Naturally occurs most often on the arid side of forest or grassland types, but often artificially created by man as a result of forest destruction.

Seasonality (of births) the restriction of births to a particular time of the year.

Sebaceous gland secretory tissue producing oily substances, for example lubricating and waterproofing hair, or specialized to produce odorous secretions.

Secondary forest (or growth) regenerating forest that has not yet reached the climax condition of PRIMARY FOREST.

Sectorial premolar one of the front lower premolars of Old World monkeys and apes, specially adapted for shearing against the rear edge of the upper canine.

Seine a fishing net with floats at the top and weights at the bottom, used for encircling fish.

Selective pressure a factor affecting the reproductive success of individuals (whose success will depend on their FITNESS, ie the extent to which they are adapted to thrive under that selective pressure).

Septum a partition separating two parts of an organism. The nasal septum consists of a fleshy part separating the nostrils and a vertical, bony plate dividing the nasal cavity.

Simian (literally "ape-like") a monkey or ape. Often used as a synonym of ANTHROPOID or HIGHER PRIMATE.

Sinus a cavity in bone or tissue.

Sirenia an order of herbivorous aquatic mammals, comprising the manatees and dugong.

Solitary living on its own, as opposed to social or group-living in life-style.

Sonar sound used in connection with navigation (SOund NAvigation Ranging).

Specialist an animal whose life-style involves highly specialized stratagems: eg feeding with one technique on a particular food.

Species a taxonomic division subordinate to genus and superior to subspecies. In general a species is a group of animals similar in structure and which are able to breed and produce viable offspring. See TAXONOMY.

Speciation the process by which new species arise in evolution. It is widely accepted that it occurs when a single-species population is divided by some geographical barrier.

Steppe open grassy plains of the central temperate zone of Eurasia or North America (prairies), characterized by low and sporadic rainfall and a wide annual temperature variation. In cold steppe, temperatures drop well below freezing point in winter, with rainfall concentrated in the summer or evenly distributed throughout year, while in hot steppe, winter temperatures are higher and rainfall concentrated in winter months.

Subadult no longer an infant or juvenile but not yet fully adult physically and/or socially.

Subfamily a division of a FAMILY.

Subfossil an incompletely fossilized specimen from a recent species.

Sublingua or **subtongue** a flap of tissue beneath the tongue in mammals, retained in most primates though vestigial in New World monkeys; particularly in lemurs and lorises.

Suborder a subdivision of an order.

Subordinate see HIERARCHY.

Subspecies a recognizable subpopulation of a single species, typically with a distinct

Subspecies contd.
geographical distribution.

Surplus killing a phenomenon where more (sometimes very many more) prey are killed than can immediately be consumed by the killer or its companions.

Suspensory movement movement through the trees by hanging and swinging beneath, rather than running along the tops of branches. See also BRACHIATE.

Taiga northernmost coniferous forest, with open boggy rocky areas in between.

Tapetum lucidum a reflecting layer located behind the retina of the eye, commonly found in nocturnal mammals.

Taxonomy the science of classifying organisms. It is very convenient to group together animals which share common features and are thought to have common descent. Each individual is thus a member of a series of ever-broader categories (individual—species—genus—family—order—class—phylum) and each of these can be further divided where it is convenient (eg subspecies, superfamily or infraorder). The SPECIES is a convenient unit in that it links animals according to an obvious criterion, namely that they interbreed successfully. However, the unit on which NATURAL SELECTION operates is the individual: it is by the differential reproductive success of individuals bearing different characteristics that evolutionary change proceeds.

Terrestrial living on land.

Territory an area defended from intruders by an individual or group. Originally the term was used where ranges were

Territory contd.
exclusive and obviously defended at their borders. A more general definition of territoriality allows some overlap between neighbors by defining territoriality as a system of spacing wherein home ranges do not overlap randomly—that is, the location of one individual, or group's home range influences that of others.

Testosterone a male hormone synthesized in the testes and responsible for the expression of many male characteristics (contrast the female hormone estrogen produced in the ovaries).

Tooth-comb a dental modification in which the incisor teeth form a comb-like structure.

Tubercle a small rounded projection or nodule (eg of bone).

Tundra barren treeless lands of the far north of Eurasia and North America, on mountain tops and Arctic islands. Vegetation is dominated by low shrubs, herbaceous perennials, with mosses and lichens.

Underfur the thick soft undercoat fur lying beneath the longer and coarser hair (GUARD HAIRS).

Ungulate a member of the orders Artiodactyla (even-toed ungulates), Perissodactyla (odd-toed ungulates), Proboscidea (elephants), Hyracoidea (hyraxes) and Tubulidentata (aardvark), all of which have their feet modified as hooves of various types (hence the alternative name, hoofed mammals). Most are large and totally herbivorous, eg deer, cattle, gazelles, horses.

Upwelling an upward movement of ocean currents, resulting from convection, causing an upward movement of nutrients and hence an increase in plankton populations.

Vector an individual or species which transmits a disease.

Ventral on the lower or bottom side or surface: thus ventral or abdominal glands occur on the underside of the abdomen.

Venule a small tributary conveying blood from the capillary bed to a vein (cf ARTERIOLE.)

Vertebrate an animal with a backbone: a division of the phylum Chordata which includes animals with notochords (as distinct from invertebrates).

Vestigial a characteristic with little or no contemporary use, but derived from one which was useful and well-developed in an ancestral form.

Vibrissae stiff, coarse hairs richly supplied with nerves, found especially around the snout, and with a sensory (tactile) function.

Xerophytic forest a forest found in areas with relatively low rainfall. Xerophytic plants are adapted to protect themselves against browsing (eg well-developed spines) and to limit water loss (eg small, leathery leaves, often with a waxy coating).

Zooplankton minute animals living near the surface of the sea (cf PHYTOPLANKTON).

INDEX

A **bold number** indicates a major section of the main text, following a heading; a **bold italic** number indicates a fact box on a single species; a single number in (parentheses) indicates that the animal name or subjects are to be found in a boxed feature and a double number in (parentheses) indicates that the animal name or subjects are to be found in a spread special feature. *Italic* numbers refer to illustrations.

Picture Acknowledgements

Key *t* top. *b* bottom. *c* centre. *l* left. *r* right.
Abbreviations A Ardea. AN Agence Nature. BC Bruce Coleman Ltd. GF George Frame. J Jacana. FL Frank Lane Agency. OSF Oxford Scientific Films. FS Fiona Sunquist.

5 Leonard Lee Rue III. 6 William Ervin. 8 GF. 12 Seaphot. 13 A. 15,16 Seaphot. 18 J. 19*t* GF. 19*b* T. N. Bailey. 22 M. Newdick. 23, 24 D. Macdonald. 25 T. P. O'Farrell. 28, 29 A. 30 BC. 31 GF. 32, 33 A. 34 GF. 35 B. Bertram. 36 World Wildlife Fund, A. Purcell. 37 Nature Photographers, M. Leach. 38 FS. 39 BC. 40*b* GF. 40*t* BC. 41 GF. 42*t* R. Caputo. 42*b*, 43 GF. 44 Natural Science Photos, G. Kinns. 45 A. 46, 47*tl*, 47*tr* GF. 47*b* BC. 48 AN. 49 BC, R. Williams. 50 Natural Science Photos. 51 Nature Photographers. 54–55 OSF. 59*t* J. 59*b* E. Zimen. 60–61 A. 61, 62*l* BC. 62*r*, 63 OSF. 64, 65*l* P. D. Moehlman. 65*r* A. 66–67 R. Caputo. 69 A. 70*t* BC. 70*b* FS. 71 OSF. 72, 72–73 A. 75 FS. 76 Anthro-Photo. 77*t* GF. 77*b* R. Caputo. 78 L. Malcolm. 79 GF. 81*t* A. J. T. Johnsingh. 81*b* E. R. C. Davidar. 82*l* BC. 82*r* J. Dietz. 83 BC. 84 A. Henley. 85*t* FS. 85*c* J. 85*b* BC. 86–87 J. W. Lentfer. 87, 88, 89, 90, 90–91 OSF. 92 F. Bruemmer. 93 J. W. Lentfer. 94 BC. 95*t* OSF. 95*b* A. 96 J. MacKinnon. 98 BC. 100 FL. 101*t* OSF. 101*b*, 102, 103 BC. 104, 104–105, 106 J. 107*t* BC. 107*c* J. 107*b* A. 110*t* BC. 110*b* A. 111*t* FL. 111*b*, 112, 113 BC. 115 FL. 116 Eric and David Hosking. 118*t*, *l* BC. 118*b* S. Buskirk. 119 J. 120 AN. 121 S. Carlsson. 122 BC. 124–125 J. 125 BC. 127 Survival Anglia. 128 N. Duplaix. 129 A. 131*t* FS. 131*b* J. 132 BC. 133 Survival Anglia. 134 A. E. Rasa. 135, 137 BC. 138 J. MacKinnon. 140 J. 141 BC. 142*t* AN. 142*b* J. 143 William Ervin, Natural Imagery. 146 D. Macdonald. 147 A. Henley. 148, 150–151 J. Rood. 152, 153 A. E. Rasa. 154 J. 156 G. Mills. 157*t* P. D. Moehlman. 157*b* BC. 158 FL. 159 P. Richardson. 160 Natural Science Photos. 162 J. 163*t* A. R. Martin. 163*b* T. Kasuya. 165 Eric and David Hosking. 166 A. 168, 169*t* BC. 169*b* William Ervin, Natural Imagery. 170 Seaphot. 171 Anthro-Photo, J. Moore. 172*t* Ekdotike Athenon. 172*c* Scala. 172*b* University Museum of National Antiquities, Oslo. 173*t* New Bedford Free Public Library. 174*l* Kingston upon Hull City Museums and Art Galleries. 174*r* National Maritime Museum, San Francisco. 175*t* Faroe Photo, Åsmundur Poulsen. 175*b* P. Morris. 177 A. R. Martin. 180 B. Würsig. 181*t* K. Balcomb. 181*b* W. N. Bonner. 184*t* Biofotos, Heather Angel. 184*b* S. S. Anderson. 185*t* A. 185*b* AN. 186 M. Würsig. 190 A. 190–191 AN. 192, 194, 195 M. & B. Würsig. 196*t* D. Gaskin. 196*b* P. Morris. 197 D. Gaskin. 202 F. Bruemmer. 203 BC. 204–205, 208–209 Sea Mammal Research Unit, Cambridge. 208*b* The Mansell Collection Ltd. 209*b* World Wildlife Fund, K. Balcomb. 210 I. Christensen. 215 BC. 217*t* AN. 217*c* BC. 217*b* A. 219*t* M. & B. Würsig. 219*b* D. A. Sutton. 220 A. 221 William Ervin, Natural Imagery. 222 Anthro-photo, J. Moore. 223 BC. 226 Institute of Oceanographic Studies, Godalming. 227*t* K. Balcomb. 227*b* W. N. Bonner. 228 BC. 229 Seaphot. 230 Survival Anglia, D. Bartlett. 231 BC. 232*t* D. Gaskin. 232*b* BC.

234*t* B. Lipton. 234*b* W. N. Bonner. 235 B. Lipton. 236–237 M. & B. Würsig. 237 Survival Anglia, J. & D. Bartlett. 238 A. 242*t* Leonard Lee Rue III. 242*b* William Ervin, Natural Imagery. 243*t* R. A. Luxmoore. 243*b* W. N. Bonner. 244 P. Wirtz. 245 U. Schürer. 246 A. Henley. 247*t* B. J. le Boeuf. 247*b* S. S. Anderson. 248–249 S. Stammers. 249 R. M. Laws. 250*t* Museum of the American Indian, New York. 250*b*, 251 W. N. Bonner. 252 R. A. Luxmoore. 253 F. Bruemmer. 254 J. 256 256–257 A. Henley. 257*c* Natural Science Photos. 257*b* Eric and David Hosking. 260 W. N. Bonner. 261 Prince and Pearson. 262 A. 263 J. 264 L. Shults. 265 K. R. Gordon. 266–267 FL. 268, 269*t* F. Bruemmer. 269*b* B. Lipton. 270*t* Robert Harding Picture Library. 270*b* J. 271 N. R. Lightfoot. 274*t* A. R. Martin. 274*b* S. S. Anderson. 275 A. R. Martin. 278–279 A. 280*t* W. N. Bonner. 280–281, 281 R. M. Laws. 282 L. Lowry. 283 Luonnonkuva Arkisto. 284 P. Veit. 284–285 Seaphot. 286*t* BC. 286*b* N. R. Lightfoot. 287 J. 289 B. L. Sage. 290*t* Prince and Pearson. 290*b* A. W. Erikson. 291 BC. 294, 295*t* J. L. Bengtson. 295*b* AN. 297 A. 298 P. K. Anderson. 300*t* Sirenia Project, DWRC, Florida. 300*b* A. 302 Seaphot. 303 R. Best. 304 A. 307*t* BC. 307*b* P. Veit. 311 A. 312–313 P. Veit. 314 R. Dunbar. 317 Frithfoto. 318 S. K. Bearder. 319 A. 322 J. Visser. 323 Natural Science Photos. 324–325 BC. 326 J. Visser. 327*t* Bob Martin. 327*b*, 328 A. 328–329, 329 J. Visser. 332 A. 333*t* BC. 333*b* S. K. Bearder. 336 P. Morris. 337 Bob Martin. 340 A. Henley. 344–345, 345, 347 BC. 348*l*. 348–349 C. Janson. 348*r* Rod Williams. 350–351 BC. 351 A. F. Coimbra-Filho. 352 BC. 353*t* Lee Leonard Rue III. 353*b* AN. 356*t* Rod Williams. 356*b* C. Janson. 357 Andy Young. 358–359 A. 363 BC. 364 C. Janson. 365 J. 366–367 BC. 367 C. Janson. 368–369 J. 369 A. 370*t* A. Henley. 370*b* AN. 371 BC. 376*t* A. 376*b* Anthro-photo. 377*t* Dawn Starin. 377*b* BC. 378*t* Eric and David Hosking. 378–379 A. 380 J. 382–383 AN. 386 A. 386–387 BC. 388 Robert Ho. 389 J. E. Fa. 390–391 Lysa Leland. 392 William Ervin, Natural Imagery. 392–393 GF. 393 Anthro-Photo, B. Smuts. 394, 394–395 H. Kummer. 398 Dawn Starin. 399 Rod Williams. 400 A. 401 J. MacKinnon. 402 J. M. Bishop. 402–403 BC. 404 A. 405 J. 409 J. M. Bishop. 410*t* A. 410*b*, 411 Anthro-Photo. 413 P. Morris. 414–415 J. MacKinnon. 415 A. Henley. 418*t* J. MacKinnon. 418*b* J. 419 BC. 422 J. 423*t* BC. 423*b* A. 424 BC. 425*t* A. Henley. 425*b* BC. 428 J. 429 J. MacKinnon. 430 Survival Anglia. 431 J. MacKinnon. 432*t* A. 432*b* BC. 433 P. Veit. 434–435 BC. 436, 437 P. Veit. 438*t* BC. 438*cl*, 438*bl* K. J. Stewart. 438*br* Syndication International. 439 P. Veit. 442 A. 442–443 BC. 443 Bob Martin. 445 BC. 446 Natural History Photographic Agency. 446–447 BC. 447 J. MacKinnon. 448 Natural History Photographic Agency.

Artwork

All artwork © Priscilla Barrett unless stated otherwise below.
Abbreviations JF John Fuller. OI Oxford Illustrators. SC Stephen Cocking. SD Simon Driver. AEM Anne-Elise Martin. MM Malcolm McGregor.

2, 3 SD. 20 JF. 21, 22 SD. 27*t* JF. 37, 38 VAP. 43, 53 OI. 57 JF. 60 John Brennan. 87 JF. 99*t* JF. 109*t* JF. 122*t* VAP. 135*t* JF. 155*t* JF. 164, 166, 167, 176, 177 SD. 178, 182 MM. 194 SD. 198, 200, 201 MM. 205, 206 SC. 207, 211, 212 MM. 214, 215 SD. 216, 218*t* MM. 218, 223 SD. 224, 225 MM. 229, 231 SD. 232 MM. 236, 240, 241, 243, 245, 246, 251, 254, 271, 282, 294 SD. 308, 309, 310, 314, 315, 316 SD. 318 AEM. 322 JF. 340 AEM. 344, 394 SD. 412 AEM. 416 SD. 440 AEM. 443 SD. Maps and scale drawings SD.